Berkeley
LIBRARY OF THE UNIVERSITY OF CALIFORNIA
D1616056

Physical Processes in the Solar System

An introduction to the physics of asteroids, comets, moons and planets

First Edition

John D. Landstreet
University of Western Ontario
London, Canada

Keenan & Darlington, Publishers London, Canada

PUBLISHED BY KEENAN & DARLINGTON, PUBLISHERS,
18 Rollingwood Circle, London, Ontario, Canada N6G 1P7

KEENAN & DARLINGTON, PUBLISHERS
18 Rollingwood Circle, London, Ontario, Canada N6G 1P7
e-mail: planets@corcaroli.astro.uwo.ca
Web: http://www.astro.uwo.ca/~jlandstr/planets

Front cover: Comet Hyakutake; back cover: Comet Hale-Bopp.
Cover images copyright © Dominique Dierick, Gent, Belgium. Used by permission.
Cover design: Sarah Margaret Landstreet

First published 2003

Printed in Canada

This book was prepared with the LaTeX document preparation system.

National Library of Canada Cataloguing in Publication

Landstreet, John D., 1940-
Physical processes in the solar system: an introduction to the origin, structure and evolution of asteroids, comets, planets and moons / John D. Landstreet.

Includes bibliographical references and index.
ISBN 0–9732051–0–5

1. Solar system -- Textbooks. I. Title.

QB 501.L35 2003   523.2   C2003–903439–9

ISBN 0–9732051–0–5 paperback

Contents

Preface

This book is an attempt to create an up-to-date text on the physics of the solar system and the objects that make it up. It thus has a rather different outlook compared to books that focus on descriptive material, on geological ideas, or on chemistry and astro-biology, although aspects of all these approaches do appear in the book. I have tried to centre the discussions on the big ideas, on how things work, on what the structure and history of various bodies has been, and on why we accept some answers to our questions and reject others. Because of this approach, the book does not provide a complete survey of the enormous amount of information now available about solar system objects. Instead I have concentrated on subjects that are thought to be (at least qualitatively) understood at present, and particularly on topics that illustrate the application of physical ideas and reasoning.

The material is examined in two different ways in each chapter: first, the subject of the chapter is discussed qualitatively and conceptually, and then towards the end of the chapter some of the same material is re-analyzed quantitatively using the tools of first year university physics and calculus. The reason for this double approach is connected with the kinds of student who took the one-semester course on "Solar System Physics" that I offered at the University of Western Ontario for a number of years, and for whom this book was written. The course originated as a part of the Astronomy Honours (four-year B. Sc.) programme at the university, and was initially designed around the goals of (a) familiarizing the students with the wide range of aspects of the solar system that can be understood using the material from the first year of university physics, and (b) using the solar system to solidify the students' mastery of that physics. I have found that the solar system provide a wonderful variety of questions that can be discussed using first-year physics, and that a course discussing such problems is very effective at helping students to realize the power of even one year of physics for understanding natural phenomena in their environment.

However, I soon discovered that a number of students other than those in honours physics or astronomy programmes were interested in taking the course. Many of these other students lacked the background in physics needed to solve the problems that formed an important part of our course, and so I developed a second version of the same solar system course, which emphasizes qualitative understanding of concepts, ability to reason with these concepts, and practice explaining basic ideas through a series of essays submitted through the semester. The only prerequisite I imposed for entrance to this more qualitative version of the course was successful completion of any first year university physical science course (astronomy, chemistry, geology, or physics, qualitative or quantitative) so that I could assume that the students would have some prior knowledge of such topics as conservation of energy and the structure of atoms.

Because of limited teaching resources, it was always necessary to teach these two versions of the course together. Thus I have tried to create a single text which could be used by both groups. Conceptual but qualitative material forms the bulk of each chapter; I found that this material could be presented in a manner that is reasonably intelligible to and appropriate for both groups, although students with different backgrounds certainly understand the material in somewhat different ways. The students in the essay version of the course read only these (non-mathematical) sections of the book. To allow the students to test their understanding of the reading as they progress, small exercises are embedded in the text, and review questions are included at the end of each chapter.

To help the students in the problem-solving course to see more clearly how the university physics they have learned may be applied to understanding the solar system, each chapter ends with a section called "Mathematical aspects", in which relevant aspects of first-year physics are reviewed (and perhaps extended), some of the most interesting applications of quantitative physics are discussed, and useful tools for analysis of problems are presented. The students in the problem-solving course read this section, as well as the rest of each chapter. Each chapter has a number of quantitative short exercises in the "Mathematical aspects" section, and students in the problem-solving group are encouraged to do all of these as they come to them. In addition, there is a selection of more challenging problems at the end of each chapter for this group; most of these are conceptually interesting problems rather than the "plug-in" type.

This system of offering two courses in one package has worked quite well, probably because any course on the solar system involves introduction of a very large number of unfamiliar ideas which need to be thought about and discussed qualitatively before they are understood – and before interesting problems can be solved. I have two classes a week for all the students, in which we discuss the big ideas of that week's reading, and a third (tutorial) class for the students in the problem-solving group, devoted mainly to discussion of the use of physics and of problem-solving in the course context. Assignments for the essay course are a series of (usually three) essays on solar system topics, based on the text and supplementary reading. The students in the problem-solving course do a series of problem sets, taken from problems collected at the end of each chapter. Tests and examinations are partly the same for both versions of the course, but the essay course has a number of essay questions on each test which are replaced by short conceptual problems for the problem-solving group.

To encourage the students to learn more about topics of interest, and to help them find suitable subjects for essays, each chapter also includes a short bibliography listing resources that I have found particularly useful. However, since each chapter's bibliography is specific to the subject of the chapter, let me mention a few general solar system texts that may be useful to teachers and students. *The New Solar System* (Cambridge: Cambridge University Press, 1999), edited by A. Chaikin, C. C. Peterson, and J. K. Beatty, provides a good general and qualitative description of the solar system, nicely illustrated with many colour photos. The *Encyclopedia of Astronomy and Astrophysics* (Bristol, U. K: Institute of Physics Publishing, 2001) has many well-written articles at a very suitable level; this encyclopedia is also available at many universities over the Web. W. K. Hamblin and E. H. Christiansen's *Exploring the Planets* (New York, NY: Simon & Schuster, 1995) is a detailed, non-mathematical survey of the geological structure and surface features of the planets in the light of space probe data, with many excellent illustrations. A very good general text on the solar system, with a strong focus on geology, rather less physics, and a little mathematics, is W. K. Hartmann's *Moons and Planets* (Belmont, CA: Wadsworth, 1999). Hartmann's book is perhaps nearest in general level and intention to this book. Finally, there are two much more advanced texts, *Physics and Chemistry of the Solar System* by J. S. Lewis (San Diego, CA: Academic Press, 1997) and *Planetary Sciences* by I. de Pater and J. Lissauer (Cambridge: Cambridge University Press, 2001). These two books contain detailed discussions of many physical, chemical, and geological aspects of the solar system. Parts of each book require a knowledge of vector calculus, partial differential equations, and chemical thermodynamics, but other parts offer very readable reviews covering a wide range of topics.

I am grateful to the many people who have helped with the preparation of successive versions of this text over the years. Barbara Landstreet and Anne Brooks typed some of the earlier versions. Tara Sopoco, Sarah Landstreet, and especially Mira Rasche have converted many of the drawings and graphs from rough sketches into clear, handsome illustrations. Successive classes have proof-read the book many times, and offered useful comments. Colleagues, particularly Professor P. Brown, have helped me to find good review material and to understand it. Professor K. Keil (University of Hawaii) and several anonymous reviewers made extremely helpful and constructive suggestions. I thank all of these people. I am also grateful to the developers of Linux, of the Gnu utilities (especially emacs), of the TeX and LaTeX document preparation system, and of the Xmgrace graph tool for the powerful (and free) working environment I have employed to prepare the book. I thank the institutions and individuals from whom I have obtained illustrations, especially NASA with its splendid policy of making all its science images available without copyright restrictions, and Mr Dominique Dierick of Gent, Belgium, who contributed the cover images. I am grateful to the many scientists who work in this exciting and fascinating field for their efforts to make their ideas accessible to the rest of us. And last but not least, I thank Barbara and Sarah Landstreet for encouraging me to persevere with what has at times seemed to be a never-ending project, and for finally getting the book into print.

I would appreciate having errors of fact, concept or proofreading called to my attention. Please drop me an e-mail at jlandstr@astro.uwo.ca.

Chapter 1

A Survey of the Solar System

1.1 Overview

In Georges Simenon's classic mystery story *Maigret à Vichy* (*Maigret in Vichy*), Detective Superintendent Maigret, taking a cure in central France, is drawn into the investigation of an enigmatic murder case. The victim is a middle-aged woman about whom the police know essentially nothing at first; there is no obvious motive, and no suspect. Gradually, however, facts come to light, one by one, sometimes by chance but mostly as a result of patient police investigation. As more and more bits of information become available, Maigret begins to try to imagine what might have happened to lead to the murder. Eventually he is successful in understanding the situation, and uncovers both the murderer and the events that led up to the crime.

Understanding the nature and history of the bodies of the solar system presents us with a problem very much like that facing Maigret. We start with the information provided by the regular movements of the bright points of light that we call the planets, the Moon, and the Sun across the sky, and try to understand the rules of organization that have led to these observed motions. To this kind of data we are now adding many wonderful new facts (images and other kinds of remote measurements, and even some samples of surface materials) provided by space probes which have visited eight of the nine planets and several comets and asteroids. By themselves, these data do not explain either the nature or the history of these bodies. We must make a major effort of imagination to try to use these facts to *deduce* the interior structure of these bodies and to *guess* how they may have formed and evolved. We then need to test our theories for consistency with other facts, and see whether they are able to make correct predictions.

As a result of these two parallel processes, the patient collection of data, and the guess-work and debate of trying to piece these data together into an intelligible story, we now understand – more or less certainly – an important part of the nature and history of the small collection of bodies that drifts through space together with our Sun. This book is an introductory account to both the data we now have and to some of the ideas that have been proposed to explain these facts. As far as possible, the book is focused on Maigret's problem: how the raw facts can be used to understand what is hidden and what is past. As a starting point for this effort, let us briefly identify the characters which will appear in the story.

The **solar system** is the family of objects, familiar and otherwise, that travel through interstellar space together with our Sun. The **Sun** itself is a **star**: a huge mass of incandescent gas, held together by gravity, intensely hot and extraordinarily luminous. Our Sun is physically similar to the thousands of other stars that we see in the sky on any clear dark night, all of which, like the Sun, are hot and intrinsically luminous. These stars are separated by enormous distances, typically of the order of a few light-years (one light-year is the distance light travels in a year, about 9,400,000,000,000 km), and they drift through space relative to one another in an ever-changing pattern, like huge, stately hot-air balloons.

As our Sun moves through space, it is accompanied by a number of much smaller objects which are held near it by the attractive force of its gravity, the same force that holds us to the surface of the Earth. Some of these objects are visible in the night sky as bright points of light that move through the pattern of the constellations of distant stars. These are the **planets**, bodies such as Venus, Mars, Jupiter and Saturn. Several of these bodies (Mercury, Venus, and Mars) are similar in size and structure to the **Earth**; four others (Jupiter, Saturn, Uranus, and Neptune) are much larger and have quite different structure than the Earth. Each planet travels around the Sun in a large nearly circular orbit. Several of these planets, like the Earth, are in turn circled by smaller satellites that we call **moons**. There are many still smaller bodies in the space around the Sun as well. Thousands of bodies the size of tiny moons, the **asteroids**, circle the Sun in principally between the orbits of Mars and Jupiter. Other small objects, physically similar to giant icebergs, reside mostly in the space far outside the orbits of the planets (though they are still bound to the Sun by its gravity). These objects occasionally venture into the inner solar. As the sunlight warms them they sublime enormous clouds of gas (mostly water vapour) and dust and become visible as **comets**. And even smaller objects are scattered through the space between the planets: when the Earth collides with one of these **meteoroids** we may see the bright flash of a **meteor** in the night sky, and sometimes we even find a remnant of the fallen rock, a **meteorite**, on the surface of the Earth.

All these objects that are bound to the Sun, and travel with it through space, make up the solar system. There are good reasons to study this group of bodies. First, simple curiosity leads us to wonder how the solar system, and the objects in it, came to exist in the first place, and how it has developed and changed through its history. Many fascinating processes, some complex and intricate, and some beautifully simple, occur in and between the solar system bodies, and it is a source of satisfaction and pleasure to begin to understand these. Secondly, for very practical reasons we need to understand our own planet better. We want to understand more clearly how concentrations of industrially important substances such as iron, copper, coal, and petroleum occurred, so that we can find such resources when they are needed and estimate the available extent of the reserves. We need to understand better how small changes in the light output of the Sun affect our climate, and how our own activities, such as burning fossil fuels, can alter the environment. This process of understanding the Earth better is enormously helped by parallel study of other objects in the solar system. Improved understanding of the Sun will lead to the possibility of forecasting its changing effects on us. Study of the internal structures and atmospheres of other planets has already helped us to understand our own planet better. Finally, of course, we want to understand the history of our world and of its immediate environment more clearly in order to assess our own place in it. A clearer comprehension of how our world has developed should help us to appreciate the significance and importance of our own activities.

This book is intended to describe the various objects that populate the solar system. We shall try to understand how solar system bodies are organized physically, and to study some of the processes operating in them. We shall also look for clues that reveal something of the history of the objects in the solar system, and of the system as a whole, to give us some idea of how this remarkable system originated and how it has developed through time. We shall concentrate our attention particularly on those aspects of solar system objects that may be understood with the aid of simple physical (or geological, or chemical, or even biological) ideas, rather than emphasizing collections of facts and statistics.

The discussion throughout the book is intended to be essentially non-mathematical, although sizes of objects and other kinds of numerical descriptions will be freely used. In most of each chapter, only those points that can be described or explained in plain English will be discussed. However, at the end of each chapter, we include a section called **Mathematical Aspects**. In this section, some of the ideas of the chapter are re-examined in the light of the tools furnished by elementary physics. This section is intended for students who have completed a year of university level physics and who have a basic knowledge of differential and integral calculus. If you lack the necessary background of physics, you may skip this section in each chapter. If you do choose to study the *Mathematical Aspects* section in some chapters, you will be delighted to discover what a wide range of topics can be understood using the ideas of first-year physics. A number of problems are also included at the end of each chapter. It is very important that any student who wishes to really understand the quantitative physical treatment of the *Mathematical Aspects* sections try to solve as many of these problems as possible. Physical ideas are only mastered when you can apply them to real situations.

Sizes and units

As we describe the various objects that we shall be studying, there will be plenty of comparisons of one object to another, so that you may have a clear idea of relative sizes and of relationships among bodies. However, it will often be necessary to give actual sizes and other measurements of things. In general, this will be done in the **SI** (Système International) system of measurement units. In this system, the basic units of length, mass and time are the **meter** (39.4 inches), the **kilogram** (2.2 lbs), and the **second**. Other convenient sizes are sometimes used in place of the basic ones: for example, the centimeter (1/100 meter), the millimeter (1/1000 meter) and the kilometer (1000 meters) are frequently used. In fact, a whole system of prefixes is available to define convenient sizes from the basic units: kilo- (1000 times larger), mega- (one million times larger) and giga- (one billion times larger) are useful to describe large dimensions, while centi- (1/100), milli- (1/1000), micro- (1/1,000,000), and nano- (1/1,000,000,000) define convenient smaller sizes.

As an example of these units, we often need to describe large amounts of time. You will often see one million years abbreviated as 1 Myr, and one billion years (one thousand million years) as 1 Gyr.

Other necessary units are given in this same system. For example, the unit for speed is the meter per second. (One meter per second, or 1 m s^{-1}, is the same as 3600 meters in 3600 s = 1 hr, or 3.6 km hr^{-1}, a slow walking pace). We shall also need a unit for the power (energy per second) emitted by a luminous body like the Sun; the SI unit is the watt, a unit familiar from ratings of light bulbs, toasters, and irons. Temperature is usually measured on the Kelvin scale, in which the size of a degree is the same as a Celsius (or centigrade) degree, but the zero point is chosen to start at absolute zero, the lowest physically attainable temperature, at -273.16 C. Any temperature given in Kelvin degrees ("Kelvins", or K), may be converted to Celsius degrees by subtracting 273 (or 273.16 if high accuracy is required).

We should mention that many physicists and astronomers actually work with slightly different units than those preferred in the SI system. In this alternative system, the basic units of distance, mass and time are the centimeter, gram (1/1000 kilogram), and second. These units, and other derived ones (power in ergs per second, for example; 1 erg $s^{-1} = 10^{-7}$ W) will often be encountered in reading in other source books.

A few useful units are specific to astronomy. Distances within the solar system are often given using the **astronomical unit** or AU as the basic length; this is simply the mean distance between the Sun and the Earth, about 150,000,000 km. (More precise values of this and a number of other useful constants and units are tabulated in Appendix B at the end of the book.) For larger distance such as those separating stars from one another, we sometimes use the **light year** or ly, the distance travelled by light in one year (about 9,500,000,000,000 km or 63,000 AU). Another unit often used for such really large distances, derived from the method by which stellar distance is measured, is the **parsec** or pc, equal to 3.26 ly.

Another area in which specialized units are useful is in measuring small angles. We often subdivide a single degree (one-360th of a circle) into 60 **arc minutes** (written 60′), and even subdivide one arc minute into 60 **arc seconds** (written 60″). In practice, we can more or less easily measure the position of a star or planet on the sky to a precision of about 1″, which is why these very tiny units of angular measure are useful.

In astronomical situations it is frequently necessary to work with *very* large (or small) numbers. These are conveniently written using **scientific notation**, in which a number written as a simpler number times a power of ten. Thus $100 = 10 \times 10$ is written as 10^2, and $10,000 = 10 \times 1000 = 10 \times 10 \times 100 = 10 \times 10 \times 10 \times 10$ is written as 10^4 (notice that the exponent of 10 is the same as the number of zeros in the original number). A more complex number such as 212,000,000 is written as $2.12 \times 100,000,000$, or much more compactly as 2.12×10^8. Small numbers are written similarly: $1/1000 = 1/10^3 = 10^{-3}$, and $2.12/100,000,000 = 2.12 \times 10^{-8}$. Multiplication of two numbers in scientific notation is quite easy: multiply together the two decimal numbers and add the exponents. For example 2.2×10^3 multiplied by 1.5×10^6 is $(2.2 \times 1.5) \times (10^3 \times 10^6) = 3.3 \times 10^{3+6} = 3.3 \times 10^9$.

1.2 An inventory of the solar system

We now turn to the actual subject matter of this book. To start, it is useful to survey in some detail the various kinds of objects found in the solar system. This will provide a general impression of the nature of the bodies as well as a useful vocabulary, and give some first hints as to how these objects are related and interact.

The Sun

The dominant body in the solar system is the Sun. It is a star, physically very similar to other stars that we see in the sky at night, except that it is about 100,000 times closer to us here on Earth than even the closest of the night-time stars. The Sun, and the hundreds of billions of other stars in the space around us, are members of a giant flattened star system that we call a **galaxy**. We call our galaxy the **Milky Way**, and it is visible in a dark sky (no Moon, no city lights) as a faint, milky band of light crossing the sky through the constellations Gemini, Auriga, and Cygnus in the (northern) winter sky, and through Scorpius, Centaurus, and Canis Major in the (northern) summer sky.

With a mass of $M_\odot = 1.99 \times 10^{30}$ kg, the Sun contains 99.87 percent of the total mass of the entire solar system (most of the rest, another .09%, is in the largest planet, Jupiter). The Sun is composed primarily of hydrogen (chemical symbol H), the first and lightest element in the periodic table of the elements, which makes up about 90% of its total mass. The next element in the periodic table, helium (He), accounts for another 9%. All other chemical elements together make up the remaining 1% of the total mass.

The Sun is not only the most massive object in the solar system, but also the largest. Its radius $R_\odot$ (the distance from the centre to the surface) is 695,000 km, about 110 times larger than the radius of the Earth. It is almost ten times larger than Jupiter, the largest of the planets.

Structurally, the Sun is a huge ball of super-hot gases. A solid body such as the Earth or the Moon supports the weight of its external layers by having interior matter which is hard to compress (like the water in a hot water bottle) because the atoms of the matter touch one another like golf balls in a pail and resist further compaction. In contrast, a star like our Sun provides outward pressure to support the weight of its upper layers by being extremely *hot* inside (the temperature at the centre of the Sun is actually about $15,000,000 \text{ K} = 1.5 \times 10^7\text{K}$). This very high temperature provides pressure in the same way the air inside a balloon stretches and supports the balloon skin: individual atoms rattle around so rapidly that their collisions with atoms above them hold up the higher layers.

Because the Sun is hot inside, heat leaks from the interior to the surface, and from there into the (almost) empty space around the Sun. Heat is lost at the enormous rate of 3.83×10^{26} W (compare this number to the total electrical energy consumption of a city like Toronto or New York, which might need only 10^{10} or 10^{11} W to heat homes, light lights, run motors in factories, drive subway trains and trams, etc.). The lost heat is actually carried off as light and heat radiation (ultraviolet, visible, and infrared rays) from the hot solar surface, or photosphere. This radiating level is much cooler than the solar interior, but with a temperature of about 5770 K (6040 C) it is still brilliantly incandescent, as anyone can easily see on a clear day.

The light output of the Sun is not the only outflow from our star. It is also boiling off a very dilute gas from its surface, which streams out of the solar system in all directions. This outflow, called the **solar wind**, carries off only an insignificant amount of mass and energy from the Sun (the Sun loses about one part in 10^{14}, or 10^{-14}, of its mass each year), but the solar wind has interesting effects on the other inhabitants of the solar system, especially comets, as we shall see later.

The planets

If we now step back from the Sun and survey the space around it, we next notice a few objects that are much smaller than the Sun. They are also far fainter than the Sun because they are not intrinsically luminous, but are visible only because they are lit by sunlight. These are the nine planets. They repeatedly travel around the Sun in enormous, roughly circular paths called **orbits**. These orbits are approximately centred on the Sun, and all lie in nearly the same plane as the Earth's own orbit around the Sun. All the planets circle the Sun in the same direction.

Some interesting properties of the orbits of the planets are assembled in Table A.1, which is in Appendix A at the end of the book for easier reference later. This table lists the nine planets, as well as the three largest asteroids (Vesta, Ceres, and Pallas), in order of their distance from the Sun. For each planet the table shows the mean distance a from the Sun (the average of the smallest and largest distances, usually called the **semi-major axis** of the orbit). This mean distance from the Sun is expressed in terms of the mean size of the Earth's orbit about the Sun, 1.496×10^{11} m, which is called an **astronomical unit** or **AU**, as the unit of length. Notice that the typical separation of planets is far larger than the size of the Sun. The distance from the Sun to the Earth (1 AU) is about 108 solar diameters. There is clearly some regularity in the spacing of the planets (especially if the asteroids are considered together as a single planet), with spacing between successive orbits increasing steadily as one looks farther and farther out in the solar system. The **mean orbital speed** v of the planet in its orbit (actually the speed in a circular orbit of the same radius as the mean distance of the actual orbit) is given in the next column. Its value decreases steadily as we look at more and more distant orbits. The time required for a planet to complete exactly one revolution about the Sun is the **orbital period** P. It is given in the table in terms of the Earth's orbital period, which is of course 1 year (1 yr, equal to 3.157×10^7 seconds). P increases steadily with mean distance from the Sun, both because the more distant planets have much farther to go to travel once about the Sun, and because they move more slowly. The outermost planets travel so slowly that neither Neptune nor Pluto has had time to complete a single revolution about the Sun since it was first discovered.

Although the planets travel around the Sun in approximately the same plane, which coincides fairly closely with the plane of the Sun's equator, the orbital planes differ slightly from one another. The **orbital inclination** i is the angle by which the orbital plane of each of the various planets is inclined to the orbital plane of the Earth. The plane of the Earth's orbit is the reference plane in the solar system, and is called the **plane of the ecliptic**. It is clear from the table that the various orbital planes (apart from those of the asteroids and Pluto) do not differ by very much.

The orbits of the planets are neither exactly circular nor precisely centred on the Sun. They are generally somewhat oval in shape, like slightly squashed circles: in fact, they are **ellipses**. The orbits of Mercury and Pluto are somewhat more elongated than the orbits of the other planets. The more elongated a planetary orbit is, the more its centre is separated from the Sun. A measure of the elongation of an orbit, and of the offset between the Sun and the centre of the orbit, is

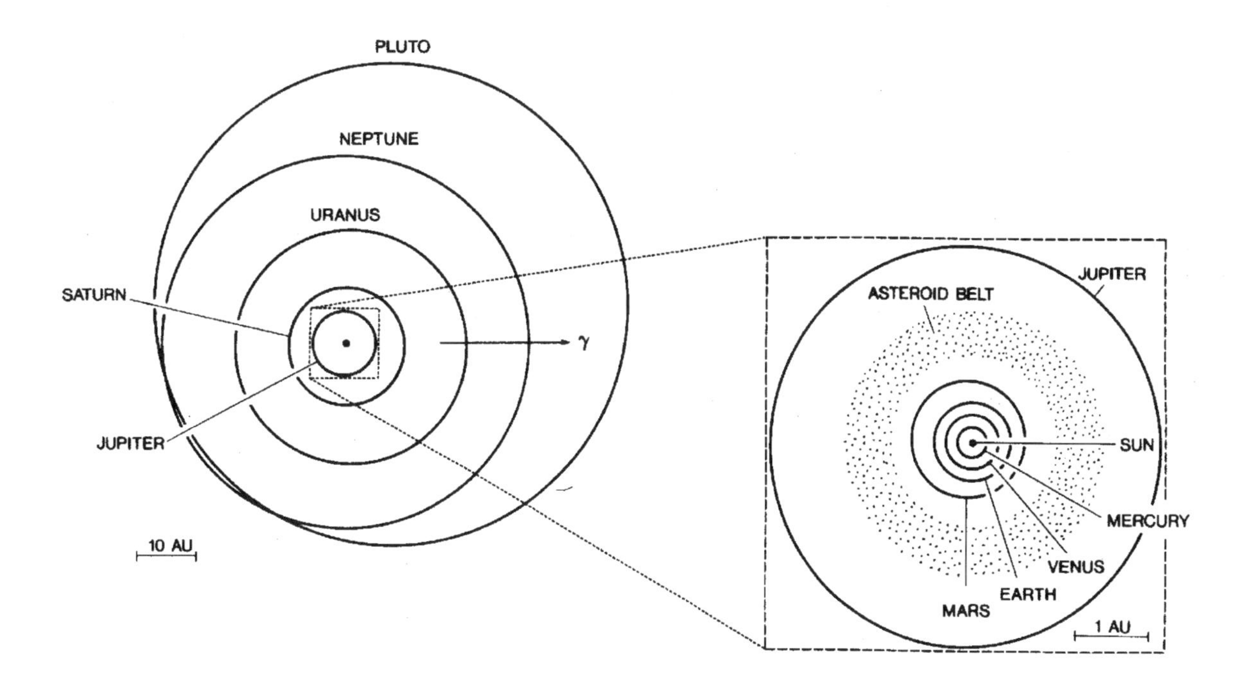

Figure 1.1: The orbits of the planets about the Sun, projected onto the plane of the ecliptic. The left part of the figure shows the planets from Jupiter out to Pluto. The inner solar system, too small to be shown adequately with the outer planets, is expanded on the right. The orbits of Mars and Pluto are clearly not centred on the Sun. The Kuiper Belt (a second asteroid belt of icy asteroids), not shown, is outside the orbit of Neptune.

the **orbital eccentricity** e, which is the distance from the centre of an orbit to the Sun, divided by half the largest dimension of the orbit (the **semi-major axis** of the orbit). The quantity e, given in the last column of Table A.1, varies from 0 for a perfectly circular orbit centred on the Sun to nearly 1 for an extremely elongated orbit (such as a comet orbit) with the Sun near one end. Ellipses and elliptical orbits will be discussed in more detail later in the chapter.

The planetary orbits are shown in Figure 1.1. Because the scale of the inner solar system is so much more compact than that of the outer part, this figure has to have two parts, one to show the planets out as far as Jupiter, and one to show the outer planets.

When we look at the various planets through a telescope, several of them have quite distinctive visual personalities. Mercury, because of its small orbit, is never seen far from the Sun. Practically no details of its surface can be seen from Earth. Venus is covered with dense clouds, and is off-white and quite featureless. It is always seen in early evening or shortly before dawn, and can be the brightest object in the sky. Mars is rather reddish, and one can make out dark and light regions on the planet, and white polar caps like those of Earth. Jupiter has alternate light and dark bands across its face, a giant red spot, and four easily visible moons. Saturn also has alternating bands like Jupiter, although they are much fainter, and is surrounded by spectacular rings, as well as one bright and several fainter moons. Uranus, Neptune, and Pluto are far enough from Earth that few details are visible, but all have one or several moons.

The planets are also rather diverse physically. Their main physical characteristics are summarized in Table A.2 (also found in Appendix A at the end of the book). In this table the mass of each planet is given as a multiple of the Earth's mass $M_e = 5.975 \times 10^{24}$ kg, and the radius is given as multiple of the Earth's radius $R_e = 6.378 \times 10^6$ m $= 6378$ km. The four inner planets are roughly similar to the Earth in size and chemical composition, and are known as the **terrestrial planets**. The largest and most massive of these planets is the Earth itself. Venus has nearly the same mass and radius as Earth, while Mars (shown in Figure 1.2) and Mercury are about an order of magnitude (that is, a factor of ten) smaller in mass than Earth, and roughly half as large in radius. The four terrestrial planets have generally similar **mean densities** (planet mass divided by total planet volume) ρ, in the range of 3900–5500 kg m^{-3}, somewhat denser than typical rocks of the Earth's surface. (Recall that the density of water is 1000 kg m^{-3}). All these planets are primarily composed of the four chemical elements silicon (Si), magnesium (Mg), iron (Fe), and oxygen (O), partly in

Figure 1.2: The planet Mars as viewed from an approaching spacecraft. The dark region in the middle of the disk is the Valles Marineris, a huge rift valley. The ovals on the left near the edge of the planet are volcanos. (Courtesy of the U. S. National Aeronautics and Space Administration [NASA].)

Figure 1.3: The planet Saturn viewed from a spacecraft. The planet's beautiful rings are prominent. Faint bands on the planet's disk parallel to the rings are cloud systems. Two small dots in the dark sky below the planet are moons. (Courtesy of NASA.)

the form of rocky material which contains all of these elements, and partly in the form of metallic iron.

The four **giant planets**, from Jupiter to Neptune, are very different from the inner four. They are quite a lot more massive than Earth, especially Jupiter and Saturn (shown in Figure 1.3), and correspondingly larger in radius. However, when we calculate mean densities, these are between 700 and 1700 kg m^{-3}, not much different from the value for water, and substantially smaller than the value for rocky material. Clearly these planets have very different chemical composition than the terrestrial planets. In fact, we believe that they all are largely composed of the same elements, H and He, that constitute the main elements in the Sun. However, they all have a higher fraction of elements other than H and He than the Sun does.

The outermost planet, Pluto, is anomalous. It is not as large as our Moon, or as massive. Tiny as it is, it has a moon of its own. It is considered to be one of the planets, but it has more in common physically with the moons of the giant planets than it does with any other planet, and it is now usually thought of as the largest of a recently discovered class of icy bodies that inhabit the regions farther from the sun than any of the planets.

The last two columns of Table A.2 give the **sidereal rotation period** (the time for one rotation relative to the stars), in (Earth) days (1 day = 86400 s), and obliquity of the rotation axis for each planet. The obliquity is the angle between the rotation axis (the imaginary line through the north and south poles of a planet) and a line drawn perpendicular to the orbit plane of the planet. Mercury, Venus, and Jupiter all have very small obliquities, which means that their rotation axes are almost perpendicular to their orbit planes. Earth, Mars, Saturn, and Neptune all have obliquities near 25°. As we shall see later, this means that all could have seasons analogous to those of Earth. This is particularly obvious for Mars, which has two polar caps which alternately grow and shrink as winter and summer come and go in each hemisphere. Finally, Uranus has an obliquity near 90°, which means that the rotation axis of the planet is almost in its orbital plane. As this planet orbits the Sun, first one of the poles points roughly towards the Sun for some years, then the Sun moves towards the equator, then towards the other pole, and so on. A potential for quite extreme seasons clearly exists!

Satellites of the planets

All of the planets except Venus and Mercury have smaller bodies circling around them, which we call satellites or moons. The Earth and Pluto have one moon each, in both cases relatively large bodies compared to the planets. Mars has two tiny moons. The giant planets, Jupiter, Saturn, and Uranus, all have systems of moons, each like a miniature solar system centred on the planet. Neptune has two fairly large moons and (at least) several smaller ones. The larger of these moons are fairly similar in size to the Earth's Moon, while the smaller ones are more nearly like asteroids. (However, unlike the Moon, most of these moons are made of a mixture of rocky material and ice.) Only Mercury and Venus have no satellites at all. Some interesting characteristics of the larger moons of each planet are collected in Table A.3. In this table, the radius of the orbit of each moon is given in units of the radius of the planet (which can be determined from Table A.2). The actual masses of the moons and their radii are compared to the mass and radius of the Earth's Moon, $M_{\rm m} = 7.35 \times 10^{22}$ kg and $R_{\rm m} = 1.738 \times 10^{6}$ m = 1738 km. (Many of the units used in these tables, such as the AU, the Earth's mass and radius, etc, are collected in Appendix A for convenient reference as needed.)

Among the terrestrial planets, the Earth is unique in having a nearly planet-sized moon. This moon is rather similar in appearance to the smallest of the terrestrial planets, Mercury. The surface is heavily marked with huge impact craters, some hundreds of kilometers in diameter. Most craters were produced during the last stage of formation of the Moon, when our satellite collided with a number of huge pieces of space debris, tens of kilometers in size, about four Gyr ago (remember, 1 Gyr means one billion years), although new craters are still produced from time to time by impacts of rapidly moving small bodies. Like the inner planets, the composition of the Earth's Moon is thought to be dominated by rocky material made of Si, Mg, Fe, and O. Because of tidal effects due to the Earth acting on the Moon, the Moon's intrinsic rotation has been synchronized with its orbital motion about the Earth, so that one hemisphere of the Moon always faces the Earth.

The only other moons found orbiting a terrestrial planet are the two tiny moons of Mars. These are only a few kilometers in diameter, and quite irregular in shape, somewhat like potatoes. Both are heavily cratered. They are probably small captured asteroids.

In contrast to the terrestrial planets, the giants are richly endowed with satellites. Jupiter has four large satellites comparable in size to our Moon, and at least a dozen smaller moons. The four large moons, discovered by Galilei (hence **Galilean satellites**) and the inner small ones form a small solar system, orbiting in the plane of Jupiter's equator. The outer satellites form two groups, each orbiting at an angle to the planet's equatorial plane, one group revolving in the same sense as Jupiter's rotation, the other group going in the opposite direction. Saturn has an equally large but more varied collection of moons. Only one, Titan, is large enough to rival the Galilean moons of Jupiter, but another eight are large enough to be seen from Earth, and several small moons were discovered by the Voyager space probes. These moons, and the spectacular ring system close to the planet that is the hallmark of its visual image (see Figure 1.3), all orbit more or less closely in the planet's equatorial plane. Only the outermost moon revolves around the planet in the opposite direction from the rest. Saturn's moon Dione is seen in Figure 1.4.

Figure 1.4: Saturn's moon Dione, one of five moons with diameters of more than 1000 km that orbit the planet. Its surface show many craters from the era when the moon was still growing by sweeping up small bodies in its vicinity. (Courtesy of NASA.)

Uranus also has a miniature solar system of moons, including five comparable to the middle-size moons of Saturn, and at least ten small moons. These bodies orbit around the equator of the planet, even though this equatorial plane lies almost at right angles to the plane of Uranus' orbit (and to the ecliptic plane). Neptune has the most bizarre moon system of the gas giants. It has one large moon, Triton, revolving around the planet in the opposite sense to the planet's rotation, and a second somewhat smaller moon, Nereid, in a highly eccentric orbit. Several tiny moons were also found here by Voyager 2. And all the gas giants have now been found to have ring systems, although only that of Saturn has enough material in it to be easily visible from the Earth.

Physically the moons of the giant planets constitute almost a new class of small planets. Although most apparently have some rocky material like that in the Earth's outer layers, most also have a large fraction of their mass in the form of frozen ices such as H_2O (water) and CO_2 (carbon dioxide, or dry ice). Temperatures in the outer solar system are so low (near 100 K), that these two substances are frozen to rock-like hardness, and are mixed up together with real rocky matter to make up the substance of the moons of the giant planets.

The moons of all the giant planets have been photographed at fairly close range by the two Voyager spacecraft. These moons exhibit an astonishing variety of surface appearances. For example, the four large moons of Jupiter range in appearance from the heavily cratered surfaces of Callisto and Ganymede, the outer two, through Europa, which has no features except a body-wide network of fine cracks, to Io, the innermost of the large moons and the most volcanically active object in the solar system, which looks in photos from spacecraft like a huge spherical pizza pie. The moons of the other outer planets are almost equally varied.

Pluto is again anomalous. It has, as far as is known, only one moon, a body not a great deal smaller than the planet in mass and radius. Probably both bodies have much the same ice and rock mixture composition, although their surface compositions are somewhat different. Because Pluto is so small, it is physically much more like other icy moons than like any of the other planets.

Asteroids

If you look at the *planetary* orbits in the map of the solar system of Figure 1.1, ignoring the zone labeled asteroid belt, there is an obvious gap in the spacing of the planets between Mars and Jupiter. There is no planet in this gap. Instead, a vast collection of small objects, the largest of which is much smaller than our Moon, orbits the Sun in the region where a planet might be expected. These bodies are so tiny that the largest of them was not discovered until 1801. Because they are so small, they do not show any visible disk through a telescope. Instead, they look like tiny points of light, similar to stars, which is how they came to be called asteroids (from the Greek word *aster*, star).

There are now many thousands of known asteroids. Their orbits resemble those of planets. They move mainly in or near the ecliptic plane, in orbits that are typically inclined to the ecliptic plane. Most orbits have inclinations of less than 30°. The orbits are usually no more eccentric than those of Mercury or Pluto. Most of the asteroid orbits have mean distances from the Sun that are between 2.2 and 3.8 AU. All asteroids orbit the Sun in the same sense as the planets. Some orbital and physical properties of the largest asteroids may be found summarized in Tables A.1 and 6.1.

Figure 1.5: The asteroid Ida and its moon Dactyl. Ida (the larger body) is about 52 km in length, and heavily cratered. Its moon is the small dot to the right of the main object in the dark sky. (Courtesy of NASA.)

The asteroids range in size from Ceres, which has a radius of 470 km, down to objects with radii (or at least typical sizes; such small objects are very unlikely to be spherical) of a kilometer or less. Only half a dozen are known to have radii as large as 150 km. Most are too small for their masses to have been measured, but the masses and densities of a few are known. Most have densities of about 2700 kg m^{-3}, but one is about half this dense and one is considerably denser. With densities of this size, these (and other) asteroids are clearly made of rock, probably very loosely packed in some. Several asteroids have now been visited by space probes, including one mission to Eros in which the probe actually orbited and then landed on the asteroid. The small asteroid Ida was photographed during a close encounter by the Galileo space probe in 1993, and is seen in Figure 1.5.

Most of the known asteroids are located in the asteroid belt, but we know that there are of the order of 1000 asteroid-like bodies a kilometer or less in diameter in orbits that cross that of Earth. Fortunately for us, collisions with these bodies are extremely rare.

A second important group of asteroids is found occupying two regions of Jupiter's orbit, 60° ahead and 60° behind the giant planet. These bodies may be as numerous as those in the main asteroid belt; they are known as the *Trojan asteroids*.

In recent years another major asteroid belt has been discovered in the region outside the orbit of the planet Neptune. Since 1992 hundreds of objects as large as the larger asteroids have been found at roughly 30 to 50 AU from the Sun, in a region known as the **Kuiper Belt**. Because they are dark and distant, little is yet known about these Kuiper Belt Objects. They are likely to be composed of a mixture of rock and ices. The planet Pluto and its moon Charon are often considered to be the largest members of this third asteroid belt.

These small floating rock piles (and ice-rock piles, in the outer solar system) are almost certainly pieces left over from the era when planets formed around our Sun. They seem to be fragments that were never swept up by any planet. They have therefore not changed much since the era when the planets formed (unlike the material of the planets, which has been intensely heated and repeatedly altered), and they provide enormously valuable clues about events that occurred during the period when the solar system formed.

Meteorites

From time to time, a rock falls to the Earth out of the sky. Only a tiny fraction of such events are actually witnessed by anyone; nevertheless, hundreds of occurrences have been recorded over the past two centuries. The fallen rock may weigh a few kilograms or more; in rare cases these objects have weighed tons. The rock may be monolithic, or several or many fragments may be found. Sometimes the surface of the rock appears to have been melted. While the rock is seen falling through the air, the fiery display is known as a **meteor**. Once the object reaches the ground safely and is found, it is called a **meteorite**.

Most of the meteorites that have been observed to fall from the sky are quite different in appearance, and in mineral and chemical content, from the usual rocks of the Earth's surface. As a result, it has been possible to identify quite a lot of other rocks found on Earth as meteorites, even though they were not seen to fall. There are now thousands of meteorites in the laboratories and museums of the world.

Many falling meteoroids have been observed (including several that were later recovered), either by automatic camera systems or by home video cameras. These observations have furnished enough information to enable the orbits of these objects around the Sun to be determined. Most of these meteorites were on orbits that carried them as far as the asteroid belt, as well as crossing the orbit of Earth, before finally colliding with Earth. This strongly suggests that most of the material currently being swept up by the Earth in the form of meteorites originated in the asteroid belt. Nature thus provides us – free – with wonderful physical samples of the asteroids with which we can study their chemical and mineral composition.

Two main types of meteorites are found. One group, which makes up about 15% of the meteorites actually seen to fall to Earth, may be called **igneous meteorites**, by analogy with igneous rocks (rocks formed from magma or molten lava) on Earth. Some igneous meteorites resemble the basaltic rock that is a common kind of volcanic lava on Earth. Others are nearly pure nickel-iron metal, similar to what we think is in the Earth's iron core. A third type of igneous meteorite has a mixture of rocky chunks embedded in a nickel-iron mass, or blobs of metallic iron in a rocky mass. All these igneous meteorites show signs of intense heating, often melting, with subsequent separation in the melted material of components of different freezing points and densities, followed by freezing of the molten material. Such meteorites appear to have been made within many asteroids much larger than the pieces that we have, which was somehow partly or completely melted. In this situation, the iron and nickel would melt and sink to the centre of the asteroid under the sorting influence of gravity, because iron is much denser than rock, while various rocky components would float to levels near the surface. Later, collisions with small objects in the asteroid belt led to breaking off of chips from these once-melted asteroids, and gravity then guided some of the chips into orbits which intersected that of the Earth.

As if it were not extraordinary enough that nature delivers to us igneous meteorites that are products of melting in the interiors of asteroids, the other great category of meteorites is just as astonishing. This group is called the **chondritic meteorites**, or **chondrites**, after small glassy spheres (usually less than one millimeter in diameter) known as **chondrules** that are embedded in the rocky mass of most chondritic meteorites. Chondritic meteorites have typical chemical compositions that are unlike any terrestrial rocks, which are the products of a long process of melting and remelting. Instead, the abundance fractions of most chemical elements (the ratios of number of atoms of various species to the number of, say, silicon or iron atoms) are quite close to the abundance fractions found in the atmosphere of the Sun. The elements for which this is *not* true are those that freeze only at low temperatures (H, He, and Ne, for example), or that evaporate fairly easily, such as indium, bismuth, lead, chlorine, or zinc. For refractory (not easily melted) elements such as magnesium, aluminum, silicon, and manganese, the abundance ratios of both abundant elements and rare ones are quite close to solar ratios.

The reason that this is an extraordinary result is that

it strongly suggests that the history of chondrites since their parent asteroids were formed has *not* included any processes leading to significant melting or other important chemical sorting of the interiors of the parent asteroids. Instead, they seem to be more-or-less unaltered remnants of the original material which coalesced to form the planets. As such, the chondrites still contain information, in the crystal grains and fragments of which they are formed, about the processes that occurred while the planets were forming. This kind of information is no longer available in the rocks of the Earth, which have been repeatedly reworked by geological activity such as volcanism, to the extent that their current mineral and chemical structures contain very little information about conditions that occurred while the planets were forming.

Thus, meteorites provide us with two enormously valuable kinds of information – information about the physical, chemical, and mineral structure of asteroids, and also information about the state of the material that coalesced to form the bodies of the solar system.

Figure 1.6: Comet Halley at the time of its most recent passage through the inner solar system in 1986. The picture shows only the part of the comet near the head. The inner tail shows many rays. (Courtesy of NASA.)

Comets

There is still one other kind of material known in the solar system that is left over from the time when the planets formed, and has remained relatively unaltered since. This material is huge chunks of intensely cold, extremely dirty ice, something like icebergs mixed with a lot of frozen mud, a few kilometers in size, that mostly orbit the Sun far outside the tracks of the planets, in a vast region called the **Oort Cloud**. Occasionally a nudge from a passing star will alter the orbit of one of these dirty icebergs, and it strays into the inner part of the solar system, inside the orbit of Jupiter. When this happens, the heat of the Sun warms the ice enough to sublimate water vapour (steam) into the space around the iceberg. As the vapour sublimes from the surface, bits of dust and dirt are carried off as well, forming a huge diffuse dust cloud around the object. This outflow of water vapour and dust is visible because it is lit by light from the Sun. In fact, sunlight streaming away from the Sun exerts enough pressure on the dust that escapes from the dirty iceberg to blow it slowly out of the solar system. The iceberg has a visible tail as well as a cloud around it.

The dirty iceberg, and the visible phenomena associated with its passage through the inner solar system, are known as a **comet**. Although several comets come into the inner solar system each year, most are extremely faint, hardly noticeable from Earth. But occasionally a spectacularly bright comet will be visible. One comet that can usually be counted on to put on a good show is Halley's comet (seen in Figure 1.6), which returns to the inner solar system every 75 or 76 years. However, on its most recent visit, in 1986, it was nearest the Sun just when the Sun was between it and the Earth, and so the view was much less impressive than usual. We had some compensation for this poor show about a decade later, however, with the easily visible comets Hyakutake in 1996 and Hale-Bopp in 1997. Comet Hale-Bopp, incidentally, has one of the largest iceberg cores ever studied, some 40 km in diameter.

The asteroids and the comets seem at first glance to be quite different kinds of objects. However, much of the chemical difference between the asteroids of the asteroid belt and the small bodies of the outer solar system (Trojan asteroids, Kuiper Belt objects, and comets) is simply a consequence of distance from the sun. In the asteroid belt, the sun raises the temperatures high enough that ice would sublime away in a relatively short time; objects farther out in the solar system are cold enough to retain ice for billions of year. What these different objects have in common is much more important: all are objects that formed by collisions of much smaller fragments of solid material early in the history of the solar system. They are thus all *planetesimals*, small bodies which then went on to accumulate by gravity into a few much larger objects that we now recognize as the planets. The asteroids, Kuiper

Belt objects, and comets are all bodies that reached the planetesimal stage, but that then escaped the final sweeping up. By exploring these objects we are able to learn something about the conditions of matter at the time when the planets first formed around the Sun.

1.3 Planetary sizes, separations, and motions

We now start our detailed study of the solar system by looking at the oldest questions of astronomy: what are the shapes and sizes of the solar system bodies, how far apart are they, and how do they move relative to one another? These closely related questions made up essentially the entire subject of astronomy during the two millennia between the birth of science in Greece during the sixth and fifth centuries B.C., and the invention of the telescope at the start of the 17th century A.D. The way in which our understanding of planetary sizes and motions developed historically is very illuminating, with many clever ideas and insights and interesting lines of reasoning, and so we shall use this development as a framework for looking at this topic.

Shape and size of the Earth

The obvious place to start our inquiry is with an effort to determine the shape and size of the Earth. This was one of the earliest problems solved by the philosophers and mathematicians of the ancient world.

Early civilizations such as those in Mesopotamia (the Sumerians, Akkadians, Babylonians, and Persians) and in Egypt, as well as the early Greeks, were inclined to accept the appearance of the world more or less at face value. They imagined it to be a large flat surface, perhaps somewhat larger than the extent of the known lands, with a ring of ocean around the outside. The sky was imagined to be a kind of inverted bowl containing the Sun, Moon, stars and planets. Gods controlled the motions of the various heavenly bodies across the sky.

The Greeks seem to have been the first to try to understand the physical nature of the Earth. The idea that the Earth is actually an isolated sphere sitting (or moving) in space, and that the Moon and Sun are also physical objects in space far from the Earth, developed slowly through a series of imaginative theories. Two main "schools" (loosely associated groups of scholars and philosophers) furnished much of the leadership for this endeavor. In the Greek islands and coastal towns of Ionia (present-day western Turkey), a group associated with Thales of Miletos (flourished 1st half of the sixth century B.C.) proposed various possible physical descriptions of the Earth and celestial bodies. Other ideas were developed in the fifth century by members of the school of Pythagoras in Syracuse, a city founded by Greeks in Sicily. By the fourth century, the great Athenian scholar and philosopher Aristotle (384–322 B.C.) was able to discuss quite correctly the nature of the Earth.

Two observations made by Greek sailors and merchants led philosophers to the view that the Earth is spherical rather than flat. First, as a ship leaves a port, the land near sea level vanishes before the peaks of hills and mountains do. Similarly, seen from land, a ship's hull vanishes before the mast and sail do. The disappearance of things near sea level before higher ones is due to the curved shape of the Earth's (or sea's) surface, which interposes a bulge between the observer and the receding object, as in Figure 1.7. The effect is a little difficult to observe casually, because objects have to be rather far away before they start to vanish; for example, if you stand on a dock at the edge of the sea with your eyes 3 m above the water level, a ship must be about 12 km away before the lowest 3 m, corresponding roughly to the height of the deck above water of a small Greek merchant sailing ship, vanishes below the horizon.

Since this effect is seen in the *same* way regardless of where on Earth a ship is, or what direction it leaves port, the curved shape of the Earth is essentially the same everywhere and in all directions. Clearly, a sphere has this property. In contrast, if the Earth were shaped like a cylinder, for example, the way in which distant objects disappear would depend on the direction in which the ship sails.

The second observation suggesting that the Earth is a sphere in space concerns what could be seen in the sky from various places on the Earth. From Greece, the arrangement of stars in the night sky, which forms a fixed pattern that was long ago divided into (artificial) small groups of stars called **constellations**, seems to pivot around a point high in the northern sky (presently quite close to the North star, Polaris). In the southern hemisphere the arrangement of stars rotates around a point in the southern sky. The pattern of constellations continually rises in the east and sets in the west through the night. The constellations visible in the sky at the end of evenings twilight are almost the same from one night to the next, but after a month or so, the constellations that were lowest in the west after sunset are no longer visible in the evening, but are replaced by the ones that a month earlier were somewhat higher in the west. The effect is as if the nightly rotation of the pattern of stars in the sky is not quite synchronized with the cycle of day and night, but as the weeks pass, the pattern seen at a particular time of night drifts slowly towards the west. After a year the pattern of stars visible at sunset is the same as that seen at the same time of night on the same date of the previous year.

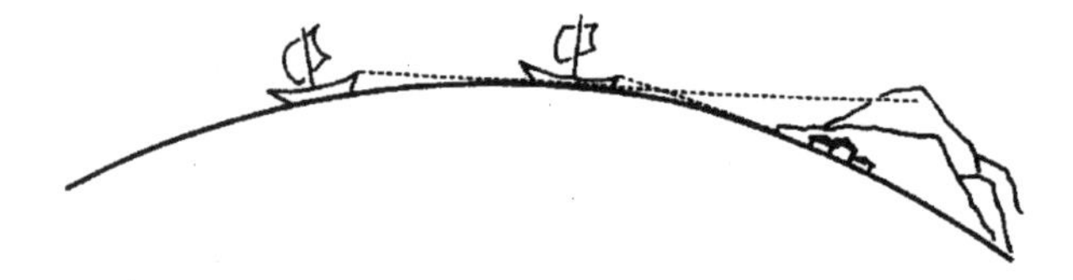

Figure 1.7: As a ship leaves the coast, the lowest place on the receding shore still visible (indicated by the dashed lines from the ship's stern to the shore) rises as the curve of the Earth increasingly comes between ship and shore.

On either the flat Earth or the spherical Earth theory, we can visualize the progression as the rotation of a sphere carrying the stars (the **celestial sphere**) around an axis. The sphere seems to turn about half way round during the night. The Sun may be thought of as having a position on the celestial sphere; when the rotation of the sphere carries the Sun above the horizon, it is day (and of course then the sky is too bright to see the stars, but they are still there). The rotation of the sphere continues during the day, carrying the Sun across the sky. This is shown in Figure 1.8.

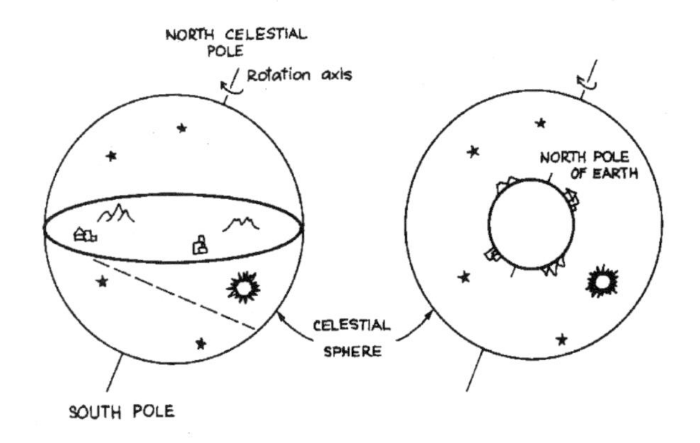

Figure 1.8: Nightly rotation of the constellations of the celestial sphere as viewed from a flat Earth (left) or a spherical one (right). There is no place on a flat Earth from which to observe the constellations to the south of the dotted line in the left-hand figure.

Now an important difference between the view of the sky from a flat Earth and that from a sphere concerns what parts of the celestial sphere are visible. From a *flat* Earth, the sky visible at a particular time (say just after evening twilight) on a particular night is the *same* from any place on the Earth. Furthermore, there is a part of the celestial sphere near the south pole that is never visible from the surface of the flat Earth, whatever the time of night or season. In contrast, the part of the celestial sphere visible from a *spherical* Earth depends on where the observer is on the Earth. A viewer near the point beneath the north celestial pole can never see the constellations of the southern celestial sphere. One near the Earth's equator can see at one time of night constellations in both the northern and southern part of the celestial sphere. One near the south pole sees only southern constellations. Thus the constellation patterns seen depend on where on Earth the observer is.

In fact, the travelers of the Greek world had observed that some constellations are visible in the sky from far to the south of Greece that are not visible from Greece itself, while even some of these vanish as one moves north from Greece. These observations support the idea that the Earth is a sphere. They conflict with the flat Earth theory. The Greek philosophers correctly concluded that the Earth is a spherical body in space.

Now, of course, if the Earth is spherical, the rotation of the celestial sphere during a night could be due either to movement of the celestial sphere or of the Earth itself. Most (but not all) ancient philosophers agreed with Aristotle that the sphere of the stars, not the Earth, should rotate. It was assumed that if the Earth rotated once per day, everything on the surface would be thrown off, blown away, or left behind. This turns out to be incorrect. The daily "rotation of the celestial sphere" is due simply to the daily rotation of the Earth about an axis (the **rotation axis**) through the north and south poles.

The actual size of the Earth was accurately measured by the geographer Eratosthenes of Cyrene (who lived about 275–194 B.C.), a scholar employed at the great library of Alexandria which was established by the Ptolemies, the family of kings who succeeded Alexander ("the Great") of Macedon as rulers of Egypt.

Eratosthenes proceeded by considering two geographic locations on Earth whose distance apart was known. He measured the angular separation between these two places on the Earth as seen from the Earth's centre. As we shall shortly see, these data enabled him to determine the circumference and diameter of the Earth.

Eratosthenes considered the two Egyptian cities Alexandria (at the mouth of the Nile) and Syene (modern Aswan, far up the Nile). Alexandria is approximately due north of Syene, and the distance between the two cities had been measured fairly accurately by royal messengers. This distance was known to be approximately 5000 stadii (the length of a "standard" stadium, probably about 157 m, was a common unit of length in the classical world), or about 785 km.

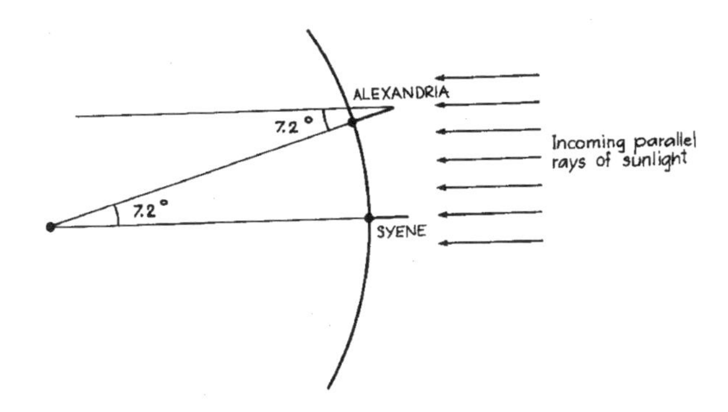

Figure 1.9: Measurement of the angle between the rays of incoming sunlight and vertical staff allowed Eratosthenes to deduce the angle between two cities as measured from the centre of the Earth.

Furthermore, Eratosthenes knew that at noon on midsummer's day, a vertical staff or rod at Syene casts no shadow, and wells are lit right to the bottom—the Sun is directly overhead at that time. On the same day, at noon, in Alexandria, a vertical staff casts a short shadow, from which it can be deduced that the stick makes an angle of about 1/50th of a circle (7.2°) with the incoming rays of sunlight. Now each of these vertical staffs points directly towards the centre of the Earth, and so (if we assume that the Sun is so far from the Earth that all the rays of sunlight arriving all over the Earth are practically parallel to each other) we conclude that the line from the centre of the Earth that passes through Alexandria makes an angle of 7.2° with the line from the centre of the Earth through Syene. This is shown in Figure 1.9.

This result means that if we take a line from the centre of the Earth that passes through Syene, and then pivot it around the Earth's centre by 7.2°, its intersection with the surface of the Earth moves the 785 km from Syene to Alexandria. Then if we were to rotate this line instead by 360°, one complete rotation, its intersection with the surface would traverse 50 × 785 km = 39,250 km. That is, the *circumference of the Earth is about 39,000 km.* If you recall from school that C = circumference = $2\pi\times$ radius = $2\pi R$, where $\pi = 3.14159$, the radius of the Earth is found to be $R = C/2\pi$ = 6250 km. This result, found by Eratosthenes in about 225 B.C., is remarkably close to the actual radius of the Earth, 6378 km.

Thus, from the time of Eratosthenes, scholars knew not only the shape of the Earth, but also its true size. In particular, they understood that the circumference of the Earth, about 39,000 km, is quite a lot greater than the extent of the world known to them. The east-west length of the Mediterranean region, from the Portuguese coast west of the straits of Gibraltar to the heart of the Persian empire (the valleys of the Tigris and Euphrates rivers, in modern Iraq), is only about 6000 km, less than one-sixth of the Earth's circumference.

The Moon

With the shape and size of the Earth established, clearly the next step is to determine the Earth's relationships with the other two large objects in the sky, the Moon and the Sun. If we suppose that these are bodies somewhere in the space outside the Earth, we need first to guess which is the nearer. There are two hints that help us with this problem.

The first hint comes from the motions of these two objects relative to the celestial sphere. If we watch the Moon during a single night, it rises in the east and sets in the west as the Sun and stars do. However, it is not fixed in position on the celestial sphere. Instead, the Moon moves during a night relative to the fixed pattern of the constellations of the night sky, in the sense that it crosses the sky from horizon to horizon somewhat slower than the stars do. From a particular time one night to the same time the next, the Moon moves about 15° on the sky (some 30 lunar diameters) relative to the celestial sphere, and rises and sets about an hour later than on the previous night. It is always found in the same belt of constellations roughly above the Earth's equator (these are in fact the constellations of the **zodiac**, familiar from popular astrology: Aries, Pisces, Aquarius, etc.) but its position changes visibly from night to night and even from hour to hour. After a bit less than one month it returns to the same constellation of the celestial sphere.

Exercise: On a clear evening, go outside and notice the position of the Moon among the surrounding stars (this is easier if the Moon is still several days from full). Go out again two or three hours later and see if you can tell that it has moved relative to the background stars.

The Sun also has a position relative to the celestial sphere. This is not nearly as obvious as the Moon's position, because whenever the Sun is up the sky is so bright that the stars of the celestial sphere cannot be seen. However, the Sun's position relative to the constellations can be found roughly by noting the constellations in the western sky just after sunset and in the eastern sky just before dawn. These are the constellations on either side of the Sun's position on the celestial sphere. From these observations it is not hard to find approximately the Sun's position on the celestial sphere. (The Sun's position can be determined more accurately by measuring the time interval between the moment when the Sun is directly south of an observer and the moment when a star of known position is directly south.) It is found that, like the Moon, the Sun is always in the belt of zodiacal constellations (though of course not always in the same place). Like the Moon, too, the Sun moves relative to the background stars, but much more slowly, by only about 1° (two solar diameters) every 24 hours. It is this drift of the Sun relative to the celestial sphere that produces the steady shift in which constellations are visible at night. (The path of the Sun on the celestial sphere marks out the plane of the Earth's orbit on the sky, and is known as the **ecliptic**).

Exercise: Draw a sketch to explain why the constellations visible in evening in winter are different from those visible on a summer evening.

The hint we need for our present problem, to decide whether the Moon or Sun is closer, is that the Moon moves much faster against the celestial sphere than does the Sun. Just as we can gauge the distance of an airplane or a bird by how quickly it crosses the sky, even if we don't know how big it is, from our experience that really distant flying things take much longer to disappear from view than similar nearby ones, the Greeks quite reasonably guessed that the quickly moving Moon is closer to the Earth than is the slowly moving Sun.

A second observation confirms this view. Very occasionally, perhaps once in twenty years from any one spot on Earth, the Sun is observed to be partly obscured (**eclipsed**) by the Moon, which passes between the Earth and the Sun. This clearly shows that the Moon is closer to the Earth than the Sun is. So we consider next the nature of the Moon.

At about the same time (dimly perceived by us in the painfully few quotations and fragments of scientific essays that have survived from before the fourth century B.C. of Plato and Aristotle) as the discovery that the Earth is a sphere in space, Greek thinkers realized (perhaps around 450 B.C.) that the Moon is a similar spherical body located in space near the Earth. Understanding that the Earth is a sphere certainly encouraged philosophers to consider the possibility that the Moon is also spherical. But more convincing evidence supporting this idea comes from the observed phases of the Moon.

As the Moon moves through the constellations, it also changes shape dramatically. The new Moon first becomes visible in the evening twilight as a slender **crescent**, setting in the west one or two hours after the Sun. Each night the crescent is wider, the Moon is higher in the sky at the end of twilight, and sets later. About a week after first appearing in the evening, the **first quarter** Moon is a semi-circle bright enough to be seen in the sky even in daylight. At this phase the Moon is high in the southern sky (as seen from the northern hemisphere) at sunset and sets about six hours after the Sun. During the following week the Moon is closer to the eastern horizon at sunset on each successive night and stays longer in the sky after sunset. Its **gibbous** shape is semicircular on the side towards the setting Sun and shows a flatter curve on the opposite side. About two weeks after new Moon, the **full** Moon is a complete circle that rises at sunset and is visible in the sky all night.

For the next two weeks, the Moon becomes smaller each night, shrinking from a full circle to a circle flattened on the other side, to the semicircle of **third quarter**, to an increasingly thin crescent. It rises an hour later each night until about $3\frac{1}{2}$ weeks after new Moon it rises just before dawn, the crescent now curved towards the rising Sun. It then disappears for two or three days, only to reappear in the evening sky after sunset to repeat the cycle of the previous month. The cycle of lunar phases repeats approximately every 29.5 days.

The key to understanding this cyclical change in the apparent shape of the Moon is the realization that the Moon, like the Earth, is lit by the Sun on one side but not the other. From Earth we sometimes see mainly the unlit side (when the Moon is crescent shaped) and sometimes mainly the lit side (when the Moon is gibbous or full).

The phases of the Moon are just the series of shapes we would see by doing a simple experiment. Outdoors at night in a large open space, suspend or set a light coloured ball at eye level. Illuminate the ball from one side with a light (such as a flashlight) also at eye level. (Doing this experiment in an open space with a beamed light reduces the amount of stray light reflected from nearby surfaces such as walls and ceiling, so that the side of the ball not directly illuminated is actually dark.) Then walk around the ball, looking at the shape of the part of the lit side that you can see. If you start your walk on the unlit side, as you circle the ball you see first a lit crescent, then a half circle. More and more of the illuminated side is seen as you move towards a position near the light source. As you continue past the light, the visible lit surface starts to decrease again, until it becomes a crescent and then vanishes as you again reach a position opposite the light source. The series of shapes you see as you walk around the ball is just the series of phases of the Moon, and this fact is very strong evidence that the Moon is also a sphere lit on one side.

In the experiment with the ball and light, the phases of the illuminated ball change as you move around the

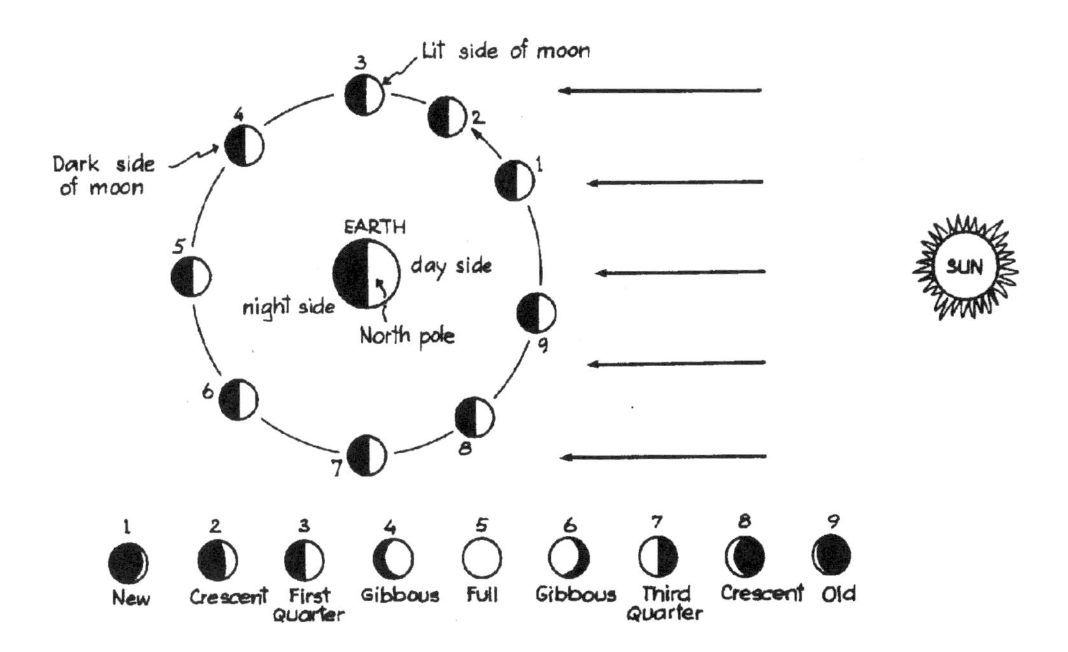

Figure 1.10: The position of the Moon in its circular orbit around the Earth, relative to the Sun-Earth line, is shown at nine phases. The corresponding appearance of the Moon as seen from Earth at each phase is shown along the bottom of the figure, where the invisible (unlit) part of the Moon is shown dark and the observed shape light. (Notice that relative distances and sizes are wildly distorted so as to be able to show the basic idea on one figure.)

ball. You see a crescent when you are on the far side of the ball from the light, so that the direction of the ball is nearly the same as the direction of the light. You see a fully illuminated ball when you are on the same side of the ball as the light is, and the light and the ball are seen in opposite directions. This is clearly also the situation with the Moon and Sun. The Moon is a crescent when it is near the Sun in the sky, and full when it is on the opposite side of the sky from the Sun. So relative to the Sun, the Earth and Moon move around one another. Is the Earth moving around the Moon, or the Moon around the Earth? This is a question that did not receive a definite answer until the development of the theory of gravitational attraction by Isaac Newton (1642–1727). In the classical era, philosophers almost always assumed that the Earth is stationary and near or at the centre of everything (at the centre of the celestial sphere, for example). As far as the Earth and Moon are concerned, this is approximately correct. So we assume for now that relative to the celestial sphere and the Sun, the Moon circles, or **orbits**, around the Earth.

The Moon must orbit at a roughly constant distance from Earth, since the size of the Moon on the sky, measured across the diameter (the largest dimension at any phase) varies by only about 10%. This can easily be confirmed by holding a ruler at an arm's length and measuring the largest dimension of the Moon on the sky. If you repeat this measurement several times during a night and during a month, you will probably not be able to detect reliably the small changes that do occur. (The impression that the Moon is larger when it is full, especially when it is near the horizon, is a perceptual illusion). This lack of size change means that the Moon's orbit about the Earth is approximately circular and centred on the Earth.

We now have a full conceptual picture of how the Moon's phases are produced by its orbital motions about the Earth. This is shown in Figure 1.10, and a dramatic illustration of how the Earth and Moon are lit by the Sun is seen in Figure 1.11.

Exercise: Use Figure 1.10 to explain why the (almost) new Moon is always seen low in the west just after sunset, while the full Moon is seen rising in the east around sunset.

Figure 1.10 suggests that the Moon may sometimes block out the sunlight reaching the Earth if it passes directly between the Sun and Earth. Since the Sun and Moon both have the same apparent size (about 30' of arc, or $1/2^\circ$) as seen from Earth, the Moon can actually cover the Sun for a short time. This phenomena is know as a **solar eclipse**. Because the Moon does not trace out exactly the same track on the celestial sphere as the Sun does, this can only happen near where the two tracks cross, and so such solar eclipses only occur

Figure 1.11: This image of the Moon (the smaller body) and the Earth (the larger one) was taken by the Galileo spacecraft as it left the Earth-moon system on its way to Jupiter. The Moon is closer to the spacecraft than the Earth is, and is moving from left to right. In addition to the huge cloud swirls, Antarctica is faintly visible at the bottom of the Earth image. Notice how the light from the sun illuminates one side of each body, while the other side is in darkness. (Courtesy of NASA.)

between two and five times a year, not every month. From Figure 1.10 it is clear that this can only happen just before the new Moon.

The Earth can also sometimes cast a shadow on the Moon, when the Moon is on the far side of the Earth and appears full. This is called a **lunar eclipse**. The occurrence of lunar eclipses makes possible a very clever method for estimating the distance of the Moon from the Earth and the size of the Moon. This method was first applied by the astronomer Aristarchos of Samos (about 320–250 B.C.), one of the greatest scientists of the Greek tradition.

Exercise: Show with a sketch that a lunar eclipse can only happen when the Moon is full.

The idea is to use the dark shadow (**umbra**) of the Earth as a measuring stick to find the size of the Moon relative to that of Earth. Because the Sun has some extent on the sky (that is, it is not just a point of light like a distant star), the really dark shadow cast by the Earth is a cone that gets smaller as one goes farther and farther from Earth, as shown in Figure 1.12(a). The dark shadow only extends to about 1,400,000 km from Earth. Someone farther from the Earth than that might see the Earth cross in front of the Sun, but the Earth would appear smaller on the sky than the Sun and would not cover the whole Sun. A **transit** of the Earth in front of the Sun would then not be able to make a total eclipse of the Sun from such a large distance.

Now the Sun is about $1/2^\circ$ (actually 0.53°), wide on the sky, so the point of the shadow opens out with an angle of $1/2^\circ$. (One way of seeing this is to imagine that you are just at the end of the shadow, watching a total eclipse. Since the Sun is $1/2^\circ$ wide on the sky, and the Earth just barely covers it, the Earth must also be $1/2^\circ$ wide on the sky, so this is the angle at the point of the shadow.) Now knowing that the shadow cone is about 13,000 km across (the Earth's diameter) where it leaves the Earth, and has a $1/2^\circ$ point, you can do a scale drawing to find that the cone must be about 110 times longer than wide, or about $110 \times 12,760 = 1,400,000$ km long.

Then, as suggested in Figure 1.12(b), you can try placing the Moon at various distances from the Earth to see what its size would be relative to the size of the dark shadow. We know that the Moon is somewhere in a cone (by sheer coincidence also $1/2^\circ$ across) that starts from the observer's eye and reaches to the (unknown) distance of the Moon. If the Moon is much closer to Earth than the length of Earth's shadow cone, then the shadow cone of Earth will be much larger than the Moon when an eclipse occurs. On the other hand, if the Moon is more than half the length of the shadow cone away from Earth, the dark shadow is smaller than the Moon and total eclipses of the Moon could not even occur. Now in fact when an eclipse of the Moon is observed, it is seen that the curved edge of the dark shadow as it starts to cover the Moon suggests the shadow is roughly three times larger in diameter than the Moon. The same result is found by measuring the time it takes for the Moon to enter the Earth's shadow, and comparing this to the time spent by the Moon within the shadow when the orientation of the shadow makes it clear that the Moon is passing through the centre of the shadow. This means that the Moon must be at a distance of roughly 350,000 km from Earth. (Incidentally, the round edge of the Earth's shadow on the Moon is strong further evidence that the Earth is a sphere). An object $1/2^\circ$ across at a distance of 350,000 km must have a diameter 1/110 as large as its distance, so the Moon's diameter is found in this way to be about 3200 km (the exact value is 3476), about one-fourth of the Earth's diameter.

This is a very interesting result on at least two counts. First, it shows that the Moon is a considerably smaller body than the Earth, so it is reasonable

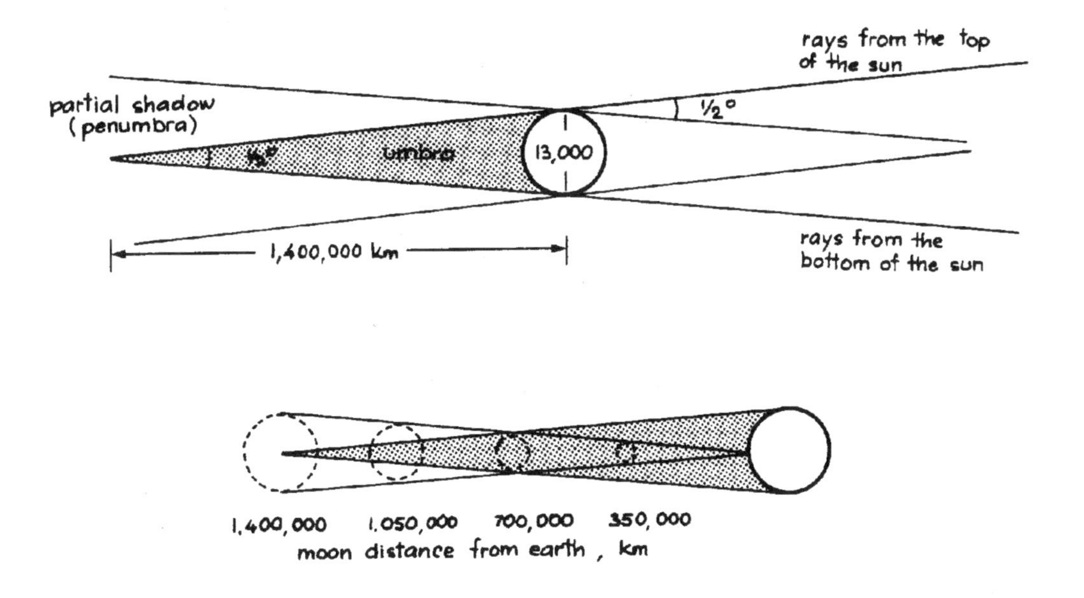

Figure 1.12: The Sun is about 1/2° across on the sky, so rays from the top of the Sun are not quite parallel to those from the bottom. Thus the size of Earth's shadow decreases with distance from Earth. The point of the shadow opens with the same 1/2° angle as the apparent size of the Sun, and since we know the Earth's diameter, a scale drawing or an easy calculation allows us to find that the cone is about 1,400,000 km long. (b) The Moon as seen from Earth is also (coincidentally) 1/2° in diameter. During an eclipse, the Moon is located somewhere in the cone that opens towards the left. The distance of the Moon from the Earth determines whether it is larger or smaller than the Earth's shadow. If the Moon is at a distance of about 350,000 km from Earth, it should be about a third as large as the shadow. At 700,000 km it would be nearly the same size as the shadow. Still farther away, the dark shadow of the Earth could not cover the whole Moon. Since the observed shadow actually seems to be about three time larger than the Moon, we estimate its distance at very roughly 350,000 km.

to suppose that it orbits the Earth rather than vice versa. However, the Moon is not a tiny body by any means. With a circumference of about 10,000 km, it is big enough to contain a land area as large as that known to the Greeks on Earth. Thus, the Earth is *not* the only large object in the solar system.

Furthermore, the extent of the solar system, even just to the orbit of the Moon, is much larger than the Earth: more than 100 times larger in linear extent, and (if the empty space around the Earth extends to the same distance in all directions) more that $100 \times 100 \times 100 = 1,000,000 = 10^6$ times larger in volume than the Earth. The Earth is clearly *much* smaller than the solar system.

The Sun

We next turn to the distance and size of the Sun. In the discussions above, we have implicitly assumed at several points that it is quite far away compared to the size of the Earth (when we assumed with Eratosthenes that all rays of sunlight arrive from the Sun nearly parallel to one another all over the Earth), or even far away compared to the size of the Moon's orbit about Earth (when we assumed with Aristarchos that the Sun's size on the sky is essentially the same from the Earth and the outer limit of the Earth's shadow cone). Now we will try to see if this is correct, or if the Sun is located just a little farther away than, and is just a little larger than, the Moon.

A nice argument that enables us to get a partial answer to this question was provided by Aristarchos. He pointed out that we should be able to measure the distance to the Sun by observing how far apart on the sky the Sun and Moon are when the Moon is exactly at first quarter. The idea is that when the Moon is exactly at first or third quarter, the Sun's rays are coming in towards the Moon at right angles (at 90°) to the line of sight from the Earth to the Moon. It is at this arrangement that we see the Moon exactly half lit and half dark. If we then watch for this precise phase to occur when both the Moon and the Sun are up (late in the afternoon at first quarter, early morning at third quarter), and then measure the angle on the sky between the Moon and the Sun, we have enough information to determine the relative distances of the Moon and the Sun. The situation is shown in Figure 1.13. With the measured Moon-Sun angle at this moment, we can

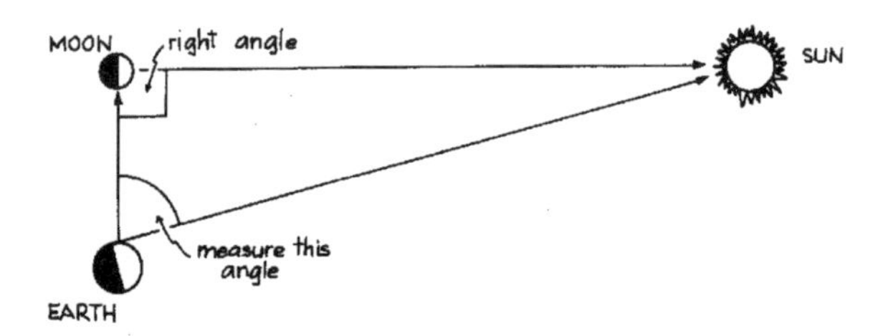

Figure 1.13: When the Moon is exactly at first or third quarter, the line of sight from Earth to Moon is at right angles to the Sun-Moon line. If we measure the angle from Moon to Sun, we may make a scale drawing of the three bodies and measure how many times larger the Earth-Sun and Moon-Sun distances are than the (known) Earth Moon distance.

make a scale drawing of the Earth-Moon-Sun triangle, and measure the ratio of the length of the Sun-Earth or Sun-Moon line to the length of the (known) Earth-Moon line. This determines how many times farther away the Sun is than the Moon.

Aristarchos assumed the Sun-Moon angle to be 87° at first quarter (he tells us nothing about how this number was obtained). It is easily found from this value that the Sun-Moon distance is about 20 times the Earth-Moon distance. With Aristarchos' figures, we deduce an Earth-Sun distance of some 8,000,000 km; we also conclude that the Sun is 20 times larger than the Moon (since it *looks* the same size but is actually 20 times farther away), and therefore that the Sun is about five times larger in radius (and $5 \times 5 \times 5 = 125$ times larger in volume) than the Earth.

This startling result led Aristarchos to make a radical suggestion; if the Sun is much larger than the Earth, perhaps the Sun, rather than the Earth, is the centre of the solar system. Other classical philosophers were aware of Aristarchos' proposal, but virtually none of them accepted it. The thought of something as big and heavy as the well-known Earth actually moving in space just seemed too unreasonable. The idea was not tried out seriously until finally Nicholas Copernicus (1473–1543) made it the basis of this theory of the solar system at the end of the middle ages.

Actually, we now know that the angle assumed by Aristarchos is wrong. It is in fact about 89.75°. The Sun is actually at 150,000,000 km from Earth, some 400 times as far away as the Moon. It is correspondingly 400 times larger in diameter than the Moon, and about 100 times larger than the Earth. It would not have been possible in classical times either to determine the time of exact first quarter accurately enough (the required accuracy would be to within an hour), nor to measure the small difference of the angle from 90° with the accuracy needed to find that it is not 90° exactly. Aristarchos' method thus does not actually provide us with a means of measuring the distance to the Sun, a problem really only solved in the 18th century. However, the Sun-Moon angle at first quarter is clearly not 70° or 80°. It is certainly within 2 or 3° of 90°. Aristarchos' method thus does clearly establish that the Sun is much farther away than, and larger than, the Moon, and even that the Sun is larger than the Earth. Aristarchos succeeded in establishing that the scale of distances between celestial bodies dwarfs the Earth itself, and that the Earth is not the largest object in the solar system.

The planets: geocentric theories

If you observe the stars of the celestial sphere night after night and month after month, you see that the patterns of the stars in the constellations are quite unchanging, although different parts of the celestial sphere are visible at different times. The only exceptions are provided by five objects that look like bright stars, and that are found in the belt of zodiacal constellations through which Sun and Moon move. These five bodies do not have fixed positions relative to the stars, but move slowly from one place to another. These are the planets, so-called after the Greek word for wanderer.

Two of the planets, Mercury and Venus, are seen only in the evening or early morning sky. Both are always quite close to the Sun on the celestial sphere and on average move along the sphere with the Sun. (In fact, Mercury is so close to the Sun that it is really hard to see by eye—when the sky is dark enough to see Mercury easily, it is already below the horizon.) The other three visible (or naked eye) planets, Mars, Jupiter, and Saturn, may be found anywhere in the zodiacal belt. Most of the time, each of these planets also drifts slowly along the zodiacal belt in the same direction as the Sun and Moon, but when one of these planets is on the opposite side of the Earth from the Sun (highest in the sky near midnight), a situation called **opposition** by astronomers, it is observed to move for some months in the opposite direction than normal. (Motion in the usual sense is called direct motion, while the period of reversed movement is known as **retrograde** motion.) This situation is illustrated for the planet Jupiter in Figure 1.14.

Each of the planets moves relative to the fixed stars at a different rate. Mercury and Venus share on average the motion of the Sun, (and thus on average each completes one circuit of the zodiac per year), but each oscillates back and forth around the Sun's posi-

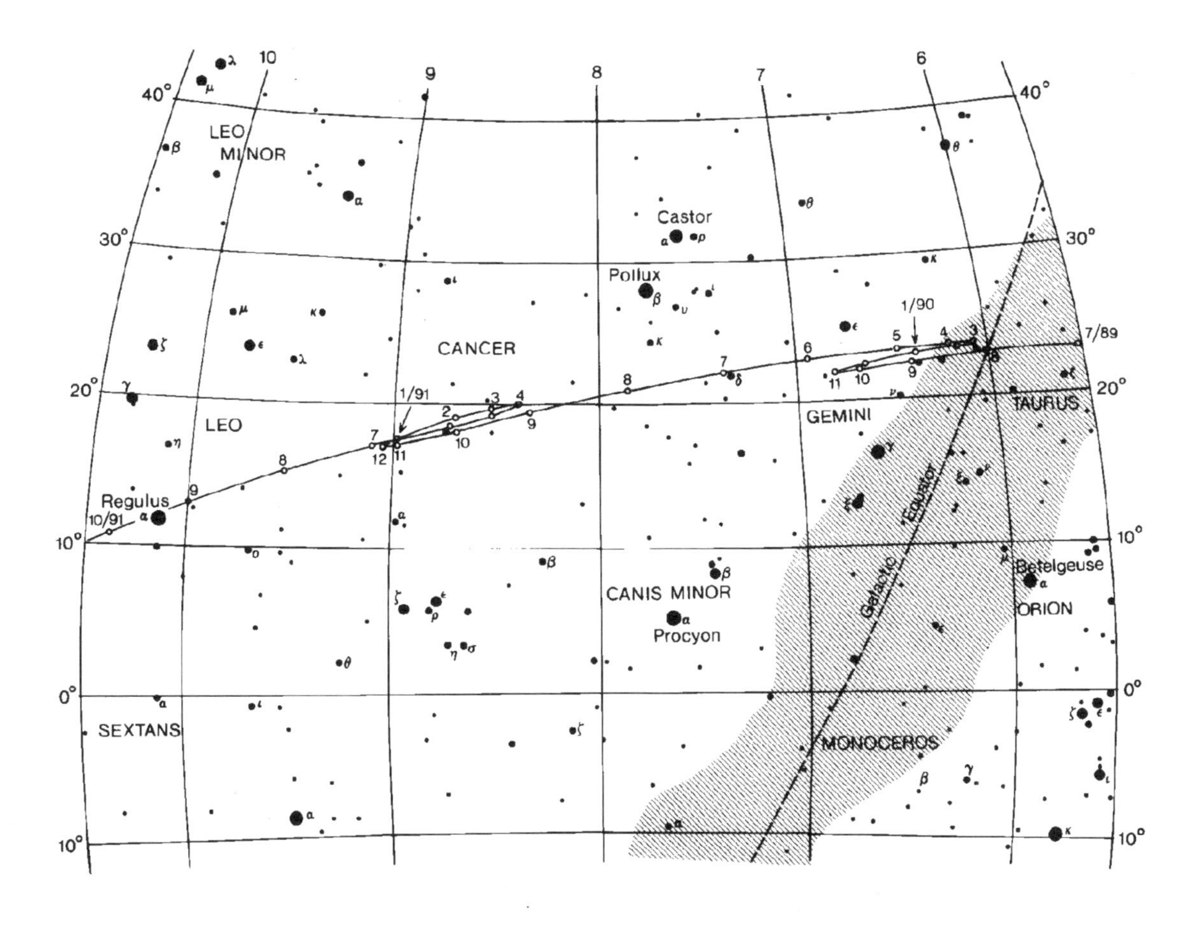

Figure 1.14: Motion on the celestial sphere of the planet Jupiter between July 1989 and October 1991. Open circles along Jupiter's path give positions at the start of each month. Numbers indicate months. Two episodes of retrograde motion are evident. The path of Jupiter closely follows the ecliptic.

tion. Mercury moves out to about 23° from the Sun on either side, repeating this motion approximately every 4 months. Venus travels farther from the Sun on both sides, out to typically 46°, and reappears at its maximum **elongation** from the Sun in the evening sky approximately every 19 months.

The other three planets visible to the eye move through the celestial sphere more slowly. Mars makes one circuit of the zodiac every 1.9 years, and has repeated episodes of retrograde motion roughly every $25\frac{1}{2}$ months. Jupiter takes almost 12 years to circle the zodiacal belt, with periods of retrograde motion every 13 months. Saturn takes $29\frac{1}{2}$ years for one circuit, and has periods of retrograde motion every $12\frac{1}{2}$ months. However the motions of the planets on the celestial sphere are not extremely regular. The width on the sky of the loops of retrograde motion vary considerably (especially for Mars), and their separation is only roughly uniform. The speed of movement is different from one period of direct movement to another.

These complex movements led the Greek astronomers to devise a fairly complicated description of the motion in order to predict future planetary positions on the sky with adequate accuracy. Because most Greek astronomers believed that the Earth is at the centre of the universe, and that all the heavenly bodies move about it, they supposed that each planet moves in a circular orbit (which they called a **deferent** circle) around the Earth. Motion along the deferent repeats with the period of revolution given in Table A.1. To explain the intervals of retrograde motion about the Sun (Mercury, Venus) or in opposition (Mars, Jupiter, Saturn), Greek astronomers placed each planet on the rim of a smaller circle (or epicycle) whose centre is fixed to the deferent. Motion about this circle, as seen from Earth, repeats with the average time interval between episodes of retrograde motion. The combination of these two movements (see Figure 1.15) gives both the steady direct motion and the episodes of retrograde motion.

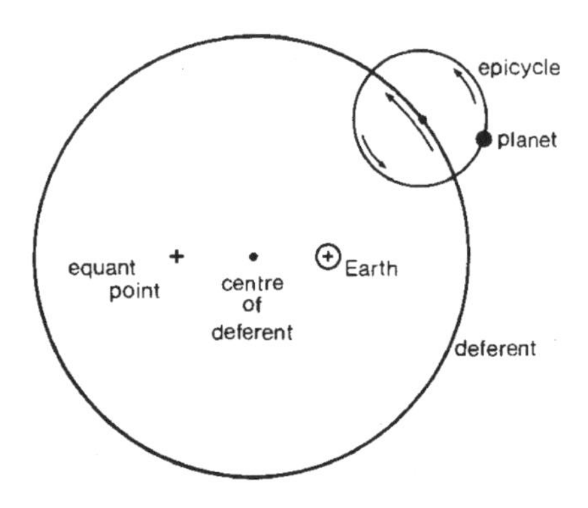

Figure 1.15: Ptolemy's description of planetary motion. The planet is on the rim of the (uniformly rotating) epicycle, whose centre moves around the deferent at a uniform rate as seen from the equant point. The Earth is displaced from the centre of the deferent opposite to the equant point.

However, so far the model predicts that retrograde movement should repeat with perfect regularity, and the retrograde loops should always be the same size, which is only a very rough approximation for Mercury and Mars. To vary the size of the retrograde loops on the sky, it was found necessary to displace the Earth from the centre of the deferent (to make the deferent **eccentric**), and to correctly describe the variations in speed of a planet, it was necessary to make the centre of the epicycle move around the deferent uniformly, not as seen from the centre of the circle, but as seen from a point (the **equant point**) on the other side of the centre of the deferent from the displaced position of the Earth. The resulting description is shown for a single planet in Figure 1.15.

This theory was also applied to the Moon and the Sun, with some differences because these bodies do not show retrograde motion.

One frustrating feature of the classical theory of the planets is that there is no way to decide on the order of the planetary orbits, or their sizes. It was generally assumed that the rapidly moving Moon is closest to Earth. Since the Sun, Mercury, and Venus all stay fairly close together on the sky, different authors made different choices as to their relative positions. It was sometimes suggested that Venus and Mercury move on the same deferent as the Sun, with epicycles more or less centred on the Sun, but this idea was not uniformly accepted. The other three planets were placed outside the Sun's orbit, in order of declining speed relative to the celestial sphere, but nothing in the classical theory demanded this order.

This rather complex description evolved over some five centuries, from the earliest known theories put forward by Eudoxus and Calippus during the time of Aristotle. Important elements were contributed by Apollonius of Perga (about 230 B.C.) and Hipparchos of Nicea (about 190–120 B.C.). The theory was perfected in the middle of the second century AD by perhaps the greatest astronomer of antiquity, Claudius Ptolemy (about 100–160 AD), who (like Eratosthenes) worked at the Library in Alexandria. Ptolemy's great synthesis, called by him (in Greek) the *Great Mathematical Synthesis*, but now known by its Arabic name of the *Almagest*, furnished both the conceptual framework and tables containing predictions of planetary positions which (with some minor updating) were still in use in the 16th century AD.

The model of Ptolemy and his predecessors forms an adequate mathematical description of the movements of the Sun, Moon, and planets, although the predicted positions are not exact. Its fundamental hypothesis, the placement of the Earth near the centre of the motions of the celestial bodies, seemed quite plausible to the Greeks on two counts. First, it was thought that rapid motion of the Earth (orbital motion or even rotation) would leave behind or blow away the inhabitants and any other loose objects. In addition, it was quite reasonably argued that if the Earth did circle the Sun, the celestial sphere should seem nearer in one direction than another. Put another way, as the Earth moves about the Sun, the separations and relative positions of the stars should change as the Earth approaches and recedes from them. This was not observed.

The planets: heliocentric theory

During the late Roman period and the middle ages, almost no progress was made on understanding planetary motions. Only in the 16th Century was the problem tackled afresh by the astronomer Nicholas Copernicus , born in Torun in what is now Poland. Copernicus rejected the Earth-centred (**geocentric**) theory of Ptolemy in favour of Aristarchos' idea that the Sun, as the largest known body, should be at the centre of planetary motions. That is, Copernicus assumed that the Earth is a planet like Venus, Mars, and the others, all circling the Sun in **heliocentric** motion. He tried to find a description of the planetary orbits (using almost the same mathematical tools of deferent circles, epicycles and eccentrics that were used by Ptolemy) that would satisfactorily account for previous observations of planetary positions and predict them in the future.

Copernicus had several reasons for preferring the heliocentric theory. Probably the most important was the fact that this theory offers simple explanations for features of planetary motion that are mysterious and arbitrary on the geocentric theory. Geocentric theory has no explanation for the fact that Mercury and Venus follow the Sun around the ecliptic, while Mars, Jupiter and Saturn can be anywhere in the zodiacal belt. The heliocentric theory explains these two kinds of motions by placing Mercury and Venus in orbits around the Sun that are smaller than that of Earth, while the other three planets have larger orbits than Earth (Figure 1.1). It is simply because of the order of the orbits that Venus and Mercury are never far from the Sun, while the other planets as seen from Earth can be near the Sun or on the other side of the celestial sphere.

Exercise: Make a sketch to explain why, on the heliocentric theory, Venus is always seen in the west not long after sunset, or in the east just before sunrise, but never high in the sky at midnight.

A second characteristic of planetary motion explained by the heliocentric theory is the fact that episodes of retrograde motion for Mars, Jupiter, and Saturn occur when the planet is on the opposite side of the Earth from the Sun. In the geocentric theory, retrograde motion is due simply to the motion of the planet around its epicycle; there is no obvious reason why the planet should systematically display retrograde movement precisely when the Earth is between it and the Sun. However, on the heliocentric theory, these episodes of retrograde movement are simply due to the motion of the Earth itself. In the case of the two inner planets, the more or less steady motion of the Sun along the ecliptic is actually due to the movement of the Earth around it. The orbital motion of each inner planet is then added onto this solar motion as a back-and-forth movement that Ptolemy described with the epicycle. As to an outer planet, its average motion along the ecliptic is due to its orbital movement about the Sun. A period of retrograde movement occurs each time the Earth comes between the Sun and the planet, since the Earth is moving about the Sun faster than any outer planet (Table A.1). The retrograde motion occurs simply because the Earth is passing the slower outer planet, and thus it occurs when the Sun, the Earth, and the outer planet are more or less in a line.

Finally, the heliocentric theory allows one to understand the different periods of time taken by various bodies to circle the celestial sphere. Simply, the planets nearer the Sun circle it quickly, both because they have relatively small distances to cover and because their velocity in space is relatively high, while the more distant planets move more slowly and have farther to go.

It is rather simple to deduce the relative sizes of the various planetary orbits in the heliocentric model of the solar system. Assuming to simplify the situation somewhat that all the planets move in circular orbits centred on the Sun, the size of the orbit of, say, Venus, relative to that of the Earth may be found simply by measuring

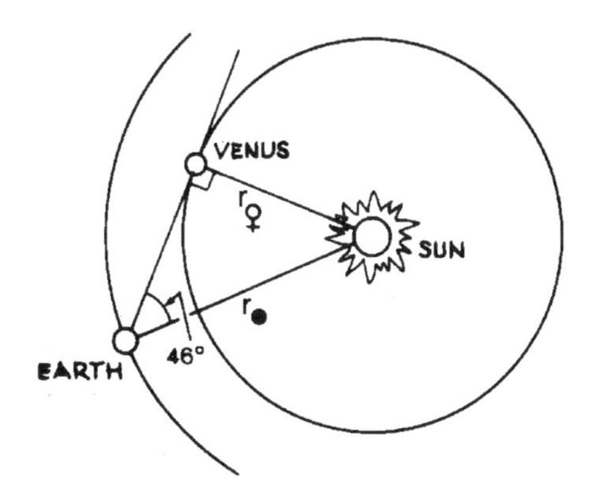

Figure 1.16: The maximum angular distance of Venus from the Sun, about 46°, occurs when the line of sight from Earth is just tangent to the orbit of Venus. Measuring the angle allows one to make a scale drawing and determine $r_{\rm venus}/r_\oplus = 0.72$.

the angular distance between the Sun and Venus when they are farthest apart on the sky, as shown in Figure 1.16. At this point in Venus' orbit, the line of sight from Earth just touches (is tangent to) the orbit of Venus, so at this moment the line of sight is perpendicular to the line from the Sun to Venus. Then with the measured angular separation of Sun and Venus, about 46°, the ratio of the radius of Venus' orbit to that of Earth, about $r_{\rm Venus}/r_\oplus = 0.72$, may be found from a scale drawing (measure Figure 1.16 with a protractor and ruler!) or from trigonometry.

Exercise: What is the phase of Venus (the shape of the lit hemisphere as seen from the Earth) for the relative positions of the Earth and Venus shown in Figure 1.16? What would be the observed phase of Venus if it were on the opposite side of its orbit from the position shown in the figure?

The relative size of the orbit of an outer planet is also easy to determine. For Jupiter, for example, one may determine accurately the time interval between two successive oppositions (these are two dates, somewhat more than a year apart, when the planet is at its highest in the night-time sky at midnight) of the planet. One quarter of this time interval later, the Earth has advanced 90° *further* around its orbit than Jupiter has around its orbit, so the radius from the Sun to Earth is perpendicular to the radius from the Sun to Jupiter. If we then measure the angle between Jupiter and the Sun on the sky at this moment, about 79°, the proportions and angles of the Sun-Earth-Jupiter triangle may be obtained from a drawing or trigonometry (Figure 1.17).

Copernicus' hypothesis of a heliocentric solar sys-

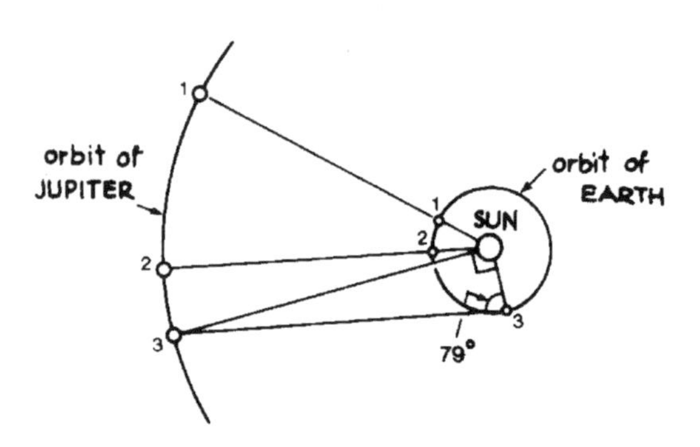

Figure 1.17: Two successive oppositions of Jupiter occur when the Earth and Jupiter are at positions 1 and 2 in their orbits. One quarter of the time interval between successive oppositions after the two bodies reach positions 2, the Earth has gone 90° further in its orbit than Jupiter has, and the two planets are at positions 3. Here the lines from the Sun to the two planets are perpendicular. Since Jupiter is then about 79° from the Sun, the ratio of Jupiter's orbital radius, $r_{\rm Jupiter}$, to the Earth's, $r_{\oplus}$, is about 5.2.

tem, described in his great book *On the Revolution of the Celestial Spheres* (1543), led to another expansion in the size of the known universe. This followed from the determination of the radius of Saturn's orbit, about 9.4 AU (recall that 1 AU is the distance from the Sun to the Earth), which thus requires that Saturn be almost ten times as far from the Sun as the Earth is. The universe must be large enough to accommodate this. But an even stronger requirement came from the fact that no change in the apparent patterns of the stars relative to one another was observed as the Earth travels from one side of the Sun to the other in its orbit. Copernicus correctly deduced from this fact that the stars must be *very* much farther away from the Earth than even Saturn, so that the Earth's movement about the Sun makes only tiny changes in the apparent stellar positions. (In fact, even the nearest stars are so far away—hundreds of thousands of AU—that their back-and-forth movement against the background of still more distant stars due to the Earth's orbital movement was only detected in the 1830's.)

The next big step forward in understanding planetary motion was due primarily to the efforts of a wealthy Danish nobleman, Tycho Brahe (1546–1601) and a German mathematics teacher, Johannes Kepler (1570–1630). Brahe became fascinated by astronomy as a young man, and devoted his adult life to measuring with the greatest precision possible the positions of the fixed stars and the movements of the planets relative to them. He accumulated during his lifetime a body of measurements far superior in both quality and quantity to those available to Copernicus. These measurements were used by Kepler, a school teacher who eventually succeeded Brahe as Imperial Mathematician (and court astrologer) to the court of Holy Roman Emperor Rudolf II, to try to refine the details of the Copernican theory of planetary motion.

Kepler found that the Copernican (or Ptolemaic) mathematical apparatus of deferents, epicycles, and eccentrics could describe the movements of the planets only approximately, even after the best possible adjustments of sizes, speeds, etc. There were small but clear discrepancies between the planetary positions observed by Brahe and the predictions of the Copernican theory. After an enormous labour, Kepler discovered a far simpler description for planetary orbits than that employed by previous astronomers, which he described in his book *The New Astronomy* (1609). He found that the planets move about the Sun in **ellipses**. An ellipse is a round or flattened closed curve that can be constructed very simply with a pencil, a length of string, and two pins, as shown in Figure 1.18. If the two pins touch one another, the curve is perfectly round (a circle); the farther apart the pins are (for a given length of string), the more flattened the curve is, until in the limit of an almost taut string the curve is almost a straight line with the foci near the extremes.

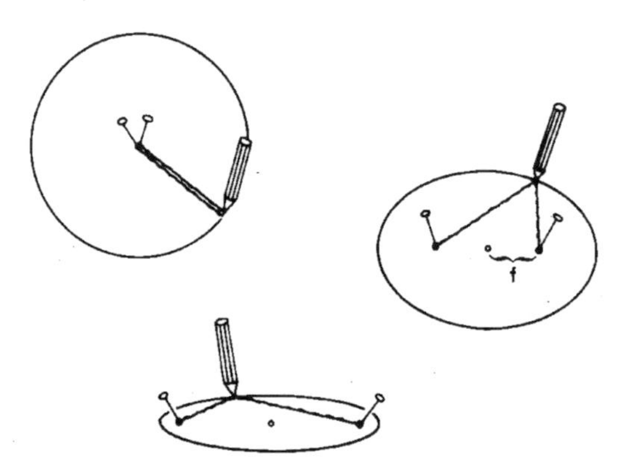

Figure 1.18: Construction of ellipses with a pencil, a string, and two pins. The ends of the string are fixed with the pins. Holding the string taut with the pencil, the pencil is moved around the pins. The path of its point traces out an ellipse. The resulting curve is circular if the pins are close together and increasingly flattened as they are moved apart.

Kepler showed that the movement of each planet about the Sun follows the shape of an ellipse. For each planet, the Sun occupies the position of one of the two pins needed to draw that ellipse (called the **focus** of the ellipse). Different planets follow ellipses of different sizes, and also of different shapes. In fact, the mean radius of the ellipse given in Table A.1 is half the length of the string needed to draw that ellipse, which is also equal to half the longest dimension of the ellipse. This length is called the **semi-major axis** of the ellipse. The eccentricity e is the distance between the centre of the ellipse and the Sun, divided by the length of the semi-major axis. Of the four easily observable planets, Mars has the largest eccentricity, and was the planet that led Kepler to his discovery. Its path is almost circular, but the centre of the orbit is offset from the Sun by almost a tenth of the orbital radius; this is visible in Figure 1.1.

Kepler also discovered two other fundamentally important features of planetary orbits. First, he found that as a planet circles the Sun, its speed changes along its orbit in such a way that the line from the Sun to the planet sweeps out equal areas in equal times (Figure 1.19). This means that as a planet moves closer to the Sun, it moves faster along its orbit, and it slows down as it moves away from the Sun. A planet whose orbit is centred on the Sun ($e = 0$; Venus has an orbit which is nearly circular and centred) keeps a constant speed all around its orbit; a planet with an orbit as eccentric as that of Mercury moves about 50% faster when it is nearest the Sun (this point of the orbit is called **perihelion**) than when it is at the farthest point in its orbit (at **aphelion**).

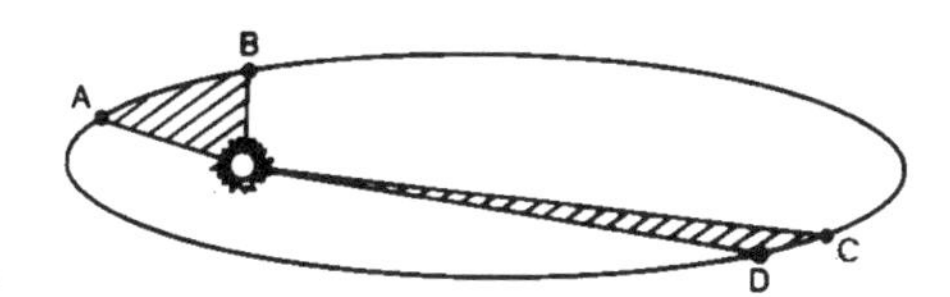

Figure 1.19: A planet moves about the Sun in such a way as to sweep out equal areas in equal times with the line joining it to the Sun. Thus it moves much farther along its orbit, and faster, in the time to go from A to B than it moves during the same time interval going from C to D. The hatched areas swept out by the planet-Sun line in equal times are the same.

In addition, Kepler discovered that the periods of revolution about the Sun (the times to complete one orbit) increase with increasing orbital size according to a definite and simple rule: the square of the orbital period in years is equal to the cube of the mean orbital radius in AU. (You should try out this rule on the data of Table A.1 with a pocket calculator; if yours can't calculate the cube of a number, just multiply it by itself three times: $a^3 = a \times a \times a$.)

Today we refer to these extremely important discoveries as **Kepler's Laws**. To summarize, they are:

1. Each planet circles the Sun in an elliptical orbit. The Sun is located at one of the foci of the elliptical path.

2. As a planet orbits the Sun, its speed varies in such a way that an imaginary line joining the Sun to the planet sweeps out equal areas in equal times.

3. The time to complete one orbit about the Sun increases with orbital size in such a way that the cube of the mean orbital radius (actually, half the largest dimension of the ellipse), as measured in AU is equal to the square of the orbital period measured in years.

Well into the seventeenth century, some astronomers (and many other people) remained sceptical of the heliocentric theory of the solar system. However, the invention of the telescope in the Netherlands, probably in 1608, had a powerful effect on the dispute after news of this invention reached Galileo Galilei (1564–1642), a professor of mathematics at the University of Padua in Italy. Upon hearing of the discovery, Galilei promptly constructed a series of telescopes of his own, which he soon turned to the heavens. By 1610 he was able to publish a small work called *Siderius Nuncius (The Starry Messenger)* in which he described observations of great interest for the dispute. He announced the discovery of the four largest moons of Jupiter, and described how they orbit the giant planet with periods of ranging from less than two days to over two weeks. He also reported seeing Venus change its apparent shape just as the Moon does; that is, he discovered that Venus shows phases. When Venus is nearest to Earth and largest, it has a crescent shape; when it is farther and smaller, it appears nearly circular. These phases are easily understood if Venus orbits around the Sun: when it is nearest the Earth, between Earth and Sun, it is lit nearly from the other side and shows a crescent disk; when it is on the other side of the Sun and farthest away, we see the fully lit side.

Thus both of these discoveries revealed that there are objects in the solar system that revolve around a centre other than the Earth. Since this goes strongly against the whole philosophy of the geocentric theory, which claimed that the Earth is the centre of all celestial motions, these discoveries gave a powerful support to the new heliocentric ideas, especially as the observations of Venus directly showed the Sun to be a centre of movement.

Exercise: From your space base on Mercury, is it possible for any of the other planets to be seen at crescent phase (like the crescent Moon)?

1.4 Gravitation

The Earth's gravitation

The great discoveries of Kepler are essentially empirical descriptions of planetary motions. No one had any way of predicting that planets should move in elliptical orbits rather than following some other type of curve. (Why aren't planetary orbits squares, for example?) Kepler speculated that planets circle the Sun because of some force that originates in the Sun and acts on the planets, but he had no idea how this force acts or how to derive the shapes of planetary orbits by postulating such force. During the 17th century, the nature of the force from the Sun was discovered, and it was found that starting from a simple set of rules (Newton's laws of motion) that describe how an object moves under the influence of a force, together with a description of the force from the Sun (the law of gravitation), Kepler's laws may be *deduced.* This change in viewpoint from a simple (kinematic) description of planetary motions to a (dynamical) theory that predicted the nature of such motions was a crucial step in the development of modern physics.

The first important discoveries in this direction were made by Galilei, who studied the movement of bodies under the influence of force of attraction from the Earth. This force attracts all material objects (you, your chair, the air, etc.) towards the centre of the Earth. We call this force the **force of gravity**, or **gravitation**. Galilei studied the effects of this force on objects near the Earth's surface. He particularly examined freely falling bodies, bodies rolling down inclined planes, and the motions of weights suspended from strings (pendulums).

The first of Galilei's fundamental discoveries concerns motion (or lack of it) in the complete absence of any forces. Until Galilei's time, it was generally assumed (following Aristotle's ideas) that the natural condition of an object is for it to be at rest—motionless. It was believed that for an object to be in motion, it must be subjected to a force, and as soon as the force is removed motion stops. This idea certainly has some relationship to reality: think of pushing a heavy box or chair across the floor. But there are clearly situations (the flight of an arrow or a ball for example) where it is hard to identify a force that acts once the object has been shot or thrown.

Galilei discovered the natural motion of an object with no forces acting on it by successively abstracting from experiments he did with pendulums. He found that when a pendulum is started off with the weight (the bob) at some height above the rest (equilibrium) position, the bob returns to the *same* height at both ends of the swinging motion (until air friction gradually wears away the movement, eventually bringing the bob to rest). Now, suppose that a pendulum string is supported by a nail on a wall, so that the bob swings near the wall. If a second nail is then put into the wall below the support nail, above the rest position of the bob, so that when the bob is lifted to one side and let go, the movement of the upper part of the string is stopped the instant it hits the lower nail, Galilei found that the bob still rises to the same height from which it started. He concluded from this that the height to which a swinging bob tries to rise does not depend on the length of the string. He boldly extended this idea to suppose that even the presence of the string does not affect the height to which the released bob tries to rise. Further experimentation showed that this is correct: a ball rolling inside a smoothly curved bowl also rises to the same height from which it is released. Furthermore, this is still true even if the bowl is steeper on one side than another. This led Galilei to consider what would happen if one side of the bowl was flattened and completely at the level of the lowest point of the bowl. He concluded that a ball set rolling down into the flat part of such a bowl would continue rolling indefinitely, trying vainly to rise back up to its original level. Thus Galilei concluded that an object set in motion will continue moving at a constant speed in a straight line until some force (such as friction) acts on it to change its motion. This fundamental discovery is known as the **law of inertia**, or Newton's first law of motion.

This idea represents a considerable abstraction from ordinary experience, in which the effects of frictional forces (such as the force acting when you slide the box across a room, or even the effect of air resistance on the pendulum) are very hard to eliminate. The idea of constant motion in a straight line as the normal state of a body not subjected to any forces is a radical change from the Aristotelian view that motion is only possible so long as a force acts. In fact, Galilei's discovery of the inertia (tendency to continue unchanged) of motion allows us to identify when a force acts: a force is present whenever the speed or direction of movement of an object is changing, that is, the presence of a force is signaled by **acceleration** (changing velocity).

Galilei's experiments on objects rolling down inclined planes revealed that the effect of the steady pull of gravity on a body is to accelerate its speed uniformly with an acceleration that is proportional to the force applied. That is, the speed of descent increases steadily from the moment the object is released. This means that as the body falls or rolls downward, in equal intervals of time it travels through larger and larger distances.

Universal gravitation

These two great discoveries, the fact that a body in motion and subject to no forces will continue in an unchanged motion, and the fact that the effect of a force is to change a body's velocity (to accelerate it) made it possible for the Cambridge scholar Isaac Newton to find the connection between the force from the Sun and the movement of the planets. As a result of Galilei's work, it was no longer necessary to ask why and how the planets move at all, but rather why, given that they move, they move in ellipses rather than in straight lines? What force acts to change steadily the direction of motion of a planet, so that it moves around the Sun? Newton supposed that the force accelerating the Moon about the Earth is the same force that causes an apple to fall from a tree, and that it is this same force again, but exerted by the Sun, that causes all the planets to move about the Sun. That is, he supposed that *every* massive body exerts a gravitational pull on every other body.

Next it was necessary to find the behaviour of this force. How does it vary with distance from the attracting centre? Newton was able to deduce the behaviour of gravitational force from Kepler's laws. He first found a simple law, also discovered independently by the Dutch astronomer and mathematician Christiaan Huygens (1629–1695), describing the acceleration (change in velocity per second) of a body moving in a circle at a given speed around a centre. The acceleration is proportional to the square of the object's velocity around the circle divided by the radius of the circle. When Newton used Kepler's third law relating the period of motion (and thus its velocity) to the orbital radius, he found that the force which must be acting to make planets move in circles of the observed sizes and periods must be proportional to $1/r^2$, where r is the orbital size, and to the mass of the attracting centre and of the attracted body. Thus for two bodies of definite mass, doubling the separation reduces the attraction of one for the other to $(1/2)^2 = 1/4$ of its previous strength. This is the **law of gravity**.

Newton then showed his superb mathematical prowess by proving that a planet moving under the influence of the gravity of a single central attraction (the Sun) must move generally in an ellipse, if the planet is moving slowly enough that it cannot escape from the Sun; a parabola, if the planet has just enough speed to escape the pull of the Sun; or an hyperbola if the planet is moving fast enough to escape the pull of the Sun with ease. These are the *only* orbital shapes possible under the action of a force directed towards the attractor that varies with separation r as $1/r^2$. Because the force of gravity on a planet is also proportional to the mass of the planet, the shape of a planet's orbit does not depend on its mass, but only on its speed at some point in its orbit. These allowed orbit shapes are shown in Figure 1.20.

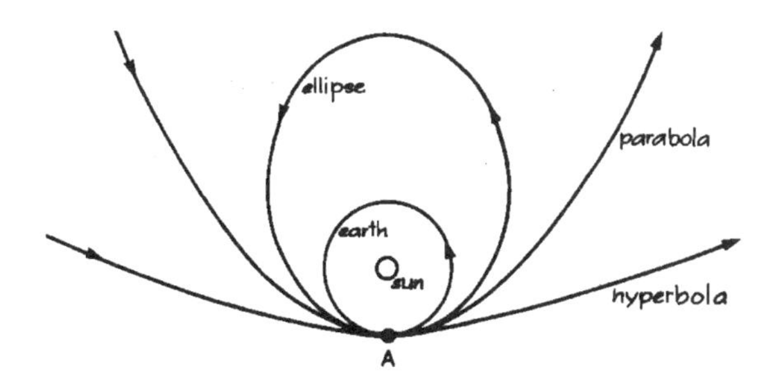

Figure 1.20: The nearly circular orbit of the Earth about the Sun is shown. The orbits followed by other bodies having larger velocities as they touch the Earth's orbit at point A are also sketched. At this point the Earth's velocity is 30 km s^{-1}; a body moving with velocity 37 km s^{-1} follows the more eccentric elliptical orbit; a velocity of 42 km s^{-1} at A leads to a parabolic orbit; and with 60 km s^{-1} at A the orbit is an open-ended hyperbola.

Newton also showed that Kepler's second law, describing how the speed of a planet varies as it traverses an elliptical orbit, is a general feature of any force directed towards the centre of attraction.

Newton thus showed that the force underlying planetary motion is the force of gravity, and that this force has exactly the right behaviour to cause just the planetary motions that Kepler had deduced from observation. This fundamental work laid out systematically all the basic ideas of the first great branch of physics, mechanics.

Galilei and Newton thus led us to our present understanding of planetary motion. In effect, we imagine a planet to have been started off (somehow) with motion roughly perpendicular to the line joining the planet and the Sun. If the Sun's gravity were not acting, the planet would continue in its original course, with constant speed in a fixed direction, because of inertia. However, the Sun does attract the planet. Hence, if we consider a short time, the planet has two motions: the unchanging motion perpendicular to the Sun-planet line, and an acceleration towards the Sun. At the end of the short time, the planet has moved a little around the Sun, and its velocity has changed direction a little. It still has a motion roughly perpendicular to the Sun-planet line. In effect the planet falls *around* the Sun, always missing it because the gravitational force on the planet has no way of reducing the planet's speed perpendicular to the Sun-planet line.

Of course, if one body (the Sun) exerts a gravitational pull on a neighbour (a planet, say), the planet will also exert a gravitational pull on the Sun. In fact, the two bodies move around their common "centre of mass". If the two bodies are nearly equal in mass, as in a system of two stars, the pull of each body on the other will be about equally important, the centre of mass of the system will be in between the two bodies, and each will orbit about this point near the middle of the system. On the other hand, if one body is far more massive than the other, the centre of mass will be close to the centre of the more massive body, and so the massive object will almost stand still while the lighter body moves about it. This is the situation for the Sun attracting the planets, and for any planet attracting its moon(s).

A more complicated situation may arise if a body is attracted simultaneously by two other objects. This can happen, for example, to a comet if it passes near a planet. In this case, to the pull of the Sun is added the pull (in a different direction) of the much lighter planet, which can still exert an important force when it is much nearer to the comet than the Sun is. In this case, the orbit followed by the comet is more complicated than in the situation that occurs when only a simple centre of force acts. If the comet passes close enough to a planet, its orbit may be radically altered by the encounter.

Energy

From Newton's description of how gravity enforces an elliptical, parabolic, or hyperbolic orbit on a small body orbiting a larger one, it soon was found that as the small object varied in distance from the larger one, its velocity changes in a very simple way with distance r from the attracting centre. We define a quantity E_k called the **kinetic energy** of the small body, given by the equation $E_k = mv^2/2$, where v is the orbital velocity at any arbitrary point in the small body's orbit, and m is its mass. We also define another quantity E_p called the **potential energy** of the small body by $E_p = -GMm/r$, where M is the mass of the larger body, r is the distance of the small body from the larger at the point where its velocity is v, and G is a universal constant that appears in Newton's law of gravity. Now what we find is that as the small body orbits the larger one, the sum $E_k + E_p = E$ remains constant throughout the orbit. That is, when the small body comes closer to the large one, so that r decreases and E_p (which is a negative number) becomes more negative, the quantity E_k becomes larger (it is always positive) in just such a way that $E_p + E_k$ stays constant. As r decreases, v increases in a completely definite way which can be computed everywhere in any particular orbit if we know the speed v of the orbiting body and its distance r from the attractor at one point in the orbit. E is called the total energy of the orbit, and this total orbital energy is a constant during the orbit. We often express this by saying that *orbital energy is conserved* (its amount is kept constant).

The distinction between hyperbolic, parabolic, and elliptical orbits is reflected in the value of the total orbital energy. An elliptical orbit always has total orbital energy E less than zero (negative). A hyperbolic orbit has positive E, and a parabolic orbit is one with total energy $E = 0$ (negative gravitational energy just equal to positive kinetic energy everywhere in the orbit).

The constancy of total orbital energy seems at first glance to be little more than a convenient means for calculating orbital speed of an object passing by another. However, it turns out to be the first hint of a much more general and powerful principle. It was gradually realized during the 19th century that if one considers other forms of energy besides kinetic and potential energy, such as internal (thermal) energy, chemical energy, electrical energy, etc., that a much more general law of conservation of energy holds, in which in a "closed system", one form of energy (say, kinetic) may be converted into another (say, chemical), but that the total energy in the system stays constant. This has come to be recognized as a very powerful and general idea, and is one which will re-appear at various points later in this book.

The idea of total energy also allows us to introduce the useful idea of **escape velocity**. Suppose we have a rocket on the Moon's surface (so that we don't have to worry about air resistance). At rest, the rocket would have a large, negative total energy (a lot of negative potential energy, and no positive kinetic energy). However, we could imagine giving the rocket enough kinetic energy to (just) completely escape from the Moon's gravitational attraction. If we did this, the rocket would have approximately zero total energy (large negative potential energy, large positive kinetic energy). The speed that is just large enough to allow the rocket to escape completely from the Moon's gravitational pull is called the escape velocity. Notice that the escape velocity depends on the mass of the planet or moon you are on (it is usually larger for more massive planets), and on just how close to the centre of the body you start from.

Exercise: Using the idea of total energy, convince yourself that an object falling to the Moon's surface from a great distance (hundreds of lunar radii away), if it started at rest, would reach the surface with the escape velocity.

1.5 Tides

Nature of tides

Gravity is also able to distort bodies, because its strength varies with distance. Consider the Moon in orbit around the Earth. The full force exerted on the entire Moon by the Earth is exactly right to hold the Moon in its present nearly circular orbit about Earth. However, because gravitational attraction falls off rapidly with distance, the force of gravity exerted by the Earth on the half of the Moon nearer the Earth is somewhat stronger than that exerted on the far side. The attraction on the near side is slightly stronger than is needed to pull the Moon around the Earth in its orbit; the attraction on the far side is slightly too weak. This causes the Moon to stretch along the Earth-Moon axis into a slightly elongated (blimp-shaped) figure. The effect is stronger when the two attracting bodies are close to one another than when they are far apart, because when they are close the size of each body is a larger fraction of the total distance separating the two. Such distortion is called tidal distortion, and the bulges raised are tidal bulges.

This is of course the effect that raises tides in the seas of Earth. At any instant, the parts of the Earth nearest the Moon are attracted by the Moon somewhat more strongly than the average attraction, while parts of Earth farthest from the Moon are attracted less strongly. This excess pull on the near side of Earth compared to that on the far side stretches the solid Earth somewhat. It also causes surface liquids in seas and oceans to slosh to the region below the Moon on the near side of Earth, and in effect pulls the Earth out from under the water on the far side of Earth, causing a similar liquid bulge on the far side of Earth. Because water is more easily distorted than solid Earth, ocean tides have greater amplitude than the tides stretching the solid Earth on which the oceans rest, and so we are aware of the ocean tides along the seashore.

Tides can have an important effect on orbits of bodies that are near one another, although this effect is realized only very slowly. In the Earth-Moon system, for example, as we have discussed, the Moon raises tidal bulges on Earth. The Earth, however, is also rotating, rather quickly (one rotation every 24 hours) compared to the rate at which the Moon revolves about the Earth (one revolution every 27.3 days). Because both solid Earth and its surface oceans experience friction, the rapid rotation of Earth carries the Earth's tidal bulges ahead of the line connecting Earth and Moon. In effect, the bulges try to line up with the line to the Moon, but friction with the rotating Earth makes the bulges always somewhat late to their destinations.

Now the bulge on the Moon side of the Earth acts

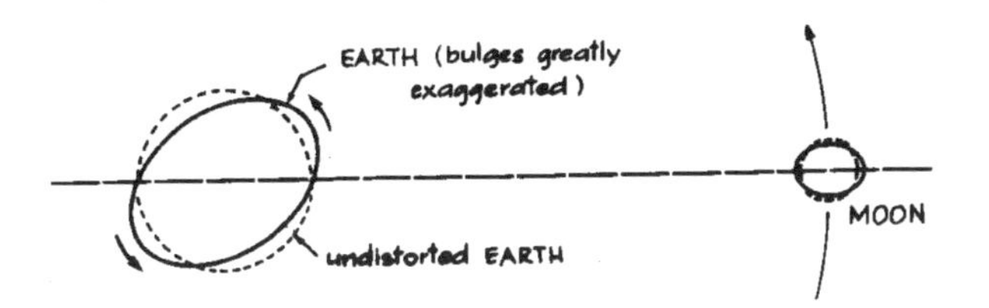

Figure 1.21: Tidal bulges on the Earth and Moon (scales greatly distorted). The Earth raises tides on the Moon, and because one side of the Moon (the side with most of the maria) always faces Earth, the bulges line up with the Earth-Moon line. The tidal bulges on Earth are carried somewhat ahead of the Earth-Moon line by the Earth's rapid rotation; the slight extra attraction between the bulge on the Moon side of Earth and the Moon speeds up the Moon in its orbit and slows the Earth's rotation.

to exert a slight extra gravitational pull on the Moon. Because this bulge is slightly ahead of the Earth-Moon line, as shown in Figure 1.21, the bulge acts to pull the Moon ahead in its orbit, or to speed it up slightly. Speeding the Moon up gives it extra energy to move in a larger orbit around Earth, so the size of the Moon's orbit is gradually increasing. Similarly, the pull of the Moon on the nearer bulge on Earth tends to slow the Earth's rotation, so the day is actually slowly lengthening. The effects in the Earth-Moon system are quite gradual. The Moon's orbit is increasing in radius by some 3.7 cm yr^{-1} at present, while the length of the day is increasing by about .0012 s per century. Over sufficiently long times, however, the effects may be appreciable. In the Devonian period, about 370 million years ago, yearly variations in the daily growth rings of corals suggest that about 400 days occurred each year, so that the day was only about 21.9 hours long. Still longer ago, the Moon was probably substantially closer to Earth than it is today, perhaps only a few Earth radii away.

The Earth-Moon system is slowly evolving towards a state in which the Earth's rotation is slowed sufficiently that it is synchronized with the orbital revolution of the Moon about Earth. This effect has already occurred for the Moon, which has one side permanently facing Earth, locked into orientation by tidal forces.

Tidal disruption and the Roche limit

A further important tidal effect that can occur when one body revolves in orbit around another is that the smaller body may be torn apart by the tidal forces of the larger body if it ventures too close to the larger body. This effect is known as tidal disruption, and the distance from the larger body at which the smaller body becomes subject to tidal destruction is known as the Roche limit.

The physical basis of this effect is the same as that of tides. Because the smaller body has some significant size, the force of gravity from the large body on the near side of the small body is larger than that on the far side. The difference between these two forces is in effect a disruptive force which tries to pull the two halves of the small body apart. The disruptive tidal force is opposed by the self-gravity of the small body, which tries to hold it together.

The self-gravity of the small body has a definite strength, which does not depend on how far the small body is from the large one (except for a slight weakening if the small body is strongly distorted in shape). The strength of the disruptive tidal force, however, is very weak for large separations of the two bodies, but rapidly increases in strength (as $1/r^3$) as the two are brought closer together and the size of the small body becomes a larger fraction of the separation r between the two. For small enough separations, the tidal force is larger than the self-gravity of the small body and it is broken apart.

The separation at which tidal disruption occurs (the Roche limit), for a large and a small body of the same density, is roughly twice the radius of the large body. If the small body is denser than the large one, its self-gravity is stronger and the Roche limit is correspondingly somewhat closer to the large body; a less dense satellite, on the other hand, is more easily disrupted and the Roche limit for it is larger.

Of course, if the small body is held together by some force other than its own self-gravity (for example, the crystalline solid-body forces that hold together a monolithic boulder or an iceberg), the relatively weak forces of gravity will not be able to disrupt the small body until the tidal force is strong enough to exceed the tensile strength of the solid (the force needed to actually break the object in two). This will not usually be the case.

The ring systems of all the outer planets that have rings (Jupiter, Saturn, Uranus and Neptune) are within the planetary Roche limits. These rings can persist because tidal forces prevent disk material about each planet from gravitationally accreting to form a moon within the Roche limit. In the case of the insignificant rings of Jupiter, Uranus, and Neptune, the present rings may have originated in from debris blasted off a moon by an impact between that moon and a passing comet nucleus. Saturn's much more impressive rings could have originated in this way, or by tidal disruption of a moon that was deflected into an orbit inside the Roche limit for example by a close passage by another satellite.

The rings of Saturn are the most extensively studied; it seems that the ring particles are mostly water ice and that some of the particles range in size up to tens of meters or even a kilometer in diameter; the individual particles clearly owe their cohesion not to gravity but to the strength of ice.

Exercise: If an old comet (one that has lost all its ices) passes close to Saturn, going *inside* the ring system but missing the planet, what do you predict will happen to the comet?

1.6 Mathematical aspects

Many of the points discussed qualitatively in preceding sections of this chapter can be treated more quantitatively using ideas from first-year university level physics and mathematics. In this section quantitative discussions of several topics are presented for readers who are interested in a more mathematical treatment of solar system physics. Similar sections on mathematical aspects will be found at the ends of most chapters. They may be skipped if you are not interested in quantitative physics or in problem-solving.

The law of gravitation

During the seventeenth century, astronomers and physicists ("natural philosophers") tried to understand what underlying principles govern the movement of the planets, making each planet move according to the laws discovered by Kepler, which are that each planet (1) moves in an elliptical orbit having the Sun at one focus, (2) moves along this orbit at such a speed that the radius vector from the Sun sweeps out equal areas in equal times, and (3) takes a time for one complete revolution about the Sun whose square is proportional to the cube of the semi-major axis of the orbit. In trying to understand this behaviour, it was not unreasonable to suppose that the observed motion is caused by attraction towards the Sun, produced by a force like the force of gravity which attracts objects to the Earth. In other words, it seemed plausible to extend the idea of gravity, as studied near the Earth's surface by Galilei, to a more general force exerted by any massive body on other objects. But this extension requires us first to guess how the attraction of gravity may vary with distance from the attracting centre. This problem was solved independently by the English scientists Robert Hooke (1635–1702), Edmund Halley (1656–1742), Christopher Wren (1632–1723), and Isaac Newton.

The first step in deriving the law of gravitation is to find the force or acceleration required to hold a planet in its orbit at a distance r from the Sun. To simplify this step we approximate planetary orbits as circles centred on the Sun. This part of the problem was solved by the Dutch mathematician and astronomer Christiaan Huygens.

Consider a body of mass m moving around a circle of radius r at uniform speed v. In a time interval dt, the object moves a distance vdt and so it moves around the circle through an angle (measured in radians) of $d\theta = vdt/r$. During dt, the direction of the velocity vector also changes by $d\theta$ (this vector is always tangent to the orbital circle and perpendicular to the radius vector), so the change in velocity dv is just $vd\theta$. Substituting, we find the familiar result that

$$a = \frac{dv}{dt} = \frac{vd\theta}{rd\theta/v} = \frac{v^2}{r}, \quad (1.1)$$

where a is the acceleration of the orbiting body. The required force $F = ma$ is thus $F = mv^2/r$.

Next we use Kepler's 3rd law, which we write as $P^2 = kr^3$ where P is the period of the motion and k is constant, to find the way in which gravity must vary with distance from the Sun in order to lead to the observed variation of P (or v) with orbital radius r. Since $P = 2\pi r/v$, Kepler's third law gives $4\pi^2r^2/v^2 = kr^3$, or an acceleration due to the gravitational attraction of the Sun equal to $a = v^2/r = 4\pi^2/kr^2$. Thus *the gravitational acceleration produced by the Sun must vary with distance as* $1/r^2$. Furthermore, Galilei showed by experiment that all bodies falling in the Earth's gravity have the same acceleration regardless of their masses, so the gravitation *force* F must be proportional to the mass of the attracted body, i.e. $F = ma = 4\pi^2m/kr^2 = Am/r^2$. And finally, if we consider the hypothetical case of two similar bodies of masses m_1 and m_2 in orbit around each other, it is clear that the force on m_1 will be Am_1/r^2. But the *equal* force exerted by m_1 on m_2 must be proportion to m_2, and so the constant A may be written as Gm_2. Thus finally we deduce that the law of gravitation must be given by

$$F = \frac{Gm_1m_2}{r^2} \quad (1.2)$$

where G is a (universal) constant called the **gravitational constant**. Its value was first determined accurately by Englishman Henry Cavendish in 1798; the value is 6.67×10^{-11} m^3 s^{-2} kg^{-1}.

Newton devised a clever demonstration that the force of terrestrial gravity studies by Galilei is in fact the same force acting to pull astronomical bodies around one another by comparing the acceleration of an apple at the surface of the Earth to the acceleration of the Moon about the Earth. At the Earth's surface, the observed acceleration of gravity is $g = 9.80$ m s^{-2}. At the Moon's distance from the Earth, 60.27 Earth radii, the acceleration a *deduced* from equation (1.2) is $a = F/m_2 = 9.80/(60.27)^2 = 2.70 \times 10^{-3}$ m s^{-2} (since the Earth's attracting mass m_1 is the same for both apple and Moon). This assumes that terrestrial gravity acting on the Moon follows the law deduced from planetary orbits about the Sun. But now the Moon orbits the Earth with a period of 27.32 d $= 2.36 \times 10^6$ s at an average distance of 3.84×10^8 m, so its mean velocity is $v = 2\pi r/P = 1.02 \times 10^3$ m s^{-1}. The acceleration *required* to keep it in its orbit, by Huygens' result (1.1), is $a = v^2/r = 2.71 \times 10^{-3}$ m s^{-2}, exactly the acceleration *predicted* from the assumption that the law of gravity (1.2) describes both terrestrial gravity and the Earth's cosmic attraction for the Moon. Newton thus showed quite clearly that the same force of gravity with which we are familiar from our daily experience also acts across the enormous reaches of space, holding the Moon to the Earth, and, by inference, the planets to the Sun.

Exercise: (a) By equating the acceleration v^2/r of a body moving in a circle about the Sun with the expression for the gravitational acceleration produced by the Sun, show that

$$P^2 = 4\pi^2r^3/GM \quad (1.3)$$

holds for circular orbital motion. Here v is the orbital velocity, P is the orbital period, r is the radius of the orbit, and M is the mass of the Sun. (b) Express this result using the units of AU for length, years for the period, and solar masses for the mass of the attracting body. Evaluate any numerical constants which remain to obtain an equation in these convenient units.

Exercise: Using the periods and orbital radii of each of the four Galilean moons of Jupiter given in Table A.3, calculate the mass of Jupiter. Are the four values in good agreement?

Elliptical orbits

It is not simple to prove in an elementary way that, when the force of attraction of a single central attractor varies as $1/r^2$ (as gravity does), the only allowed orbits are in fact ellipses, parabolas and hyperbolas. However, we can study some aspects of such orbits without excessive mathematical effort.

First, let's look for the equation describing an ellipse, starting from the geometrical construction shown in Figure 1.22. The algebraic description of this curve is that it is the locus of points for which the sum of the distances from two given points (the foci, at f_1 and f_2) is equal to a constant. To express this in a convenient form, recall that Kepler showed that the Sun is at

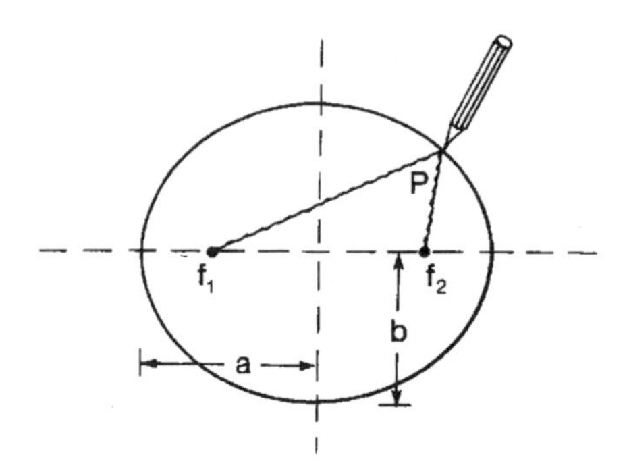

Figure 1.22: Construction of an ellipse. The dimensions labelled a and b are respectively the semi-major and semi-minor axes of the ellipse, f_1 and f_2 are the positions of the two foci, and P is an arbitrary point on the ellipse.

one of the foci of each elliptical orbit, so let us put the origin of polar co-ordinates (r, θ) at that focus. Then if we call half the length of the long axis of the ellipse (the semi-major axis) a, and the distances from each of the two foci to a particular point on the ellipse a_1 and a_2, it is easily seen that $2a = a_1 + a_2$. Now if the origin of our coordinates is at f_1, clearly $r = a_1$, and the two components of a_2 are $(r\cos\theta - 2f)$ and $(r\sin\theta)$, where $2f$ is the distance between the two foci. Then we have $2a = r + [r^2\sin^2\theta + (r\cos\theta - 2f)^2]^{1/2}$. Solving for r, we find

$$r(\theta) = \frac{a^2 - f^2}{a - f\cos\theta} = a\left[\frac{1 - e^2}{1 - e\cos\theta}\right], \tag{1.4}$$

where the **eccentricity** $e = f/a$ is a measure of how far off centre the foci are, and how flattened the ellipse is. Equation (1.4) gives the distance r from one focus to the orbit as a function of polar angle θ for given values of a and e.

Exercise: Fill in the missing steps in the derivation above. Start by showing that $2a = a_1 + a_2$.

It is easily shown as well that

$$f = (a^2 - b^2)^{1/2} \quad \text{or} \quad e = (1 - \frac{b^2}{a^2})^{1/2} \tag{1.5}$$

where b is the semi-minor axis, half the length of the minor axis (the short axis: see Figure 1.22).

Exercise: Starting from Figure 1.22, prove the two relations above.

We can also extrapolate this expression to the limit $e \to 1$, $a \to \infty$ to find the limiting form of an ellipse as one focus recedes to infinity. If we call the periapsis distance of the orbit (the smallest distance from the attracting focus to the orbit, on the major axis) q, we can use the equalities $a = q + f$ and $e = f/(q + f)$, eliminate f from the expression for a in favour of e and q, and find

$$r = q\frac{1 + e}{1 + e\cos\theta} \underset{e\to 1}{\longrightarrow} \frac{2q}{1 + \cos\theta}, \tag{1.6}$$

the polar equation of a parabola.

Exercise: Carry out the steps to derive the expression above for the shape of a parabolic orbit.

Exercise: The eccentricity of the lunar orbit is 0.0549, and the semi-major axis of the orbit is 384,000 km. Calculate the Earth-Moon distance q at perigee (closest approach) and Q at apogee, and the corresponding largest and smallest values of the lunar angular diameter as seen from Earth. Should this variation in angular diameter be obvious to the casual observer?

Exercise: Calculate, using the parameters of the Earth's orbit given in Table A.1, (a) the minimum and maximum distances from Earth to the Sun, and (b) the maximum and minimum velocities of Earth in its orbit around the Sun.

Angular momentum and Kepler's Second Law

One of the important properties of planetary orbits discovered by Kepler is a consequence of the conservation of angular momentum, and so we recall here a few results about angular momentum discussed in elementary physics texts.

The **angular momentum** of a point mass (an object whose internal motions we can ignore because it is so small) is defined with respect to a specific point or origin, O. If the mass of the small body is m, the radius vector (vectors are printed in **bold face type**) from O to the mass is $\mathbf{r}$, and its instantaneous velocity vector is $\mathbf{v}$, then the angular momentum of the mass $\mathbf{L}$ is defined as the vector cross product of $\mathbf{r}$ and the linear momentum $\mathbf{p} = m\,\mathbf{v}$,

$$\mathbf{L} = m\,\mathbf{r} \times \mathbf{v}. \tag{1.7}$$

The angular momentum of the point mass about O is altered by the application of a force acting perpendicular to the vector $\mathbf{r}$. We define the vector **torque** $\mathbf{T}$ exerted by a force $\mathbf{F}$ acting on the mass about the point O as the cross product of $\mathbf{r}$ and $\mathbf{F}$,

$$\mathbf{T} = \mathbf{r} \times \mathbf{F}. \tag{1.8}$$

It is easily seen from Newton's Second Law ($\mathbf{F} = d(m\,\mathbf{v})/dt$) how the time rate of change of angular momentum is related to the torque. If we take the time derivative of $\mathbf{L}$, using equation (1.7), we find

$$d\mathbf{L}/dt \;=\; m(d/dt)(\mathbf{r} \times \mathbf{v})$$

$$\begin{aligned} &= m[(d\mathbf{r}/dt) \times \mathbf{v} + \mathbf{r} \times (d\mathbf{v}/dt)] \quad (1.9) \\ &= \mathbf{r} \times d(m\,\mathbf{v})/dt, \end{aligned}$$

where the first term in $(d/dt)(\mathbf{r} \times \mathbf{v})$ vanishes because $d\mathbf{r}/dt = \mathbf{v}$, and the cross product of a vector with itself is zero. Then substituting for the derivative of $m\,\mathbf{v}$ from Newton's Second Law, we find finally

$$d\mathbf{L}/dt = \mathbf{r} \times \mathbf{F} = \mathbf{T}. \quad (1.10)$$

Thus angular momentum $\mathbf{L}$ is altered by the application of a torque, just as linear momentum is altered by the application of a force – no torque, no change in $\mathbf{L}$.

An important aspect of equation (1.10) is that not all forces acting on a body change its angular momentum. In particular, if we measure the angular momentum of a small body around a much larger one (e.g. the angular momentum of the Earth in its motion around the Sun) from the centre of the larger body, or from the centre of mass of the system (which lies on the line joining the two objects), the attractive force pulling the small body towards the larger one is *parallel* to the radius vector to the small body and so the torque $\mathbf{r} \times \mathbf{F}$ *vanishes* because the cross product of two parallel vectors is zero. In this case, even though there is a force (gravitational attraction) acting on the small body, there is no torque, and so the angular momentum of the small body is constant ("conserved") as it moves around the larger body.

This fact leads directly to Kepler's Second Law, which states that the radius vector from the Sun to a planet sweeps out equal areas in equal times. Now (see Figure 1.19) the triangular area swept out in dt by the radius vector from the attracting mass to an orbiting object is just $dA = (1/2)r(v_\perp dt)$, where $v_\perp$ is the component of orbital velocity perpendicular to the radius vector. But $(1/2)rv_\perp$ is simply half the scalar value of the vector cross product $\mathbf{r} \times \mathbf{v}$, which is constant because of the constancy of $\mathbf{L}$. Thus Kepler's law of equal areas, $dA/dt =$ constant, holds for any kind of orbit of one body around another that conserves angular momentum, and in fact is true for two bodies acted on by any force which has a component only along the line joining their centres of mass.

Velocity at a given point in an orbit

We may easily find the velocity of an orbiting body at any point in its orbit by using the equations expressing conservation of angular momentum and of energy in the orbit. To do this, we must know how the potential energy of a body in a gravity field varies with distance r from the attractor. Clearly, since the work done by the force of gravity $F = -GMm/r^2$ (negative because the attractive force of gravity is directed towards smaller values of r) in attracting one body of mass m at a distance r from the source M of gravitational attraction through a radial distance dr is simply $dW = F\,dr$, the potential energy difference between two points r_1 and r_2 is simply

$$\begin{aligned} \Delta E_g &= -\int_{r_1}^{r_2} F(r)dr \\ &= \int_{r_1}^{r_2} \frac{GMm}{r^2} dr \quad (1.11) \\ &= -GMm\left[\frac{1}{r_2} - \frac{1}{r_1}\right]. \end{aligned}$$

If we take as a reference point $r_1 \to \infty$, the potential energy at $r = r_2$ is

$$E_g(r) = -GMm/r, \quad (1.12)$$

which is zero at $r \to \infty$ and gets steadily more negative as one comes closer and closer to the attractor. The negative value of gravitational potential energy corresponds to the fact that we must do positive work on the body to return it to infinity against the pull of gravity.

Now conservation of energy states that the sum of the potential energy $E_g(r)$ and the kinetic energy $E_k(v) = (1/2)mv^2$ is a constant E for any orbit:

$$E = mv^2/2 - GMm/r = \text{constant}. \quad (1.13)$$

If we specify v at some r, then the value of E is determined and the value of v at any other r allowed by the orbit form is given by solving equation (1.13) for v.

Of course, it may not be particularly convenient to determine the total energy by specifying the value of v at some particular r, although we must specify *some* two constants to determine the shape of the orbit uniquely. Instead, we may prefer to specify the geometrical parameters of the orbit, for example the semi-major axis a and the eccentricity e of the ellipse. The dependence of v on r and the two parameters a and e in this situation may be found with some algebra. Write down the expression for the total energy at both perihelion (closest approach to the attractor), $r = q$, where $v = v_q$, and at aphelion (farthest distance from the attractor) where $r = Q$ and $v = v_Q$, and equate the two expressions. Do the same for the *scalar value* of angular momentum at the same two points in the orbit, using the fact that at these two points in the orbit the velocity vector is perpendicular to the radius vector and so the $\sin\phi$ factor from the cross product (ϕ is the angle between $\mathbf{r}$ and $\mathbf{v}$) is equal to 1.0. Use the relation found from angular momentum conservation in the energy equation to eliminate v_Q and find an expression for v_q in terms of q and Q. Simplify this expression as far as possible. Then evaluate E at q using the expression for v_q, and the fact that $2a = q + Q$, and obtain an explicit expression for the total energy E that depends on a (but not on e). Now total energy E is constant over the orbit, so this value of E applies anywhere in the orbit. Putting the expression for E back into equation (1.13), one obtains

$$v^2(r) = 2GM(1/r - 1/2a), \tag{1.14}$$

known as the **vis viva** equation.

Exercise: Carry out the algebra needed to verify the correctness of Equation 1.14.

This equation allows us to evaluate the velocity $v(r)$ at any allowed distance r from the attractor for an orbit of specified a. Notice that $v(r)$ does not depend explicitly on the eccentricity e at a given r; the way e enters the problem is in the allowed range of r for various orbits of the same a but different e values: r can range between $q = a - f = a(1 - e)$ and $Q = a + f = a(1 + e)$. Notice also that in general there is no place in a closed orbit in which the velocity of the orbiting body reaches zero, not even at aphelion, unless $Q = 2a$, which only occurs if the ellipse is a straight line with $e = 1.00$.

Escape velocity

Finally, equation (1.13) allows us to calculate a very interesting quantity called the **escape velocity** v_e, which is the velocity a body would have to be given at a distance r from an attractor of mass M in order to just barely enable the small body to escape the gravitational influence of the attractor. If we look at equation (1.13), the condition for an orbiting body to just be able to escape (to reach $r \to \infty$ with $v \to 0$) is simply $E = 0$, from which we deduce that at a distance r, v_e is given by

$$v_e^2 = 2GM/r. \tag{1.15}$$

Thus v_e is equal to $\sqrt{2}$ times the velocity for a circular orbit ($r = a$ in equation (1.14)).

Notice that v_e is the velocity which, once supplied, allows the escapee to get away without any further external force being exerted. It is also possible to escape from an attractor with a velocity which is always less than v_e if a force (say, the push of a rocket engine) is supplied over the escape route.

Finally, it should be clear that if any object starts at rest at $r \to \infty$ and falls in towards an attractor of mass M, at any distance r from M it will have a velocity $v = v_e(r)$.

Exercise: Calculate (a) the escape velocity from the Earth's surface, and (b) the escape velocity from the Sun (i.e. from the solar system) starting from the Earth's orbit. (c) Why is the escape velocity from the Sun so much larger than from the Earth? What consequences does this have for efforts to send space probes to other star systems?

Exercise: What is the *minimum* velocity with which a meteorite, large enough that atmospheric friction is negligible, would strike the Earth? Justify your answer.

1.7 References

Boorstin, D. J. 1983, *The Discoverers* (New York, NY: Random House, Inc.). A fascinating general history of scientific and scholarly discovery that contains an extensive section on the history of efforts to understand the solar system, and much else of interest.

Cohen, I. B. 1981, "Newton's discovery of gravity", *Sci. Am.*, Mar., 166. Newton's discovery of the law of gravity ushered in modern physics.

Corey, C. 1984, "The Earth's orbit and the ice ages", *Sci. Am.*, Feb., 58. The roughly ten ice ages that have occurred during the past million years may have been caused by small changes in the Earth's orbit around the Sun.

Gingerich, O. 1973, "Copernicus and Tycho", *Sci. Am.*, Dec., 86.

Gingerich, O. 1982, "The Galileo affair", *Sci. Am.*, Aug., 132. Galileo's arguments in favour of the Copernican world system had an important effect on scientific thought – and got him into a lot of trouble.

Gingerich, O. 1986, "Islamic astronomy", *Sci. Am.*, Apr., 74. During the Middle Ages the most important astronomical work was carried out by Islamic scholars who built on the Greek traditions.

Gingerich, O. 1992, "Astronomy in the age of Columbus", *Sci. Am.*, Nov., 100. The new world discovered by Columbus helped to prepare the minds of Europeans for other radical new ideas, such as the new cosmology of Copernicus.

Koestler, A. 1959, *The Sleepwalkers* (New York, NY: Macmillan Co.). Psychologist and novelist Arthur Koestler looks closely at the personal lives and work of Copernicus, Brahe, Kepler, and Galilei, in a historically accurate set of linked biographies that reads like a novel.

Wilson, C. 1972, "How did Kepler discover his first two laws?", *Sci. Am.*, Mar., 92.

Wolf, A. 1950, *A History of Science, Technology, and Philosophy in the 16th and 17th Centuries* (New York, NY: Macmillan Co.). The development of astronomical ideas from Copernicus to Newton is discussed in much technical detail in this excellent historical treatise.

1.8 Review questions

1.1 What is the relationship of the solar system to the rest of the universe, and in particular to the Milky Way galaxy?

1.2 What planets are currently visible in the sky in the evening? Which of these will still be visible six months later?

1.3 What is the essential function served in the geocentric theory of planetary orbits by the epicycle? What observational fact does it mainly serve to explain?

1.4 What questions left unanswered by the geocentric theory of the solar system were answered satisfactorily by the heliocentric theory?

1.5 From your space base on the equator of one of the moons of Jupiter, can Mars ever be seen high in the sky at local midnight?

1.6 Why does the Moon not fall onto the Earth because of the Earth's gravitational attraction?

1.7 Why is Mercury harder to see in the sky by eye than Venus or Mars?

1.8 How does Jupiter shine? What is the origin of the light we see coming from the planet?

1.9 What causes tides?

1.10 Why does Jupiter take longer to orbit the Sun than Venus does?

1.11 In the chapter we discuss how the *relative* distances of the planets from the Sun are found. How can the real scale of the solar system (i.e. the size of one Astronomical Unit) be measured from Earth?

1.9 Problems

1.1 The aim of this question is to solve approximately the problem of how far below the horizon a distant object is, and to apply the result to an interesting case. (a) Consider a line of sight (a horizontal line) tangent to a circle (the Earth). The circle has radius R, and in coordinates (X, Y) from its centre is given by $X^2 + Y^2 = R^2$. The sight line touches the Earth at $(X, Y) = (O, R)$. The problem is to find a simple expression for the distance from the sight line to the smooth surface of the Earth as a function of distance X away from the contact point. Make a change of coordinates to (X, Y') where $Y' = Y - R$. This Y' is the vertical distance from the sight line to the circle at a given X. Change to the variable Y' in the expression for the circle and solve for Y' exactly. (b) For $X/R \ll 1$, expand the square root of the solution in a Taylor's series, keeping only the smallest 2 terms, to find a simple approximate expression for $Y'(X)$. (c) Suppose that your eye is on this sight line at some position X_e such that your eye is 3 m above the surface of the Earth. Calculate the distance X_e which separates you from the point where your sight line touches the Earth's surface. (This distance is the distance out to which, from your spot on the beach, you can see the surface water of a lake or sea. You should find a value for X_e that is some km in length.) (d) Now suppose you are watching a receding ship from this position 3 m above the water level. Calculate and plot a graph showing how much of the ship's height has dropped below the horizon as a function of distance from your position out to 30 km away from you. Be sure to include the distance between your post and the point where your sight line contacts the surface of the water as well as the distance beyond this point out to the boat.

1.2 The object of this question is to test the correctness of some of the assumptions implicitly made in the calculations of Eratosthenes and of Aristarchos. (a) Eratosthenes' method for measuring the diameter of the Earth assumes that the rays of incoming sunlight at Syene and Alexandria are *parallel*. Calculate the minimum distance d_e at which the Sun would have to be located in order for rays from a single point on the centre of the solar disk to arrive at both Alexandria and Syene with no more than $1/2^\circ$ difference in direction. Compare this distance to the actual distance to the Moon and to the Sun. Then calculate the difference in direction of incoming rays at Syene and Alexandria from the centre of the Sun's disk with the Sun at its actual distance. (b) For Aristarchos' method of measuring the distance from the Earth to the Moon to work reasonably accurately, the shape of the Earth's shadow must be known (Aristarchos assumed that the Sun is so far away that its angular size from the end of the Earth's shadow cone is almost the same as the Sun's angular size as seen from the Earth). As a quite different possibility, suppose the Sun were the same physical size as the Earth, and were at such a distance that it would still be $1/2°$ in diameter on the sky. Calculate the distance at which the Sun would satisfy these two requirements, and compare it to the results of Aristarchos' measurement of the distance to the Sun. What would be the Sun-Moon angle at lunar first quarter (Figure 1.13) be if this were the real situation? Deduce the shape of the Earth's dark shadow in this case, and estimate how much the deduced distance and diameter of the Moon would be increased compared to their values assuming the correct shape for the shadow cone.

1.3 On 26 July 1953 a nearly central eclipse of the Moon took place (that is, the Moon passed almost precisely through the centre of the Earth's shadow). The Moon first touched the Earth's dark shadow (umbra) at 10:32.5 UT. It finished entering the umbra at 11:29.9 and began to re-emerge at 13:11.4. It lost contact with the umbra at 14:08.8. At the time of the eclipse, the Moon subtended $0.518° = 31'05''$, and the Sun subtended $0.524° = 31'27''$. The Earth's diameter is 12750 km. Using Aristarchos' method (i.e. without prior knowledge of the Moon's dimensions, and assuming that the Sun is very far away), find (a) the ratio of the diameter of the Moon to the diameter of the Earth's dark shadow at the Moon's distance from Earth, (b) the distance from Earth to the Moon when the eclipse occurred, and (c) the diameter of the Moon.

1.4 As seen from the Earth, the maximum angular distance on the sky between the Sun and Mercury during one period of the planet's visibility either in the evening or morning sky (the *greatest elongation of the planet*) during its orbit can vary from as little as 17° 52´ to as much as 27° 49´. (a) Assume that the largest and smallest values of greatest elongation occur when the line of sight from Earth is perpendicular to the major axis of Mercury's orbit, contacting it at aphelion and perihelion respectively. Sketch the line-of-sight triangles that describe the largest and smallest values of greatest elongation. (b) Assuming that the Earth's orbit is circular and coplanar with that of Mercury, calculate the semi-major axis (in astronomical units, AU) and eccentricity of Mercury's orbit from these observed extreme values of greatest elongation. Compare to the values in Table A.1 of the text.

1.5 (a) Planet 1 has an orbital period of P_1 about the Sun. Planet 2 has a period of P_2. *Derive* a general equation expressing the time interval t_0 between successive oppositions of planet 2 as seen from planet 1, assuming that both planets are in coplanar circular orbits and $P_2 > P_1$. (Recall that from one opposition to the next, the inner planet will make exactly one *more* revolution about the Sun than the outer planet.) (b) Apply your expression to find the approximate intervals between oppositions of Mars as seen from the Earth, and of Jupiter as seen from Mars.

1.6 Using conservation of angular momentum in an elliptical orbit, show that

$$(rv \sin \phi)^2 = GMa(1 - e^2) = GMq(1 + e),$$

where r is the distance from the attracting body to the orbiting body, v is the velocity of the orbiting body, ϕ is the angle between the radius vector from the large to the small body and the velocity vector of the small body, a is the semi-major axis of the orbital ellipse, e is the eccentricity, and q is the minimum (perihelion) distance between the two bodies.

1.7 Saturn's ring system extends from a radius of about 71 000 km to about 138 000 km. (a) Calculate the circular velocity and period of revolution for a ring particles on the inner edge, and on the outer edge, of the rings. How many revolutions does the inner particle make for one revolution of the outer one? (b) Find the difference in velocity and orbital period for two ring particles whose orbits are both circular with $a = 100000$ km if one has an orbital semi-major axis 1 meter larger than the other. (Hint: differentiate the expression for circular velocity as a function of semi-major axis size to get an expression which can be evaluated without keeping many significant figures.) Compare the result obtained this way with a direct calculation of the velocity difference.

Chapter 2

Matter and its Atomic Structure

2.1 Overview

Now we turn from the (very!) macroscopic scale of planetary motions to the microscopic scale of atoms and even of electrons and atomic nuclei. To understand many aspects of solar system physics requires a general knowledge of the states and structure of matter. In this chapter, we shall review some of the most useful concepts.

We begin by looking at how the idea of chemical elements originated, and how the notion of the atom was developed by chemists in the 19th century. We then survey the work of the physicists who discovered and mapped the internal structure (electrons, atomic nuclei) of those atoms early in the 20th century. We discuss a number of aspects of the behaviour of matter that may be understood with a knowledge of atoms; for example, we look at various states of a substance (solid, liquid, gas) that can exist at different temperatures and pressures; we consider how various elements can combine chemically to form new and interesting substances (compounds); and we look at the structure of the solid compounds (minerals) that make up the building material of many objects such as planets in the solar system. This final topic will bring us into the realm of geology, of course, and the non-mathematical part of the chapter will end with an introduction to the main types of rocks with which it is useful to be familiar in studying the solar system.

2.2 Atomic nature of matter

Chemical elements

The idea that matter is actually composed of a modest number of elementary substances or chemical elements, which combine to form the enormous variety of materials found in nature, is at least as old as Greek science. Aristotle considered the elementary substances to be earth, water, air and fire (which we now think of as states of matter – solid, liquid, gas, plasma – rather than chemical elements), while many medieval alchemists considered salt, sulphur, and mercury to be the fundamental substances from which all others were formed. The modern view of elements only began to emerge in the late 17th century, when in 1661 the Irish chemist Robert Boyle (1627–91) proposed that those substances should be considered chemical elements that cannot be decomposed by any chemical means into two or more other substances.

The difficulty with this idea at first was the problem of deciding whether a substance is divisible or not. For about a century Boyle's view had little impact, but during this period two extremely important developments occurred that finally paved the way for modern chemical and atomic theory. The first of these was the development of methods for handling, separating, combining, and studying gases. These advances made it possible to quantitatively study particularly simple situations involving transformations and combinations of substances that turn out to be elements, two or three at a time. The other development was a growing interest in measuring the amounts (weights or volumes) of materials participating in chemical reactions, which led in the middle of the 18th century to the clear recognition that when substances react chemically, *the total mass (or weight) of the original substance is equal to the mass of the final product.* Thus, for example, if a quantity of paper is burned inside a sealed container containing air, the paper turns to ash and decreases in weight, but the mass of gas increases. The total weight of the containing vessel and its contents does not change during the reaction. As a result of many such experiments, chemists gradually became convinced during the 18th century that the quantity of matter is conserved in all chemical reactions.

The identification of the chemical elements, the fundamental indivisible substances, was a major preoccupation of some of the best chemists of the late 18th century. The intellectual leader was the Frenchman Antoine Lavoisier (1743–1794). As an example of the work of experiment and interpretation that Lavoisier carried out, and of the difficulties of identifying chemical elements, consider the situation of oxygen. Lavoisier knew that when a substance such as mercury is heated in a closed container filled with air, the mercury is transformed into a new substance, called a calx by chemists of the day (we call it an oxide), while the volume of air decreased by about one-fifth. It seemed clear that air is composed of two substances, one of which is involved easily in chemical reactions and one which is not (we now know that air is a simple mixture of the oxygen and nitrogen). The problem was how to separate the two. A method for doing this occurred to Lavoisier when he met the English experimenter Joseph Priestley (1733–1804), who described to Lavoisier how he had found that really strong heating of calx of mercury releases a gas that supports combustion (burning of paper, etc.) much *better* than ordinary air. Lavoisier immediately understood that this experimental result gave him the tool he needed to separate air. First, he mildly heated mercury in air to form a calx. He kept the residual air from this experiment, put the calx of mercury into a new container and heated it strongly. It gave off Priestley's gas, which indeed supported burning extremely well, while the residual air from the first experiment did not support any combustion. Finally, combining the two gases produced a gas indistinguishable from normal air. Lavoisier had demonstrated the composite nature of air in the most convincing possible way, by taking it apart and putting it back together again.

In a similar way, Lavoisier showed the composite nature of another of the Greek elements, water. It can be produced by explosive combination of the gases hydrogen and oxygen; or if steam is passed over red-hot iron, a calx of iron is formed and hydrogen is left. Thus, like air, water can be formed from more elementary substances (hydrogen and oxygen) and decomposed into them. Using similar reasoning, many other elements were also identified.

Atomic theory

The next really big step forward was the development of a workable atomic theory by the English chemist John Dalton (1766–1844). Dalton was certainly not the first to propose that matter is made of tiny, discrete building blocks; some Greek philosophers had suggested this two millennia earlier, but had found no way to test the idea. Dalton's great contribution was to find a connection between atoms and experimental chemistry. He assumed that any kind of matter is composed of a vast number of tiny indestructible particles, and that the atoms of different elements have different weights. In this view, chemical analysis (separation of substances) and synthesis (combinations of substances) are nothing more than separating and reuniting the distinctive particles of one element with those of one or more others. If atoms are indestructible, we have a theoretical basis for the conservation of matter in chemical reactions.

Two principal experimental facts seem to have led Dalton to his atomic theory. First, when two elements combine to form a particular compound (hydrogen and oxygen to form water, or mercury and oxygen to form the oxide of mercury), the ratio of the two substances needed to form the third is always exactly the same regardless of how large a quantity of the compound is made, how quickly it is made, etc. (This is the **law of definite proportions**; it is true for gases and many simple substances but not by any means for all compounds). Secondly, Dalton himself discovered a simple rule describing what happens when a given pair of elements can form two *different* products (for example, a given quantity of carbon combines with a little oxygen to form carbon monoxide, while it combines with ample oxygen to form carbon dioxide). If one keeps constant the amount of one substance (say the carbon in our example), then the weights of the other substance (here the oxygen) needed to form the different final products are in the ratio of small integers (the **law of multiple proportions**). In our example, exactly twice as much oxygen combines with a given amount of carbon to form carbon dioxide as is needed to form carbon monoxide from the same amount of carbon.

These two facts led Dalton to suppose that the explanation for the observed behaviour is that a chemical compound is formed of little groups of atoms (we call these groups **molecules**), in which one or at most a few atoms of one element combine with a small number of atoms of one or more other element. These molecules then form the building blocks of the compound substance. In the case of formation of carbon monoxide and carbon dioxide, Dalton's theory suggests that carbon monoxide forms when one atom of carbon combines with one of oxygen, while carbon dioxide molecules each contain one atom of carbon and two of oxygen. Thus, it was the assumptions that molecules form the building unit of compounds, and that only small numbers (say, normally between 1 and 4) of atoms of any one element are involved in these molecules that enabled Dalton to use his theory to explain observed behaviour.

Dalton then set to work to determine the relative weights of different atoms, starting from the known relative weight of substances that must be combined to exhaust both reacting materials to form a compound. Working with such simple substances as water (composed of hydrogen plus oxygen), ammonia (hydrogen and nitrogen) and carbon monoxide and carbon dioxide (carbon and oxygen), he was able to find relative weights for the atoms of many substances and to show that indeed the atoms generally combine in simple ratios.

The work of Dalton led the Swedish chemist J. J. Berzelius (1779–1848) to propose the modern notation for chemical substances, based on their atomic composition as determined by Dalton and others. He suggested giving one atom of an element a one- or two-letter symbol, such as C for carbon, Cl for chlorine, Cr for chromium, and Co for cobalt, and then expressing the molecular constitution of a substance with a simple formula giving the symbols of the elements involved and numbers of each kind of atom in the basic molecule. Thus water (two hydrogen atoms, H, combined with one oxygen atom, O) is written as H_2O; carbon dioxide (one carbon atom with two oxygen atoms) written as CO_2. This system is so easy to use and so informative that it quickly gained universal acceptance. Since this notation shows the number of atoms involved in the basic molecular building block of a substance, it is readily adapted to show what happens at an atomic level when a chemical reaction occurs. Thus when oxygen (which in air is actually in the form of little pairs of O atoms, written O_2) combines with carbon to form carbon monoxide or carbon dioxide, we may describe the reactions symbolically as

$$C + O_2 \rightarrow CO_2$$

and

$$2C + O_2 \rightarrow 2CO,$$

where obviously the second equation means "two C atoms combine with two O atoms (in O_2) to form two molecules of CO, carbon monoxide".

Another line of evidence pointing to the existence of atoms came from the study of chemical reactions between gases. In situations where two gases react at the same temperature (say at 0 C) and pressure (say, sea level atmospheric pressure; this combination of temperature and pressure is called "standard temperature and pressure", or STP), a remarkably simple relationship between the volumes of the two gases needed to complete the reaction is found. The ratio of the two volumes of gas needed is a ratio of small whole numbers. Thus, for example, two volumes of CO combine with one volume of O_2 to produce two volumes of CO_2. Complex ratios such as 1 volume of one gas to 1.143 volumes of the other are never found, as long as both gases are at the same temperature and pressure. This extraordinary fact was reported by Joseph Gay-Lussac (1778–1850) in 1808, and is called Gay-Lussac's law, or the **law of combining volumes**.

The very simple relationship between volumes of reacting gases strongly hinted at the presence in the combining gases of little units that combined in simple ratios, and Gay-Lussac's law was quickly interpreted by an Italian lawyer and amateur chemist, Amadeo Avogadro (1776–1856). He boldly guessed that equal volumes of all gases having the same temperature and exerting the same pressure contain equal numbers of molecules (**Avogadro's Law**), and that the observed ratios of combining volumes simply reflect the numerical ratios of combining atoms. Thus, for example, one volume of gaseous H_2 combines with one volume of gaseous Cl_2 (chlorine) to make two volumes of (gaseous) hydrochloric acid, HCl. We write this reaction as

$$H_2 + Cl_2 \rightarrow 2HCl,$$

which says that one molecule of H_2 combines with one molecule of Cl_2, to form two HCl molecules. Avogadro's law explains the relative *volumes* of gases involved in this reaction by supposing that equal volumes (say 1 ℓ each) of H_2 and Cl_2 contain equal numbers of molecules, which react with one another in such a way that one molecule of H_2 and one of Cl_2 result in two molecules of HCl, and thus (at the same temperature and pressure as before reaction) yield two volumes (2 ℓ) of HCl.

The usefulness of Avogadro's principle for determining molecular weights of molecules in gases and of atoms was first clearly understood by the Italian chemist Stanislao Cannizzaro (1826–1910). Because equal volumes of gas at a given set of conditions (e.g. STP) contain equal number of molecules, the ratio of masses of two different molecules is just the ratio of the densities of the two gases under the same conditions. Thus, for example, the mass of 1 ℓ of CO_2 is 22 times the mass of 1 ℓ of H_2. Taking the unit of mass as the mass of one H atom (half of an H_2 molecule), since H is the lightest of the atoms, we find that the mass of a CO_2 molecule is 22 times the mass of an H_2 molecule, which is two mass units, so the mass of a CO_2 molecule is 44 units.

Table 2.1: Composition of some carbon molecules.

Compound	Molecular weight (H = 1)	C fraction by weight	Mass of C in molecule (H = 1)
Methane	16	0.75	12
Hydrogen cyanide	27	0.44	12
Ethane	30	0.80	24
Carbon dioxide	44	0.27	12
Propane	44	0.82	36
Cyanogen	52	0.46	24

One can use the molecular masses determined in this way to determine the mass or weights of constituent atoms as well, since experiments of making compounds from elements, or of breaking down compounds into elements, reveal the fraction of the mass of a molecule that is made of one particular element. An example will show how this is done. In Table 2.1, we list several carbon compounds. The mass of the molecules (called the **molecular weight**) relative to the H atom is given, and then the fraction of the total mass of each molecule which is made of carbon is listed. The last column shows the mass of carbon in each molecule. Since each molecule must contain one, or two, or some small number of C atoms, these masses must be either the mass of the C atom, or that mass times a small integer. The smallest mass of C is 12, and all the other masses are integer multiples of 12. We conclude that the mass of the C atom (the **atomic weight** of C) is 12 times that of H.

However, through most of the 19th century, atoms could not be observed directly, and doubts persisted about their reality. The actual sizes and masses of atoms were unknown as well, although *ratios* of atomic masses were deduced from the results of chemical experiments. Since single atoms could not be seen in microscopes, they must be less than about 10^{-6} m (= 1 μm = 1 micrometer) in diameter, but this could be (and is) a very generous upper limit to atomic size. A further hint on atomic size could be obtained from soap and oil films, formed by stretching a tiny drop of liquid on a metal frame or on a water surface. Such films always break once they have been pulled or blown out to a large enough size. If it is assumed that this happens when the film has been stretched out to a layer only one molecule thick, then the volume of the film at the instant of breaking (its measurable surface area times its unknown thickness) should equal its original, also measurable, droplet volume. This provides a way of calculating the thickness of the film when it is one molecule thick; one finds thicknesses of 10^{-9}–10^{-10} m at the breaking point, (correctly) suggesting that molecules and atoms are of this rough size.

Size and structure of atoms

Starting in the second half of the 19th century, the main work showing the existence of atoms, measuring their sizes, and studying their nature and internal structure was carried out by physicists. This work eventually resulted in a knowledge of atoms far more detailed and exact than could have been imagined by the chemists who first struggled to find clues about atoms in their experiments. To the astonishment of all, the experiments of the physicists revealed that atoms are not fundamental, indivisible bricks, but that they have a rich and complex internal structure. The first part of this structure to be detected by experiments, surprisingly, is the lightest part, the electron.

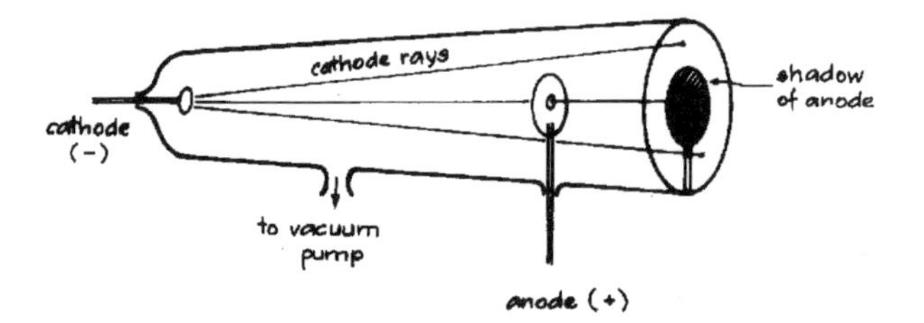

Figure 2.1: A cathode-ray tube. A high voltage applied between the cathode and anode of an evacuated glass tube causes rays to pass from the cathode to the anode. Those that miss the anode make the glass at the right end of the tube glow. This is the prototype of the cathode-ray tube (CRT) in a television set or computer monitor.

Atoms and their parts were studied in experiments involving electric currents passed through a near vacuum in a glass bottle. A typical experiment is shown in Figure 2.1, where a high voltage (a few kV) is applied between the (negative) cathode and the (positive) anode. Rays stream from the cathode towards the anode, visibly lighting up the inside of the bottle if the vacuum is not too good. Those that miss the anode cause the end of the glass tube to glow; the shadow of the anode is clearly visible, showing that the rays come from the cathode, and travel in straight lines.

When electric or magnetic fields are applied across the long axis of the tube, the cathode rays are deflected. This shows that the rays are electrically charged, rapidly moving particles. They are produced and behave in the same way regardless of what material is used for the cathode from which they are emitted; they are evidently part of all matter. These rays were christened **electrons**.

The deflection of a beam of electrons by an electric or magnetic field depends on the electrical charge e of the particles in the beam (the larger the charge, the larger the deflection) and on the mass m of the particles (the larger the mass the smaller the deflection), and so Joseph J. Thompson (1856–1940) was able to measure the ratio of charge to mass, which has a value of $e/m = -1.76 \times 10^{11}$ C kg^{-1} for all the electrons of cathode rays. (C is the coulomb, the amount of electrical charge that passes a point in one second when a current of one ampere flows).

The actual charge on the electron was measured early in this century in experiments by Robert Millikan (1868–1953) and several of his students. They established that the electron's charge is $e = -1.60 \times 10^{-19}$

C, so that the mass of an electron is a tiny $m = 9.11 \times 10^{-31}$ kg.

Other experiments with cathode-ray tubes were used to study whole atoms. If a small amount of a single kind of gas (H_2, O_2, Ne, etc.) is left in the glass tube, then a second kind of ray, attracted towards the cathode, is observed. These rays are made up of molecules (and atoms which may be produced from molecules disrupted by collisions with electrons) that have had one or more electrons removed by the impact of an electron streaming from cathode to anode. These atoms that have lost an electron (we call them ions) are now positively charged and are attracted to the cathode. As before, some miss it and go on to illuminate the glass end of the discharge tube. These ions also move in straight lines. Their trajectories can be bent by electric and magnetic fields, but only by much stronger fields than affect electron beams, showing that they are much more massive than electrons. By measuring the deflection, the ratio of charge-to-mass can again be determined. The largest charge-to-mass ratio is found for hydrogen gas; an ionized H atom has

$$e/m_{\mathrm{H}} = 9.58 \times 10^{-7} \text{ C kg}^{-1}.$$

Since atoms are normally electrically neutral, we assume that a positively charged H atom has lost an electron, so the charge on the atom is the same as that of the electron, but positive. We then derive

$$m_{\mathrm{H}} = 1.67 \times 10^{-27} \text{ kg}$$

for the mass of a single H atom, a value 1836 times larger than the mass of an electron. This establishes the scale for all other masses determined from chemical experiments, and in fact masses for other atoms measured in a discharge tube show the same ratios to H as one finds from chemistry. With the cathode ray tube, the physicists had found a way to weigh individual atoms.

Knowing actual masses of individual atoms (C, with atomic weight 12, has a mass of $12 \times 1.67 \times 10^{-27} = 2.00 \times 10^{-26}$ kg, for example), we can now estimate the sizes of atoms from the density in solid or liquid state by assuming that in these states, the atoms are essentially in contact with one another. Copper has an atomic weight of 63.5 and a density (mass per unit volume) of 8900 kg m^{-3}. Hence one cubic meter of Cu contains $8900 \text{ kg}/(63.5 \times 1.67 \times 10^{-27} \text{ kg/atom}) = 8.39 \times 10^{28}$ atoms, so the (roughly cubic) volume occupied by each atom is $1.00 \text{ m}^3/8.39 \times 10^{28} \text{ atoms} = 1.19 \times 10^{-29}$ m^3/atom, and this cubic volume has a dimension of $(1.19 \times 10^{-29})^{1/3} = 2.28 \times 10^{-10}$ m on a side. Thus if we think of atoms as actually being spherical, the radius of a Cu atom is about 1×10^{-10} m, about 1 Å (Angstrom unit; 1 Å $\equiv 10^{-10}$ m). This turns out to be roughly the size of atoms of all elements, within a factor of two or so (see Table 2.6). No wonder atoms aren't visible through microscopes!

Further experiments, such as Ernest Rutherford's (1871–1937) experiment of shooting twice ionized He atoms through very thin gold foil, reveal that atoms are mostly empty space. In fact an atom has a structure quite reminiscent of the solar system. Virtually all the mass of an atom is concentrated in a small positively charged sphere called the nucleus. This nucleus has a radius of between 10^{-15} and 10^{-14} m, larger for heavier atoms. The electrons, each almost 2000 times lighter than the lightest nucleus (that of H) orbit around this nucleus in orbits of typically 10^{-10} m radius, which define the size of the atom. (These orbits, however, are not regularly spaced and in one plane as are planetary orbits, but are often elongated, like cometary orbits, and inclined to one another). Thus the nucleus is smaller in size by a factor of 10^4 or 10^5 than the atom as a whole, even though all but a very tiny fraction of the total mass of the atom resides there.

It is found that the nucleus, small as it is, defines chemical identity by its electrical charge. Atoms of different chemical elements have different amounts of positive charge in the nucleus. This charge always occurs in integer multiples of the charge of the electron. An atom of H has a nuclear charge of one electron (but opposite in sign, i.e. positive), the nucleus of an atom of He has the charge of two electrons, C has six, O eight, etc. This nuclear charge (number of positive e charges) is called the **atomic number** of the element, and is usually given the symbol Z. In Table 2.2, which lists some common chemical elements that will be of particular interest to us, Z is tabulated along with a number of other qualities that will be explained as we go along.

Normally a number of electrons equal to the atomic number Z surround the nucleus, so that the atom as a whole is electrically neutral. This situation can be changed, of course, if the atom has an electron knocked off (for example by a collision with another atom in a really hot gas, from being irradiated with ultraviolet radiation, or even by giving up an electron to a neighbouring atom in a chemical bond). In this case, the nucleus keeps the same electrical charge—and chemical identity—as before, but due to the shortage of electrons the atoms as a whole is no longer electrically neutral—it becomes an ionized atom, or **ion**.

Roughly speaking, an atom with a large atomic number Z has its Z electrons arranged in nested or concentric sets of orbits. They are given names like 1s, 2s, 2p, 3s, 3p, 3d, etc. to denote successively larger orbits (indicated by the integers 1, 2, 3, 4 etc., where each

Table 2.2: Most abundant chemical elements in the solar nebula

Atomic number Z	Name	Chemical symbol	Atomic weight (^{12}C=12)	Melting point at 1 atm (K)	Boiling Point at 1 atm (K)	Abundance (atoms per 10^3 Si atoms) solar atmosphere	CI chondrites
1	Hydrogen	H	1.01	14.0	20.3	28 200 000	5 600
2	Helium	He	4.00	–	4.2	2 400 000	–
8	Oxygen	O	16.00	54.8	90.2	19 000	7 700
6	Carbon	C	12.01	3 820	?	9 330	810
10	Neon	Ne	20.18	24.5	27.1	3 390	–
7	Nitrogen	N	14.01	63.3	77.4	2 340	40
12	Magnesium	Mg	24.31	922	1 363	1 070	1 050
14	Silicon	Si	28.09	1 683	2 628	(1 000)	(1 000)
26	Iron	Fe	55.85	1 808	3 023	890	870
16	Sulphur	S	32.06	390	718	600	435
13	Aluminum	Al	26.98	934	2 740	83	85
18	Argon	Ar	39.95	84.0	87.5	71	–
20	Calcium	Ca	40.08	1 112	1 757	65	62
11	Sodium	Na	22.99	371	1 156	60	58
28	Nickel	Ni	58.69	1 726	3 005	50	49
24	Chromium	Cr	52.00	2 130	2 945	13.2	13.5
17	Chlorine	Cl	35.45	172	239	8.9	5.3
15	Phosphorus	P	30.97	317	553	7.9	10
25	Manganese	Mn	54.94	1 517	2 235	6.9	9.3
19	Potassium	K	39.10	336	1 033	3.7	3.8
22	Titanium	Ti	47.88	1 933	3 560	3.0	2.4
27	Cobalt	Co	58.93	1 768	3 143	2.2	2.2
30	Zinc	Zn	65.38	693	1 180	1.1	1.3
9	Fluorine	F	19.00	53.5	85.0	1.0	0.85
29	Copper	Cu	63.55	1 357	2 840	0.46	0.54
23	Vanadium	V	50.94	2 163	3 653	0.28	0.29

Sources: N. Grevesse & A. J. Sauval 1998, Space Sci. Rev., 85, 161; *CRC Handbook of Chemistry and Physics*, 1986–87 Ed. (Boca Raton, Fla: CRC Press, Inc.), B-5.

integer refers to what is called a **shell**), and more elongated ones (successively s, p, d, etc., where each letter refers to a particular **subshell**). As one goes from light nuclei to heavier ones, the larger nuclear charge pulls the innermost orbits closer and closer to the nucleus, so that the outer orbits have roughly the same size for all atoms. The electron orbits have a much less well-defined character than planetary orbits do— each orbit is a kind of cloud in which the electron is located, but the electrons do not follow a regularly repeated path. Very importantly, each orbit (subshell) also has a maximum number of electrons it can accept: two for an s subshell, six for p, 10 for d, etc. A schematic sketch of a carbon atom ($Z = 6$) is shown in Figure 2.2. Its $1s$ subshell (the smaller circle) and the $2s$ subshells (the two oval orbits) are filled, but the $2p$ subshell (two larger circle) has only two of six possible electrons.

Light and other kinds of electromagnetic radiation

Crucial information about the nature of the orbits followed by the electrons inside the atoms was revealed by experiments concerning the interaction of single atoms (in gases) with light. These experiments are particularly relevant to us because much of the information we have about distant astronomical objects comes to us through light they emit or reflect, and so a knowledge of how atoms interact with light helps us to understand better the objects we observe. To look more closely at the interaction of light and atoms, we need first to recall some basic properties of light itself.

Light is one of many closely related kinds of **electromagnetic radiation**. It is physically almost identical in nature to radio waves (the radiation that carries radio or television signals from a transmitting antenna to a radio or television receiver that obtains its sig-

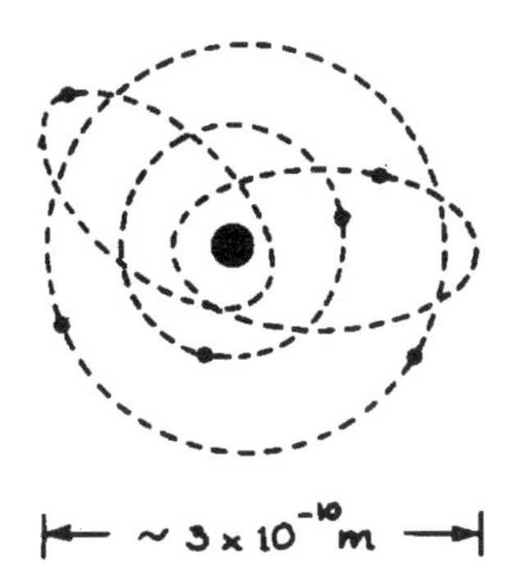

Figure 2.2: Sketch of a C atom. The largest dot is the nucleus with a charge of $-Ze = -6e$. Six electrons are in orbits of various sizes and orientations around the nucleus. The sizes of the electrons and the nucleus are enormously exaggerated compared to the size of the atom overall, and the orbits (dashed lines) are shown as being much more definite than they really are.

nals independently of a cable), to infrared radiation (the radiation that warms your skin when you sit near a fire or an electric space heater), to ultraviolet light (radiation that gives you a sunburn when you sit too long in the sunlight), and X-rays (the penetrating radiation that a physician uses to look at structures inside your body). All these different kinds of radiation share the basic characteristic that they are waves of electricity and magnetism that, once generated, travel freely through space. These waves all travel at the same speed in space, a speed that we call the **speed of light**, which has the enormous value of $c = 300\ 000$ km s^{-1}. A beam of radio waves, or of light, takes only about 1 1/3 sec to travel the 385,000 km from the Earth to the Moon, and only 8 1/3 min to travel from the Sun to the Earth.

The quality which distinguishes one kind of electromagnetic radiation from another is the **frequency** or **wavelength** of the wave, so we need to look at the meaning of these two closely related characteristics of a wave. Imagine a regular series of waves coming in towards the beach at the lake or seaside. The speed v of the wave is simply the speed of one of the wave crests or troughs over the lake or sea floor. It is measured in the usual units for speed, for example m s^{-1} or km hr^{-1}. The wavelength of the waves, usually called λ, is the distance from one wave crest to the next, or from one trough to the next. It is a length, measured in convenient units such as m, km, cm, or Å. The frequency, usually called f or ν, is the number of waves which pass a fixed point (say, the end of a pier or an anchored buoy) every second. Frequency is measured in waves per second; one wave per second is known as one Hertz (abbreviated Hz). For waves near the shore of a lake, typical values might be $v \approx 5$ m s^{-1}, $\lambda \approx 20$ m, and $f \approx 0.25$ waves per second or 0.25 Hz (i.e. one wave every four seconds).

The speed, frequency, and wavelength are related in a simple way. Imagine again the waves coming towards the beach. If each wave is 20 meters long from crest to crest, and 1/4 wave passes you in one second, then the distance that the pattern travels in one second, which is of course the speed of the wave, is simply the length of one wave times the number of waves passing each second, or $20 \times (1/4) = 5$ m s^{-1}. We can express this idea, that speed = (length of one wave) × (the number of waves per second), as an equation which should be understandable by even the most math-phobic:

$$v = \lambda f. \tag{2.1}$$

Because of this simple relationship, and the fact that all electromagnetic waves travel through space at the same speed c, we may identify a particular wave by *either* its wavelength *or* its frequency, since the other can easily be computed from equation (2.1).

Not only are different kinds of electromagnetic waves distinguished from each other by wavelength, but within each kind of radiation different waves can be identified in the same way. For example, on your FM radio dial the numbers usually range from 88 to 108. These numbers are simply the frequencies of the various radio stations to which you can tune the radio, expressed in millions of Hz (or megahertz, MHz). The CBC2 station in London, Ontario, for example, broadcasts at a frequency of 100.5 MHz; this broadcast could also be labeled by the corresponding wavelength of 2.99 m. Similarly, different kinds of visible light (that is, light that can be detected with the eye) are perceived as different colours. These colours are distinguished by their different wavelengths, ranging from red at about 0.7 μm or 7000 Å, through the middle colours of the rainbow – orange, yellow, green, blue – to violet at 0.4 μm = 4000 Å.

The identities, and wavelength and frequency ranges, of a number of kinds of electromagnetic radiation are summarized in Table 2.3. You should remember the meaning of the terms visible light, ultraviolet radiation, and infrared radiation, and what they mean; we will meet these terms many times again later in the book.

Electron orbits and energy levels inside the atom

Now that we have looked at how light is described, we can discuss how it interacts with atoms, and how that interaction led to an understanding of atomic structure.

The relationship between light and atoms was first studied experimentally during the 19th century. Typi-

Table 2.3: Wavelengths and frequencies of electromagnetic radiation

Identity of waves	wavelength range	frequency range
AM radio broadcast band	600 – 200 m	500 – 1600 kHz
Short wave radio bands	200 – 6 m	1.6 – 50 MHz
TV broadcast bands	6 – 2 m	50 – 150 MHz
FM radio broadcast band	3.4 – 2.8 m	88 – 108 MHz
Radio astronomy	10 m – 3 mm	30 MHz – 1×10^{11} Hz
Atmosphere completely opaque	2 mm – 30 μm	1.5×10^{11} – 1×10^{13} Hz
Infrared (IR or heat) radiation	300 – 0.7 μm	1×10^{12} – 4.3×10^{14} Hz
Visible light	0.7 – 0.4 μm or 7000 – 4000 Å	4.3×10^{14} – 7.5×10^{14} Hz
Ultraviolet (UV) radiation	4000 – 100 Å	7.5×10^{14} – 3×10^{16} Hz
X-rays	100 – 0.1 Å	3×10^{16} – 3×10^{19} Hz
Gamma rays	below 0.1 Å	above 3×10^{19} Hz

cally, light emitted by a flame containing both a combusting gas and some other gas was passed through a device called a spectrograph, which, by using a prism or diffraction grating, spreads the light out into the different colours that make it up. The spread-out light is called a **spectrum**. At first, the spectrum of the light source was observed by eye, but when photographic plates began to be used in laboratories in mid-century, the spectrum could be recorded and studied at leisure, and reproduced for others to see. We now usually display spectra by graphing the brightness of the light source at different colours (that is, we graph brightness against wavelength or frequency). An example of a graph of a spectrum is shown in Figure 2.3.

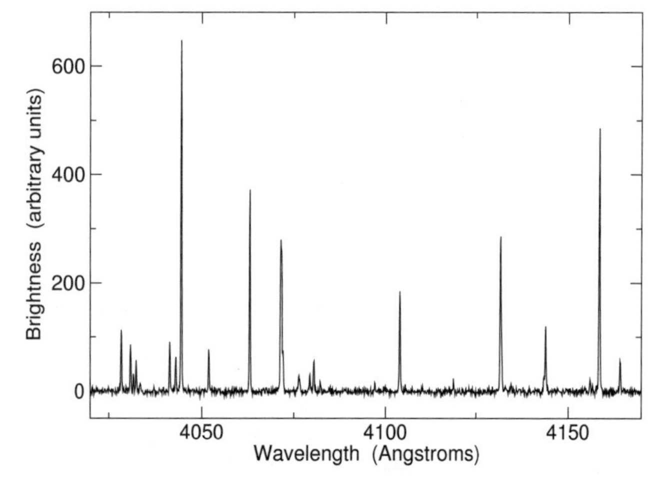

Figure 2.3: A small portion of the emission spectrum (in the violet part of the visible light spectrum) of a heated gas of neutral iron and argon atoms. Notice how the gas is only bright at certain wavelengths, and quite dark at most. The bright colours are called spectral lines. The spectral lines at 4044, 4104, and 4158 Å are due to the atoms of argon; the rest are produced by the iron atoms.

The spectra observed from flames and other heated gases have a form which is really quite astonishing. Most of the light emitted is concentrated into certain quite specific colours, while very little or no light is emitted at most colours. This behaviour is clearly seen in Figure 2.3, which shows part of the spectrum emitted by a mixture of heated (!) iron vapour and argon gas. In this graph, the height of each of the tall vertical lines (appropriately called **spectral lines**) shows the brightness of a particular colour emitted strongly by this gas. A brightness of zero is recorded for intermediate colours lying between the spectral lines. Such a spectrum, in which isolated individual colours are bright while most are dark, is called an **emission line spectrum**.

It was found from many such experiments during the 19th century that each chemical element has a specific, characteristic set of colours that it emits when heated. Some elements, such as atomic hydrogen, emit very simple patterns; the emission line spectrum of H has only four spectral lines in the whole visible spectrum, at 6563 Å (red), at 4861 Å (blue-green), at 4340 Å (violet), and at 4101 Å (deep violet). Others atoms such as iron emit thousands of specific visible colours, as one may guess from the small sample in Figure 2.3.

These same characteristic colours reappear in a different guise when a gas of some particular kind of atom is placed in front of a light source, such as an incandescent lamp, that emits light of all frequencies ("white" light). When light from the lamp, after passing through the gas, is spread out into a spectrum, many of the same characteristic colours that the gas itself emits when heated are observed to be weakened or absent in the spectrum of the lamp. In this situation the gas is apparently *absorbing* the same particular colours that it emits when heated. The particular colours which are emitted or absorbed thus serve as a kind of fingerprint for the atoms or ions of a specific chemical element, and the presence in a spectrum of the pattern of spectral lines produced by a particular atom provides unambiguous evidence that that atom is present in the gas.

A theory which explains this remarkable behaviour was developed in 1913 by the Danish physicist Niels Bohr (1885–1962), who developed ideas that had been introduced in 1900 by German physicist Max Planck (1858–1947) to explain the radiation from an incandescent solid. Essentially, Bohr's explanation of spectral lines is made up of three parts, one concerning the nature of electron orbits, one concerning the way that light carries energy, and one concerning how the atoms and light interact.

The first part of the theory is that each electron in an atom (for example, each of the six electrons in neutral C) has only certain allowed orbits that it can occupy. In fact, the actual trajectory in the space around the nucleus followed by the electron is not at all well defined; it is more correct to think of the electron as simply being "somewhere" in a limited space, a sort of cloud, near the nucleus, than it is to think of the electron moving in definite track like a planetary orbit. Although the orbits do not follow definite tracks in space around the nucleus, each allowed orbit of an electron has a definite energy, leading us to name the various orbits **energy levels**. When an electron is raised from one particular allowed orbit to another, a definite amount of energy must be supplied. This same amount of energy is required whenever an electron makes this particular upward orbit change, in any atom of the element in question. If the electron reverses the orbit change, going downward in energy from the higher energy level to the lower one, the same amount of energy is liberated as had to be supplied for the upward change.

The second part of Bohr's theory concerns the way in which a light beam (or any electromagnetic wave) gives up or acquires energy when the light is absorbed or emitted. In such interactions, light behaves as if it carries energy in little packets which we now call **photons**. A light beam having only light of a single specific frequency (or colour) f contains *only* photons (energy packets) of one particular energy. The energy E carried by each photon is the amount

$$E = hf, \tag{2.2}$$

where $h = 6.63 \times 10^{-34}$ J s is a universal constant called Planck's constant. This means that only atoms which are able to accept energy in packets having the amount of energy E given by equation (2.2) can absorb the colour of frequency f, and an atom which needs to give up an amount of energy E by radiating will radiate light of frequency f.

The final part of Bohr's explanation of the spectra of heated gases is to combine these two ideas. Because light of a single colour carries energy in packets all having a single energy, only light of the appropriate colour can provide the right amount of energy to allow an electron to make the change from one specific orbit (energy level) to another. Each particular orbit change that occurs using energy provided by photons of light thus requires the availability of light of a particular colour. Conversely, if an electron in an atom spontaneously shifts from a higher energy level to an orbit of lower energy, the atom must rid itself of the corresponding energy. It can do so by emitting light, but the photon of light emitted will have the particular colour that corresponds to the energy released as the electron drops from the higher energy level to the lower one.

Thus a particular kind of atom, such as an atom of neutral carbon, which has a large number of accessible electron orbits, each of definite energy, will also have a considerable number of specific colours that it can absorb (raising an electron one orbit to another orbit of higher energy) or emit (when an electron drops to an orbit of lower energy). However, only these colours that correspond to jumps from one energy level to another can be absorbed or emitted. The interaction of light with an atom is shown schematically in Figure 2.4.

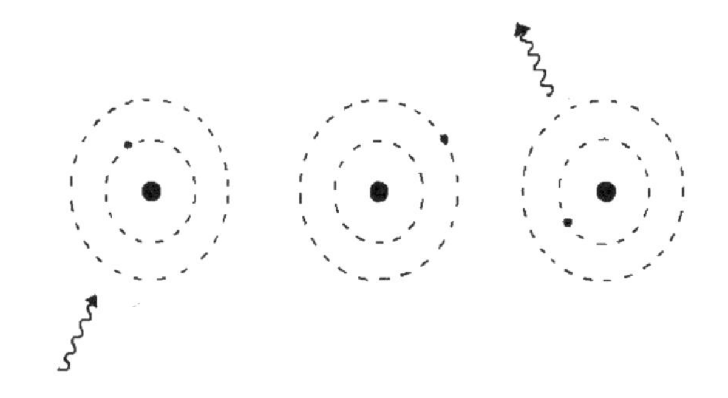

Figure 2.4: An atom absorbs a photon, which raises an electron from its original energy level to one of higher energy. After as short while, the electron drops back to the original energy level, getting rid of the excess energy by emitting a photon of the same frequency as the one originally absorbed, but which is moving in a different direction. The electron could instead drop down to some *other* level than the one from which it started, emitting a photon of a *different* frequency than that originally absorbed.

Atomic nuclei

The atomic building bricks of chemical matter, conceived originally by chemists as the smallest indivisible units of matter, were thus found by the physicists to have quite an elaborate structure, even having some parts (electrons) that can easily be removed. Not long after the beginning of the 20th century, even the atomic nucleus itself was found not to be a simple indivisible structure, but to be further subdividable into distinct pieces.

The first hint of this structure in the atomic nucleus came from the occurrence of natural **radioactivity**. Certain chemical elements (radium, uranium) were discovered to spontaneously emit energetic and penetrating rays. These rays are found to be of several types. One, gamma rays, are very energetic electromagnetic radiation, like X-rays. A second, beta rays, are simply very high-speed electrons. A third kind of emission, called alpha rays, are high-speed, completely ionized He nuclei. These rays turn out to be the symptom of spontaneous ejections from certain atomic nuclei of part of themselves, and reveal that atomic nuclei must not be monolithic objects, but have an internal structure.

During the 1930's it became clear that every atomic nucleus is actually a little swarm of heavy particles, like a bag full of marbles. Two types of heavy particles are found: protons and neutrons. A **proton** has essentially the mass of one H atom. In fact, the nucleus of an H atom is simply one proton. Each proton has exactly the same electrical charge as one electron, but of opposite sign. The number of protons in the nucleus determines the total charge and thus the atomic number Z. Since the electrical charge of the nucleus also determines the number (Z) of electrons that make the atom neutral, and since the number of electrons determines the way in which the atom interacts with other atoms chemically, *the number of protons in the nucleus determines the chemical identity of the atom.* The second type of particle, the **neutron**, is almost identical to the proton except that it has no electrical charge (it is electrically neutral, hence the name). The neutron's mass is about 0.14% larger than that of the proton.

In an atomic nucleus, these two kinds of massive particles are packed closely together, essentially touching one another. In relatively light atoms, up to about $Z = 20$ (Ca), the number of neutrons is approximately equal to the number of protons. Elements of Z above 20 tend to have a modest excess of neutrons over protons. Lead, for example, has 82 protons but about 125 neutrons. However, for most elements, the number of neutrons is not completely fixed. Oxygen, for example, occurs in three forms in nature, all with 8 protons, but with 8, 9 or 10 neutrons. These various forms are called **isotopes** of the element. Most elements have more than one naturally occurring isotope; tin has 10!

The radius of both the proton and the neutron is about 1.3×10^{-15} m. Since these particles are virtually touching in the nucleus, the physical size of a nucleus is larger for heavier (high-Z) elements than for light ones. The nucleus of tin ($Z = 50$), with about 120 particles, is roughly five times larger in diameter than a single proton (H nucleus). The mass of the nucleus, and thus essentially the mass of the atom is determined by the total number of protons and neutrons: with one electron per roughly two nuclear particles, or **nucleons**, only about 0.03% of the atomic mass is in electrons. The total number of nucleons (neutrons plus protons) is called the **mass number**, A, of the nucleus. A is close to, but not the same as, the atomic weight of a particular element measured chemically. There are two differences. First, A is for a particular isotope. For naturally occurring nuclei of one element, usually several values of A are found. These various isotopes are not equally common; in a particular sample, the fraction of atoms of one isotope can be quite different from the fraction of another isotope. The **atomic weight** of an element is an average of the atomic weights of different isotopes, weighted by the relative numbers found on average in nature of each isotope. Secondly, a given value of A does not correspond to a definite mass, because neutrons and protons have slightly different masses. For example, both ^{46}Ca and ^{46}Ti have the same mass number $A = 46$, but because Ca has 20 protons while Ti has 22, the nuclei of these two isotopes do not have quite the same mass. Rather than use either the proton's or the neutron's mass as a standard of nuclear mass, the unit of atomic weight $m_u = 1.6605 \times 10^{-27}$ kg (see Appendix A) is now defined as 1/12 of the mass of a C atom with $Z = 6$, $A = 12$, also written $^{12}_{6}$C. Thus, the atomic weights in Table 2.2 are essentially the mean weight of the naturally occuring isotopes of an element in units of m_u.

It is easy enough to understand that the atom as a whole is held together by electrical forces, since the positively charged nucleus attracts the negatively charged electrons, and holds them in orbits around the nucleus. But the positively charged protons of the nucleus *repel* one another electrically. What holds the positive and neutrally charged particles of the nucleus together? This is accomplished by a different kind of force, which acts only between nucleons. The **nuclear force**, or **strong force**, is a very short-range force, and acts only over a distance of a few proton diameters. Thus it plays no role in interaction either with electrons or with other atoms. However, within the nucleus it is much stronger than the repulsive electrical forces between the protons. This short-range behaviour is very different from the electrical force between protons and electrons, which is a force that acts over long distances, although it falls off with distance as $1/r^2$, like gravity.

Radioactivity, which first drew attention to the nature of atomic nuclei, turns out to be a result of an internal imbalance in a nucleus. For a given number Z

of protons, the nucleus is most stable—holds together most firmly—if the numbers of protons and neutrons are nearly equal (except that for heavy nuclei, electrical repulsion between the protons shifts the most stable state in favour of more neutrons and fewer protons). Any nucleus with a ratio of neutrons to protons very far from the optimal value will spontaneously change sooner or later to a more stable state, often by ejecting either an alpha particle or an electron (which converts a neutron into a proton). However, other pieces may also be ejected, such as a positive electron (positron), a single proton or neutron, or even a heavy nucleus which represents a sizeable fraction of the total nuclear mass. Some nuclei, especially artificially made ones, are so unstable that they break apart within a tiny fraction of a second. Others take billions of years to "decay".

The various chemical elements occur in the universe in widely differing amounts. Overall in stars and in very thin gas in space, about 90% of all the atoms present are H atoms. Most of the remaining 10% are He atoms. Less than 1% of all atoms in the universe are anything other than H or He; these less abundant elements range in abundance from C and O (one atom in 2000 and one atom in 1400 respectively) to such very rare species as lead (Pb, about one atom in 10^{10}). As an approximation to the cosmical abundances of various elements, we give in Table 2.2 the relative abundance in the atmosphere of the Sun. The **abundance** of an element is the fraction of the total number of atoms in a sample (say one cubic meter of solar gas, or a particular rock, or the whole Earth) that are atoms of that element, or sometimes the number of atoms of the element in a sample relative to the number of atoms of some reference element (for example H or Si). The elements in Table 2.2 are in order of decreasing abundance in the Sun. Note that (for reasons which will become clear later) the Earth has very little H and almost no He; thus the overall abundance pattern of Table 2.2 is not found in the Earth, although the relative abundances in the Sun of the heavier elements of Table 2.2 (beyond O) do resemble fairly closely the relative abundances inside the Earth.

Table 2.2 also gives abundances of the tabulated elements relative to Si in a sample of carbonaceous chondrites. Recall from Chapter 1 that these meteorites are thought to be more or less unchanged samples of the matter which froze out as solids in the early history of the solar system, and was later incorporated into planets, moons, etc. These chondrite abundances should give us a good idea of the overall chemical composition of the inner planets and asteroids.

2.3 States of matter

Solid, liquid, gas

Everyone knows that water can exist in three quite different states: as a solid (ice, snow), a liquid (normal water), and a vapour (steam, humidity). We call these three possible forms **states** (or **phases**) **of matter**. Water makes the transition from one state to another as its temperature changes. Liquid water freezes when the temperature is lowered, and boils away when it is raised. But water is not the only substance to undergo such changes. Virtually all chemical substances can exist as solid, liquid or gas. This is not so familiar from everyday life only because few common substances make the transition from one state to another at easily accessible temperatures. Nitrogen (N_2), the main constituent of air, is already a gas at 130 K = -143 C; iron becomes a liquid at about 1535 C and a gas at 2750 C. Melting and boiling temperatures (at normal atmospheric pressure) of a number of chemical elements are given in Table 2.2. Although these refer only to pure elements, they give an idea of the range of temperatures at which substances change state.

When the process of changing state from solid to liquid, liquid to gas, or even solid directly to gas, is studied more closely, other interesting features emerge. Imagine doing the experiment of inserting a thermometer in a pot filled with a block of really cold ice which is then placed over a heat source such as the flame on a gas stove. At first as heat is added, the temperature of the ice block rises steadily. When the block reaches 0 C and begins to melt, the temperature stops rising. It stays steady at 0 C until all the ice has melted. Then the temperature starts to rise again, and continues to rise steadily until it reaches 100 C, when the water boils. At this point the temperature again stops rising as the water gradually boils away, escaping as steam. No further temperature rise occurs until the pot is empty, at which point we lose touch with the vaporized water (steam) because of the crudeness of our apparatus. However, we notice again that the change of state from liquid to gas requires a considerable heat input from the flame, during which no temperature rise occurs.

We note three interesting points from this experiment. First, heat input is needed to raise the temperature. Secondly, as the temperature of the water rises, at certain temperatures two different phases can coexist. Finally, when the state of the water is changing, heat input is required to make the change, but does not raise the temperature. In what follows, we look at the various states in which matter can exist, and at the processes of change from one phase to another, in more detail.

Conservation of energy

Before we go any farther, however, we need to recall an important idea from basic physics. In Chapter 1 we saw that in motion under the influence of gravity, a quantity called energy is constant. This energy is made up of a kinetic part and a potential energy due to gravity. As the potential energy of a small body orbiting another larger one decreases (or becomes more negative), the kinetic energy (and the speed) of the small body increases, and vice versa.

During the 19th century, it gradually became clear following the work of Benjamin Thompson, (Count Rumford, 1753–1814), Sadi Carnot (1796–1832), Julius Robert von Mayer (1814–1878), James Prescott Joule (1818–1889) and others that heat is related to energy, and that the principle of conservation of energy is more general than the special case for gravitational motions.

That kinetic energy or gravitational potential energy may be converted into heat is familiar enough. If you rub your hands briskly together, the conversion of energy of motion into heat warms them. Similarly, if you tie a heavy weight to a rope wrapped around a horizontal axle, and let the weight turn the axle as it descends, and then resist the rotation of the axle by holding or clamping it almost but not quite tightly enough to stop the weight from descending, the clamp (a brake) quickly grows hot.

It is also true, but to a more limited extent, that heat can be turned into mechanical energy. If you hold a child's pinwheel above a hot stove element, rising hot air heated and lifted by the stove element will turn the pinwheel. More seriously, in a steam locomotive heated water is used to propel the engine and its train.

We are thus led to view heat as a form of energy. In fact, it is found that generally in nature, the energy in a closed or isolated system is constant, but can be transformed back and forth among numerous forms such as kinetic energy, gravitational potential energy, electrical energy, chemical energy, etc., and to a lesser extent, heat energy. Thus, mechanical energy (kinetic or gravitational) may be used to heat an object such as a pot of water. The energy used is effectively stored as internal energy in the heated water. Thus we measure heat input and output from an object in the same units that are used for mechanical energy: total energy is measured in joules, and energy transfer per second in the unit joules per second, more commonly known as watts, the unit used to rate the heat output of irons, space heaters, and toasters, or the electrical energy input required for a light bulb, a refrigerator, an electric motor, or a stereo. In normal life the commonest unit of total energy consumption (what you are charged for by your supplier of electricity) is kilowatt-hours, the number of kilowatts consumed times the time (in hours) during which they were consumed (1 kilowatt-hour = 1 kWh = 3,600,000 joules, about the amount of energy needed to raise the temperature of a bathtub full of water by 5 C).

Gases

Let us now look at the various phases of matter one by one. The gas phase, structurally the simplest form of matter, is familiar mainly from the behaviour of air, which is a mixture of about 78% N_2 and 21% O_2 with small amounts of H_2O vapour, CO_2, and other gases.

The gas state of a substance is the form reached at "high" temperature. Further heating of a gas does not lead to any new state of matter (although when a gas is heated to a temperature of several thousand K, molecules dissociate into atoms and atoms begin to lose electrons and become ionized, a state referred to as a **plasma**). As we have seen, some substances are already gaseous at temperatures near absolute zero, while others only become gaseous at temperatures above 3000 K.

A distinctive characteristic of gases is that they have very low density. If you weigh a closed container full of water, say, and then empty it and weigh it again full of air, and then *really* empty it (by pumping the air out and leaving a vacuum) in the container, you will hardly be able to detect the weight of the air, while the water weight will be easily measured (if the container isn't too big!). A cubic meter (about the capacity of a bathtub, a refrigerator, or a freezer) of water weighs 1000 kg = 1 tonne (so the density of water, the mass divided by the volume, is 1000 $\mathrm{kg\,m^{-3}}$). A cubic meter of air at room conditions weighs about 0.64 kg; its density is more than 1000 times smaller than that of water.

A second property of gases is that they are compressible. When you pump air into a tire, or pump it out of a container with a vacuum pump, the air's density is changed. In a car tire it is normal to have air at about three times its usual density; in a racing bike tire the air may be six or seven times its usual density. When you kick an inflated soccer ball, the dent your foot makes momentarily decreases the volume of the ball, and increases the density.

A gas offers resistance to compression, however: gases exert **pressure** on their surroundings. This is pretty clear when you blow up a balloon or pump up a tire. The compressed air inside exerts pressure on the walls of its container, pushing them outward. If you blow up a balloon far enough, the air pressure bursts it. Conversely, if you remove the air from a container, the pressure of the air outside the container may well be strong enough to crush it. The pressure exerted by a gas in (or around) a container is a force exerted on each square centimeter or square meter of surface. The larger the surface, the larger the total force. At sea level, the Earth's atmosphere exerts a pressure equivalent to a *weight* of one kg on each cm^2, or 10000 kg (10 tonnes) on each square meter; this is just the weight of the column of air above that square cm or square m. This pressure is large enough to crush a tin can from which the air has been removed. The pressure of air is often measured by scientists in units of newtons per m^2, also known as the **Pascal**. The Earth's atmospheric pressure is normally 101 kPa (kiloPascals) = 1.01×10^5 Pa at sea level, a pressure also referred to as **one atmosphere** (atm). The fact that the pressure at the base of the atmosphere is almost equal to a round number in Pa has led to one other unit often used by planetary scientists: 100 kPa is also called **one bar**, (and also 1000 mbar) so the earth's surface pressure is 1010 mbar.

Another interesting characteristic of gases is that they mix, or diffuse into one another, easily. If you open a bottle of bleach or perfume at one end of a room, the odour is soon detectable all over the room. Two or more gases can easily be mixed together: they may or may not be able to react chemically. The N_2 and O_2 in air virtually do not react, but a mixture of H_2 and O_2 reacts explosively when heated.

The way in which gases react when subjected to external pressure was studied in the 1660's by Robert Boyle; how gases react to changes of temperature was determined by Jacques Charles (1746–1824) and Joseph Gay-Lussac between 1787 and 1802. Remarkably, all gases show essentially the same behaviour, as long as they are not very highly compressed, and are considerably hotter than the temperature at which the liquid phase becomes gaseous. Basically, the density of a gas which is kept at constant pressure (one could imagine the gas enclosed in a cylinder by a freely sliding, weighted piston, for example) *decreases* in direct proportion to an increase in absolute (Kelvin) temperature. If you double the temperature (as measured from absolute zero), the volume occupied by the gas doubles and the density of the gas is reduced to half its previous value. On the other hand, at constant temperature the gas density increases in direct proportion to the external pressure. If you double the total force on the imaginary cylinder described above—including the force due to the external air—the volume of the gas drops half its previous value, so the density doubles. This behaviour is known as the **ideal gas law**, and the fact that this law applies to many different chemical species of gases (as long as they are not too dense or cool) shows that it reflects some fundamental characteristic of matter.

The behaviour of gases may be easily understood by thinking about how the atoms making up the gas act. Because gases have so much lower density than liquids or solids, it is clear that the atoms must be far apart. At room conditions, in fact, each atom in a gas is separated from its nearest neighbours by very roughly ten atomic diameters; only about 1/1000 of the volume is actually occupied by atoms. This is why a gas is relatively easy to compress. Nevertheless these atoms exert pressure on the walls of their container, and fill any container from top to bottom. Clearly, the atoms must be in constant motion, bouncing from one wall of the container to another like ping-pong balls (that never run out of energy...), and occasionally colliding with one another. The pressure on the container walls is due to the enormous number of collisions per second of the contained atoms against the walls of the container. (The atoms are very tiny, but the number of collisions is enormous: atoms collide with the interior walls of a one-litre bottle full of air about 10^{26} times per second.)

The motions of these atoms are evidently connected with temperature, since pressure increases with temperature. In fact, as we heat the gas, the energy that goes into the gas from the heat source simply increases the kinetic energy (energy of motion) of the individual gas molecules. In other words, heating the gas makes the molecules move faster. As a result, they cross the container at a higher average speed, and strike the walls more often. They also strike the walls harder. Thus increased pressure when the temperature is increased is simply due to the increased energy of the individual molecules.

The ease with which two different gases mix follows from the wide separation of individual molecules. Individual molecules of one species have no trouble moving into the wide-open spaces between molecules of the other species. Furthermore, it is clear that if two gases mix together, the pressure exerted on the container walls by one gas is not affected by the presence of the other gas. The total pressure is just the sum of the *partial pressures* due to each gas.

Exercise: Start with a 1-litre container of N_2 at STP, and a 2-litre container of O_2 also at STP. Transfer the contents of both containers to a third 1-litre bottle at 0 C. What is the pressure exerted by the mixed gas on the walls of its container?

Liquids

In contrast to gases, liquids are practically incompressible. The density of a liquid is almost independent of the pressure exerted on it. (Actually this is not exactly true. At the pressures found in the deep interior of the Earth, 10^4 or 10^5 times larger than the atmospheric pressure at sea level, liquids are compressed by a factor of roughly two. But this is not at all comparable to the great compressibility of gases.) This lack of compressibility goes along with a density thousands of times higher than the density of a gas at room temperature and pressure. It is clear that in a liquid, in contrast to a gas, the atoms essentially touch one another, like marbles in a bag. Incompressibility is simply a consequence of the great energies needed to distort the atoms themselves.

And yet, liquids can flow. Evidently the atoms are able to touch one another without getting locked into fixed positions, as happens in a solid. This is because the atoms in a liquid still possess a fair amount of kinetic energy (internal energy). The atoms touch one another, but they vibrate and jostle ceaselessly. This continual motion keeps them from locking into a grid, and allows them to flow. This is why liquids cannot generally get too cold without freezing solid. But even though forces between atoms are not strong enough to let atoms get locked into fixed positions, they are strong enough in a liquid to bind the atoms together. A liquid is not simply a gas compressed to the point where the molecules touch; as a not-too-hot gas is compressed or cooled, some gas condenses out as a liquid far before the gas density has reached the point where atoms touch. The atoms in the liquid are held together by inter-atom or inter-molecule attractive forces.

Suppose now that a liquid, water, for example, is placed in a closed container (held at constant pressure) several times larger than the volume of liquid, with some other gas (air, say) than the gas of that liquid (water vapour) present. At first, there is no water vapour above the liquid water. However, even well below the boiling temperature, some of the water molecules at the surface of the water are vibrating fast enough to escape from the attraction of their neighbours, and leap into the nearly empty space above the water surface. Gradually more and more water vapour fills the empty space above the water. But now, as more and more water molecules join the gaseous water above the liquid, more and more of them collide with the surface of the water, where they usually stick, due to the attraction of other water molecules. Eventually an equilibrium is reached, in which the density (or partial pressure) of water vapour above the liquid is high enough that exactly as much water returns to the liquid state each second as evaporates each second. Once this situation is reached, no further net change occurs, as long as the container volume and temperature are held constant. In the closed container, liquid water and water vapour coexist. The air space above the water has as much water vapour as it can maintain; we say that the air above the water is **saturated** with water vapour; the **relative humidity** is 100%.

If we then raise the temperature of the closed container, water molecules evaporate much more frequently from the surface. The density of water vapour in the air space must rise in order to re-establish the balance of one molecule returned to the surface for each one that evaporates. The partial pressure, or density, of water in the gas phase is higher, but the air is still saturated with water vapour, and the relative humidity is still 100%. (The partial pressure of vapour needed to just balance evaporation and maintain equilibrium is called the **vapour pressure** of the liquid.)

As we raise the temperature further, more and more of the liquid enters the vapour, until we reach the **boiling point** or **vaporization temperature**, at which the vapour pressure just equals the total pressure applied to the container. At this point, the pressure of evaporating gas is high enough that bubbles can form in the interior of the liquid (they could not form as long as the vapour pressure of the liquid was less than the applied pressure, because the applied pressure squeezed them flat). These bubbles rise rapidly to the surface in the motion we call boiling. If the temperature is kept at this point by addition of further heat, the water boils until it has become completely vaporized, and the transition to the gas phase has been made. Any further rise in temperature expands the container (still at constant pressure) but does not alter the gas.

The energy that must be supplied at the boiling point to evaporate all the liquid (the **latent heat of vaporization**) is required to give each molecule the energy it needs to break free of its neighbours and join the gas. For a particular substance (at a specific temperature and pressure) the amount of heat that must be supplied to cause melting, per kg, is constant. Once all the molecules have broken loose, and the liquid is fully evaporated, further heating simple raises the temperature of the gas. If we carry out the same experiment in reverse, lowering the temperature from a high value, at the vaporization temperature (now the condensation temperature) the gas begins to condense to a liquid. Further extraction of heat (the same amount per kg must be removed to allow condensation as was required to vaporize) causes most of the vapour to condense at the boiling point, and then as the temperature is reduced below the boiling point, more and more gas condenses into the liquid until only a tiny fraction is left as vapour.

If the container with the heated liquid is open to the air so that the vapour can escape, then the situation is somewhat different again. In this case the vapour never reaches the vapour pressure above the liquid and continuous evaporation can take place. The liquid can completely evaporate at a temperature below the boiling point, because lost molecules are not replaced by returning ones from the vapour. This is how a puddle evaporates on a cool day.

The temperature at which boiling occurs is quite definite at a particular applied (total) pressure. Water at sea level boils at 100 C = 373 K. However, if the applied total pressure is changed, the boiling point does too. At 1500 m above sea level, where the atmospheric pressure is only 0.84 atm, bubbles form at lower vapour pressure and water boils at 95 C. Since cooking is often done with boiling water (which conveniently provides a fixed temperature as long as the pot does not boil dry), it is clear that food must be boiled longer at high altitudes than at sea level because it is cooking at a lower temperature.

In the other direction, a pressure cooker is simply a sealed pot in which a weighted escape valve allows the vapour pressure inside the pot to rise above atmospheric pressure. In this situation the boiling point rises and the food cooks more quickly than normal.

Exercise: You fill the ice cube tray for your refrigerator and put it in the freezer section. After the ice cubes have frozen entirely, is there any water vapour at all in the air in the freezer compartment? Explain.

Solids

When a liquid is cooled sufficiently, at a particular temperature it changes to a solid. (An exception is He; even at T = 0 K it remains liquid). There is no dramatic change in density associated with this phase change; the atoms or molecules are essentially just touching in both liquid and solid phase. Normally the solid is slightly denser than the liquid. (Water is an exception; the solid state has about 87% the density of the liquid. This is why ice floats in water.)

Again there is a **latent heat of fusion**, like the latent heat of vaporization, a fixed amount of heat per kg that must be supplied for melting, or removed during solidification. As heat is removed from the liquid, the temperature falls until crystals of solid begin to form. As further heat is removed, more and more of the liquid crystallizes (the liquid and solid phases may coexist at the freezing or melting temperature) until the substance has become completely solid. The temperature remains constant during the change from liquid to solid. Then as further heat is removed, the temperature once again begins to drop.

Unlike the liquid, the solid does not flow. It keeps the shape it freezes into. The thermal vibrations of the individual atom have dropped to a low enough level that those atoms can become locked into position relative to one another by atomic forces. When a solid melts, enough energy must be fed into the solid to loosen all these little fixed atomic bonds. When a liquid freezes, the energy released as the atoms lock into their places must be removed to keep the process going. This is the origin of the heat of fusion. Note that because much less energy is required just to set atoms free to roam around one another than is needed to evaporate them completely from the surface of the substance, the heat of fusion per gram is normally considerably less than that of vaporization.

To give some idea of energy requirements for various steps in heating a substance, Table 2.4 gives the latent heats (at atmospheric pressure) for water. In this table you will also find the **specific heats**, the energy required to change the temperature of one kg of water by one K (or one degree C) in the solid, liquid, and gaseous states.

Table 2.4: Latent heats and specific heats of water.

Quantity tabulated	value and units
Specific heat of ice (125 – 273 K)	1000 – 2000 J kg^{-1} K^{-1}
Melting temperature of ice	273 K
Latent heat of fusion of ice	3.34×10^5 J kg^{-1}
Specific heat of water	4180 J kg^{-1} K^{-1}
Vaporization temperature of water	373 K
Latent heat of vaporization of water	2.26×10^6 J kg^{-1}
Specific heat of water vapour	2000 J kg^{-1} K^{-1}

Source: *CRC Handbook of Chemistry and Physics, 1986–87 Ed.* (Boca Raton, Fla.: CRC Press, Inc.).

Putting some of these results into more familiar form, about 0.1 kW-hour of energy is required to melt one kilogram of water, another 0.1 kW-hour raises the temperature from 0 C to 100 C, and some 0.6 kW-hour is needed to vaporize it.

Not only can a solid melt, it can also pass directly to vapour, a process called **sublimation**. Even at low temperature, the occasional surface molecule will by chance be given enough thermal energy to escape. If the solid is in a closed container, a small (!) vapour pressure will be established above it. If the temperature is raised at rather low pressure (for water, less than 6×10^{-3} atm), a temperature will be reached at which the solid will vaporize directly. At higher pressures, the solid first becomes liquid and then at a different, higher temperature becomes a vapour.

The various states that a substance can have, and the temperature at which various transitions are made, are often illustrated with the aid of **phase diagrams**. A pressure-temperature phase diagram for water is shown in Figure 2.5. This is a graph with temperature and

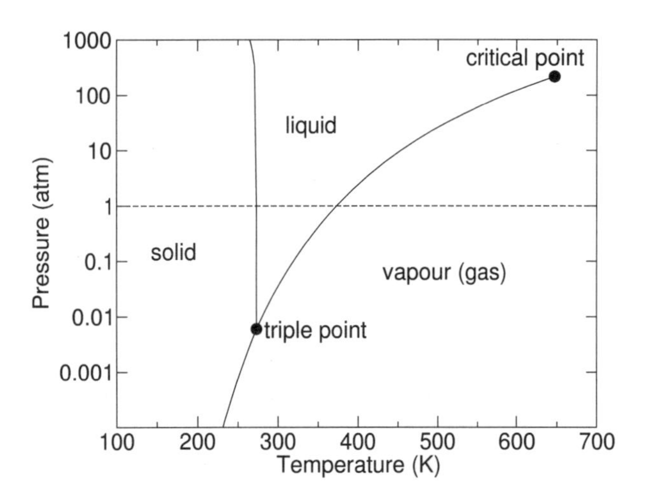

Figure 2.5: Pressure-temperature phase diagram for water (H_2O). Pressures are given in atmospheres (1 atm = 10^5 Pa), temperatures in degrees K. The meaning of the various regions (vapour, liquid, and solid) and the lines dividing them is discussed in the text. A sample of water held at atmospheric pressure follows the dashed line as the temperature is raised or lowered. Source: *CRC Handbook of Chemistry and Physics*, 1986–87 Ed. (Boca Raton, Fla.: CRC Press, Inc.l) D-189 and F-64.

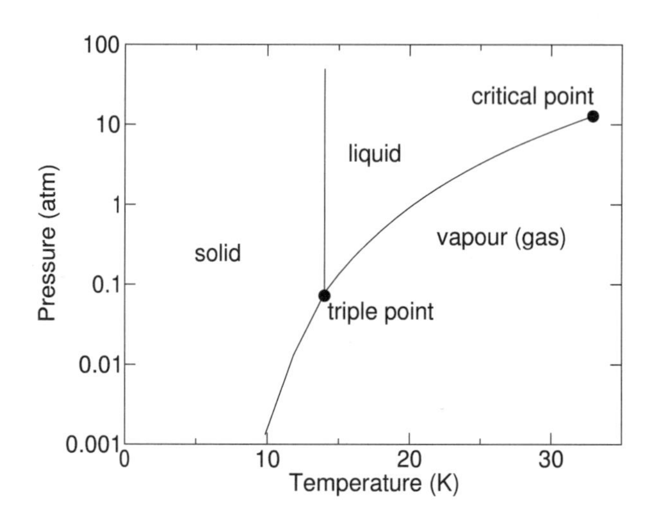

Figure 2.6: Pressure-temperature phase diagram for H. Notice that all transitions occur at far lower temperatures than for water (Figure 2.5). Source: *CRC Handbook of Chemistry and Physics*, 1986–87 Ed. (Boca Raton, Fla.: CRC Press, Inc.), D-193.

pressure as co-ordinates. In the diagram are plotted curves showing the temperature at which water boils for various pressures (the line marked vaporization, separating regions labeled vapour and liquid), the temperature at which ice melts at various pressures (the line marked fusion, between regions labeled solid and liquid), and the temperature at which the solid sublimes for various pressures (the line marked sublimation, separating the regions labeled solid and vapour). At temperatures higher than the **critical point**, the substance is gaseous at all pressures: no phase transition with gain or loss of latent heat is observed. At the **triple point**, all three phases can coexist. (At the temperature of the triple point, if the applied pressure, for example in a cylinder closed by a sliding piston, is higher than that of the triple point, all the vapour is forced into the solid or liquid. If the pressure is too low in a closed container at the triple point temperature, the vapour will evaporate until the pressure rises to the value on the diagram.)

A similar phase diagram for H_2 (Figure 2.6) shows the same general features but with greatly different values of temperatures and pressures.

The significance of the phase diagram of a substance can be appreciated better by doing some imaginary experiments and looking in the diagram to see how conditions will change. Imagine a sample of water in a cylinder closed by a piston, whose temperature and pressure can be changed at will, by heating or cooling the bottom, say, and by increasing or decreasing the weight on the piston. Now imagine keeping the total pressure on the cylinder equal to atmospheric pressure (but not allowing any air into the cylinder). If we start the cylinder at very low temperature, say -200 C), the water is completely solid. At one atmosphere applied pressure, the piston will rest directly on the ice: the vapour pressure of water at this temperature is far too low to lift the piston. If we then raise the temperature of the water, keeping the pressure constant, conditions will change along the horizontal dashed line at 1 atm in Figure 2.5. At a temperature of 0 C (273 K) the ice will melt, becoming finally completely liquid once enough heat has been added. There will still be no vapour; the vapour pressure at 0 C, about 6×10^{-3} atm, is still much too low to lift the piston, and so it will sit right on the water surface. We continue to raise the temperature, and at 100 C (373 K) the vapour pressure of the water reaches 1 atm. Bubbles of gas form in the liquid, and it boils. Vapour pushes the cylinder up, and the water is partly liquid, partly gas. After enough heat has been added, the liquid boils completely away, becoming vapour at a pressure of 1 atm. As the temperature is raised still further, the water vapour (steam) becomes hotter and hotter, and because it is kept at constant pressure, it becomes less and less dense. No further phase changes occur until the temperature is so high (at around 4000 K) that the water molecules begin to break apart into H and O atoms, a transition we do not show in this diagram. Reversing the direction of motion along the dashed line (reducing the temperature at constant pressure) reverses the sequence.

If we keep the temperature constant and vary the pressure, a different set of changes occurs. Suppose we start off at -25 C (248 K), say, at a very low pressure, such as 1×10^{-4} atm (most of the weight of the piston will have to be supported, perhaps by a spring or a pulley and weights). Under these conditions, water is gaseous, even though the temperature is low. (Recall that if the air is dry, snow can evaporate completely in winter even when the temperature stays steadily below freezing.) As the pressure is raised, at pressure of 6.3×10^{-4} atm, the vapour condenses to become a solid. As the pressure continues to rise, even well above the atmospheric value, the water stays solid. A similar experiment at +25 C (298 K) finds the water a vapour until a pressure of 3.1×10^{-2} atm is reached, at which point the steam condenses to become a liquid, which it remains at higher pressure. If this experiment is run at 400 C (673 K), no transition at all occurs. As the pressure is raised, the water gets denser and denser, but there is no definite point at which it changes phase. Eventually, the water becomes more or less incompressible, and in this sense it has become a liquid, but no actual transition is observed.

Comparing the phase diagrams of water and H_2, Figures 2.5 and 2.6, we see that both have very similar appearance, although the temperature scale is quite different for the two. In both cases, the triple point is the point that sets the scale. Normally, the boundary between solid and liquid is a nearly vertical line above the triple point. The melting temperature is only slightly affected by pressure; it usually rises very slightly with increasing pressure (for substances that expand on melting, the normal case), but in rare substances such as water (or gallium or bismuth) that expand on freezing, the melting temperature decreases slightly with increased temperature. And in both figures, we see that the line where solid and vapour coexist drops away to lower temperature as the pressure is lowered, while the transition between liquid and vapour goes from the triple point toward higher temperature as the pressure is raised, until the critical point is reached. In fact, if one knows the temperatures and pressures of the triple point and the critical point for a substance, a rough phase diagram for the substance can be sketched just by following the models of Figures 2.5 and 2.6. Triple points and critical points for a number of substances that will be needed later are given in Table 2.5.

Exercise: Using the data in Table 2.5, sketch a phase diagram for the main constituent of the Earth's atmosphere, N_2.

Exercise: Why does the relative humidity in a closed space rise as the temperature falls, until condensation occurs?

Exercise: Explain why is the air inside your house relatively dry in winter. Does this mean that the relative humidity outdoors is low?

Table 2.5: Triple points and critical points.

	triple point		critical point	
Substance	T(K)	p(atm)	T(K)	p(atm)
H_2, hydrogen	13.80	0.069	33.25	12.90
Ne, neon	24.57	0.426	44.46	25.9
O_2, oxygen	54.8	0.00026	154.58	50.16
N_2, nitrogen	63.15	0.124	126.05	33.76
CO, carbon monoxide	68.2	0.15	133.0	34.5
CH_4, methane	90.7	0.0926	190.65	46.09
NH_3, ammonia	195.5	0.0596	405.55	112.44
CO_2, carbon dioxide	216.6	5.2	304.2	72.9
H_2O, water	273.2	0.00603	374.1	218.3

Source: *CRC Handbook of Chemistry and Physics, 1986–87 Ed.* (Boca Raton, Fla.: CRC Press, Inc.), Secs B, C, D, & F.

2.4 Chemical bonds

Recall from the beginning of this chapter that the basic nature of atoms as the building blocks of common substances was first discovered by studying the proportions with which different chemical substances will combine with one another. This led to the discovery of the atoms and molecules and the identification of chemical elements and compounds. But what force causes atoms to stick together? This is an important question both for the formation of gaseous molecules such as O_2 and CO_2, and for the cohesion of liquids and solids. And how does this sticking force affect the resulting structures of the solids, liquids, and molecules? In this section, we will look briefly at some of the answers to these questions.

Ionic bonds

The only force available between atoms is the force of electrical attraction between unlike charges (between an electron and an atomic nucleus, for example), and the repulsion between like charges (of one electron for another). The nuclear force is much too short range to act between atoms, as atoms are roughly 10,000 times larger than the range of this force. Gravitational forces between atoms, although long-range, are far too weak to have any effect. But now if each atom is an electrically neutral object, with the negative charge of Z electrons, canceling the positive charge of Z protons, why is there any residual forces between atoms?

The answer comes from several different effects. One of the most important has to do with the nature of the allowed energy levels in an atom. Recall that each subshell ($2s$, $3p$, etc.) has a maximum number of electrons it can accept. In fact, an atom which has its highest occupied subshells exactly filled is extremely stable. For most atoms, however, the number of electrons which exactly fills all of the occupied electron energy levels is not the same as the number Z of protons in the nucleus, so the atom can only fill its outermost subshell by being electrically charged. The C atom of Figure 2.2, for example, could achieve the happy state of a filled outer subshell either by losing two electrons, leaving it with a full $2s$ state, or gaining four to get a full $2p$ state.

Atoms can achieve the highly stable state of filled outer electron level by exchanging electrons with other types of atoms, and this is one way in which an electrical attraction between two atoms may be created, leading to a bond between the atoms and making solids and liquids possible. For example, a sodium atom, which in isolation has filled $1s$, $2s$, and $2p$ energy levels and one electron alone in the $3s$ energy level, could give up its single $3s$ electron to a chlorine atom, which has filled $1s$, $2s$, $2p$, and $3s$ subshell and five of the six allowed electrons in the $3p$ subshell. This would put both the Na and the Cl atoms into the favoured situation of having filled outer electron subshells, at the expense of giving the Na atom a positive charge of one electron unit, and the Cl atom an equal but negative charge. But in this state the two atoms are not electrically neutral, and so can attract one another. This kind of exchange allows Na and Cl to form a **chemical bond** with one another. We call this kind of bond an **ionic bond**, because each of the atoms involved essentially becomes an ion (an electrically charged atom) in the process of forming the bond.

Notice that the number of electrons available or needed determines the proportions of Na and Cl in their compound, NaCl (sodium chloride, better known as table salt). Because Na has one electron to offer, and Cl needs one, each Na atom pairs with one Cl atom, and the resulting compound is NaCl, not Na_3Cl or $NaCl_2$.

Each type of atom has a definite electron structure, and thus has available—or needs—a certain number of electrons to fill out its outer energy level. We call the number of electrons that an atom can give up in forming an ionic bond with one or more other atoms the **valence** of the atom. An atom which prefers to accept electrons has a negative valence, which is the number of electrons needed. An atom which can achieve filled subshells by giving up one or more electrons, becoming positively charged, has a positive valence. Ionic bonds form between electron donors (positive valence, generally metals) and electron acceptors (negative valence) in the particular proportion that has the number of donated electrons equal to the number of accepted electrons. That is, in an ionically bonded compound, the sum of all the valences of the atoms involved, each multiplied by the number of atoms from the chemical formula, is zero. Thus in NaCl, the sum of one valence +1 (Na) and one valence −1 (Cl) is zero. A more complex example might be the combination of aluminum (Al, valence +3) with oxygen (O, valence −2). The particular combination Al_2O_3 (aluminum oxide) provides

Table 2.6: Valences and radii of common elements.

Z	Chemical symbol	Valence	Radius atom (Å)	Radius ion (Å)
1	H	-1	0.7	1.8
2	He		1.2	
6	C		0.75	
7	N	-3	0.7	1.92
8	O	-2	0.6	1.40
9	F	-1	0.6	1.31
10	Ne		1.3	
11	Na	+1	1.95	0.95
12	Mg	+2	1.58	0.72
13	Al	+3	1.39	0.58
14	Si	+4,-4	1.21	0.47 (+4)
15	P	-3	1.2	2.3
16	S	-2	1.1	1.91
17	Cl	-1	1.0	1.80
18	Ar		1.6	
19	K	+1	2.6	1.32
20	Ca	+2	2.1	1.04
22	Ti	+2	1.6	
23	V	+2, +3	1.5	
24	Cr	+2, +3	1.4	
25	Mn	+2, +3	1.4	0.84 (+2)
26	Fe	+2, +3	1.3	0.77 (+2)
27	Co	+2, +3	1.3	0.75 (+2)
28	Ni	+2	1.2	0.72
29	Cu	+1,+2	1.3	0.96 (+1)
30	Zn	+2	1.4	0.77

Sources: C. W. Allen 1973, *Astrophysical Quantities*, 3rd Ed. (London: Athlone Press), § 19.
C. E. Mortimer 1979, *Chemistry, a Conceptual Approach* (New York: D. Van Nostrand), Chap. 3.

three electrons each from two Al atoms (= 6 electrons) for three O atoms, each of which needs two electrons (= 6 electrons). Thus the total charge of the compound is $2 \times 3 + 3 \times (-2) = 0$.

For the 26 elements included in Table 2.2, Table 2.6 tabulates the resulting valence. The valences listed in Table 2.6 are those relevant to ionic bonds. No atom gives up or accepts more than three or four electrons in such a bond. Table 2.6 also lists one or two radii for each element, with sizes given in Å units. The radii given for neutral atoms are sizes estimated from theory and from atomic collision experiments. The sizes for ions are the sizes that the ions have in ionic compounds or metals. When more than one valence state is possible, the valence state whose radius is tabulated is in parentheses following the radius. Notice that negative ions (electron acceptors) are larger than neutral atoms, while positive ions are smaller than the corresponding neutral atoms because they have lost some electrons. A remarkable fact is that the size of an atom is almost independent of Z!

Ionic bonds are particularly important in joining metals, such as Mg, Al, Ca, Fe, etc. (most of which—see Table 2.6—are electron donors with positive valences) to oxygen (**oxides**), to the halogen elements fluorine, chlorine, bromine, etc. (**halides**), and to the sulphur (**sulphides**), all of which are electron acceptors of negative valence. At room temperature, compounds joined by ionic bonds are generally crystalline solids. That is, their atoms are arranged in a regular, rigid array in which electron donors and acceptors alternate in some regular way. Normally a donor will be closest to one or more acceptors, as is the case for sodium chloride (Figure 2.7).

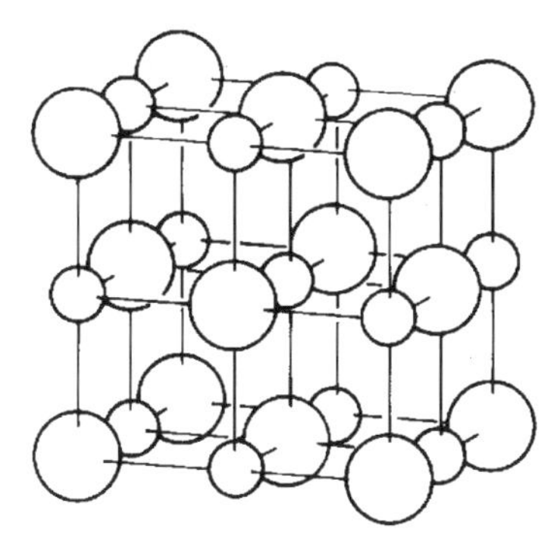

Figure 2.7: Crystal structure of sodium chloride, NaCl. The Cl ions are about twice as large as the Na ions. All ions have been shrunk to show crystal structure clearly; in reality, they touch one another.

A particularly simple example is that of NaCl, which forms the crystal structure shown in Figure 2.7. In this crystal, atoms are arranged in neat rows along three perpendicular axes, with one atom of Na alternating with an atom of Cl. This arrangement respects reasonably well both the valence requirement, which insists on the ratio of an Na atom to one atom of Cl, and the sizes of the atoms, with large (3.6 Å diameter) Cl ions alternating with smaller (1.9 Å diameter) Na ions. The NaCl crystals reflect this microscopic arrangement of atoms in their visible structure; the crystals split (cleave) most easily alone planes parallel to the rows of atoms, and so grains of table salt are tiny cubes.

Literally thousands of chemical compounds are formed on this general model. (Fortunately, we will need to get better acquainted with only a few!) Depending on the ratios of the two (or more) elements involved, and on their sizes, quite a number of different crystal structures are possible. If all the atoms are of about the same size, for example, the crystal may have atoms arranged in planes one above another, but with successive planes offset so that the atoms of one plane fall into the depressions between atoms in the plane below, like tennis balls packed in a large box. This is illustrated in Figure 2.8.

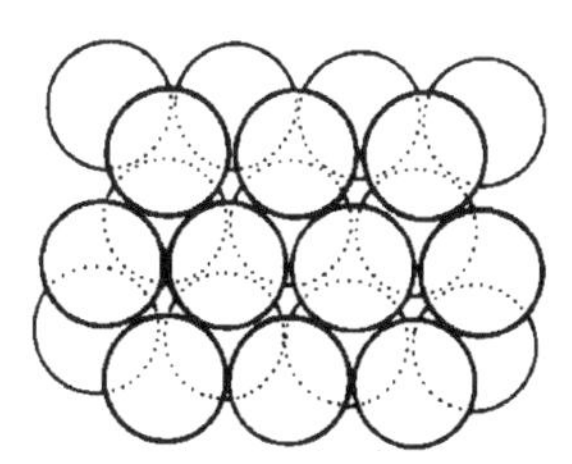

Figure 2.8: One of the closely packed arrangement adopted by atoms in a solid when all have the same size. Successive (vertical) layers are offset so that the atoms of the second layer lie over the holes between the atoms of the first layer. Atoms in the third layer (not shown) lie directly above those of the first layer.

Compounds bound with ionic bonds generally melt only at rather high temperatures, typically of 1000 K or more, and become gases at still higher temperatures. In the solid and liquid state, most such compounds have essentially no tendency for the atoms to form the distinct molecules that might be expected from a formula such as NaCl; in fact, the formula merely expresses the requirement of specific proportions for the constituent atoms.

Exercise: Is the crystal structure of Figure 2.8 the only possible closely packed structure for identical atoms?

Metallic bonds

Another method by which atoms can bind together is found in solid metals, such as Na, Al, Ca, Ti, Cu, etc. Metals are distinguished from other kinds of chemical elements by the fact that their outer (valence) electrons can be removed with relative ease from the atom (technically, they have lower first ionization potentials than non-conducting elements and noble gases). In a solid elemental metal, since all atoms have the same valence, ionic bonding is not possible. Instead, each atom contributes one or more valence electrons to a common pool, which is then shared among all the atoms. This turns out to be a state of lower total energy than is the state of isolated atoms (at least at moderate temperatures), and so again results in a means of bonding atoms together in a solid or liquid.

A metallic solid generally does not take on the particular structure of NaCl. A metal composed of atoms of only a single element has all atoms of the same size, and so tends to go to the structure of tennis balls in a box, as in Figure 2.8. But mixtures of metals are possible, giving rise to solids with atoms of more than one size, and so other crystal forms occur. Note that because there is no exchange of electrons, as in ionically bonded compounds, metals may be mixed in more or less arbitrary proportions. To distinguish substances made of more than one metallic chemical element, and held together by metallic bonds, from ionically bonded crystals which must respect the proportions required by valence, we call metallic compounds **alloys**. A typical example of an alloy is the alloy of tin and copper, called bronze, which provided humans with their first widely useful metal.

Like ionically bonded solids, most metals melt at a relatively high temperature, of the order of 1–2000 K, and boil roughly another 1000 K higher, testifying to the strength of the metallic bond.

Small molecules and covalent bonds

Yet a third type of chemical bond, somewhat similar to the metallic bond, operates in small molecules of substances that tend to be gaseous at room temperature, such as H_2, N_2, O_2, CO_2, and NH_3. In some of these molecules, the fact of having two identical atoms makes ionic bonding impractical. Instead, the two atoms share valence electrons. Thus, in the H_2 molecule, each H atom furnishes one valence electron, and the two electrons orbit around both nuclei. This turns out to be a state of lower total energy than two free H atoms, and so such structures are bound. Such bonds are called **covalent**.

A fourth type of bond is of importance in substances in which covalent (or ionic) bonds do create actual small molecules that have an individual identity, such as the molecules of Table 2.5. These are all molecules which continue as molecular units even when they have become gaseous, only dissociating into individual atoms at temperatures of 3–4000 K. In such molecules, the bonds that hold the molecules together do not extend directly to making larger structures, and so these substances actually condense and freeze only at rather low temperatures, in the range of 10–400 K (see Table 2.5). The force that holds these molecules together (weakly, as is clear from the very low temperatures at which they become gaseous) is called the **van der Waals bond**. Essentially it relies on the fact that even in an electrically neutral molecule, the electrons are not distributed about the nuclei in a completely spherically symmetric way. As a result, there are places on the periphery of a molecule which are slightly positively or negatively charged. These slightly charged regions are strong enough for a negative patch on one molecule to attach to a positive patch in another, thus binding the molecules into a liquid or solid, at least if the temperature is low enough. Thus in the case of small molecular units, a hierarchy of bonding operates: the atoms are (strongly) bound by covalent (or ionic) bonds into molecules, which at low enough temperature bond (weakly) into liquids or solids by the van der Waals bond.

2.5 Minerals

The four inner planets Mercury, Venus, Earth, and Mars, are essentially solid bodies, as are the moons of Earth and Mars. The asteroids, the meteorites that derive from them, the moons of the outer planets, and the nuclei of comets are also solid. Most of these bodies are composed of rock, but comet nuclei and moons of the outer planets have large amounts of ice, and comets in particular are primarily composed of ices. In our study of these bodies it will be valuable to know something about the specific solid chemical substances that make up the rocks and ices of these bodies, and so we turn to a brief discussion of minerals.

Most of the 91 naturally occurring chemical elements are found in some amounts everywhere in the solar system, and so the variety of chemical substances present is extremely large. This is true even at the surface of the Earth; most rocks contain tiny amounts of dozens of chemical elements, and here and there, significant naturally segregated amounts of rare substances (silver, gold, lead, tin, and copper, for example) are found. However, we shall gradually realize that only a few chemical elements dominate the bulk (overall) chemical composition of most solar system bodies. The inner planets are composed primarily of only four elements: oxygen (O), silicon (Si), magnesium (Mg), and iron (Fe). These four elements account for about 93% of the mass of the Earth, for example. A few more elements (sodium, aluminum, calcium, nickel) are present in substantial amounts; in the Earth, these total 5 or 6% of the mass. All other elements combined contribute less than 3% of the total.

Similarly, the moons of the outer planets (and nuclei of comets) have compositions dominated by a few elements. These bodies are usually mixtures of ice and rock. The rock almost certainly has roughly the same composition as terrestrial rock, and is made primarily of O, Si, Mg, and Fe. The ices also are composed largely of four elements: hydrogen (H), carbon (C), nitrogen (N), and oxygen (O).

Because of the relatively simple bulk chemical compositions of these solid bodies, we can gain insight into the most common kinds of chemical combinations that occur by looking at the solid compounds formed by only a few elements. We shall do this in two parts. In this section we look at the simple solid chemical substances that are produced by combinations of the dominant chemical elements. These substances are called **minerals**. In the next section, we shall discuss how these minerals combine to form the actual **rocks** that you find along a stream bed, on a cliff face, or at the seaside. We shall also look at some of the naturally occurring processes that segregate specific minerals into particular types of rocks.

Silicate minerals

Let us look first at the minerals formed by the most abundant elements in the inner planets. In principle, with four primary elements and three or four secondary ones, the number of imaginable chemical combinations is very large. Fortunately for us, only a tiny fraction of all conceivable combinations of O, Si, Fe, Mg (with Na, Al, Ca and Ni) actually occur. In fact, with the single important exception of pure (metallic) iron, which can occur alone or mixed (alloyed) with some nickel, *all* the combinations of these elements that occur frequently in nature are combinations of Si and O with one, two, or three of the other elements. Normally, Si and O combine (partly covalently and partly ionically) to form a single (more or less covalently bonded) unit, SiO_4 (which acts like an atom with valence -4), and which combines with one or more of the (positive valence, see Table 2.6) metal ions to form very stable compounds. These compounds of metals with SiO_4 units are the basic minerals from which rock forms.

The basic SiO_4 unit from which silicates are built has a characteristic structure which is related to the sizes of the atoms involved. The most abundant atoms vary considerable in size (see Table 2.6). O has by a considerable margin the largest ion, and Si has the smallest. The basic SiO_4 unit is built from these two elements in the form of a tetrahedron. Three of the four O atoms form a triangular base, with the fourth sitting on the other three. The tiny Si atom is tucked into the interior of the O tetrahedron. The arrangement is shown in Figure 2.9. The silicate tetrahedron then combines with one or more metal atoms in a repetitive structure, in which the particular metal atoms of the mineral are packed in amongst the SiO_4 units as compactly as possible. With different metal ions of different sizes, quite different crystal structures (arrangements of the atoms in the solid) occur.

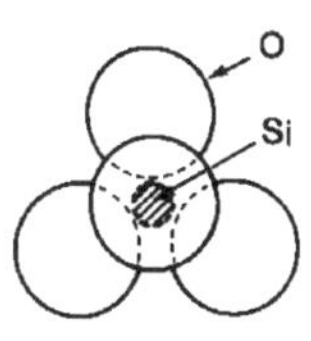

Figure 2.9: The SiO_4 tetrahedron which is the basis of the structure of silicate minerals. The small Si atom (hatched) is at the centre of the four large O atoms which are arranged in a pyramid.

The proportions of metal to Si and O in silicate rock generally incorporates about as much O as possible. The material is fully oxidized because the parent compounds from which all rock formed were built in an environment in which many more O atoms than metal atoms (see Table 2.2) were present. This allows us to think of silicates of combinations of metal oxides (FeO, MgO, Na_2O, etc.) with silicon dioxide (SiO_2). In fact, geologists often express fractions by weight of a rock as so much of this oxide and so much of that.

Three of the major families of minerals (of the six or seven that geologists identify as the major minerals in terrestrial volcanic rocks) that are widely expected throughout the solar system, and that are found in moon rocks and meteorites, are listed in Table 2.7. The simplest of these mineral families (in chemistry, not crystal structure) is **olivine**. Like the other families, this mineral has a definite crystal structure, but a limited range of metal ions is allowed. One limiting form of olivine has the chemical formula Fe_2SiO_4 = $(FeO)_2(SiO_2)$. Its structure is shown in Figure 2.10. As may be seen in the figure, SiO_4 tetrahedra are cemented together by Fe ions regularly placed throughout the crystal. However, some or all of the Fe atoms in this structure may be replaced by Mg atoms, which have the same valence and nearly the same size as

Table 2.7: Silicate mineral families.

Mineral family	Density ($kg\ m^{-3}$)
Olivines	
$(Mg,Fe)_2SiO_4$	
(a) forsterite	3190 – 3330
$Mg_2SiO_4 = (MgO)_2(SiO_2)$	
(b) fayalite	3910 – 4340
$Fe_2SiO_4 = (FeO)_2(SiO_2)$	
Pyroxenes	
$(Mg,Fe,Ca)SiO_3$	
(a) orthopyroxenes (Ca < 5%)	
$(Mg,Fe)SiO_3$	
(i) enstatite	3100 – 3430
$MgSiO_3 = (MgO)(SiO_2)$	
(ii) bronzite	
$MgSiO_3$, some Fe	
(iii) hypersthene	3400 – 3500
$MgFe(SiO_3)_2 = (MgO)(FeO)(SiO_2)_2$	
(b) clinopyroxenes (Ca > 5%)	
(i) pigeonite	
$MgFe(SiO_3)_2$, 5–15% Ca	
(ii) diopside	3200 – 3380
$CaMg(SiO_3)_2$, Fe < 10%	
(iii) augite (Ca-rich)	3200 – 3600
$Ca(Mg,Fe,Al)(Al,Si_2O_8)$	
Feldspars	
(a) orthoclase (potassic feldspar)	2560
$KAlSi_3O_8 = \frac{1}{2}[(K_2O)\ (Al_2O_3)(SiO_2)_6]$	
(b) plagioclase series	
(i) albite (sodic feldspar)	2610 – 2640
$NaAlSi_3O_8 = \frac{1}{2}[(Na_2O)(Al_2O_3)(SiO_2)]_6$	
(ii) anorthite (calcic feldspar)	2700 – 2760
$CaAl_2Si_2O_8 = (CaO)(Al_2O_3)(SiO_2)_2$	
Hydrated silicates	
serpentine	2500 – 2600
$(Fe,Mg)_3Si_2O_5(OH)_4$	

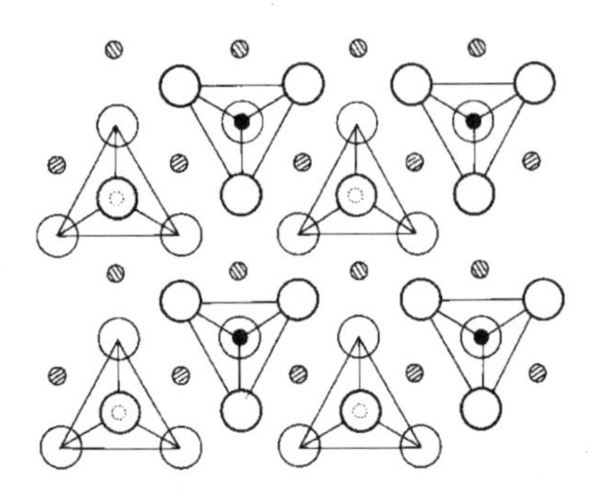

Figure 2.10: Crystal structure of olivine. The SiO_4 tetrahedra are held together by small ions of Fe and/or Mg. In alternate planes, the SiO_4 tetrahedra point up (Si atoms are dashed) and down (Si atoms are solid). Mg or Fe ions lie in two intermediate planes, shown with different cross-hatching.

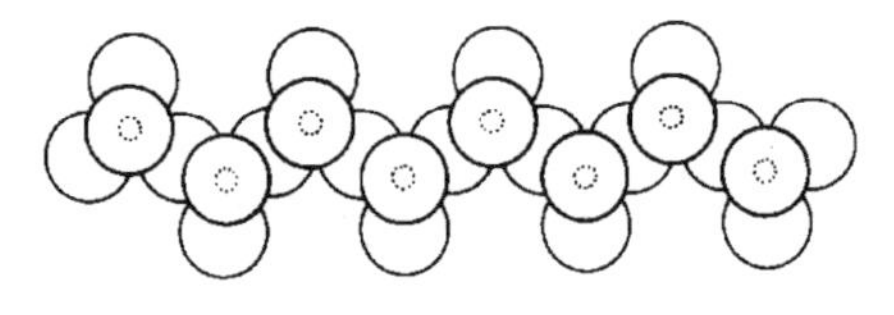

Figure 2.11: The crystal structure of pyroxenes is based on long chains of SiO_4 tetrahedra in which successive tetrahedra share O atoms as shown. Many such chains are bound together in a cable structure by ions of Fe or Mg between the chains.

the Fe atom. Thus another limiting form of olivine is $Mg_2SiO_4 = (MgO)_2SiO_2$. The allowed range of composition for olivine may be written with the notation $(Mg,Fe)_2SiO_4$, which simply means two metal ions for each SiO_4 tetrahedron, with Mg and/or Fe in any proportion.

A second family is the **pyroxenes**. In these compounds, the basic structural unit is a chain of SiO_4 tetrahedra in which each tetrahedron shares an O atom with each neighbour along the chain. The chemical formula along the chain thus becomes SiO_3, even though it is a chain of SiO_4 tetrahedra. The arrangement of a chain is shown in Figure 2.11. Chains are cemented to one another by metal ions (Fe, Mg, Ca or Al) between the chains. A simple pyroxene involving only Mg and/or Fe is the orthopyroxene series, which may be described chemically as $(Mg,Fe)SiO_3$. Clinopyroxenes have similar crystal structure, but some of the Mg or Fe is replaced by Ca and/or Al. Several pyroxenes of importance in solar system materials are listed in Table 2.7. These are mainly forms found in meteorites.

Finally a third silicate family of importance is the **feldspars**. Like the olivines and pyroxenes, these minerals are found in terrestrial rocks and also in meteorites. They are particularly interesting as the main compound of the rocks of the lunar highland. The feldspars derive their structure from that of simple silicon dioxide (silica or quarts) SiO_2. In this substance, the SiO_4 tetrahedra are organized so that every O atom is actually shared by two tetrahedra. This allows valence balance to occur while still building with the highly stable SiO_4 tetrahedron. The feldspars have the same basic crystal structure as quartz, but one Si atom in four (in potassic and sodic feldspar), or one Si atom in two (in calcic feldspar) is replaced by an Al atom, which has about the same size, but a valence of +3 rather then the effective value of +4 of Si. The extra electrons needed by the O are supplied by one extra atom of K or Na per Al atom (in potassic or sodic feldspar), or one Ca for every two Al (in calcic feldspar). The result is to convert quartz, which we may write as SiO_2 or equally as Si_4O_8, into respectively $KAlSi_3O_8$, $NaAlSi_3O_8$, and $CaAl_2Si_2O_8$. The feldspars are thus a family of silicates in which the less abundant elements Ca, Na, Al, and even K play an essential role, while Mg and Fe are absent. Notice that the feldspars have significantly lower density than the olivines and pyroxenes.

Other structures are possible, such as the double chains found in the amphiboles (e.g. hornblende), and the sheets of silicates in phyllosilicates (e.g. mica), but these minerals, though common on Earth, are not prominent elsewhere in the solar system. This is partly because many of these minerals contain water, a substance largely absent from most meteorites and entirely absent from lunar rocks. However, hydrated silicates are found in some particularly primitive meteorites, and a hydrated form of olivine, serpentine, is included in Table 2.7.

Ices

Among the many kinds of solids that form naturally from the various chemical elements, we have explained above that the most widespread ones are those that form from the three elements Mg, Si, and Fe in combination with O. Minerals composed Mg, Si, and Fe are widespread because these are the most abundant elements in the mix from which the Sun and the planets formed that freeze even at high temperatures (say greater than 1000 K). But the elements C, N, O and Ne are even more abundant than Mg, Si, and Fe (see Table 2.2 yet again). Does this group of elements form any interesting kinds of minerals under any common solar system conditions?

The answer to this question is yes, in the outer solar system where temperatures of no more than 1–200 K occur, for example on the moons of the outer planets, in the Kuiper belt, and in comets. In these extremely cold regions, compounds of C, N, and O form solids which we can reasonably regard as minerals, although because they are liquid or gas on Earth we call these minerals **ices**. In contrast, the element Ne, a "noble gas", is so unreactive that it forms no real compounds at all, and its melting and boiling points are so low that it is gaseous essentially everywhere in the solar system.

The main forms of C, N, and O found in the solar system have been listed already in Table 2.5. From that table we see that each of this group of elements can occur at low temperatures in two or more forms: O can be present as O_2 or H_2O, N may be in the form of N_2 or NH_3, and C can occur in CO, CO_2, or CH_4. It is tempting – but incorrect – to assume that with the very large numbers of H_2 molecules present in the gases from which the solar system formed, spontaneous chemical reactions such as

$$3H_2 + N_2 \rightleftharpoons 2NH_3$$

would insure that almost all the the molecules of C, N, and O would occur in combinations with H. In fact the balance that is struck in the gases that formed the solar system depends strongly on temperature. Because N_2 and CO are more strongly bound molecules than their competitors NH_3 and CH_4, they are favoured at high temperature (between a few hundred and about 2000 K) in spite of the fact that their formation requires two relatively uncommon atoms (compared to the much larger number of H atoms) to find one another. (However, H_2O is favoured above O_2 even above 1000 K.) At lower temperature, where collisions do not break up the molecules that include H so easily, the balance between the molecules without H and those including H may shift strongly in favour of NH_3 and CH_4, provided enough time is available (millions of years or more at the densities of the gases in the gas cloud from which the Sun formed). In fact, in the solar system both of the competing types of molecules are found in large amounts.

Water ice forms one additional type of mineral that is of considerable interest when we try to understand the chemistry of the atmospheres of terrestrial planets. The crystal structure of water ice is rather porous, and it is easy for atoms and even molecules of other elements to become trapped in the water ice in significant amounts. Ices in which this occurs are called **clathrates**. . An example is the formation of methane hydrate,

$$CH_4 + 7H_2O(s) \rightarrow CH_4 \cdot 7H_2O(s)$$

.

Finally, it is interesting to ask why it is that compounds of C, N, and O form solids only at low temperatures while Mg, Si, and Fe are solid well about 1000 K. The reason is that all the abundant ices are compounds in which strong (usually covalent) bonds exist at the level of individual molecules, but these molecules bond into solids (or liquids) only with the weak van der Waals bond, and thus melt and even evaporate at rather low temperatures. (Notice from Figures 2.5 and 2.6 that, unlike the melting point, the vaporization temperature varies fairly strongly with the local partial pressure of the substance.)

It is this tendency to become vapour at the least excuse that has separated these ices from rocky minerals in the solar system. We believe that as the Sun formed, the cores of the planets formed from material in the cloud around the forming Sun that was condensed into solid particles. In the inner solar system, only refractory minerals (silicates, metallic iron) condensed, and thus the inner planets are made of these substances. In the considerably cooler regions farther from the new Sun, the abundant ices were also able to condense, and thus joined rocks as main constituents of planetary moons (and as cores of the giant planets as well).

2.6 Rocks

Rock types

The minerals that are discussed in the previous section are essentially pure chemical compounds. In nature they are less likely to occur in pure form than in fairly complex solidified mixtures, usually containing large amounts of two or three minerals in the form of interlocking mineral grains, plus small amounts of many other chemical elements. Such solid mixtures are known as **rocks**. These are the substances that you actually find on the ground!

Terrestrial rocks are classified by geologists into three main categories, which correspond to the basic types of processes by which the rocks on Earth are formed. **Igneous** rocks form from the molten state, for example from surface lavas extruded by volcanic eruption, or from intrusion of a body of molten rock into a layer or hollow in the ground that is forced open by the intruding material. Basalt and granite are typical igneous rocks. **Sedimentary** rocks may form by chemical precipitation of crystals from a water solution. Limestone (calcium carbonate, $CaCO_3$) and common salt (sodium chloride, NaCl) may be deposited in this way from seawater. Sedimentary rocks may also form from aggregates of more-or-less ground up debris from erosion and weathering, perhaps sorted and transported far from its origin by flowing water. Such rocks start as loose deposits of particles that are gradually cemented together either by being later soaked in some kind of "glue" (for example a solution of calcium carbonate) or by being compressed and heated. Examples of sedimentary rocks are sandstone, formed mainly from grains of very insoluble quartz (silica, $Si0_2$) weathered out of rocks, and shale, formed from very tiny particles of aluminosilicates that may even be weathered from the same rocks (and that may be transported long distances by flowing water because of their small size), which aggregate first as clay and then solidify. **Metamorphic** rocks form out of either of the first two classes when they are subjected to heat and/or pressure, for example when solid rock is heated by intrusion of lava nearby or when rocks are buried, compressed, and heated as a result of mountain building processes. Heat and pressure convert shale into slate, limestone into marble, granite into gneiss, and sandstone into quartzite or quartz schist.

These categories are not always easily applied to objects in the solar system outside the Earth. On the Moon we find igneous rocks (highland anorthosites and mare basalts, for example) but most of the single rocks found are actually **breccias**, rocks formed from pulverized fragments made of the earlier igneous rocks by meteorite impacts that are later cemented by further impacts. On Mars, the photographs returned by the two Viking landers show what are clearly igneous rocks, some of which show bubble holes and derive from gassy, bubbly lava. There may also be sedimentary and metamorphic rocks and breccias. In meteorites, we certainly find some igneous components, such as the iron-nickel metal found in iron and stony-iron meteorites, and the chondrules of chondrites meteorites, but much meteoric material appears to have formed by condensation directly from a vapour having temperatures somewhere in the range of 300–1700 K. This process does not produce terrestrial rocks at all.

Igneous rocks

Igneous rocks are quite common in the inner solar system On Earth, the common forms of such rocks have a rather limited range of chemical or mineral composition, illustrated (and simplified) in Figure 2.12.

Each general chemical composition (for example, half ferromagnesians such as olivine and pyroxene, and half plagioclase feldspar, called basalt or gabbro) can occur in a fine-grained variety, in which individual mineral grains are scarcely visible, and a coarse-grained variety in which the grains are quite prominent and may be several mm across.

The igneous rocks that one finds on Earth have mainly been produced as a result of one of a few processes acting on material which has been melted as a result of deep burial, or which is molten material rising from the upper mantle, or is in contact with such material. This melted material may undergo various kinds

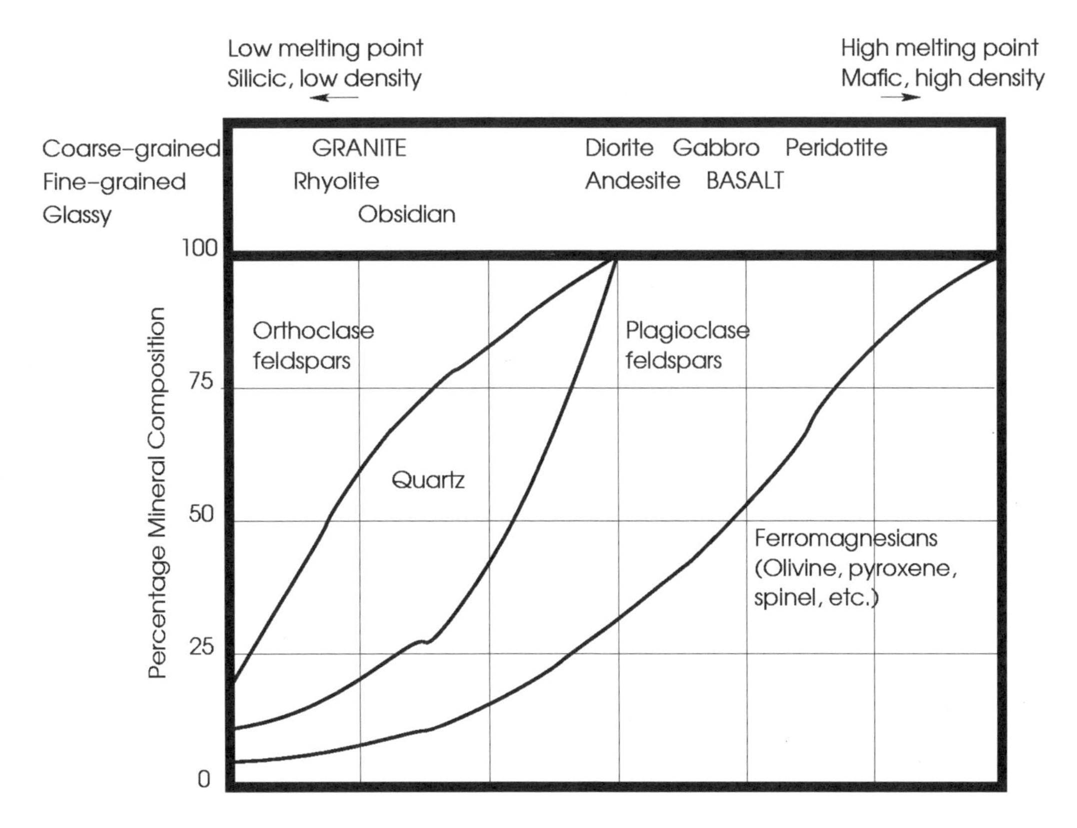

Figure 2.12: Mineral compositions of a number of common terrestrial rocks and their names.

of separation processes, and finally deposit part or all of its original mass near or on the surface. The result is that rocks having a variety of chemical and mineral compositions are found in various places on the Earth's crust.

The simplest process forming surface igneous rocks is by the cooling and solidification of molten rock (called **magma** when it is deep in the crust of the Earth, and **lava** when it erupts onto the surface) when it rises close enough to the surface that heat loss cools it below the melting point of its various constituents. This freezing process, however, is not as simple as you might suppose. Unlike a specific chemical element or a molecular compound, a mass of molten rock does not simply solidify completely at a single temperature. Instead, some parts solidify at fairly high temperature (as high as 15–1600 C) while others do not solidify until the temperature has dropped as low as perhaps 700 C. Suppose we start with a very hot magma which contains roughly the proportion of elements found in the Earth, so that it is rich in Mg, Fe, Si and O, and has minor amounts of Ca, Na and K. Suppose now that the temperature of the magma drops. As it cools, the first minerals to crystallize (freeze out to become small solid crystal grains in the liquid magma) are Ca-rich feldspar and Mg-rich olivine. As the temperature continues to drop, some of the olivine grains will gradually take on more SiO_2 from the magma, and change into pyroxene. At this point, the Fe, Na, K and some of the Si and O will still be in the magma. At still lower temperature, iron begins to be incorporated into the olivine and pyroxene, and more and more olivine changes over to pyroxene. As the temperature nears 1000 C, Na will begin too be incorporated into grains of anorthite, changing it in part into sodic feldspar, or albite. Some K will begin to form potassic feldspar, or orthoclase. Gradually as well the pyroxenes will change crystal structure, take on some water if any is dissolved in the rock, and become amphibole and biotite. Some SiO_2 will remain isolated and freeze out as quartz. Eventually when the temperature drops below 6–700 C, the whole mass of rock will have frozen solid.

Thus, in a cooling magma of a fixed chemical composition, the part of the magma that is solid, and the minerals that make up the solid crystals depend on the magma temperature. As the temperature changes, the mixture of solids and liquids, and the composition of each, changes. We say that at each temperature there is an *equilibrium* mineral composition.

The nature of the crystals formed depends on the speed with which the magma cools. This could vary greatly; a deeply buried magma body could take centuries to cool, while lava that flows out onto the flanks of a volcano might cool in a few hours. If the molten rock cools quickly, only tiny crystals have time to aggregate; they may be too small to see by eye! Slow cooling allows larger crystals to accumulate, sometimes more than 1 cm across. Furthermore, if a really hot magma cools quickly, the mineral transformations that occur in a slowly cooling lava (olivine changing to pyroxene, anorthite changing to albite) may not have time to occur, and unusual mineral mixes may be left in the cold rock.

This simplest cooling process depends on the mass of magma staying homogeneous throughout, typically as a result of fairly quick cooling. If the magma cools slowly under conditions in which settling or rising of crystals can occur, important kinds of mineral separation can occur. Such separation is known as **crystal fractionation**. In a cooling magma, crystals of olivine and (later) pyroxene tend to sink to the bottom of the magma pool, because they are slightly denser than molten rock. Thus olivine and pyroxene accumulate at the bottom of the magma pool, while the chemical composition of the remaining magma become gradually depleted in Mg and (later) Fe. Ca, in anorthite, is relatively low in density and may rise to the top of the magma chamber. As the remaining magma solidifies, it will be poor in olivines, pyroxenes, and calcic plagioclase, but rich in sodic and potassic feldspars and in silica (quartz, SiO_2). The final solid rock mass may thus have a layered rock composition which changes from the bottom to the top of the original magma body. Just such changes with height in exposed rock bodies may be found in the Palisades, a rock cliff exposed in the Hudson River valley across from New York City.

A related complication can occur if lava leaks out of a magma chamber as it cools. In this case, the first lava flows released, when the magma is still quite hot, may be full of Mg-rich olivine and pyroxene. Later lava flows will have successively less of these high temperature crystals, and be more and more enriched in silica and in sodic and potassic feldspar. This progression is found in the layers formed by successive lava flows, for example at Tristan de Cunha in the southern Atlantic.

Still another possibility arises if a solid rock mass is subjected to new heating, sufficient to melt the low melting temperature minerals but not the high melting temperature grains. In this case, the liquid magma may then be forced out of the original rock mass, typically because its density is less than that of the solid rock. It may rise towards or to the surface and solidify. Rocks produced by this process are said to be due to **partial melting**. Clearly, this process may separate low melting point minerals such as silica and orthoclase feldspar from such high melting point substances as plagioclase feldspar pyroxene and olivine. The magma melted out of a rock of a particular composition will itself have a definite composition as well (which will depend somewhat on how hot the parent rock mass becomes). As an example, lunar mare basalts appear to be a product of partial melting of the lunar mantle.

The compositions of common types of igneous rocks shown in Figure 2.12 correspond essentially to the type of mineral separation produced by crystal fractionation or by partial melting. Rocks at the right side of the diagram such as peridotite and basalt are rich in high melting point minerals and may have been separated as the sinking or floating crystals in crystal fractionation, or be the residue left after partial melting. These rocks, whose composition resembles the bulk composition of the Earth, and particularly that of the Earth's **mantle** (the rocky outer two-thirds of the Earth's total mass, which overlies the **core**, the central sphere containing about one-third of the Earth's mass, and largely made of metallic iron), and are called generally **mafic** or **basic rocks**. (The term "mafic" recalls the predominance of *ma*gnesium and iron = *fe*.) Rock on the left side are the types of rocks that might have been separated as low temperature magma after crystal fractionation or partial melting. These are the types of rocks that make up much of the Earth's **crust** (the thin veneer of low density rocks, from 3 to 40 km thick, depending on the location, that covers the Earth's mantle). Such rocks are often referred to as **felsic** (after feldspar, a major component).

2.7 Mathematical aspects

The gas law

As we have discussed earlier in the chapter, the changes in pressure in a gas in response to variations in the volume, temperature, and mass of the gas were the subject of numerous experiments. The results of these experiments is summarized in the famous ideal gas law, which describes quite accurately the behaviour of all gases when they are well above their condensation temperatures, and at a density far below that of the liquid phase of the same substance. The ideal gas law, as it was established by chemists during the 19th century, states that

$$pV = n_{\rm m} R_{\rm g} T. \tag{2.3}$$

Here p is the pressure (force per unit area) exerted by the gas on its surroundings (the wall of a container, for example, or the ground, or simply on an adjacent volume element of gas. V is the volume occupied by the quantity of gas of interest (this may or may not be enclosed in a container, but the gas law applies to a fixed amount of gas). T is the temperature measured from absolute zero (-273.15 C), i.e. the absolute or Kelvin temperature. The quantity $n_{\rm m}$ is the number of **moles** of the gas, which we define as the total mass of the gas in grams (not kg!) divided by the atomic or molecular weight μ of the gas. In turn, we define the molecular weight of the gas as the physical mass of one molecule of the gas divided by the unit $m_{\rm u}$ of atomic weight ($m_{\rm u} = 1.6606 \times 10^{-27}$ kg), which is almost but not exactly equal to the mass of one H atom. For a gas of simple atoms (Ne, for example), the molecular weight μ is almost equal to the average atomic mass number A of atoms of that element, and is the quantity tabulated in Table 2.2 as the atomic weight. For gases in which the basic unit is a diatomic molecule (for example O_2 or N_2), the molecular weight is quite close to twice the atomic weight given in Table 2.2. $R_{\rm g}$ is a single universal constant, the same for all gases, which has the value 8.314 $\rm J\,mole^{-1}\,K^{-1}$. Two very striking features of the ideal gas law are its extreme simplicity and great generality.

It is worthwhile to think for a moment about the way in which a gas that is described by the ideal gas law behaves. Imagine that a sample of some gas is confined in a cylinder closed on the top by a freely sliding piston which has a weight sitting on it. The gas law states that if the weight on the piston is left constant, a change in the temperature of the gas leads to a corresponding change in volume. Doubling the (absolute or Kelvin) temperature doubles the volume in the cylinder that the gas occupies. On the other hand, if the volume is maintained constant, say by adding or subtracting weights as needed, then a change in temperature leads to a corresponding change in pressure. Doubling the temperature doubles the internal pressure, so that the total weight of the piston and its weights must be doubled to maintain the same volume as before. If the temperature is held constant, then a change in the volume (produced by adding or removing weights) leads to an inverse change in pressure, which of course means that if you double the weight of the piston, so that the gas must supply twice as much pressure as before to support it against gravity, the volume will be reduced to one-half the earlier volume.

The gas law can also be written in other convenient forms. Clearly we may write the number of moles of gas as $n_{\rm m} = 1000\ M/\mu$, where M is measured in the usual SI units of kg. The factor of 1000 must be put in because the meaning of one mole of a chemical is a weight in gm equal to the molecular weight of one molecule. If we divide both sides of equation (2.3) by the volume V, and recall that the total mass M divided by the total volume V is just the density $\rho = M/V$ of the gas, the gas law may be written as

$$p = 1000\,(M/V)(R_{\rm g}T/\mu) = 1000\,\rho RT/\mu. \qquad (2.4)$$

Now recall that Avogadro correctly hypothesized that in a given volume of gas at a particular temperature and exerting a given pressure, there is always a fixed number of molecules of gas, regardless of what gas may be present. We call the particular number of molecules, which together have the same numerical weight in grams as the molecular weight μ of the gas, Avogadro's number $N_{\rm A}$. $N_{\rm A}$ has the values 6.022×10^{23} molecules per mole. (In fact, the SI *definition* of one mole of a gas is the quantity of that gas containing exactly $N_{\rm A}$ molecules.) Thus one kg of a gas of particles each having a mass of exactly one atomic mass unit $m_{\rm u}$ will contain $1000\,N_{\rm A}$ molecules, and so $1000\,N_{\rm A}m_{\rm u} = 1$, or $m_{\rm u} = 1/(1000\,N_{\rm A})$. Then defining a new constant, Boltzmann's constant k, by $k = R_{\rm g}/N_{\rm A} = (8.314/6.022 \times 10^{23}) = 1.381 \times 10^{-23}\ \rm J\,K^{-1}$, we may rewrite (2.4) in the simple form

$$p = 1000\,m_{\rm u}R_{\rm g}\rho T/\mu m_{\rm u} = \rho kT/\mu m_{\rm u}. \qquad (2.5)$$

In this form, the volume occupied by the gas has disappeared, to be replaced by the bulk density ρ. This form is particularly convenient for discussing extended (unconfined) gases of indefinite volume, as in planetary atmospheres.

Finally, if we notice that the mass in a unit volume, ρ, divided by the mass of a single molecule, $\mu m_{\rm u}$, is simply the number of molecules per unit volume, the **number density** n, we may rewrite (2.5) in the form

$$p = nkT \qquad (2.6)$$

Here we have the gas law reduced to its simplest terms, with pressure seen to be directly proportional to absolute temperature and to the number of molecules per unit volume, with the same constant k regardless of the composition of the gas. This rule neatly expresses Avogadro's idea that the number n of molecules in a given (unit) volume is the same for a particular T and p regardless of what kind of molecule is present. This expression, incidentally, is probably the most useful form of the gas law to memorize for future use. Boltzmann's constant turns out to have fundamental importance in the kinetic theory of gases and in statistical mechanics, the microscopic physics underlying the thermal behaviour of matter.

Exercise: Using the gas law together with the fact that the air pressure at sea level is 101 kPa, estimate the number of molecules per cubic meter, and the average separation distance between molecules in air at 20 C.

Exercise: The density of metallic Ti is 4540 kg $\rm m^{-3}$. Assume that the Ti atoms are arranged in a cubic lattice in the metal (that is, that the Ti atoms are arranged in neat rows parallel to each of three orthogonal axes). Estimate the radius of the Ti atoms and compare to the value in Table 2.6. The atomic weight of Ti is 47.8.

Kinetic theory and the gas law

The gas law was derived as a description of the behaviour of macroscopic samples of gas. However, we know that a gas is composed of a very large number of atoms or molecules (one cubic cm of air at normal atmospheric conditions contains 2.7×10^{19} molecules), all bouncing around inside the container, or passing through the volume of gas we are looking at if we consider a particular volume inside an extended gas. The macroscopic pressure exerted on the walls of a container, or on a boundary of the imaginary gas volume, is simply due to the collisions of the molecules against the walls. In fact, we can easily understand the significance of the gas law from a consideration of the average behaviour of the molecules of a gas.

Consider for convenience a cubic container, with each side d one meter in length and width. Orient the edges of the container along the x, y and z axes of a rectangular coordinate system. Now look at one molecule. It has mass m and speed v, which may be resolved into velocity components $v_{\rm x}$, $v_{\rm y}$, and $v_{\rm z}$ along the three axes. Ignore the (infrequent) collisions between molecules. Now suppose that the molecule is at first moving in the positive x direction, and collides elastically with the wall at $x = 1$ m. In the collision, the x component of the momentum of the molecule changes from $mv_{\rm x}$ to $-mv_{\rm x}$. Now the molecule speeds off towards the wall at $x = 0$ m, which it strikes after a time $t = d/v_{\rm x} = 1/v_{\rm x}$. After another time t it returns to the original wall at $x = 1$ m, so the total time between impacts of the molecule is $2t = 2/v_{\rm x}$, and the molecule makes $1/(2t) = v_{\rm x}/2$ round trips per second. At each collision, the molecule has its momentum changed by a total of $2mv_{\rm x}$, and so in one second the wall at $x = 1$ m must deliver a total momentum of $(v_{\rm x}/2)(2mv_{\rm x}) = mv_{\rm x}^2$ to the molecule. But from Newton's second law, this requires a force numerically equal to the momentum change of the molecule at the wall. According to Newton's third law, this force is equal to the force that this one molecule exerts on the wall. Since the wall has unit area, the force per unit area, or pressure, exerted by one molecule is thus $mv_{\rm x}^2$.

Now if there are actually n molecules in the box, so that the number density of the gas (which occupies one m^3) is also n, each will exert a similar force on the wall at $x = 1$ m. Each will have a somewhat different velocity, but clearly the total force exerted by the wall on the n molecules, or the force exerted on the wall by those molecules, will be equal to $nm\overline{v}_{\rm x}^2$, where $\overline{v}_{\rm x}$ is a suitable average x-component of velocity. Therefore the pressure exerted on the wall, since it has unit area, is equal to $nm\overline{v}_{\rm x}^2$.

The other two velocity components, $v_{\rm y}$ and $v_{\rm z}$, have no effect on this calculation; they lead to collisions on the two y sides and the top and bottom of the box. Collisions among the molecules also have no effect. This is easily understood when we consider that conditions in the box do not change with time (as long as no heat is exchanged with the exterior, and the volume and contents of the box remain unchanged). The way in which the system stays always in the same macroscopic state is by what is called detailed balance: for every collision which knocks a particular molecule out of a particular trajectory (path and speed), another collision sooner or later will put some other molecule back into this trajectory.

Now certainly the motion of the molecules in the box is essentially the same in all directions, apart from the very small effects of gravity. Thus we expect that $\overline{v}_{\rm x}^2 = \overline{v}_{\rm y}^2 = \overline{v}_{\rm z}^2$. But now the mean kinetic energy of a molecule in the box is just $e_{\rm k} = (1/2)m\overline{v}^2 = (1/2)m(\overline{v}_{\rm x}^2 + \overline{v}_{\rm y}^2 + \overline{v}_{\rm z}^2) = (3/2)m\overline{v}_{\rm x}^2$. Thus we find that the pressure in the box is given by

$$p = (1/3)nm\overline{v}^2 = (2/3)ne_{\rm k}. \tag{2.7}$$

This expression looks very much like equation (2.6), except that in place of the temperature term kT we have $(2/3)e_{\rm k}$. But we have simply calculated the gas pressure of a gas from microscopic arguments, and so equation (2.7) must be the *same* as the gas law that was arrived at from experiment. Therefore we make the identification

$$e_{\rm k} = (1/2)m\overline{v}^2 = (3/2)kT, \tag{2.8}$$

and we see that the average kinetic energy per molecule is simply proportional to the absolute temperature. That is, from this calculation we learn that the microscopic meaning of temperature is internal kinetic energy. As the gas is made hotter, the internal average kinetic energy per particle rises directly with absolute temperature T, leading to a proportional rise in pressure because the collisions with the container walls are more energetic.

From this microscopic interpretation of the gas law, we derive immediately one other interesting fact. Clearly the pressures of two mixed gases, each of whose molecules are independently banging against the walls of the container, will simply add. That is, the total gas pressure on the walls of a vessel is simply the sum of the pressures of the individual gases calculated for example from Equation (2.6), with the appropriate number density n_μ of molecules of each type. Another way of stating this is that the total pressure in a mixed gas is the sum of the partial pressures of the individual gases, a law originally deduced from experiment by John Dalton, and known as Dalton's law of partial pressures.

2.8 References

Bransden, B. H. and Joachain, C. J. 1983, *Physics of Atoms and Molecules* (Harlow: Longman Group Ltd.). Chapter 1 of this excellent advanced undergraduate textbook on the quantum mechanics of atom and molecules has a very clear, if brief, description of historical developments in physics that led to the modern understanding of the atom. The treatment is mathematical but at about the level of the "mathematical aspects" sections in this book.

Holmyard, E. J. 1958, "The Chemical Industry: Developments in Chemical Theory and Practice", in *A History of Technology*, vol. 4, ed. C. Singer, E. J. Holmyard, A. R. Hall and T. I. Williams (London: Oxford University Press), pp 214–229. This article is a beautifully written and concise history of the development of the modern chemical theory of atoms.

Lewis, J. S. 1997, *Physics and Chemistry of the Solar System* (San Diego, CA: Academic Press). Chapter IV of Lewis' excellent advanced book has much detail about the chemistry that can occur in the mix of elements available in the gas cloud that formed the solar system.

2.9 Review questions

2.1 How do chemists identify chemical elements among the millions of naturally occurring substances?

2.2 What led Dalton to the idea of atoms?

2.3 Why does the law of definite proportions work for gases but not always for solids such as metal alloys?

2.4 What is the atomic description of pressure in a gas?

2.5 Different atoms and molecules have different masses. When two equal containers at the same temperature have equal numbers of two different molecules, one kind in each container, how can the two different gases exert the same pressure?

2.6 When water in a closed pot boils, what gas is the main substance found in the space above the liquid? Why does the lid bounce?

2.7 Why do you float higher in salt (sea) water than in fresh water?

2.8 What is the difference between a mineral and a compound? Between a mineral and a rock?

2.9 Why does solid water have relatively low density compared to solid rock? Why is solid lead denser than solid aluminum?

2.10 Problems

2.1 Take 1 liter of N_2 gas at 20 C and atmospheric pressure. Inject into the same container H_2 gas from a 3 liter container in which the H_2 is at 20 C and atmospheric pressure. (a) Assume that the two gases simply mix, but do not react chemically. What is the pressure in the 1 liter bottle containing the mixture? (b) Now, remove the gas mixture and allow it to react to form NH_3. Return all the resulting NH_3 to the 1 liter bottle. Still at 20 C, what is the pressure in the bottle?

2.2 Start with a one-liter bottle containing H_2 gas at atmospheric pressure and at 20 C. Take a second one-liter bottle containing O_2 gas also at 20 C and normal atmospheric pressure, and inject the contents of this bottle into the first one-liter bottle with the H_2. (a) Assuming that the contents do not react, but only mix, at 20 C what is the resulting pressure? (b) Now allow the contents to react to form as many H_2O molecules as possible with the available atoms. What is the resulting chemical composition of the gas (i.e. what fraction of the gas is in H_2O molecules and what fraction is other molecules). Calculate the resulting pressure in the one-liter bottle at 20 C.

2.3 (a) Using the data in Table 2.5, sketch a rough phase diagram for methane. (b) Suppose that a planet has a rocky surface above which the only volatile substance is methane. The total weight of methane above each square meter is 3 tonnes (3000 kg), adding together the methane in all forms, so if all the methane were gaseous the pressure would be 0.3 atm at the planetary surface. Describe qualitatively the changes of phase that would occur if the planetary surface temperature gradually rose, as a result of the increase of the luminosity of the planet's star, from 50 K to 250 K. Sketch the variation of atmospheric (gas) pressure with temperature for these conditions at the bottom of the atmosphere (i.e, at the top of the solid layer of methane, if there is one, otherwise, at the rock surface). (c) How would the behaviour of the CH_4

change if 1 atm of N_2 (10 tonnes per square meter) were present on the surface with the CH_4?

2.4 Assume that Mars formed from chemical elements that were able to freeze out of the cloud of gas around the forming Sun, and that the relative abundances in this frozen-out material was the same as that of solar atmosphere (Table 2.2) for Mg, Si, Fe, Na, Al, and Ca. Assume that all elements except perhaps Fe are fully oxidized when they freeze out (as MgO, SiO_2, FeO, Na_2O, Al_2O_3, and CaO). Calculate and tabulate the fractions of the total mass of Mars which are accounted for by O, Na, Mg, Al, Si, S, Ca, and Fe under each of the following three plausible hypotheses (the range of answers will give you some idea of the uncertainty of such calculations). (a) No S is accreted, and the Fe is entirely metallic, as in the Earth's core (that is, it brings with it no O). (b) No S is accreted, but the Fe is fully oxidized as FeO, so that there is no metallic core in the planet. (c) The S is fully frozen out in the relative amount given in Table 2.2, combined with Fe as FeS; the remaining Fe is oxidized as FeO. You may neglect in this calculation H, He, C, N, Ne, Ar (which do not condense at high temperatures), and all elements less abundant than sodium (which contribute little to the total). In your answer, please tabulate the mass fractions for each element, not the mass fractions of various oxides.

2.5 Assume that a typical moon of one of the outer planets is composed of a mix of ices and rocky material, with the elements C, N, and O and Mg, Si, and Fe in the proportions of Table 2.2. Assume further that all the Mg, Si, and Fe have combined with O in the proportions of MgO, SiO_2, and FeO, that C and N are completely in the form of CH_4 and NH_3, and all the remaining O is in the form of H_2O. (a) Calculate the relative numbers of each of the six molecular forms above in this moon. (b) Next, using the masses of each molecular form and the relative numbers from (a), compute the fraction of the total mass of the moon contributed by rocky (Mg, Si, Fe-rich) material and the mass fraction in ices. (c) Finally, assume that the ice fraction has a density of 900 kg m^{-3}, and the rocky fraction has a mean density of 3500 kg m^{-3}. Calculate the overall mean density of the mix of these two materials that you have found. (Actual densities of the main moons of the outer solar system are found in Table A.3. Your result should lie in this range!)

Chapter 3

The Sun and the Astronomical Environment

3.1 Overview

For several reasons it is relevant to step back and examine the broad astronomical environment in which the solar system exists. First, the formation of the solar system is believed to have been an essential part of the process in which the Sun formed from a gas and dust cloud of the interstellar medium. We may learn something about this phase of the solar system's development by studying star formation in other parts of the Milky Way. Secondly, the solar system is strongly affected by the Sun's surface activity (sunspots, flares, etc) and by its evolution. When in the course of its development, some 5×10^9 years from now, the Sun becomes a red giant and literally swallows the inner planets, the solar system will be greatly altered. Thus it is worthwhile to survey what is presently known of stellar evolution. A third point is that the non-volatile heavy elements that make up almost all of the mass of the inner planets were not present in the galaxy from its beginning, but have been manufactured by nuclear reactions in the interiors of stars and subsequently scattered through the interstellar medium. The present chemical composition of various solar system objects is thus a result of past stellar evolution. Finally, we must keep the astronomical environment in mind for its possible direct effects on the solar system. Because stars are very far apart these may not occur frequently, but they may nevertheless be important. An example concerns comets. Millions of potential comet nuclei are believed to be present in a vast reservoir of iceberg-like small bodies on the outer fringes of the solar system. From time to time the orbit of one of these objects around the Sun is altered enough by the gravitational field of a nearby star, or by the tidal effect of the bulge of the Milky Way, to send it into the inner solar system. Normally, this merely produces a brilliant show, but when one of these bodies crashes into a planet, quite a lot of damage can be inflicted. In fact, it is widely believed that such an impact ended the reign of the dinosaurs on Earth—and the Mesozoic era—about 65 million years ago.

It is thus appropriate to survey the astronomical setting of the solar system, and to review what is known of how stars form, evolve, and eventually die. These are the topics discussed in the present chapter.

3.2 The Milky Way galaxy

Stars in the galaxy

Our Sun and its system of planets are located within a huge assembly of some 10^{11} stars known as a galaxy. Galaxies are huge isolated clouds of stars that are found scattered throughout the universe; literally billions of galaxies may be seen from Earth with a large telescope. Our own galaxy is known as the Milky Way, and is visible on a dark night as a faint band of light running across the sky through the constellations Orion, Perseus, Cassiopeia, Cygnus, Sagittarius, and Scorpius.

All galaxies, including our own, are essentially huge star groups, containing between 10^8 and 10^{12} stars. They occur in three basic forms. Elliptical galaxies are roughly spherical in shape, often somewhat flattened. Spiral galaxies are disc-shaped, round but very thin. Irregular galaxies are irregular and amorphous in structure. Our own galaxy is a spiral. Its appearance is sketched in Figure 3.1. An image of a real spiral galaxy (not the Milky Way, which we cannot see like this because we are inside it, but instead the galaxy Messier 81, a near neighbor in the universe) is shown in Figure 3.2.

The disk of the Milky Way has a diameter of about 100,000 light years, or 10^{18} km. (One light-year, abbreviated ly, equals 9.46×10^{15} m). The Sun itself is located about 30,000 light-years from the galactic centre, almost on the main plane of the disk. The central bulge has a maximum thickness of perhaps 8,000

Figure 3.2: The nearby galaxy Messier 81, a spiral galaxy that probably looks much the same as the Milky Way would if viewed from the exterior. The individual stars scattered over the image are foreground stars in our own Milky Way galaxy. (Courtesy of the U. S. National Optical Astronomy Observatory/Association of Universities for Research in Astronomy/National Science Foundation, or NOAO/AURA/NSF.)

light-years, while the disk has a thickness of only about 3–5,000 light-years. These dimensions are fairly typical for spiral galaxies.

The shape of the galaxy is a consequence of the motions of the stars that make it up. All these stars attract one another with their mutual gravitation; from the point of view of a star (such as the Sun) located out in the disk of the galaxy, the combined attraction of all the other stars resembles the attraction that would be exerted by a single huge star at the centre of the galaxy. The means by which the stars of the galactic disk prevent themselves from falling towards the galactic centre is the same means by which planets avoid falling into the Sun—the stars move in orbits around the galactic centre, falling around rather than in. In fact, the motions of stars in the disk of a spiral galaxy such as the Milky Way are very neatly organized; almost all of them move in the same direction in orbits that depart by only a few percent from circular form, lying nearly in a single plane. The result is that although stars near the Sun are all moving about the galactic centre at speeds of about 250 km s^{-1}, they move relative to one another by only about 20 or 30 km s^{-1}. Stars in the central bulge of the galaxy have a greater variety of orbits. Their orbits are often more elongated and highly inclined to the main plane of the Milky Way. The stars of the central bulge are distributed through the volume fairly uniformly, but those of the disk show some tendency to clump into spiral-shaped lanes that run outward from the central bulge towards the periphery. It is because of this effect that disk galaxies are known as spiral galaxies.

In the disk of the Milky Way, the stars are separated by typically a few light-years. Thus, the nearest stars to the Sun are the three members of the α Centauri system, at a distance of 4.3 light years. Most of the disk stars are stars roughly similar to the Sun in size (the **solar radius** $R_\odot = 6.95 \times 10^8$ m), mass (one **solar mass** is $M_\odot = 1.99 \times 10^{30}$ kg), and surface temperature (the Sun's **effective temperature** is 5800 K), and are in the long-lasting stage of stellar evolution that we call the **main sequence phase**. A small fraction of our

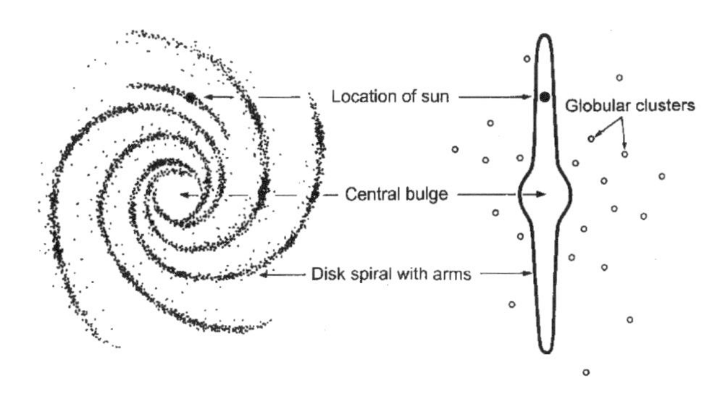

Figure 3.1: Face on and side views of the Milky Way galaxy, a typical spiral galaxy like billions of others in the universe. Stars in the disk orbit around the centre mostly in a single plane, in much the same way that planets orbit the Sun. They are held in roughly circular orbits by the combined gravitational attraction of the other Milky Way stars. Smaller groups of perhaps a million stars each, called globular clusters, orbit chaotically around the centre of the Milky Way; these clusters contain some of the oldest stars in the galaxy.

neighboring stars have radii that are of the order of 10 to 1000 times larger than that of the Sun, and are known as **red giants**; another small fraction are stars about the size of the Earth, or 1% of the solar diameter in size, and are called **white dwarfs**. The principal characteristics of the stellar population near the Sun are indicated in Table 3.1. Masses and radii are given relative to the Sun. Main sequence stars more massive than the Sun are singled out for a separate line in the table because, as we shall see later, these are short-lived stars that have been made relatively recently.

Approximately half of the stars near the Sun are not single but are members of **binary systems** made up of two stars circling one another. A small fraction of stars belong to triple star systems, usually with two stars close together circled by a third at a much greater distance. Some are members of groups of stars that we call clusters, which may contain only a few dozen stars or nearly a million.

The population of stars making up the central bulge of the galaxy is similar to that of the galactic disk with one significant exception: there are virtually no stars present that are more massive than the Sun. Their absence indicates that in the galactic bulge there has been almost no recent star formation.

The stars of the galactic disk are similar in chemical composition to those of the bulge. All are composed essentially of the two lightest elements, hydrogen and helium. About 90% of the atoms are hydrogen and most of the remaining 10% are helium. Both bulge and disk stars also contain a very small sprinkling of heavier chemical elements, no more than a slight impurity, accounting for about 0.1% of all the atoms present. Although this heavy element fraction includes some atoms of virtually all known stable chemical elements, it is mainly made up of eight elements: C, N, O, Ne, Mg, Si, S, and Fe (see Table 2.2).

Interstellar matter in the galaxy

Stars are not the only component of the Milky Way. In between the stars is a thin haze of gas and dust known as the interstellar medium. In the Milky Way, such dust and gas makes up a few percent of the mass of the galaxy as a whole. This interstellar matter is concentrated mainly in the disk of the galaxy. As in the stars of the Milky Way, about 90% of the atoms of the interstellar matter are hydrogen, slightly less than 10% are helium, and about 0.1% are atoms of heavier chemical elements. Most of the hydrogen is in the form of single atoms (H) or hydrogen molecules (H_2). The helium is essentially all atomic (He). The heavier atoms, again mainly those of C, N, O, Ne, Mg, Si, S, and Fe, are found both in atomic form and also locked up in more or less complex molecules and in small condensed solid particles that we call dust grains.

The gas and dust is not at all uniformly distributed through the galaxy, but is found to be strongly aggregated into clouds and clumps, and particular types of clouds preferentially occur in certain regions of the galaxy.

Hydrogen is found in atomic form (single atoms rather than molecules) mainly in the region between about 25,000 and 40,000 light-years out from the galactic centre, in the part of the disk where the Sun's galactic orbit lies. Perhaps half the neutral hydrogen is found in **H I clouds** some 10 or 20 light-years across, with internal temperatures of about 50–100 K, densities of $n \sim 2 \times 10^7$ atoms m^{-3}, and total masses of the order of $10^2\ M_\odot$ (10^2 times the mass of the Sun). In between these clouds, there is a similar total amount of hydrogen, in the form of a thin substratum with much lower density, $n \sim 1\text{–}2{\times}10^5$ atoms m^{-3} , but far higher temperature, around 7000 K. The outward pressure exerted by the dense but cold clouds is roughly balanced by the pressure exerted by the surrounding hot thin **intercloud medium**, so neither clouds nor intercloud matter tend to expand or contract.

Closer to the centre of the galaxy, but still in the disk, between perhaps 10,000 and 25,000 light-years from the centre, there is rather little hydrogen in atomic form. About 90% of the hydrogen in this inner region is instead found in the form of molecular H_2 in large cold clouds that are known as **molecular clouds** because of

Table 3.1: Properties of common stars in the Milky Way galaxy.

Star type	Radius ($R/R_\odot$)	Mass ($M/M_\odot$)	Surface temperature (K)	Fraction of stars near Sun (%)
Main sequence (larger than Sun)	1 – 10	1 – 50	6 000 – 50 000	4
Main sequence (smaller than Sun)	0.3 – 1	0.1 – 1	3 000 – 6 000	88
Red giants	10 – 10^3	1 – 20?	2 000 – 7 000	1
White dwarfs	10^{-2}	0.7	4 000 – 50 000	7

Source: C. W. Allen 1973, *Astrophysical Quantities* (London: Athlone Press), Sec. 118.

the variety of molecular species found in some of them. A typical molecular cloud, like a hydrogen cloud, might be 10–100 light-years across and have a temperature of 10–60 K, but it would have a much larger mass ($\sim 10^3$–$5 \times 10^5\ M_\odot$) and density (n $\sim 10^8$–10^{10} molecules m^{-3}). Such clouds would also usually have large numbers of such molecules as CO and OH, and in the densest clouds we even find quite complex molecules such as ammonia (NH_3), water vapour (H_2O), formaldehyde (H_2CO) and ethyl alcohol (C_2H_5OH). Interestingly, regions of recent star formation, as marked by short-lived hot stars, are usually found on the edges of such molecular clouds. Such hot young stars have a dramatic effect on the gas cloud matter near them. Ultraviolet light from the hot stars dissociates molecules (breaks them into constituent atoms) and ionizes atoms (frees electrons from them). When a free electron finds and recombines with an ion (an atom that has lost one or more electron), photons of light are emitted as the electron drops from one energy level in the atom to another. In this way the gas around the hot star gives off light to form the characteristic glowing clouds of gas that we call **H II regions** ("H-two regions", after the old term H II used by spectroscopists for ionized H). Such H II regions usually have a red colour because of the strength of the red spectral line Hα given off by a hydrogen atom as it recombines with an unattached electron.

Finally, a significant fraction of the volume between the stars is occupied by yet another form of interstellar matter. This is an extremely low density (n $\sim 10^2$ or 10^3 ions m^{-3}), very hot (10^5 or 10^6 K) gas known as **coronal gas**. This is gas heated and expanded by the effect of blast waves produced from time to time in the galaxy by the explosions of collapsing massive stars in what are called supernova events or explosions. Although this intensely heated gas accounts for only about 0.1% of all the gas atoms of the interstellar medium, it permeates perhaps half the volume of the disk in the form of bubbles and tubes blown up in the otherwise relatively dense interstellar medium.

The total mass of gas in the Milky Way in the form of H I clouds is about $1.2 \times 10^9\ M_\odot$; in the intercloud gas regions there is about $1.4 \times 10^9\ M_\odot$; in giant molecular clouds there is about $4 \times 10^9\ M_\odot$. About 5% of the $1.4 \times 10^{11}\ M_\odot$ total visible mass of the galaxy is thus in the form of interstellar matter. Almost all of this matter is found in the disk of the galaxy. The central bulge has much less interstellar matter.

3.3 Structure of main sequence stars

One of the great scientific achievements of this century was the gradual discovery by Emden, Eddington, Chandrasekhar, Bethe, Hoyle, Fowler, and others of how a star is organized internally and how it changes during its life history. The picture we have built up of this process will be the subject of the next several sections. We begin by summarizing what is known about the structure of a star during its main sequence phase of development.

Support against gravity

Stars are observed to be very massive: the Sun, for example, is 3×10^5 times more massive than the Earth. This means that a star has very strong self-gravity. The downward force on a kilogram of matter at the surface of a typical main sequence star is more than 10 times greater than the force at the surface of the Earth. Thus the material of a star is held together by the strong gravitational attraction of each part for every other part. But what holds it up? What keeps a star from collapsing under the influence of gravity, and shrinking to the size, say, of a beach ball?

The answer is provided by another observation,

namely that stars are hot. With a surface temperature in excess of 3000 K, we expect that the interior of a star is so hot that the H and He that makes up almost all the material of the star must be gaseous. Now a hot, compressed gas exerts an outward pressure, produced by the high-speed random motions of the atoms that make it up. The force that holds up a star against gravity is thus essentially the same force that prevents an automobile tire from collapsing under the weight of the car it supports: gas pressure.

Most stars, like the Sun, are observed not to vary in size. The gas pressure force outward and the gravitational force inward must therefore balance exactly, and this must be true at each depth in the star. In effect, the gas pressure at each depth must be just large enough to support the weight of the overlying layers of gas. But as one looks deeper and deeper into the star, the weight of the overlying layers gets larger (just as the water pressure increases with depth in the ocean) and so the deeper one looks, the greater the outward pressure that must be provided by the star's gases. To provide this pressure, a star is both much hotter and much denser deep in the interior than it is at the visible surface.

Internal energy sources

But a body like the Sun that supports itself against gravity with gas pressure has another problem not faced by a body like the Earth that supports itself by having its matter in a solid or liquid state which strongly resists compression. For a gas ball to support itself against its self-gravity, it must be hot inside, and so it inevitably leaks heat out into the cold space around it, and thus gradually loses the heat that it needs to support itself. In fact, the Sun leaks heat (we call the energy radiated each second a star's **luminosity**) at the prodigious rate of 4×10^{26} watts. Even at the distance of the Earth from the Sun, about 150 million km, or more than 200 $R_{\odot}$, this luminosity leads to an **energy flux** (the energy per second passing through a square meter) of about 1.4 kilowatts per square meter perpendicular to the flow of energy. So, unless the gas ball has an energy source inside itself to replenish the lost heat, its internal pressure will gradually fall below the level needed to balance gravity, and the star will slowly shrink.

A star could conceivably supply the internal heat needed to balance gravity through shrinking. By shrinking, in effect the outer layers of the star are allowed to fall inward. They release gravitational energy as they fall, converting it to energy of motion that ultimately becomes heat. In this way, the leakage of heat could cause a change in the star's structure that would replenish the lost heat and continue to allow the star to support itself against gravity.

However, it has been clear since the turn of the century that this could not be the whole story, at least for the Sun. If the Sun were to support itself against gravity with heat provided by shrinkage, it could supply only enough energy by shrinking from a very large size to its present size to maintain its present luminosity for about 10 million years. But it has been known for many years that the geological record found in the rocks of the Earth's crust required hundreds of millions of years to create. If we make the very reasonable assumption that this required the Sun to function almost unchanged for hundreds of millions of years, then we must look for another energy source to supply the lost heat. The discovery of nuclear transmutations at the turn of the century eventually provided an answer to the puzzle, and by 1940 it had become clear that conditions at the centre of a star are so hot that hydrogen nuclei there can combine to form helium nuclei with a great enough release of energy to supply the energy flowing out from the star's surface.

A star like the Sun thus exists in a double equilibrium. It has a pressure equilibrium between the inward force of gravity and the outward pressure of the hot compressed hydrogen and helium gas. It also has an energy equilibrium between the energy flowing out of the surface and the energy released by hydrogen fusion reactions in the hot interior. Having achieved a structure in which both these equilibria exist, a star can continue almost unchanged for as long as its nuclear energy source holds out.

Assuming that stars originally form from matter that is chemically identical to the diffuse gas found in the interstellar medium, one can calculate both the structure expected for a star of a given total mass, and the length of time that the star can continue more or less unchanged, living on its nuclear fuel. The sizes, surface temperatures, and luminosities calculated for stars having various masses turn out to describe the commonest kind of stars around the Sun that we have labeled **main sequence** stars in an earlier section. A main sequence star is thus a nearly chemically homogeneous star replacing its energy losses by nuclear reactions that convert hydrogen to helium at the centre of the star. Table 3.2 lists several observable quantities for main sequence stars having a few typical mass values. In this table, masses are given relative to the Sun's mass $M_{\odot} = 1.985 \times 10^{30}$ kg; the surface temperature is the typical temperature of the radiating atmosphere of the star; the luminosity is the total energy radiated each second by the star in all directions, in watts; the radius is the distance from the centre of the star to the radiating atmosphere; and the surface gravity is the acceleration at the level of this atmosphere. The values given for a star of one solar mass correspond to a younger star than the Sun, which has a slightly lower luminosity and radius than the present-day Sun.

A star can persist as a main sequence star, it turns out, until about 10% of its hydrogen fuel has been converted to helium. At that point it begins to feel strongly the effect of fuel shortage at the centre where the energy-liberating nuclear reactions occur, and its structure must change to accommodate the new situation. The shortage of fuel at the centre means that the energy released by nuclear reactions no longer balances that lost from the centre, and so the centre of the star shrinks and becomes hotter. This increases the energy release from hydrogen fusion, because with higher temperature the H nuclei can fuse more easily. The luminosity of a massive star remains roughly constant, while that of a low-mass star actually increases. Paradoxically, the shrinkage and higher temperature at the centre cause the outer layers of the star to swell enormously, until the star reaches a size about 10 times larger than the Sun. The surface temperature drops considerably, to a value around 2–3000 K. This is the structure that we have previously identified in the stellar population of the Milky Way disk as the **red giant** phase. Red giants, in other words, are stars that have begun to exhaust their available hydrogen fuel.

Table 3.2: Properties of main sequence stars

Mass ($M/M_\odot$)	Surface temperature (K)	Luminosity (W)	Radius (m)	Main sequence lifetime (yr)
15	34 000	8×10^{30}	3×10^9	1×10^7
9	25 000	2×10^{30}	2×10^9	2×10^7
5	19 000	2×10^{29}	2×10^9	7×10^7
2.25	11 000	1×10^{28}	1×10^9	5×10^8
1.0	5 800	3×10^{26}	6×10^8	8×10^9
0.5	3 800	1×10^{25}	3×10^8	8×10^{10}

Source: R. J. Tayler 1970, *The Stars: their Structure and Evolution* (London: Wykeham Publs.).

Main sequence lifetimes

A significant feature of the main sequence phase can be observed by examining the data in Table 3.2. The masses of the table range over a factor of 30 from smallest to largest, but over this range the luminosities vary by a factor of almost one million. This has an important consequence. The available nuclear fuel is proportional to the mass of the star, but the rate of use is proportional to the luminosity. Massive stars have more fuel than low mass stars, but not very much more. But they use this fuel so much faster than low mass stars that they exhaust the available fuel, and cease to be main sequence stars, in far less time than low mass stars do. Main sequence lifetimes calculated for the stellar masses are listed in Table 3.2.

The most remarkable facts in this table are the long main sequence lifetimes of all stars, and the extent to which the lifetimes of the low mass stars exceed those of more massive stars.

Now the Milky Way as a whole is believed to have an age of between 10 and 15 Gyr ($1.0 - 1.5 \times 10^{10}$ yrs). Clearly when we observe a massive star that can remain on the main sequence for only 10^7 or 10^8 years after it becomes a main sequence star, it must have been formed long after the Milky Way had settled into essentially its present state. The observation of massive stars in the disk of the galaxy is therefore clear evidence that star formation has occurred very recently, and is presumably still going on in the disk.

On the other hand, the stars of the galactic bulge, and of globular clusters, have such low masses that they could well have been formed at the time that the galaxy formed. The absence of *any* stars in such regions of the galaxy that have main sequence lifetimes significantly less than the age of the galaxy strongly suggests that in the galactic bulge and in the globular clusters essentially no new stars have been formed since the era when the galaxy itself formed.

We can even determine approximately how long ago star formation in a cluster or association stopped, and thus obtain a rough age, if we make the reasonable assumptions that each cluster when formed contains stars with a great range of masses, and that each cluster formed within a fairly short time, all at once. A cluster that now contains main sequence stars with masses of up to $5M_\odot$, but none with greater masses, must have an age since star formation stopped of about 7×10^7 years. If it were much younger it would presumably have more massive but shorter-lived stars still on the main sequence. If it were much older, even the $5M_\odot$ stars would all have evolved off the main sequence (see Table 3.2), and only lower mass stars would be still on the main sequence. Using this kind of reasoning, we find that the open clusters of the galactic disk mostly have ages ranging between 2×10^7 and 10^9 years. Open clusters whose ages are nearly as large as the age of the galaxy are found, but they are quite rare. In contrast, all globular clusters in the Milky Way have ages determined in this way of about 1×10^{10} years. The fact that all the globular clusters have similar ages is one of the strongest pieces of evidence suggesting that their common age is also the age of the galaxy itself.

Nuclear reactions in main sequence stars

Let us look a little more closely at the nuclear reactions that power a star's luminosity, and at how the star changes in response to the changing availability of nuclear fuel, until ultimately the available fuel is converted to non-usable forms and exhausted, and the star ends its life as a tiny white dwarf, or explodes in a cataclysmic event known as a supernova, perhaps leaving a neutron star or black hole as a remnant.

The nuclear reaction that supplies energy to make up for that lost from the surface of a star while it is on the main sequence is the combination of hydrogen nuclei to form helium nuclei. This is a typical nuclear reaction. It is a process analogous to a chemical reaction, such as the combination of atoms of hydrogen (H) and oxygen (O) to form molecules of the chemical compound water (H_2O), with a release of heat energy. However, in a chemical reaction the atoms combine, by sharing or exchanging electrons, without any change to the atomic nuclei. The energy released in a typical chemical reaction is a few electron volts (1 eV $= 1.6 \times 10^{-19}$ joules) per atom, or roughly 10^8 joules per kilogram-mole of reacting matter. (For an atomic species of atomic weight A, one kilogram-mole is A kilograms of the material). In contrast, in a nuclear reaction it is the atomic nuclei that combine to form, not chemical compounds, but different chemical elements. A typical nuclear reaction releases a few million electron volts (MeV) per nucleus, or some 10^{15} joules per kilogram-mole of reactant. From the chemical combination of one kilogram of hydrogen and oxygen, in the right proportions, one would get enough energy to light a 100 watt light bulb for about $1\frac{1}{2}$ days. From the conversion of one kilogram of hydrogen into helium, one could provide the electric power consumed by a city of one million for $1\frac{1}{2}$ days.

Nuclear reactions do not occur at room temperature (300 K) because all atomic nuclei are positively charged due to the protons that they contain, and strongly repel one another electrically. They cannot get close enough together to combine. In contrast, the temperature at the centre of a main sequence star is typically somewhat hotter than 10^7 K. At such a high temperature the atoms are moving extremely rapidly (H at typically 300 km s^{-1}), and collisions between atoms are frequent and violent. They are so violent, in fact, that atoms of all sorts are stripped of their electrons, which also move around rapidly but unattached to atomic nuclei. The collisions between the bare atomic nuclei are so violent that low-mass nuclei (which have only one or at most a few protons) sometimes approach close enough to one another, in spite of their electrical repulsion, for the short-range but very powerful nuclear force to cause the two colliding nuclei to stick together to form a heavier nucleus.

In a main sequence star large quantities of the least electrically charged atomic nuclei, that of hydrogen, are available at the centre of the star, and it is hydrogen that is involved in the most important fusion reactions in such stars. The hydrogen is gradually converted into helium by means of two reaction sequences. The simpler one, called the proton-proton sequence, is the most important in stars of about 1 $M_\odot$ or less. This sequence starts with two normal H nuclei (i.e. protons), which collide to make a very anomalous helium nucleus, ^{2}He, composed of two protons. This nucleus is radioactive (spontaneously unstable), however, and so most such collisions are immediately undone. Very rarely, however, one of the protons spontaneously changes to a neutron by emitting a positive electron, e^+, and a neutrino, ν. This changes the resulting nucleus to stable heavy hydrogen or deuterium (^{2}H), composed of one proton and one neutron. This may be written in a form analogous to a chemical equation,

$$^1\mathrm{H} + {}^1\mathrm{H} \rightarrow {}^2\mathrm{H} + \mathrm{e}^+ + \nu \quad (1.2\ \mathrm{MeV}).$$

The 1.2 MeV represents the energy released by the reaction. It includes the energy released when the e^+ is annihilated by a normal e^- electron. However, the neutrino escapes immediately from the star, and the 0.3 MeV that it carries off into space on average is not included in the 1.2 MeV released.

Because the ^{2}He nucleus is so unstable, it took physicists a long time to realize that deuterium could actually be produced by this reaction. The rarity of the successful reaction is also responsible for the fact that nuclear energy production by H reactions occurs at a relatively slow rate which is completely determined by this very severe bottleneck.

The ^{2}H deuterium nucleus that results from a successful positron – neutrino emission is quickly struck by another proton, to produce a light helium nucleus. This reaction may be written

$$^2\mathrm{H} + {}^1\mathrm{H} \rightarrow {}^3\mathrm{He} \quad (5.5\ \mathrm{MeV}).$$

Again there is a release of energy. Finally, once a significant number of ^{3}He nuclei have been produced, they begin to collide with one another to form a normal helium nucleus ^{4}He, with two protons left over:

$$^3\mathrm{He} + {}^3\mathrm{He} \rightarrow {}^4\mathrm{He} + {}^1\mathrm{H} + {}^1\mathrm{H} \quad (12.8\ \mathrm{MeV}).$$

The overall reaction sequence has the effect of fusing together four protons into one ^{4}He nucleus. Since the last step involves two ^{3}He nuclei, to make the ^{4}He each of the first two reactions must happen twice, and so the total energy released by the formation of one ^{4}He nucleus is $2\times(1.2)+2\times(5.5)+12.8 = 26.2$ MeV (about

6.5 MeV per H nucleus) and the whole sequence may be summarized as

$$4\,{}^1\mathrm{H} + 2\mathrm{e}^- \rightarrow {}^4\mathrm{He} + 2\nu \quad (26.2\ \mathrm{MeV}).$$

An alternative sequence of reactions, using ^{12}C nuclei as catalysts, is found to occur more readily than the proton-proton cycle in stars more massive than the Sun.

Exercise: Fundamentally, why do nuclear reactions provide so much more energy per reaction than chemical reactions?

3.4 Stellar evolution and the synthesis of heavy elements

The red giant stage

The helium formed in the core of a main sequence star is unable to undergo fusion reactions at a temperature of $\sim 10^7$K. The He remains as an inert "ash" produced by the fusion. As H is converted to He in the stellar core, the amount of usable fuel declines steadily. By the time the hydrogen fuel is nearly gone in the innermost 10% of the star's mass, the effects of a shortage of available fuel are beginning to be felt, and the star begins to change towards a red giant structure. The energy production at the centre of the star is no longer high enough to supply energy losses from the surface, the central pressure falls below the value required to balance gravity, and the core of the star contracts and heats. This general temperature rise allows hydrogen fusion to occur farther and farther from the centre of the star, until eventually fusion ceases at the core but continues in a shell surrounding the core of He ash. At the same time, the outer layers of the star swell outward to a size typically a hundred times larger than their main sequence size.

During the red giant phase a significant fraction of the star's total mass is ejected from the outer layers back into space before it has a chance to be used as nuclear fuel. This ejection occurs as a steady evaporation of matter from the surface in what is called a **stellar wind**. A stellar wind is found even in many main sequence stars such as the Sun (where it is called the solar wind), but it only has an important effect on main sequence evolution for stars more than 30 or 40 times more massive than the Sun. The mass ejection rate in the Sun is low enough that only about 0.01% of the Sun's total mass will be blown away during the Sun's main sequence life. In red giants, however, the mass loss rate is very rapid, and by the time all available nuclear fuels have been used, a star may have lost as much as 80% of its original mass back into space.

In red giants this mass loss is probably driven mainly by radiation pressure. The outer atmosphere of a red giant is cool enough (less than 2000 K) for small solid grains of refractory (high melting and boiling point) material to condense or freeze out of the gas. These particles are composed mainly of the most abundant chemical elements (except for He, N and Ne, which do not combine readily with other elements and which freeze out only at very low temperatures), and could be, for example, silicates such as $FeMgSiO_4$, or organic carbon compounds such as are found in soot. The grains are then driven out of the stellar atmosphere into the surrounding interstellar space by radiation pressure, the same force that cleans small particles out of the solar system. As they move outward, the grains drag along much gas by viscous friction, thus producing a strong stellar wind.

This wind has the same chemical composition as the star's atmosphere. If the atmosphere has a chemical composition unchanged from the composition at the time the star formed, the stellar wind will return material to the interstellar medium that has the same composition as the interstellar medium itself. However, a red giant has very strong convection (boiling motions) throughout much of its volume, and this convection mixes to the surface some material from near the core that has undergone nuclear fusion. This matter is richer in He than the original matter in the star was, because of the conversion of hydrogen. If the red giant is massive enough for most H fusion to occur via the CNO cycle, then the material mixed up from the interior is also relatively poor in ^{12}C and rich in ^{14}N. This is because the slowest step in the whole CNO cycle is the fourth step, in which ^{14}N is made into ^{15}O. Thus, as the CNO cycle proceeds, most of the ^{12}C is fairly quickly turned into ^{14}N, while ^{14}N is only destroyed very slowly. Eventually the abundance of ^{12}C in the reacting region falls so low that ^{12}C nuclei are transmuted only as often as ^{14}N nuclei are transmuted, and an equilibrium is attained. In the region where this equilibrium holds, the N/C ratio is about 20:1 instead of the 1:3 value found, for example, in the Sun. Thus matter mixed to the surface from the reacting region is richer in N and poorer in C than it was originally. Therefore the gas returned to the interstellar medium from the star at this particular evolutionary stage has the effect of changing the chemical composition of the interstellar gas, enriching it in He and N but making it poorer in C.

As the star uses up the hydrogen near the core, the central temperature gradually rises. Eventually it reaches roughly 10^8 K, about ten times hotter than the temperature at which H fusion can occur. At the higher temperature, collisions between He nuclei finally become energetic enough for the helium ash to become a usable nuclear fuel, and the He nuclei begin to fuse to form beryllium and then carbon and oxygen with the reactions

$$\begin{aligned} {}^4\text{He} + {}^4\text{He} &\rightarrow {}^8\text{Be} \quad (-0.1 \text{ MeV}) \\ {}^4\text{He} + {}^8\text{Be} &\rightarrow {}^{12}\text{C} \quad (7.4 \text{ MeV}) \\ {}^4\text{He} + {}^{12}\text{C} &\rightarrow {}^{16}\text{O} \quad (7.2 \text{ MeV}). \end{aligned}$$

The first reaction is a severe bottleneck to this process. ^{8}Be is not stable (note that energy is not released when it is made, but must be added) and spontaneously decays back to two ^{4}He nuclei. However, this does not happen instantaneously, and when the temperature has risen to $\sim 10^8$ K, ^{8}Be nuclei are being formed rapidly enough that at any one time there is roughly one ^{8}Be nucleus for every 10^{10} ^{4}He nuclei that has not yet decayed back to two ^{4}He nuclei. This turns out to be enough ^{8}Be for the second reaction to occur. ^{12}C is stable, and once formed is only likely to be destroyed by reactions making still heavier nuclei, such as the last of the reactions above.

The occurrence of helium ignition provides the star with a fresh source of fuel, although it can only power the star's energy output for about 10–15 % of the time it spent as a main sequence star. The star again readjusts its structure, with the centre becoming less dense and the size of the outer layers decreasing somewhat. As helium burning progresses, the star develops a layered structure, like an onion. At the centre is a sphere rich in C and O produced by He-burning. Around this C-O rich region is a shell made up mainly of He produced by earlier H-burning. Finally, the outer layers of the star are H-rich, and have still approximately the chemical composition with which they started, apart from the changes in He, C, and N that occurred as the star first became a giant.

What happens next depends on the mass with which the star started. A star that started its main sequence life with about 8 $M_\odot$ of material or less finishes its He-burning phase by ejecting into space almost all the remaining hydrogen-rich material, leaving only a core rich in C and O that has already essentially become a white dwarf. A star initially more massive ends its life by exploding violently as a supernova; the material ejected back into the interstellar medium is likely to include much gas that has undergone considerable nuclear processing. After a supernova explosion there may be no remnant at all, or the core of the star may remain as a tiny neutron star or an invisible black hole.

White dwarfs

For the star that starts with a mass of less than about 8 $M_\odot$, the helium-burning phase is the last phase of major nuclear activity that the star goes through. As the He at the stellar core is exhausted, the star faces a problem similar to the one that it had when central H was exhausted and the star had to become a giant. Energy output from the burning of He does not suffice to replenish heat lost from the surface, so the pressure falls below the value needed to support the outer layers. The weight of the outer layers forces the core to shrink, and it heats up somewhat. He is able to convert to C farther from the centre; after a while the He-burning is going on in a shell around the inert core of C-O ash.

At this point, the density of the gas at the centre of the star is more than 10^7 kg m^{-3}, or 10^4 times higher than the density of water. This extremely dense condition brings about a change in the physical state of the matter at the core of the star. As the gas is compressed to greater and greater densities, the electrons of the gas (which have mostly been freed from their atoms by the high temperature and resulting violent collisions between particles) are also packed closer and closer together. Now the basic laws that govern the behaviour of atoms and electrons (quantum mechanics) require that when electrons are closely packed, they must all have different energies from one another. This rule operates on isolated atoms, where it requires that each electron occupy a separate orbit around the nucleus, so that only two electrons (with oppositely oriented spins) can be in the lowest energy level; all the others must fill up orbits of higher energy. This requirement of separate orbits (or energy levels) is called the Pauli exclusion principle. In the core of the red giant the matter is dense enough that the Pauli exclusion principle comes into operation. It requires that only a few electrons have low energies; most must have fairly high energies. As the matter becomes denser and denser, more and more electrons are packed into each cubic meter, and as new electrons are forced in, they must occupy trajectories of higher energy than the electrons already there. The fact that most of the electrons must have high energies means that they exert a considerable pressure, since they are moving very rapidly. This effect of the Pauli principle in a hot gas (a plasma) is called **degeneracy**, and the resulting pressure is known as (electron) **degeneracy pressure**.

The important feature of degeneracy pressure to the star is that it is different from normal thermal gas pressure; it is present even if the matter is cold. Once the degeneracy spreads through much of the material remaining in the star, the gradual exhaustion of fuel no longer produces an overall pressure imbalance with resulting shrinkage. The outer, non-degenerate layers where He fusion is occurring still shrink and heat as fuel is exhausted, but the degenerate core remains largely unaffected.

After the red giant has developed a degenerate core of non-reacting C-O ash, and while He-burning is going on in a shell around this core, another significant phenomenon occurs. The helium burning becomes unsteady, and a regular series of He-burning flashes occur. During these flashes the heat lost from the star is largely provided by He-burning; in between, it is mainly provided by H-burning somewhat farther out. These He shell flashes power strong convection, and it appears that some of the products of helium fusion, such as C and O, will be mixed up to the surface to be returned to the interstellar medium by the star's wind. But the mixing that accompanies the He burning pulses also brings N from the H-burning region down into the He-burning zone where it is partly converted to heavier elements by such reactions as

$$\begin{aligned} {}^{14}\mathrm{N} + {}^{4}\mathrm{He} &\rightarrow {}^{18}\mathrm{F} \\ {}^{18}\mathrm{F} &\rightarrow {}^{18}\mathrm{O} + \mathrm{e}^{+} + \nu \\ {}^{18}\mathrm{O} + {}^{4}\mathrm{H} &\rightarrow {}^{22}\mathrm{Ne} \\ {}^{22}\mathrm{Ne} + {}^{4}\mathrm{He} &\rightarrow {}^{25}\mathrm{Mg} + \mathrm{n}. \end{aligned}$$

The last reaction is particularly interesting because it can release many free neutrons. These neutrons are not electrically charged, so they have no difficulty in interacting with atomic nuclei, even ones with very high numbers of protons. In fact, the production of all types of atomic nuclei heavier than iron in stars is almost certainly carried out by successive additions of neutrons to atomic nuclei of the iron group (Fe, Ti, V, Cr, Ni etc.). Thus, the development of He-burning flashes allows a wide range of really heavy atomic nuclei to be produced (though in small amounts) and subsequently to be returned to the interstellar gas. When this process of neutron addition goes on rather slowly, over a period of many thousands of years (as in a red giant), it is known as **slow neutron addition**, or the **s-process.**

Eventually, the advance of nuclear burning outward through the star, and the steady loss of matter from the surface, reduce the mass of the H- and He-rich outer envelope to a value of the order of 0.1 $M_\odot$. At this point almost all the remaining outer envelope is blown off at a greatly accelerated rate (a superwind) leaving behind essentially only the degenerate C-O core. The loss of the outer envelope with almost all the remaining fuel brings an end to nuclear burning, and the small amount of gas around the degenerate core shrinks onto the core. As this gas contracts it heats, and soon the star has such a high surface temperature ($\sim 30,000$ K) that ultraviolet photons emitted from it cause the departing superwind matter to glow by fluorescence. This state in the star's development is called a planetary nebula phase, from the resemblance of the glowing gas cloud around the star to the appearance of a planet when seen through a small telescope. Gradually the glowing gas cloud disperses, leaving the very compressed C-O core of the red giant.

This C-O core, which usually contains about 0.7 $M_\odot$ of matter, no longer needs to be hot inside to support itself against gravity; the required pressure is supplied by degeneracy pressure. Because the core is very dense, it is extremely small compared to the size of the original star, with a radius of roughly 10^4 km, about the size of the Earth. It has become a white dwarf. Since the star no longer has any nuclear burning, and cannot shrink, it gradually loses its internal heat out into space. Because it has a rather small surface for radiating heat away, this cooling process requires about 10^{10} years before the surface temperature drops so low that the white dwarf is no longer readily seen through a telescope from a distance of a few light-years.

Supernovae, neutron stars, and black holes

For the tiny fraction of main sequence stars that start out with more than about 8 $M_\odot$ of material, evolution after helium ignition is rather different from that of a lower mass star. Such stars do not shut off nuclear reactions after He-burning by developing enough degeneracy pressure to support themselves against gravity without shrinking and becoming hotter at the centre. Instead, they become hot enough ($T > 5 \times 10^8$K) to begin to use the C and O ash as a fuel, with reactions such as

$${}^{12}\mathrm{C} + {}^{12}\mathrm{C} \rightarrow {}^{23}\mathrm{Na} + {}^{1}\mathrm{H} \quad (2.2 \text{ MeV}),$$

$${}^{12}\mathrm{C} + {}^{12}\mathrm{C} \rightarrow {}^{20}\mathrm{Ne} + {}^{4}\mathrm{He} \quad (4.6 \text{ MeV}),$$

and occasionally

$${}^{12}\mathrm{C} + {}^{12}\mathrm{C} \rightarrow {}^{24}\mathrm{Mg} + \gamma \quad (13.9 \text{ MeV}).$$

Another potentially interesting reaction series occurs using protons liberated by reactions like the first of those above:

$$\begin{aligned} {}^{1}\mathrm{H} + {}^{12}\mathrm{C} &\rightarrow {}^{13}\mathrm{N} \\ {}^{13}\mathrm{N} &\rightarrow {}^{13}\mathrm{C} + \mathrm{e}^{+} + \nu \\ {}^{4}\mathrm{He} + {}^{13}\mathrm{C} &\rightarrow {}^{16}\mathrm{O} + \mathrm{n}. \end{aligned}$$

The significance of this reaction series is that (like the series involving ^{22}Ne that can occur in He-burning flashes) it can produce neutrons, which are able to make elements heavier than iron by reactions with moderately heavy nuclei already present in the gas.

For stars that start out with between about 8 and 13 $M_\odot$, the density becomes high enough at the centre as carbon burning begins to slow down there (due to fuel exhaustion) that the centre of the star becomes degenerate. As the density rises, electrons are forced to higher and higher energies, and they eventually have high enough energies to begin to be captured by protons inside atomic nuclei by the reaction

$$\mathrm{p} + \mathrm{e}^- \rightarrow \mathrm{n} + \nu \quad (-0.8\ \mathrm{MeV}).$$

Capturing an electron turns a proton into a neutron, so atomic nuclei begin to change chemical identity. Furthermore, the electrons have been providing a large part of the total pressure, and as they are absorbed by nuclei, the central pressure falls. The star shrinks, the density rises, more electrons are captured by protons, the central pressure continues to decrease, and the process accelerates to a catastrophic collapse. As the star collapses, most of the protons in nuclei near the centre capture electrons and become neutrons. The density near the star's centre becomes so large ($\sim 10^{17}\ \mathrm{kg\,m^{-3}}$) that individual nuclei begin to merge, and the core of the star becomes a kind of giant atomic nucleus made up largely of neutrons.

The sudden collapse of the core to the dimension of a small asteroid, $\sim$ 10 km across, does not go unnoticed by the rest of the star. Exactly what happens is not fully clear, but the sudden shrinkage of the core releases an enormous amount of gravitational energy, which in turn causes the explosive ejection of most of the matter left in the outer layers of the star in a giant fireball. The material explodes away from the central star at an enormous rate, about 5000 $\mathrm{km\,s^{-1}}$ (more than 1% of the speed of light). For a period of weeks, the fireball (the expanding cloud of hot gas) radiates energy at some 10,000 times higher a rate than the star did as a main sequence star or giant. The result is one of the most spectacular cosmic events that nature can produce, a **supernova explosion**.

The consequences of this collapse are twofold. On the one hand, the core of the star is left as a tiny remnant, a sphere of roughly nuclear density about 10 km across, composed mainly of neutrons. This **neutron star** is often detectable for perhaps 100 million years due to pulsed radio emission it emits; during this stage, the star is also known as a **pulsar**. On the other hand, the ejected material eventually rejoins the interstellar gas. The matter of the fireball has enhanced abundances of those chemical elements such as He, N, C, and O that are formed by hydrogen and helium burning. It also includes heavy atomic nuclei formed in the intense heat of the first moments of the fireball. The gas returned to the interstellar medium by the fireball thus alters the chemistry of the interstellar gas by raising slightly the total fraction of the gas in the form of helium and heavier elements. The Crab Nebula (Figure 3.3) is such an expanding cloud of gases enriched in heavy elements.

Figure 3.3: The explosion of a massive star in the year 1054 was recorded by Chinese and Korean astronomers. The mass of gas expelled in the explosion has been expanding ever since, and now forms the beautiful Crab Nebula. The expanding gas is greatly enriched in elements heavier than He; these elements will be mixed into the interstellar gas and participate in the next generation of star formation. (Courtesy of the European Southern Observatory.)

Stars heavier initially than 13 $M_\odot$ also go through a carbon burning stage like that of stars in the 8–13 $M_\odot$ range, but the more massive stars are hotter at the centre than their lower mass counterparts and so do not become degenerate at the centre even after carbon burning. Instead, they become hot enough ($T > 10^9\ K$) for further nuclear reactions involving ever heavier nuclei to occur.

As the centre of the star becomes progressively hotter, these reactions lead to production of heavier and heavier elements: Si, S, Ar, Ca, and finally the elements of the iron group (Ti, V, Cr, Mn, Fe, Ni). Each reaction releases some energy and helps to hold the star up for a time, but as each fuel is depleted at the centre, the central temperature rises and allows the reaction to occur farther from the centre while preparing conditions for the next, higher temperature reaction. The star thus develops a structure like an onion, with concentric shells of different dominant chemical compositions. Finally, with the development of an iron core the process finishes. No further energy can be extracted from nuclear reactions in the core; forming heavier nuclei from iron does not release energy, it requires it. But the temperature at the centre at this point is approaching 5×10^9 K. At such high temperatures the iron nuclei begin to be broken up by the intensive heat radiation. This, of course, removes energy from the centre, cooling it and reducing the pressure. The star reacts by shrinking and reheating the centre. As more iron nuclei are shattered, the process gathers speed and soon a catastrophic collapse is under way.

As with less massive stars, this collapse probably leads to a supernova explosion, and to the formation of a neutron star – or, if the initial star was extremely massive, to a **black hole**, a star so completely collapsed that even light cannot escape from it. However, in this case the matter ejected in the supernova fireball is enriched in most of the chemical elements up to iron, as well as some very heavy nuclei that may be formed during the early stages of the explosion. (Production of free neutrons and creation of heavy elements goes very quickly in supernova explosion, and is therefore known as **rapid neutron addition**, or the **r-process**). In fact, nucleosynthesis in such really massive stars, with subsequent supernova explosions, is thought to be the means by which almost all the atomic nuclei between Ne and Fe are synthesized and then added to the interstellar medium. These newly minted atomic nuclei are then incorporated into the next generation of new stars to form. Thus, all of the common chemical elements found in the Earth (O, Mg, Si, S, Ca, Cr, Fe, Ni) were produced by generations of supernovae. *The relative abundances of these elements in the solar system are the direct result of the various nucleosynthesis reactions that have occurred in early generations of stars in the Milky Way galaxy.*

3.5 The star in the solar system: the Sun

The Sun's general structure

We have already noticed that the solar system's own star, the Sun, is a fairly typical main sequence star, neither one of the largest and brightest stars, nor one of the really small and faint stars. It is sufficiently typical that we normally use the solar mass and radius as units of size for measuring other stars. A star of this mass has a main sequence lifetime (Table 3.2) of about 10 Gyr. From radioactive dating of meteorites (see Chapter 5), we have deduced that the solar system, and the Sun, were formed about 4.5 Gyr ago. The Sun is thus about half-way through its main sequence life. Since the oldest stars in the Milky Way galaxy are about 12 or 13 Gyr old, the Sun was formed long after the first burst of star formation. As a consequence, about 2% of the Sun's mass is composed of elements heavier than He that were formed in earlier generations of massive stars and their supernovae, and subsequently incorporated first into the general interstellar medium and then into later generations of stars. With a mass of 1 $M_\odot$, the Sun will eventually become a red giant, (and lose about a third of its mass during this phase by a very strong stellar wind), and then eject a planetary nebula and finish life as a white dwarf.

The Sun has essentially the structure we have described above for a main sequence star. The core has a central temperature of about 15 million Kelvins, and close to the core nuclear reactions are converting H into He to replace the 4×10^{26} W lost from the surface. The density of the gas at the centre of the Sun is about 150,000 kg m^{-3}, more than ten times the density of lead. This is only possible because the atoms there are almost entirely stripped of their electrons, and so can be packed far more closely together than normal neutral atoms can.

As we come out from the centre towards the surface, the density, pressure, and temperature drop. Heat leaks gradually out towards the surface, carried by X-ray photons that frequently collide with electrons and ions. About 70% of the way out, at about 500,000 km from the centre, we come to a level above which the solar gas is in constant boiling motion. Between this level and the surface, heat is transported outward by **convection**: by the physical rising of blobs of hot gas, which are replaced by descending blobs of slightly cooler gas. The process is similar to the one that carries heat up into the room air above a heated radiator or heating element in your home in winter, or to the flow of liquid you can see in a pot of thick soup on the stove just before it reaches the boiling point.

At the top of the convective layer, we reach the radiating surface of the Sun, the layers which lose heat directly into the dark space around the Sun. We call this layer the **solar atmosphere** or **photosphere**. The region from which radiation is emitted is actually about 500 km thick, but this is so thin compared to the total radius of the Sun (700,000 km) that it looks like a sharp surface to observers on Earth. The temperature falls as one rises in the atmosphere; a typical temperature for this layer (the **effective temperature** of the Sun) is about 5800 K. At this level the density of the gas is a mere 2.5×10^{-4} kg m^{-3}, almost a billion times (10^9 times) less than at the Sun's centre.

When we observe the visible light emitted by the hot surface layers, at low magnification we see a surface that shows very few features. The only obvious features that we sometimes see are dark, irregular spots. Several such spots are visible in the white-light image of the Sun shown in Figure 3.4. We call these dark

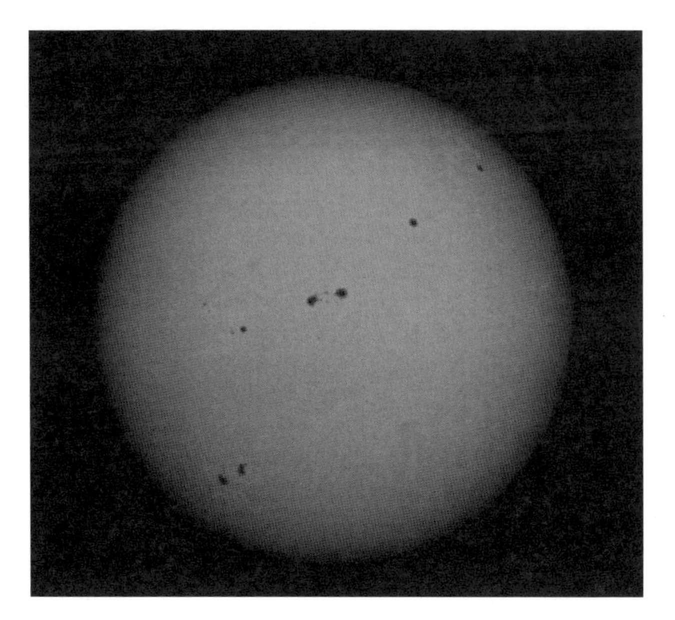

Figure 3.4: An image of the Sun taken in white light (that is, detecting the light you see with your eyes). The Sun is seen to be essentially featureless except for several dark sunspots scattered across the image from lower left to upper right, parallel to the Sun's rotational equator, which happens to be oblique in this image. (Courtesy of the U. S. National Solar Observatory, NSO/AURA/NSF.)

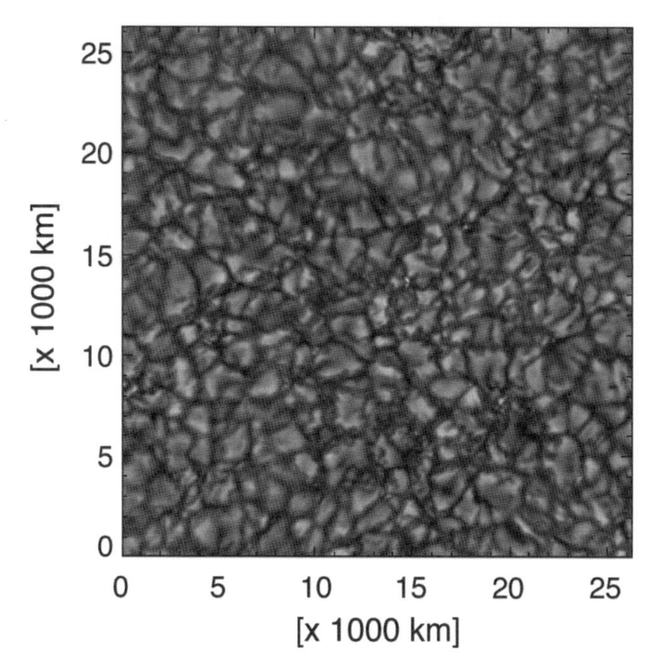

Figure 3.5: At the highest useful magnification, the Sun's surface is seen (in white light) to be covered with an irregular pattern of bright patches outlined by a delicate darker tracery. This pattern, the solar granulation, reveals the rising hot blobs of gas (the bright polygons) and the descending cooler gas (the darker lines) of the convection that transports heat through the outermost 30% of the Sun's radius. (Courtesy of T. Rimmele/NSO/AURA/NSF.)

patches **sunspots**. When a sunspot is visible near the edge of the visible disk (the **limb** of the Sun), it is surrounded by a larger irregular area, known as a **plage** or **facula**, where the brightness is slightly *higher* than on the general solar surface. When we observe sunspots daily over a period of weeks, we notice first that they all move across the Sun's visible disk, parallel to the plane of the ecliptic, going from one limb of the Sun to the other in about two weeks, and we deduce that we are observing the **rotation** of the Sun. The Sun takes about 27 days to turn once on its axis, which is almost perpendicular to the plane of the Earth's orbit, so that the solar equator is approximately in the plane of the ecliptic. (In fact, the Sun's surface does not all rotate at the same rate; at the equator one rotation, for example of a sunspot, takes about 25 days, at 30° latitude above or below the equator the rotation takes about 27 days, and near the poles one rotation requires more than 36 days! The Sun does *not* rotate like the Earth or other rigid bodies.) We also see that each sunspot changes shape from one day to another, and that individual sunspots appear, persist, and then vanish over a period of a few weeks.

When we observe the Sun's surface with greater magnification, we discover another kind of surface feature. The entire surface is covered with a delicate network of irregular oval or polygonal bright patches, separated by a network of less bright lines, somewhat like fine lace or a cobweb. The bright spots are typically a few hundred km across, near the limit of our ability to discern detail on the surface of the Sun through the Earth's unsteady atmosphere. This pattern of lighter and darker regions is clearly visible in Figure 3.5, and is called the **solar granulation**. The granulation is the visible symptom of the convective motions that carry heat outward through the outermost 30% of the Sun's radius. The physical process of convection occurs as relatively hot blobs of gas float upwards through their surroundings, like hot air balloons rising in the cooler Earth's atmosphere because of their buoyancy. As they rise, these blobs carry their excess heat upward with them, and eventually release this heat as they dissolve into their surroundings. In between the hot blobs are cooler streams which descend because they are slightly denser than their surroundings, finally cooling the layers in which they dissolve. The bright regions of the granulation are simply the rising, somewhat hotter parcels of gas, which are cooling by radiating their excess heat out into space, while the darker lines separating these bright blobs are the flows of cooled gas back into the Sun. When we observe the solar granulation carefully, we find that the hotter gases are rising at a few hundred meters per second, while the cooler material is descending at a similar speed. Individual blobs persist for a few minutes before being replaced by others rising from below them. The existence of the solar granulation provides direct confirmation of the theoretical prediction that the outer layers of the Sun are in a state of convection.

The solar spectrum and the chemical composition of the Sun

The Sun is the largest single object that resulted from the formation of the solar system (it contains almost 99.9% of the total mass of the present system, although there may once have been as much as a few percent of the Sun's mass in the cloud of material around the young Sun – the proto-solar nebula – from which the planets formed). It is also the object whose present chemical composition is most nearly the same as that of the original cloud from which the whole system formed. As we shall soon see, information about the chemical composition of the original solar nebula is quite helpful in understanding the chemistry of other solar system objects, both for identifying those (particularly certain meteorites) which have been altered very little since the original formation of the system, and in seeing how more complex bodies have developed their present chemical compositions. So it is of interest to determine the chemical composition of the Sun's outer layers.

But how is this to be done? One cannot send a space probe to the Sun to get samples of atmospheric material; the probe would vaporize before reaching the visible surface of the Sun. Instead, we study the Sun's radiation, which turns out to contain abundant clues about the chemical composition of the photosphere, as well as about the temperature, pressure, movements of blobs of gas, presence of magnetic fields, and other interesting physical characteristics.

However, it is not obvious what it means to study the radiation from the Sun. One aspect of such a study is to take pictures of the solar surface (we now call this "obtaining images" or "imaging") and to study the features that we see. We have already seen above some of the kinds of information contained in such pictures. But to obtain information about the chemical composition, temperature, etc., we must turn to the method of **spectroscopy**. We have to spread out the light of the Sun into different colours and look at how the Sun's brightness varies from one colour to another.

To understand the results of such an experiment, we need to recall the general nature of thermal (heat) radiation from opaque hot objects. All opaque objects that are warm or hot radiate energy into the space around them, thereby losing some of their internal heat energy. The Sun's luminosity is an example of this tendency, but even much cooler object (your hand, for example, or an ice cube) radiate heat continuously. The radiation from each square meter depends primarily on the temperature of the object, and rises very rapidly with increasing temperature (in fact, the energy loss rate increases as the temperature to the fourth power, T^4). Every square meter of the Sun's atmosphere radiates more than 100,000 time more strongly than a square meter of wall in your living room! A fundamental feature of the radiation from an opaque warm or hot object is that the radiation is emitted around a characteristic wavelength which depends only on the temperature of the object. The Sun's atmosphere, with a temperature of about 5800 K, radiates most strongly in visible light around 0.5 μm. Your wall, at about 300 K, radiates most strongly at around 10 μm, well into the infrared which your eye cannot see (which is one reason you can't read by the light of the radiation from your wall). Radiation from a cold interstellar gas cloud at 10 K occurs primarily around 300 μm, far in the infrared. (The characteristic wavelength varies as $1/T$.)

Opaque warm bodies do not radiate simply at a single wavelength or frequency, however, but in a range of wavelengths around the characteristic value. Most of the radiation emitted from such a body is radiated at wavelengths between about 0.5 and 3 times the wavelength at which the radiation is strongest. The Sun, for example, radiates pretty strongly in all colours of visible light as well as at adjacent infrared and ultraviolet colours. If we spread out the Sun's radiation into a spectrum (that is, we separate the radiation into the different component colours) and measure the Sun's brightness at each colour, we find the result shown in Figure 3.6. We see that most of the Sun's radiation is emitted between about 0.25 μm (2500 Å) and 1.5 μm, with a maximum at about 0.5 μm (5000 Å). Outside of this rather narrow band, the Sun's radiation is much weaker. In spite of its nearness and brightness, the Sun is not a brilliant source of X-rays or radio waves.

The way in which the Sun's radiation varies with wavelength is typical of the radiation from opaque heated objects. By comparing the solar spectrum of Figure 3.6 with the theoretical predictions for radiation from hot objects of various temperatures, we deduce a characteristic atmospheric temperature for the Sun of 5770 K.

However, in Figure 3.6, the Sun's light is not spread out very greatly. What do we see if we spread the light out one thousand times more finely? The result of do-

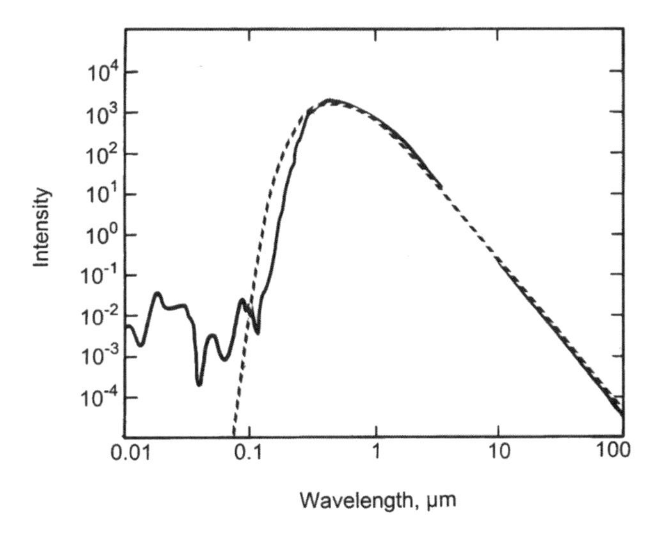

Figure 3.6: The overall solar spectrum (the solid curve), showing the amount of energy lost per second (in mW m^{-2} nm^{-1}) at various wavelengths (colours). The spectrum of the Sun is very similar to that of an ideal radiating body with a temperature of 5770 K (dashed curve), except shortward of 0.1 μm. Note however that the intensity scale is logarithmic, so that the "excess" ultraviolet light (compared to an ideal radiator), which is mostly produced in the solar corona (discussed below), actually involves very little energy. (Adapted from J. Lean 1991, Revs. Geophys., 29, 4, 505.)

ing this is shown in Figure 3.7, which shows a small part of the Sun's spectrum between about 0.485 and 0.487 μm (4850 to 4870 Å). This spectrum covers less than 1% of the total spectrum of the Sun in visible light alone. In it we see a wealth of detail not visible in the more general spectrum of Figure 3.6. The main characteristics of this spectrum are (a) the presence of a general level of brightness at most colours, as we saw in Figure 3.6, and (b) the weakening of many particular colours relative to this general brightness. If you recall the discussion in Chapter 2 about absorption and emission of light by atoms, you will not be too surprised to see these weakened colours. The weakened colours are simply **absorption lines**, colours strongly absorbed by atoms of specific elements in the Sun's atmosphere. Atoms of essentially all known elements are present in the gas making up the Sun. Most light escapes into space from the level in the solar atmosphere at which the general absorption of photons of all colours (mostly, in the Sun, by hydrogen atoms that have acquired a second electron) has diminished enough to make escape possible, but some particular colours are very strongly absorbed by atoms high in the atmosphere. This makes the Sun somewhat darker at these specific colours than at other, nearby colours that are not especially strongly absorbed by neutral or once-ionized atoms of any of the elements present.

Exercise: Where on Figure 3.6 is Figure 3.7?

The presence of absorption lines in the solar spectrum provides us with a very powerful tool for studying conditions in the Sun. Of course, as soon as we have identified a particular set of colours as those absorbed by one particular element, we know that that element is present in the Sun's atmosphere. The small spectrum shown in Figure 3.7 reveals the presence in the Sun of H, Ti, V, Cr, Fe, Co, Ni, and perhaps the "rare earth" element neodymium (Nd). However, we can obtain much more information than simply identifying atoms present in the Sun. We can use our knowledge of physics to calculate the spectrum expected from a hot gas under the conditions present in the Sun's atmosphere, and by comparing such calculations with the observed spectrum, and adjusting the conditions assumed in the calculation until the computed spectrum matches the observed one, we can determine the temperature, pressure, and chemical composition of the Sun's atmosphere. The relative numbers of various elements (abundances) in the solar atmosphere tabulated in Table 2.2 have been determined by such modelling of the observed solar spectrum. About 70 of the 92 naturally occurring chemical elements have been detected, and their abundances relative to H determined, through study of the solar spectrum. Similar studies of the spectra of other stars allow us to say with some confidence what the chemical compositions of their outer layers are, and comments earlier in this book about the chemical composition of various types of stars, interstellar clouds, and so on are based on the study of their spectra.

Exercise: How do you think that the spectrum of Figure 3.7 would change if the amount of Ni in the solar atmosphere were reduced by a factor of ten while all other conditions remained the same?

One of the most fundamental aspects of the chemical composition of the Sun shown in Table 2.2 is the overwhelming preponderance of the lightest element, H, and of the second lightest element, He. All other 90 elements combined make up less than 0.2% of the atoms in the solar atmosphere. As a first approximation, we could think of the Sun (and all other main sequence stars) as being made up only of H and He. This must also have been true of the interstellar cloud from which the Sun formed, and indeed is true of all interstellar clouds in the Milky Way galaxy.

Among the elements heavier than H and He, we find further regularities in the deduced abundances. The next most abundant group after H and He is made up

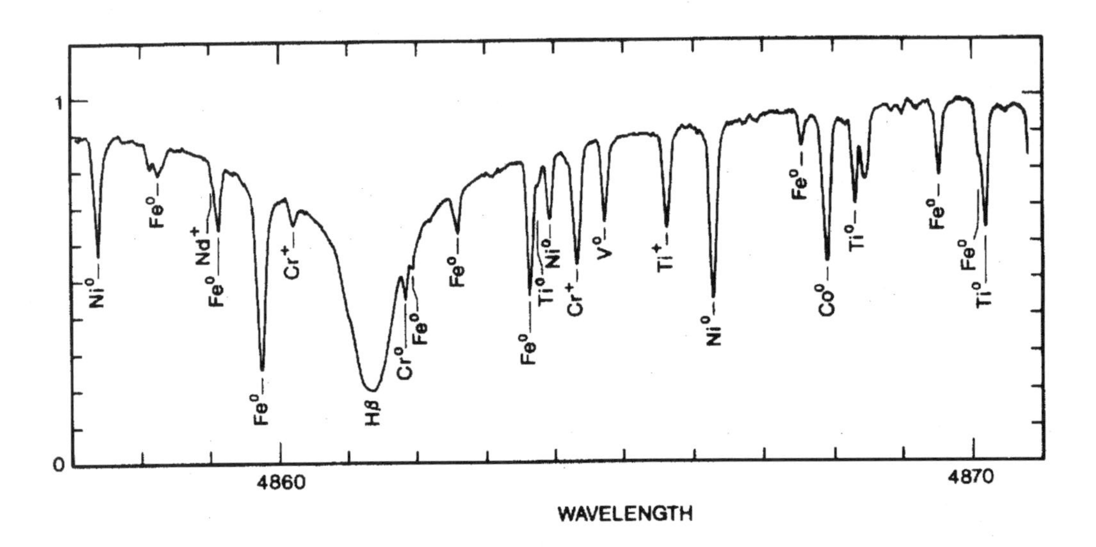

Figure 3.7: A very small part of the visible spectrum of the Sun is shown in detail. The brightness of the Sun (normalized to a maximum of 1) is plotted against wavelength in Ångstrom units. In this small region, many particular colours are weakened because they are absorbed in the Sun's atmosphere by atoms of specific chemical elements. The element responsible for each of the stronger absorptions is noted on the Figure, together with the state of ionization involved: thus Ti^0 indicates a colour absorbed by neutral titanium, while Ti^+ indicates absorption by once-ionized Ti. The strong, broad absorption at 4863 Å labelled Hβ is due to neutral H, the most abundant element in the solar atmosphere.

of the light elements C, N, O and Ne. Apart from O, which combines readily into compounds that are solid even at high temperature, all these light elements are fairly volatile, and we shall see that because of this they are not nearly as abundant in the terrestrial planets (relative to such refractory elements as Si or Fe) as they are in the Sun. The third group in importance is made up of Mg, Si and Fe. Because these elements all form compounds (particularly with oxygen) that are solid at high temperatures, these are the elements, with O, that are most abundant in terrestrial planets and the asteroids. Other elements are still less abundant in the Sun, with relative amounts that tend to decrease fairly steadily as the atomic weight increases. The heaviest elements (such as gold, thorium, and uranium), not listed in Table 2.2, are present in ratios of about 10^{-4} atom per 1000 Si atoms, about 10,000 times less abundant than any elements listed in the table. It is not surprising that the heavier elements are not major constituents of any solar system bodies.

Spectroscopy also allows us to discover two very surprising facts about the sunspots. When we obtain a spectrum of the relatively dark (but still quite luminous) surface of a sunspot, (see Figure 3.8) we find (by studying the proportion of atoms that are lifted to high energy levels, or even ionized) that the spot is considerably cooler than the surrounding, brighter atmosphere of the Sun. Instead of a characteristic temperature near 5800 K, we find that the darkest part of a sunspot has a temperature of 4500 K or less. It is because this temperature is substantially lower than that of the general photosphere that a sunspot appears (relatively) dark; it is emitting half or less the light from each square meter that the general solar atmosphere does.

The second surprise is that the sunspots are regions of intense **magnetic fields**. Magnetism is the force that orients compass needles here on Earth, and causes a small iron bar magnet to pick up nails. Almost everyone knows that the Earth has a general magnetic field rather like that of a bar magnet which is roughly aligned with the Earth's rotation axis, with a north and a south pole. Around a bar magnet, or the Earth, the magnetic field exerts a force on compass needles that tends to align the compass needle (itself a tiny magnet) with one end pointing towards the north pole of the magnet and the other towards the south pole. We can visualize the magnetic field of a bar magnet as a series of loops that connect one pole to the other, and that show the direction in which a compass needle points when it is held in various locations near the magnet. We call these loops **lines of force**.

When atoms are placed in a strong magnetic field, the energies of the various electron orbits are all changed a little; each orbit splits into several orbits of very similar energy. As a result, the spectral line (caused by absorption of light of a colour corresponding to the energy required to jump from the lower level to the upper level) splits into several closely space spec-

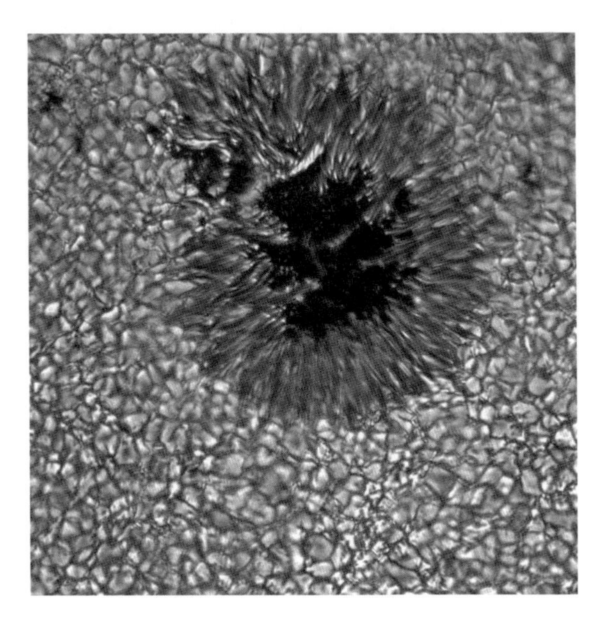

Figure 3.8: An image of a sunspot and its surroundings. The central region of the spot is about 1500 K cooler than the general photosphere, leading to its very dark appearance. A strong magnetic field is present in the spot. Around the spot, the granulation (also seen in Figure 3.5) is clearly visible. Courtesy of T. Rimmele/NSO/AURA/NSF.

tral lines as the splitting of the orbital energies allows the atom to absorb several slightly different colours. This splitting is known as the **Zeeman effect**, and it is clearly observed in the spectrum of light from a sunspot. It is found that a typical sunspot is a region with a magnetic field that can easily reach several thousand times the strength of the magnetic field at the surface of the Earth. Sunspots usually occur in pairs (aligned roughly parallel to the solar equator) with opposite polarity, so that a north and a south pole are usually found near one another.

It is believed that the magnetic field in a sunspot is connected with the relative coolness of the spot, which seems to be due mainly to the fact that the magnetic field inhibits the convective motions of the gas within the spot and hence does not allow as much heat to flow into it from below as reaches the surrounding surface. The blocked heat is apparently stored in the convective layers of the Sun and only gradually leaks out later. Another possible cooling effect is that the magnetic field may help to carry heat *out* of the sunspot into the upper atmosphere of the Sun, thus cooling the spot relative to its more weakly magnetic surroundings.

The solar chromosphere and corona

It is not normally easy to observe the levels in the solar atmosphere above the visible photosphere, as the gas is too thin to absorb or emit very much light, and its emissions are lost in the glare of the radiation from the photosphere, which lights up the Earth's atmosphere to its familiar bright blue colour. One way to observe these higher layers is to observe an eclipse of the Sun by the Moon. As the Moon covers the bright solar disk and the sky goes dark, we can briefly see the higher solar atmosphere just before it too is covered. During this brief moment, we can also record the spectrum of these higher layers. When we study these spectra, we find that the density declines steadily as we go upward in the Sun's atmosphere, and the temperature in the outer layers drops to a low of about 4400 K a few hundred km above the brightest layers of the photosphere. However, when we look still higher, we discover the surprising result that the atmosphere of the Sun does *not* continue to become still cooler, or even to settle to a constant temperature. Instead, the temperature in these very low density regions (measured by observing the spectral lines produced in this region) appears to *rise* again, and we find a layer, which we call the **chromosphere**, in which the temperature seems to increase from about 4400 to 25,000 K. This layer is about 2000 km thick, but of such low density that it is almost completely transparent, and its heat radiation is only about 0.01% of that of the photosphere.

Even stranger, above the chromosphere there is an abrupt jump (in a height interval of perhaps 300 km) in the temperature of the gas from about 25,000 K to a temperature of over 10^6 K. We deduce the temperature of this outer gas layer from the presence of atoms that have lost several electrons, such as Mg ions with nine of its 12 electrons removed, or Fe ions lacking as many as 13 of the 26 electrons. Around the Sun out to a distance of more than one $R_\odot$ above the surface we find a tenuous outer layer at this astonishingly high temperature. This region is called the **corona**. The corona is directly observable during an eclipse of the Sun, as a faint pearly crown of light around the dark disk of the Moon, as in Figure 3.9. It is also observable in an image of the Sun taken from space with a camera sensitive to X-rays, shown in Figure 3.10; in such an image the photosphere (which is far too cool to emit any significant amount of X-rays) appears as a dark central ball surrounded by a bright, irregular glowing cloud of light emitted by the enormously hot gases of the corona. The fact that the corona emits brightly in X-rays confirms the very high temperature deduced from its spectrum. The X-ray images of the Sun reveal another very interesting feature of the corona, namely that (unlike the almost featureless photosphere) it is highly structured, with loops and whorls which are visible above the surface in Figure 3.10. These loops reveal that the structure of the corona is structured and controlled by the looping lines of force of the photospheric magnetic field rising above sunspots and other magnetic regions. This magnetic control of the corona occurs because the density of the coronal gas is so low that more energy per m^3 is present in the magnetic field than in the gas!

Figure 3.9: An image of the Sun made during a 1970 total eclipse. The dark circle in the centre is the dark side of the Moon, which briefly covers the bright solar photosphere and allows us to see against the blackness of space the faint, irregular glow of the solar corona (from the Latin word for crown) surrounding the Sun. (Courtesy of NOAO/AURA/NSF.)

The gas of the corona is so hot, in fact, that it is not gravitationally anchored to the Sun, but instead continuously evaporates off into space as the very low-density **solar wind** which flows out of the solar system in all directions. This evaporation takes place particularly from regions of the corona which on Figure 3.10 appear dark, such as the y-shaped region at the top of the figure; because the coronal gases boil off freely from these regions, they have relatively low density and low brightness in X-rays. These source regions for the solar wind are called **coronal holes**.

As the solar wind passes the Earth, it has a density of only about 10^6 ions m^{-3}, or about one ion per cubic centimeter, and has a temperature near 10^5 K. It flows by Earth at about 500 km s^{-1}, or sometimes even faster. This wind continues outward in all directions through the solar system, and eventually collides with the interstellar gas at a (poorly known) distance of the order of 100 AU from the Sun. This wind, of course, has no appreciable effect on any of the large bodies of the solar system, such as planets or asteroids. However, we will find later that even such an incredibly low density flow can have quite observable effects as it interacts with the coma of a comet.

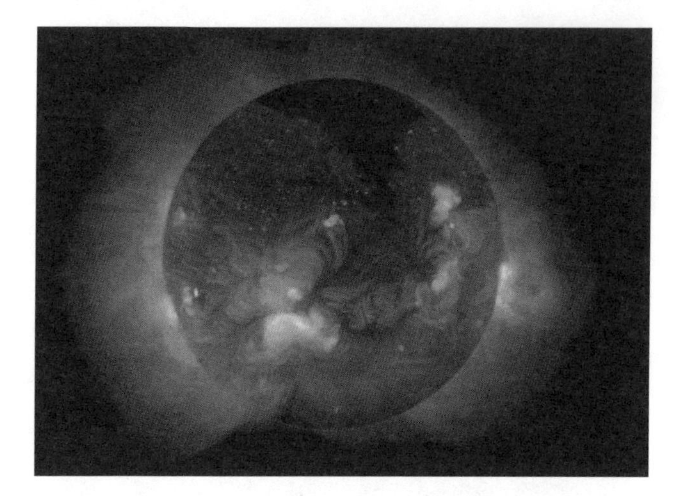

Figure 3.10: The Sun as viewed by the Japanese satellite Yohkoh, which makes images using the X-rays emitted from the solar corona. The dark ball underneath the bright haze is the photosphere of the Sun, which is too cool to emit significantly at X-ray wavelengths. The bright haze around photosphere is visible in the light of X-rays emitted by the hot tenuous gas of the corona. The brightest spots are regions of the corona that are above sunspots on the Sun's surface. The complex features seen against the dark solar disk show the degree to which looping magnetic lines of force from the photosphere control the structure of the corona. The dark region at the top of the figure is a coronal hole, from which the solar wind is escaping. (Courtesy of NASA's Marshall Space Flight Center.)

The fact that emission from the chromosphere indicates that it is (at least some of the time) at a higher temperature than the photosphere, and that the gas of the corona is at a still very much higher temperature, presents us with something of a puzzle. We all know from our experience that heat does not flow spontaneously from cool regions (here the Sun's photosphere) to hotter ones (the chromosphere and corona). It is not possible for these outer layers to owe their high temperatures to heating by radiation from the photosphere. Instead, we must look for some mechanism more nearly akin to heating your hands by rubbing them together, so that the mechanical energy you put into the motions through your muscles is converted into heat by the friction between the palms.

In the Sun, one source of mechanical energy that can be turned into heat is the boiling motions of the convecting layers below the photosphere, visible in Figure 3.5. This convection generates sound waves that spread out in all directions, including outward, and as they move into layers of lower and lower density they become more and more violent until they finally break like waves on a beach, depositing their energy as heat in the chromosphere. Another, more indirect, method involves the magnetic field that we have already noticed in the sunspots, and that is found in small patches all over the Sun. This magnetism is generated in the highly electrically conducting interior of the Sun by a combination of the rotation of the Sun and its convection, and where the magnetic field emerges above the Sun's surface it can deposit energy by abrupt changes in its structure. This mechanism probably contributes part of the heating of the chromosphere. It also probably contributes the major heating of the corona, whose most luminous regions as seen in X-rays (Figure 3.10) are closely related to regions of intense magnetism in the photosphere below.

The total energy budget of the corona is a little difficult to determine, since we still do not understand in detail how the corona is heated. However, we can estimate the total energy put into the corona by looking at the ways the corona *loses* energy: by boiling off the solar wind, by radiating photons (mostly X-rays), and by losing heat that is conducted back to the photosphere by the ionized gas of the corona. We find that the total energy loss per second of the corona is about 10^{-4} of the total solar luminosity. We deduce that this much energy must be injected into the corona every second from below, probably by the magnetic heating effects mentioned above. This clearly does not represent much of a drain on the total energy output of the Sun, and thus the presence of the corona has almost no effect on the Sun's interior structure.

The solar cycle and solar activity

We have already noticed that sunspots are not permanent features on the surface of the Sun. There are often several sunspots visible on the Sun's surface, but these individual sunspots last for only a few weeks. As old sunspots vanish, new ones appear, often near the locations of the old ones. However, when we observe the Sun's disk regularly, month after month, we notice slow systematic changes in the way in which sunspots appear. Over a period of about 11 years, the Sun goes through a *cycle* of sunspot activity. At the start of a cycle, there are few or no sunspots visible on the solar surface. Then sunspots begin appearing, mostly at about 30° latitude above and below the solar equator. As time goes on, sunspots appear in greater numbers, and ever closer to the equator. Finally as sunspots are being formed only a few degrees from the equator, the cycle comes to an end and sunspots largely cease to be formed. After two or three years during which very few sunspots are visible, new spots start to be formed again near 30° from the equator and a new cycle of sunspot production begins. This cycle is known as the **solar cycle** or the **solar activity cycle**. Sunspots and their variations turn out to be key components in the many other less obvious variable features of the Sun's outer layers.

As we saw earlier, spots tend to occur in pairs of opposite magnetic polarity (one spot is a magnetic north pole, and nearby one usually finds a spot that is a magnetic south pole), roughly aligned parallel to the solar equator. During one solar cycle, the leading spots (relative to the Sun's rotation) in almost all the spot pairs in the northern hemisphere have a particular polarity (for example, north polarity), while the leading spots in the southern hemisphere have the opposite polarity (for example, south polarity). The overall situation is the same in the next solar cycle, except that all the spot pairs have reversed polarity relative to the preceding cycle (in the next cycle spots of south polarity would be the leading spots in the northern hemisphere). Thus the entire solar cycle is not 11 but 22 years long.

Remarkably, this cycle that we find repeated more or less steadily decade after decade sometimes *stops*. Shortly after the invention of the telescope early in the seventeenth century led to the clear recognition of sunspots by the German Jesuit scholar Christopher Scheiner and by Galileo Galilei, sunspots *ceased to appear on the surface of the Sun*. From 1645 on hardly any spots were seen for nearly 70 years. Then suddenly in 1715 spots began to appear again, and the cycle that we are familiar with began as though nothing had happened.

The magnetic fields of the Sun turn out to be connected with a variety of other kinds of activity on and above the surface of the Sun. However, most of this activity is invisible in white light images of the Sun. To discover these less obvious and quite variable solar phenomena, it turned out to be necessary to observe the Sun in other, subtler, ways.

We have already seen how eclipses and X-ray images allow us to see the faint and tenuous corona, which is completely invisible in normal white-light images such as Figure 3.4. We now consider what might be seen in images taken in a single colour of visible or ultraviolet light. Suppose we choose to observe the Sun using a filter that allows through (transmits) only light that is very strongly absorbed by one of the most abundant kinds of atoms in the Sun's atmosphere. We might choose the red spectral line of H at 6563 Å, known as H-alpha or Hα, or the tremendously strong line of ionized Ca at 3933 Å, called the K-line. Photons emitted with either of these colours at the level of the Sun's normal photosphere have no chance at all to escape into space, because they are too easily absorbed. Instead, they can only escape into space from a level several hundred km higher in the atmosphere, where the density of the gas has dropped to such a low value that the photons have a chance to slip out between the atoms waiting to absorb them. Thus if we observed the Sun through a filter that allows through only one of these tremendously absorbed colours, we see light emitted from a layer several hundred km above the normal photosphere. How does this change what we see?

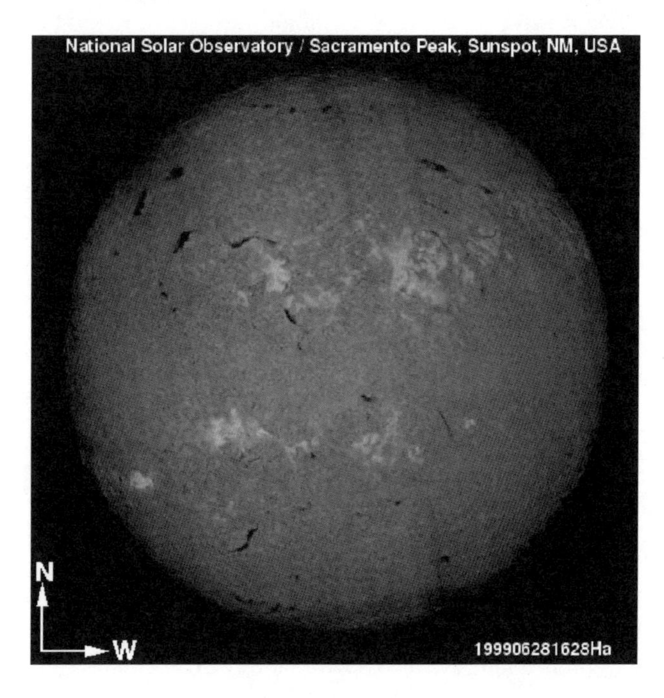

Figure 3.11: An image of the Sun as seen through a filter which transmits only light absorbed by the H-alpha line of hydrogen. We see a layer several hundred km above the usual photosphere, where the atmosphere is very inhomogeneous. Bright plages define active regions above and around sunspots; dark filaments occur near such active regions. (Courtesy of NSO/AURA/NSF.)

Seen in white light, the sum of all the colours which emerge from the photosphere, the Sun is almost uniform in appearance. It is completely bland on the largest scale; as we look more closely we sometimes see sunspots, the only obvious features on the Sun. At still finer scales, near the limit of the detail we can see on the solar surface because of the turbulence of the Earth's own atmosphere, we see the granulation caused by convection. This is essentially uniform everywhere on the Sun, except that it is suppressed in sunspots. When we look at the higher layers of the solar atmosphere through an H-alpha or K-line filter, all this changes. We see a completely different kind of "surface" on the Sun, one with far more variations from one place to another. The surface at this altitude is mottled and extremely irregular. Over sunspots, we find regions of greatly enhanced brightness. Around these very bright areas are larger, quite irregular regions not as bright as over the sunspots but still rather bright. We call these regions **plages**. Between sunspots we sometimes find irregular dark structures (sometimes hundreds of thousands of km long) called **filaments**. When filaments are seen at the edge of the Sun during eclipse, they turn out to be huge glowing loops or hedge-like structures extending far above the atmosphere into the corona, which we call **prominences**. Outside of the plages many other bright points occur in a very irregular network. These features may be seen in Figure 3.11. We are now looking at the level of the solar chromosphere.

At this altitude, the heating is no longer controlled mainly by the transport of heat from the interior to the surface by the convective motions, which effectively heat every part of the Sun's surface in the same way. Instead, here the heating is largely controlled by the magnetic field that emerges from the photosphere up into the outer layers of the Sun, much like the situation in the corona, which we have already seen is completely structured by the Sun's magnetic field. The extent to which the chromosphere is heated and controlled by the Sun's magnetic field is immediately clear from the fact that the brightest regions in the chromosphere occur directly above sunspots. More detailed observations show that almost all the brightest regions in the chromosphere are associated with small patches or ropes of magnetism on the solar surface that occur over much of the solar surface, particularly near big sunspots, but elsewhere as well. This very patchy distribution of the magnetic field, which has almost no significant effect on the appearance of the photosphere except for the sunspots, is dramatically reflected in the brightness and structure of the chromosphere.

Filaments are also closely related to the structure of the magnetic field rising up from the photosphere into the chromosphere. They generally occur along the line dividing a magnetic region of north polarity from one of south polarity. A filament has a lifetime similar to that of a sunspot, and often ends its existence weeks after it is formed by lifting off into the upper corona from its place over a sunspot pair, and disappearing. Filaments, like the sunspots with which they are connected, are much more numerous when sunspots are common than when they are rare. From the appearance of a filament (as a prominence) in Hα or K-line images when it reaches the limb (edge) of the Sun, we deduce that the filament is a mass of gas having chromospheric conditions of temperature and density, but which is embedded in the corona. Compared to coronal gas, the gas of a filament is much denser and cooler.

This poses for us (at least) three problems: what causes cool gas to accumulate in the corona into a filament, what supports its mass (which is comparable to the mass of a terrestrial mountain!) high above the rest of the chromosphere, and how can it stay much cooler than the surrounding corona?

We still do not understand very clearly how filaments form; perhaps most of them simply condense (like the puddle of condensed atmospheric water vapour that soon surrounds a cold bottle of pop sitting on a table during a hot, humid day) out of the much thinner coronal gas. The filament appears to be supported against gravity by magnetic forces ultimately produced by the sunspots over which it forms: the magnetic field lines from one spot to the other form an arch or arcade which is capable of supporting the ionized (and electrically conducting) gas of the filament. The fact that the filament can stay much cooler than the corona in which it is embedded is well understood, however: the same magnetic field that supports the filament enormously inhibits thermal conduction of heat from the corona into the filament, and in any case the filament is so much denser than the corona that it easily radiates away the small amount of heat that is conducted in from the corona.

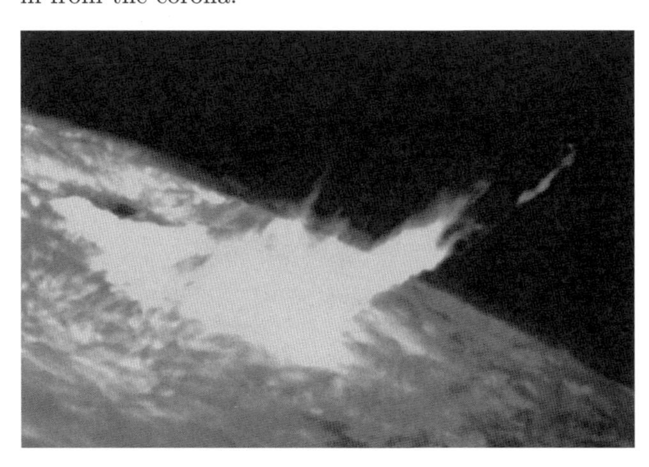

Figure 3.12: A brief, brilliant solar flare seen through an H-alpha filter. The explosion ejects a spray of hot, dense gas in a surge that rises far above the photosphere. (Courtesy of NSO/AURA/NSF.)

Another phenomenon generally visible only with the aid of a chromospheric filter is the occurrence of a sudden explosion above the solar surface, which we call a **solar flare**. These events always occur in or around the strong magnetic fields of sunspots, and they are generally visible as a quick, intense brightening (in an Hα or K-line image) of a small region of the chromosphere near a sunspot over a period of some seconds. When we observe such a flare obliquely, as in Figure 3.12, we can see that the flare ejects material up into the corona in the form of a fountain or surge of material, a bit like briefly turning on a lawn sprinkler. The energy powering a flare comes from a sudden re-arrangement of the magnetic field above the photosphere. This can release a huge amount of energy, enough to briefly raise the temperature of the chromospheric gas around the flare to a level of many millions of degrees K. The flare explosion ejects a large burst of charged particles (electrons and protons) and high-energy radiation (x- and even gamma-rays) into space, and if a filament is present over the flare region (not an uncommon situation) the filament is blown away by the flare. Below the flare, if it is energetic enough, it will heat a region of the photosphere enough for the explosion to be briefly visible in white light. Some high speed particles from the flare reach the Earth only minutes after the flare, while a slower-travelling disturbance (a "shock wave") in the solar wind will often reach Earth a day or two later, causing brilliant auroral displays, radio communication interruptions, and sometimes even massive power blackouts. Solar flares are the form of solar activity that have the most important immediate effects on Earth, and are being intensely studied by such agencies as NASA in the U. S.

Other kinds of solar activity occur as well, but since these phenomena cannot really be understood at the level of this book, we end the discussion of solar activity here. The basic point is that all kinds of solar activity are ordered by, and provided with energy from, the very non-uniform solar magnetic field that we see most clearly in sunspots, but which is also present, rather spottily, all over the solar disk.

In spite of much work, the origin of this magnetic field remains rather poorly understood. We think that it is produced in the convection zone of the Sun through the complex motions of this boiling, rotating, electrically conducting gas, through some kind of "magnetic dynamo". The magnetic field that emerges on the surface of the Sun is a manifestation of strong magnetic fields deeper in the Sun. The dynamo that produces these fields appears to depend on the fact that the Sun does not rotate like a solid body; instead, the equator rotates more rapidly than the polar regions, and this has the effect of drawing out the magnetic loops inside the convecting layers into long tubes wrapped around the Sun, parallel to the equator. This is probably the reason that pairs of sunspots, where a loop of magnetic lines of force projects above the surface, tend to be aligned parallel to the equator. But we do not yet understand the generation of this field very clearly. We do not understand very well why it comes and goes cyclically with the 11- (22-) year solar cycle, nor why this cycle sometimes stops completely. Solar activity, particularly because of the significant effects it can have on Earth, is certain to remain an important area of study by astronomers and physicists for years to come.

3.6 Mathematical aspects

Support against gravity by internal pressure

Almost all stars, like the Sun, are observed to have essentially constant size. (Some oscillate slightly in size, but even these stars have a constant mean size.) The fact that the size of a star is not changing in size means that the inward attraction of gravity for the gas at any layer is just balanced by an equal an opposite outward force; if this were not true, the layer would be accelerated inward (or outward) and the size of the star *would* change. In fact, the inward attraction of gravity is balanced at each level by the outward pressure of the hot, compressed stellar gas.

There are two ways to look at this balance. One is to say that at each level in the star (at some definite distance r from the centre) the weight of all the layers above r (out to the total radius R) is exactly supported by the pressure $p(r)$ at this level. That is, the total outward force at r due to gas pressure on the overlying layers,

$$f_{\text{press}} = 4\pi r^2 p(r) \tag{3.1}$$

is just equal to the total weight of the overlying layers,

$$W = \int_r^R 4\pi r^2 \rho(r) g(r) dr, \tag{3.2}$$

where $\rho(r)$ is the local density of the gas and $g(r)$ is the local gravitational acceleration. However, this way of stating the condition which must be satisfied for the star to be static turns out not to be the most convenient for solving problems. An alternative, more useful way of looking at the situation is to focus on a single small volume of gas, a slab of surface area A and thickness dr between r and $r+dr$. To have this slab motionless, the *difference* between the force downward on the top of the slab, which is equal to $p(r+dr)A$, and the force upward on the bottom of the slab, $p(r)A$, must just support the weight dW of the slab, equal to its volume Adr times its density $\rho(r)$ times $g(r)$. That is, equilibrium requires that

$$[p(r+dr) - p(r)]A = dpA = -dW = -\rho(r)g(r)Adr, \tag{3.3}$$

or

$$\frac{dp}{dr} = -\rho(r)g(r) \tag{3.4}$$

where the minus sign arises because $p(r)$ must be *larger* than $p(r+dr)$ to support dW. This equation is called the **equation of hydrostatic equilibrium** and plays a very important role in many areas of physics and astrophysics.

Equation (3.4) is an example of a major type of equation that occurs in many physical situations. It is a **differential equation**, an equation that contains one or more derivatives. Such equations often describe situations in which you know something about a physical system at some point, and you want to extend your knowledge into neighboring regions. In this case, the differential equation allows you to start at the point where you know the conditions (a place where you know the value of the pressure p, for example), and move away from that known point in little steps in the independent variable (here r), calculating for each step the small change in p that accompanies each step in r. After a number of such calculations, you can obtain the functional dependence of one variable on the other, $p(r)$ for example, over some region of interest.

Differential equations make up a major field of study in applied mathematics. They can be quite difficult to solve, particularly if you want an analytical result, and the nature of the solutions can depend strongly on the kind of information you have about values of some of the variables (the "boundary conditions" or "initial conditions"). In this book, we will only use differential equations in situations in which they can be solved by the most straight-forward of all methods, direct integration. The application of Equation (3.4) in the next section is an example of direct integration.

Exercise: Use Equation (3.4) to show that the pressure at any depth in an atmosphere is simply equal to the weight per unit area of all the material above that depth. (This is a very useful way of looking at hydrostatic equilibrium.)

Hydrostatic equilibrium in the solar atmosphere

Let us get a better idea of the usefulness of Equation (3.4) by looking at how it may be used to understand something of the structure of the outer layers of the Sun. First look at the **photosphere**, the surface layer from which the sunlight that we observe originates. The temperature in the photosphere is not constant, of course, but increases steadily as we go into the Sun. However, it does not change by more than about a factor of two in the layer that we can see, and for a simple first approximation to the structure of this layer, we can take the temperature of the solar photosphere to be constant and equal to a characteristic value, the **ef-**

fective temperature, of about $T_e = 5800$ K. Now we take Equation (3.4) and use the ideal gas law as expressed in Equation (2.5) to eliminate the density ρ, and obtain

$$\frac{dp}{dr} = -\rho g = -\frac{\mu m_u p g}{k T_e} \equiv \frac{p}{H}, \tag{3.5}$$

where the quantity

$$H = \frac{k T_e}{\mu m_u g} \tag{3.6}$$

has the dimensions of length and is called the **scale height** of the atmosphere. With our rough approximation that the photosphere is at a constant temperature, H is also approximately constant, and Equation (3.5) can be integrated from one level r_0 (which we might take to be the "base" of the photosphere) to another higher level r_1:

$$\int_{p_0}^{p_1} \frac{dp}{p} = \ln(p_1/p_0) = -\int_{r_0}^{r_1} \frac{dr}{H} = -\frac{r_1 - r_0}{H}, \tag{3.7}$$

or

$$p(r_1)/p(r_0) = \exp[-(r_1 - r_0)/H]. \tag{3.8}$$

We see that the pressure in the atmosphere decreases (approximately) exponentially with increasing height $r_1 - r_0$ above r_0, and that the scale height H is the distance over which the pressure decreases by a factor of $1/e$. Equation (3.8) is known as the **barometric law**.

An important point about the integration we carried out in the paragraph above needs to be emphasized. Effectively, we started from a point r_0 at which the pressure has some known value p_0, and used the (differential) Equation (3.5) to determine the value p_1 at some other point r_1. That is, our result (3.8) expresses p_1 in terms of p_0. This was taken explicitly into account from the start because we did the integration as a definite integral. However, the same outcome would have been found if we had done the calculation as an indefinite integration. In that case, we would write Equation (3.5) as

$$\frac{dp}{p} = -\frac{dr}{H} \tag{3.9}$$

which when integrated becomes

$$\ln(p) = -r/H + C, \tag{3.10}$$

where C is the constant of integration. *Do not forget the constant of integration!* If you do, you will probably end up with a meaningless, incorrect result. Here, we use C to set up our result so that it refers to some point r_0 where we know p_0. If we substitute these two values into Equation (3.10), we find

$$\ln(p_0) = -r_0/H + C. \tag{3.11}$$

Solving this equation for C, substituting the value into Equation (3.10) and rearranging the terms, we have

$$\ln(p/p_0) = -(r - r_0)/H, \tag{3.12}$$

which is evidently the same as Equation (3.8). Thus, we get the same result as before by doing an indefinite integration and evaluating the inevitable constant using conditions at r_0.

The scale height H gives a measure of the effective "thickness" of the atmosphere, or at least of the most significant part of it. This is easily seen if we look at the total mass per unit area σ_0 above the level r_0, where the pressure is p_0 and the density is ρ_0. We use the fact that at constant temperature $p(r)/p_0 = \rho(r)/\rho_0$ and then the barometric law to find that

$$\begin{aligned} \sigma_0 &= \int_{r_0}^{\infty} \rho(r) dr = \rho_0 \int_{r_0}^{\infty} \frac{p(r)}{p_0} dr \\ &= \rho_0 \int_{r_0}^{\infty} \exp[-(r - r_0)/H] dr \\ &= \rho_0 H \int_0^{\infty} \exp(-u) du = \rho_0 H. \end{aligned} \tag{3.13}$$

Thus the total mass per unit area above the level r_0 where $\rho = \rho_0$ is the same as the surface mass density in a substance of uniform density ρ_0 and thickness H. It is easily shown by a similar integration that the shell of thickness H above r_0 contains 63% (about 2/3) of the total mass above r_0.

Exercise: Prove this result.

Thus it is reasonable to use H as a measure of the thickness of the photosphere, even though actually the atmosphere has no definite upper limit.

To evaluate H, we need to know the mean molecular weight μ of the gas. Because the solar photosphere is composed mainly of neutral H (90% of the atoms; see Table 2.2) and neutral He (10% of the atoms), the average mass of an atmospheric atom is about $0.9 m_H + 0.1 m_{He} = m_u(0.9 \times 1.0 + 0.1 \times 4.0) = 1.3 m_u$, and the average molecular weight μ of the gas is 1.3. Then using the mass ($M_\odot = 1.985 \times 10^{30}$ kg) and radius ($R_\odot = 6.95 \times 10^8$ m) of the Sun to evaluate the surface gravity, we find that $H = 1.34 \times 10^5$ m, so we may take 130 km as an estimate of the thickness of the radiating layers of the Sun. Because this number is tiny compared to the total radius of the Sun, about 700,000 km, the Sun appears to have a sharp edge even though the photosphere does not actually end abruptly anywhere, but just keeps on getting thinner and thinner as one goes up.

Exercise: The gas density at the bottom of the photosphere of the Sun is about 3×10^{-4} kg m^{-3}. Estimate the mass of the solar atmosphere both in kg and as a fraction of the Sun's total mass. (Hint: you may need some data from Table B.2.)

Another application of these ideas is to understand why the thickness of the solar corona is a significant fraction of the solar radius in thickness, a fact clearly evident in photographs taken during a total solar eclipse, such as Figure 3.9. We again assume that the corona is in hydrostatic equilibrium (not quite true: the solar wind is due to a small departure from equilibrium) at constant temperature (also only a rough approximation). We estimate the effective thickness of the corona by evaluating the scale height for the conditions there using Equation (3.6). We take the characteristic temperature of the corona to be $T \approx 1 \times 10^6$ K as determined from X-ray observations. The gas has about the same chemical composition as the photosphere, roughly 90% H and 10% He atoms by number, but because of the very high temperature these atoms are completely ionized. Their essentially weightless electrons contribute pressure but hardly any mass to the mean molecular weight. Since each H atom contributes one electron and each He atom contributes two, a typical small volume containing 9 H atoms and 1 He atom also contains $(9 + 2) = 11$ free electrons, so the total number of particles in the volume is 21. Then the mean mass of the particles in this volume is $(9/21)m_{\rm H} + (1/21)m_{He} + (11/21)m_{\rm e} = m_{\rm u}[(9/21)\times 1.0+(1/21)\times 4.0+(11/21)\times 0.0] = 0.62 m_{\rm u}$, and we have $\mu = 0.62$. If we now take the gravitational acceleration to be roughly constant and equal to its value at a distance of $1.1 R_\odot$ from the Sun, the scale height of the corona $H \approx 5.9 \times 10^7$ m, or about 60,000 km, about 1/10 the solar radius, and almost 500 times larger than the scale height of the photosphere. This is approximately what is observed in eclipse photos. In fact, the great radial extent of the corona was one of the first really strong hints that the temperature of the corona is *much* higher than that of the visible photosphere.

Exercise: Equation 3.8 can be applied to the Earth's atmosphere. For the mix of O_2 and N_2 found there, the mean molecular weight $\mu = 29.0$. Show that the scale height of the Earth's atmosphere is about 8 km. Why is it so much smaller than that of the Sun?

Conditions at the centre of the Sun

It is often valuable to start exploring a new topic by investigating the general order of magnitude of quantities to be studied before doing a lot of work to solve difficult problems precisely. Determining the general size of physical parameters of a problem can help one to be confident of using the right physics in more detailed study, and can make it easier to find appropriate approximations and simplifications. We will often use equations discussed in this book to find orders of magnitude, as we do in this section.

Results from such work are often correct to no more than a factor of ten or so either way, but they can still be valuable. For example, from observation we can determine that the surface layers of the Sun have a typical temperature of about 6000 K. But what about the interior? We observe no heat radiation from the centre of the Sun. Is the temperature there colder than at the surface? About the same temperature? About 10^6, or 10^9, or 10^{12} K? There is clearly an interest in establishing roughly how hot the interior of the Sun is even if we cannot solve this problem exactly. We can find the order of magnitude of the interior temperature by using the equation of hydrostatic equilibrium (Equation (3.4)) and the gas law.

We start by using Equation (3.4) to obtain an order of magnitude estimate of the pressure $p_{\rm c}$ at the centre of the Sun. For this purpose we treat Equation (3.4) not as a differential equation which must be satisfied throughout the star, but as an approximate difference equation. That is, we effectively use the approximate known size of some of the quantities in this equation to determine roughly how large other quantities must be to be consistent with the known ones. Replace the term dp/dr with the rough estimate of its size $(p_{\rm s} - p_{\rm c})/R_\odot$ where $p_{\rm s}$ and $p_{\rm c}$ are the surface and central pressures and $R_\odot$ is the solar radius. The quantity $p_{\rm c}$ is the unknown which we want. The surface pressure $p_{\rm s}$ is certainly much, much smaller than $p_{\rm c}$, and we will take it to be 0. The radius $R_\odot$ is an observed quantity. For the right-hand side, estimate ρ to be $\overline{\rho} \approx M_\odot/(4\pi R^3/3)$, the mean density of the Sun (certainly the real density of the Sun in its deep interior must be of this general size). Estimate g to be a typical gravity $g \approx G(M_\odot/2)/(R_\odot/2)^2$ evaluated with half the solar mass, at one-half the solar radius. Again, this is a reasonable guess of the size of this quantity. Note that the result does not depend very strongly on factors of two that we include (or not) according to taste. Now solving for the central pressure $p_{\rm c}$ (taking $p_{\rm s} = 0$), we find

$$p_{\rm c} \approx (3/2\pi) G M_\odot^2 / R_\odot^4 \approx 6 \times 10^{14} \text{ Pa}. \qquad (3.14)$$

Exercise: Carry out the algebra leading to Equation 3.14.

This result is not expected to be very accurate, but it nevertheless indicates that the central pressure in the Sun is (as one might guess) thousands of times larger than at the centre of the Earth (about 3.6×10^{11} Pa, see Chapter 8). In fact, this estimate is about a factor of ten less than the result of precise calculations, so it is not very accurate, but it does *not* mislead us.

Next we use our estimate of central pressure to find a typical interior temperature $\overline{T}$ for the matter inside the Sun. For this we make a preliminary guess that the matter will be hotter than at the surface, and probably gaseous, so we use the gas law from Equation (2.5). Let us make an estimate of $\overline{T}$ for a point about half way into the star, where we estimate that the pressure is roughly $\overline{p} \approx 0.5 p_c$. For the density we use the mean density of the Sun, $\overline{\rho} = M_\odot/(4\pi R^3/3) = 1410$ kg m^{-3}. We anticipate that the matter will be hot enough to be ionized, and take the molecular weight, as in the corona, to be $\mu \approx 0.62$. Our result is that the typical interior temperature is

$$\overline{T} \approx \overline{p}\mu m_u/(k\overline{\rho}) \approx 1.6 \times 10^7 \text{ K}. \quad (3.15)$$

The typical interior temperature is of the order of 10 million K, confirming that the material will be essentially gaseous and highly ionized. Our estimate this time is a few times larger than the more precise result, but again a reasonable order of magnitude evaluation.

Notice that we do not have enough physics here to derive even the order of magnitude of the solar interior conditions without some help from observations; we had to use both the observed radius and mass of the Sun to determine p_c and $\overline{T}$. It is not surprising that we needed to specify the mass: stars can have various masses, and we needed to specify how massive a star we wanted to consider. However, the *size* of a star of given mass is determined on the main sequence not only by the condition of hydrostatic equilibrium but also by another equation that expresses the idea that (in equilibrium) heat should not build up anywhere within the star. We have avoided doing the more difficult calculation by using the observed solar radius in our estimates.

Energy sources in the Sun

Our next project is to carry out another order of magnitude reconnaissance, this time of possible energy sources for the Sun. We observe the luminosity of the Sun to be $L_\odot = 3.85 \times 10^{26}$ W. This represents an enormous energy leakage from the Sun. What is the source of this radiated energy, which the Sun is able to lose year after year without any obvious change in structure?

One obvious possible source is gravitational energy. As we have discussed in the preceding chapters, energy released by an object descending into a gravitational well (getting closer to another massive object) converts gravitational energy into kinetic energy or heat. Let us estimate how effective this energy source might be at powering the Sun. From Equation (1.12), the gravitational energy released as a mass m approaches another mass M from a great distance to a separation r is

$$E_g = GMm/r. \quad (3.16)$$

We can use this result to estimate the amount of gravitational energy released as the Sun formed. Let us imagine dividing the Sun into two equal parts, each of mass $M_\odot/2$. Then an estimate of the energy released by the accretion of the second half of the Sun onto the first half is

$$\begin{aligned} E_{g\odot} &\approx G(M_\odot/2)(M_\odot/2)/(R_\odot/2) \\ &\approx GM_\odot^2/(2R_\odot) \approx 1.9 \times 10^{41} \text{ J}. \quad (3.17) \end{aligned}$$

This is clearly only a rough approximation, but it should give us the magnitude of the total energy available from gravitational contraction of the Sun to its present size. Further energy is available if the Sun contracts further.

Next, we estimate the length of time that this energy could power the Sun's radiation at roughly the present rate. That is, we want an estimate of the maximum time that this energy source would be able to supply the energy losses of the Sun. To get such an estimate, we take the total available energy estimated from Equation (3.17) above, and divide it by the observed luminosity $L_\odot \approx 4 \times 10^{26}$ W of the Sun, which gives the energy loss per second, to find the number of seconds of radiation we have available. The result is

$$t_{KH} \approx E_{g\odot}/L_\odot \approx 5 \times 10^{14} \text{ s} \approx 1.5 \times 10^7 \text{ yr}. \quad (3.18)$$

This time, the length of time that gravitational energy release could power the Sun at its present rate, is known as the **Kelvin-Helmholtz timescale** after the physicists who first made this estimate.

The striking feature of t_{KH} is that it is too short. From the geological record and from radioactively dated ages of terrestrial rocks, we know that the Earth has been here, and had an environment recognizably like the present one, for at least 4 Gyr. This number is more than 200 times longer than t_{KH}, and even with the uncertainty in our estimate of t_{KH}, it is not reasonable to suppose that the Sun could have been powered gravitationally with little change during the long time that the Earth has been bathed in sunlight. It was this fact that stimulated the search for some other possible source of solar energy, and led to the discovery of the nuclear reactions that power the Sun.

Earlier in the chapter we have discussed the actual nuclear reactions that replenish the heat lost from the Sun each second. However, it is not necessary to look at these details to estimate the length of time $t_{N\odot}$ for which such reactions could power the Sun's radiation. Instead, we again make an order of magnitude argument.

In a nuclear reaction, it is found from many experiments in nuclear physics that roughly 1% of the rest mass energy $E = mc^2$ of a nucleus can be released, provided one starts with nuclei that are not already the most stable possible forms (i.e. nuclei of iron). The surface of the Sun is predominantly composed of H, and we suppose that the interior must be too. H is indeed capable of undergoing nuclear reactions, although it was not easy to discover exactly how the reactions proceed, because the very first reaction, the one that makes deuterium from normal H, was known to lead to a completely unstable nucleus. However, we ignore the details, and estimate that the total nuclear energy available from all the H in the Sun is of the order of

$$E_{N\odot} \approx 0.01 M_\odot c^2 \approx 1.8 \times 10^{45} \text{ J}. \quad (3.19)$$

This energy reservoir potentially provides some 10^4 times more energy than that provided by $E_{g\odot}$, and correspondingly the "nuclear" time $t_{N\odot}$ over which nuclear reactions could potentially power the Sun with little change in structure is also about 10^4 times larger than t_{KH}:

$$t_{N\odot} \approx E_{N\odot}/L_\odot \approx 5 \times 10^{18} \text{ s} \approx 1.5 \times 10^{11} \text{yr}. \quad (3.20)$$

Even if we allow for considerable inefficiency in the release of nuclear energy (for example, only a small fraction of the Sun's H is in the centre where conditions allow nuclear reactions to occur), $t_{N\odot}$ is large enough to explain the length of time for which the Sun has warmed the Earth. We conclude that although a significant amount of energy was released as the Sun formed, the great bulk of the solar radiation has been of energy released by nuclear reactions.

Similar estimates of t_{KH} and t_N may be made for other types of stars by using their observed masses, radii, and luminosities.

Thermal radiation

Finally we turn to looking briefly at the radiation from stars and other hot objects, and recall a few useful expressions from first-year physics.

All warm objects radiate heat to their surroundings, in the form of electromagnetic energy. As the temperature of the object rises, the typical wavelength at which the strongest radiation occurs moves from the infrared (for objects at room temperature) into the visible (for objects as hot as stars) and even to X-ray wavelengths (for objects having temperatures approaching a million degrees, such as the solar corona). It is also found that the amount of energy radiated per unit area of the object rises rapidly with temperature.

The radiation from real objects varies somewhat from one object to another at the same temperature. It is found from laboratory studies that materials such as metals, which are relatively reflective, are rather poor radiators compared to darker, more absorbent materials. At a particular temperature, the radiation from a block of silver and from a block of graphite will have the same qualitative character and occur at approximately the same wavelengths, but there may be a difference in energy loss per unit area of a factor of three or four. It is found that the simplest, most easily described, behaviour is shown by objects which are essentially black – completely absorbent – at all wavelengths of interest. An object of such a material is called a **black body**, and its radiation is called **black body radiation**. As you may recall from your physics text, the best way to make a black body in a laboratory is to look at radiation from a hollow cavity in a heated object. Such a cavity is essentially black – it absorbs almost all the radiation that enters it – and so it behaves as a black body in emission.

The radiation of black bodies was intensely studied in the laboratory at the end of the 19th century, and simple laws were found to describe this radiation. The first is that the total energy loss per second per unit of area $\mathcal{F}$ (say in watts per square meter) is given by

$$\mathcal{F} = \sigma T^4, \quad (3.21)$$

where T is the temperature of the objects in Kelvins, and $\sigma = 5.67 \times 10^{-8}$ W K^{-4} m^{-2} is known as the Stefan-Boltzmann constant. This quantity is called the **energy flux** or simply **flux** from the radiating object. Thus the radiation per square meter from the atmosphere of the Sun, with a temperature of nearly 6000 K, is more than 10^5 times larger than the radiation per square meter from the wall of your room, which is at about 300 K. Similarly, the apparent blackness of sunspots on the surface of the Sun is simply a consequence of their cooler temperature compared to the rest of the photosphere. With an umbral temperature of about 4500 K compared to a general photospheric temperature of 5800 K, the emission from a sunspot is about 1/3 as intense as from a region of similar size in the photosphere, and sunspots appear quite dark compared to other parts of the photosphere.

Exercise: Use the tabulated values of solar luminosity and effective temperature from Table B.2 to calculate the radius of the Sun and confirm the value in that table.

The radiation from a non-black real object, with an average **albedo** (reflectivity) A over the wavelength region in which most of the thermal radiation is emitted, is less efficient, and the power output per square meter is

$$\mathcal{F} = (1 - A)\sigma T^4. \tag{3.22}$$

The albedo varies of course both with temperature and from one material to another. Metals have fairly high reflectivity, typically 0.75 (75%), and consequently the radiated power from a heated metal is of the order of one-quarter of that from a black body. In contrast, dark rock, such as the surface of many asteroids and of chondritic meteorites, may have an albedo of only a few percent, and in this case the radiation can be fairly similar to that from a black body at the same temperature.

To describe the actual distribution of the radiation from a black body over wavelength or frequency, we use a quantity called the **specific intensity**. This is simply a quantity which describes how much radiation energy passes each second through a unit area of surface, in a definite interval of wavelength (or frequency), into a specific solid angle in a definite direction. (Note that we measure solid angle using a unit called a **steradian**, which is the area on a unit sphere subtended by the solid angle; the solid angle subtended by all possible directions thus measures 4π steradians.) The units of specific intensity per unit wavelength, I_λ, are watts per square meter per steradian per unit of wavelength (e.g. per meter or per Ångstrom unit). The specific intensity emitted by a black body per square meter of surface area (projected perpendicular to the direction of the radiation), usually denoted by B_λ, is given by a simple expression discovered and explained by Max Planck (1858 – 1947) in 1900,

$$B_\lambda = \frac{2hc^2}{\lambda^5} \frac{1}{e^{hc/\lambda kT} - 1}, \tag{3.23}$$

where $h = 6.626 \times 10^{-34}$ Joule-sec is the fundamental constant of quantum mechanics, c is the speed of light, λ is the wavelength of the radiation (in meters if you are using SI units), and T is the temperature of the body. The explanation of this equation led to the discovery of the quantized nature of atoms and eventually to the whole of quantum mechanics, the physical theory that describes atomic and smaller particles.

The essential information in this equation of interest to us is that it shows the variation of the power radiated by thermal emission with wavelength. Its normalization (to unit solid angle, etc.) is much less interesting. The distribution of radiated power over wavelength according to Equation (3.23) is shown in Figure 3.13 for a fixed emitting area and for the temperatures 3000 K (the lowest curve), 4000, 5000, and 6,000 K (the highest curve), for visible and near infrared wavelengths. The highest temperature is approximately that of our own Sun; the lowest is characteristic of red giants such as Arcturus and Betelgeuse. You can easily see that the total energy emitted per unit area (the area under each curve) rises rapidly with increasing temperature, in accordance with Equation (3.21). (In fact, Equation (3.21) may be obtained from (3.23) by integrating over frequency and solid angle.) The wavelength at which the specific intensity is largest decreases with rising temperature, from about 1.0 μm for the red giants down to about 0.5 μm for the Sun. Hotter stars would radiate still more intensely than any of those plotted (per unit of area), and would peak at shorter wavelengths, for example at about 0.28 μm for Vega or Sirius, which have characteristic temperatures of about 10,000 K. Similar curves can be calculated for bodies at planetary temperatures, but because the emission is so much less intense than from stars, the curves would not differ from the horizontal zero axis on the scale used in Figure 3.13.

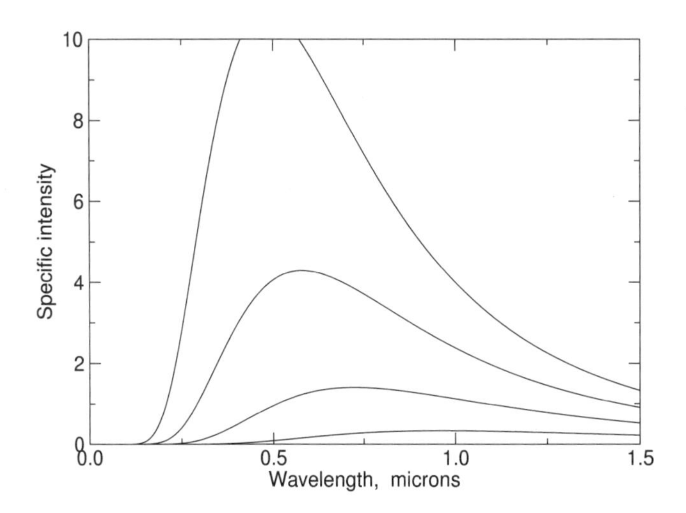

Figure 3.13: Specific intensity as a function of wavelength for black bodies having temperatures of 3000 K (the lowest curve), 4000 K, 5000 K, and 6,000 K (the upper curve). The radiation is from the same arbitrary area for all black bodies. Radiation from the Sun is similar to the 6000 K black body; most of the energy is emitted as visible light. The 3000 K black body has an energy distribution similar to that of an incandescent light bulb, and mostly emits near infra-red radiation.

By differentiating B_λ from Equation (3.23) with respect to λ, it is easily found that the wavelength $\lambda_{\rm m}$ at which B_λ is greatest is given by

$$\lambda_{\rm m} T = 2.90 \times 10^{-3} \text{ m K} = 2.90 \times 10^7 \text{ Å K}, \tag{3.24}$$

where the two forms are appropriate for wavelengths measured in m and in Å respectively. Thus thermal radiation from your wall, at about 300 K, is strongest around 10^5 Å = 10 μm in the middle infrared, while thermal radiation from the Sun, at about 6000 K, is strongest at about 5000 Å = 0.5 μm, in the middle of the visible spectrum.

Exercise: Carry out the calculation to derive Equation 3.24 from Equation 3.23. (Hint: you will arrive at an equation that you cannot solve algebraically. You may find a solution graphically or by successive approximations.)

Although the equations above describe radiation from an idealized radiator, they furnish a useful approximate description of the radiation of opaque real bodies. The distribution of sunlight over wavelength, and its absolute intensity, are reasonably well described by Equation (3.23) with $T = 5770$ K. Important deviations occur only far from the visible spectral region, in the ultraviolet (where the hot corona provides excess emission) and in the far infrared (where again the corona provides some excess). We shall meet these equations several times again in chapters to follow.

3.7 References

Eddy, J. A. 1977, "The case of the missing sunspots", *Sci. Am.*, May, 80. Eddy describes the historical detective work that showed that solar activity has almost completely stopped for decades at a time in the past, and that the overall level of activity may have an important effect on climate.

Foukal, P. V. 1990, "The variable Sun", *Sci. Am.*, Feb., 34. Foukal describes the many ways in which the Sun's activity and even its luminosity vary with time.

Foukal, P. V. 1990, *Solar Astrophysics* (New York: John Wiley and Sons). This is an excellent, up-to-date textbook for advanced undergraduates studying physics and astronomy.

Kirschner, R. L. 1994, "The Earth's elements", *Sci. Am.*, Oct., 58. Most of the material that makes up the Earth – and its inhabitants – was produced inside stars, particularly in supernovae.

Lang, K. R. 1997, "SOHO reveals the secrets of the Sun", *Sci. Am.*, Mar., 40. SOHO is a remarkable satellite that has studied many aspects of the Sun, from its core to its wind. The various instruments on it are catalogued in this somewhat superficial article.

Noyes, R. W. 1982, *The Sun, Our Star*, (Cambridge, Mass.: Harvard Univ. Press). Noyes' book presents a clear general description of the Sun at the level of a good Scientific American article, without any significant mathematics.

Shklovskii, I.S. 1978, *Stars: Their Birth, Life and Death*, (San Francisco: W. H. Freeman and Co.). This book is a semi-popular discussion of all aspects of stellar evolution, especially of star formation and star death.

Tayler, R.J. 1970, *The Stars: Their Structure and Evolution* (London: Wykeham Publications Ltd.). This short book presents a clear description of the basic physics underlying stellar structure and evolution at about the level of second or third year of university.

Williams, G. E. 1986, "The solar cycle in Precambrian times", *Sci. Am.*, Aug., 88. Efforts to understand the solar cycle may be aided by records in 700-million year old rocks.

Wolfson, R. 1983, "The active solar corona", *Sci. Am.*, Feb., 104. Studies of the solar corona from space and at many wavelengths are helping us to understand this complex structure.

Zirin, H. 1988, *Astrophysics of the Sun*, (Cambridge, U. K.: Cambridge Univ. Press). Zirin's book is an informal, authoritative, and personal description of the Sun, and is lavishly illustrated with excellent black-and-white photos. Parts of the book are completely descriptive, while other parts assume a considerable background in physics.

3.8 Review questions

3.1 Main sequence stars are observed to shine with unchanged output for decades and centuries. They are clearly in a state of equilibrium. What is the essential role of the high internal temperature of a star in maintaining this equilibrium? What is the role of nuclear reactions?

3.2 Why does a main sequence star burn hydrogen at all? Why does it burn H first, and only later burn He?

3.3 Why do main sequence stars of only moderately different masses have such very different main sequence lifetimes? What event ends the main sequence life of a star and sends it into the red giant state?

3.4 What effects do the most massive stars have on the interstellar gas, future star formation, and the evolution of the Milky Way galaxy?

3.5 When the Sun ends its life and collapses, what will its final state be? Why?

3.6 The Sun's chromosphere and corona have visibly complex structure while the photosphere (except for a few sunspots) is boringly uniform. What leads to this striking difference?

3.7 How can the chromosphere and corona of the Sun be hotter than the solar photosphere? What basic energy source heats them? How is this energy probably transferred into the chromosphere and corona?

3.8 Describe a few of the variable features observed on and above the surface of the Sun. How do these features typically vary individually? How are they affected by the solar cycle? What is the fundamental physical link between these variable structures?

3.9 Problems

3.1 Consider a sample of stars of various masses but all having the same chemical composition as the Sun, which can be approximated as 90% H and 10% He (by number of atoms, not by weight). Everything else can be neglected. (a) Compute the number of H atoms and the number of He atoms in one kg of stellar gas. (b) Assume that the energy released by conversion of four H nuclei into one He nucleus is 26 MeV. Calculate the total energy in J released by conversion of all the H nuclei in one kg into He nuclei. (c) Now assume that the main sequence lifetime of a star is approximately the time taken to convert 10% of the total mass of H into He. For the masses listed in Table 3.2, compute the total energy in J released during the main sequence life of stars of each of mass. (d) The luminosity of the star characterizes the rate at which energy released by nuclear reactions leaks out of the star. Use the total energies computed in part (c) and the luminosities in Table 3.2 to compute the time spent as main sequence stars, and compare the times you calculate to those tabulated as "Main sequence lifetime" in the Table.

3.2 The Planck function B_λ (Equation 3.23) describes the energy emitted in a unit *wavelength* interval. For many purposes, it is more convenient to use the equivalent function B_ν which describes the energy emitted into a unit *frequency* interval. (a) Using the relation between frequency ν and wavelength λ, find the size of a small interval $d\nu$ corresponding to a given interval $d\lambda$. (b) Now the energy emitted by a blackbody in $d\lambda$ is $B_\lambda d\lambda$. Clearly the same amount of energy must be computed using $B_\nu d\nu$ if ν takes the value corresponding to λ and the size of $d\nu$ corresponds to the interval $d\lambda$ as found in part (a). Use the equality $B_\nu d\nu = B_\lambda d\lambda$ to show that

$$B_\nu(T) = \frac{2h\nu^3}{c^2}\frac{1}{\exp(h\nu/kT) - 1}.$$

(c) Now we use the expression for B_ν to determine the fraction of the radiation from a really hot star that falls within the range of visible radiation easily detected from the ground, roughly from $\lambda = 300$ nm (the ultraviolet limit due to atmospheric cutoff) to about 1000 nm (the useful long wavelength sensitivity limit of CCD detectors). Compute the frequencies ν_3 and ν_{10} corresponding to these two wavelengths, and then compute the value of $h\nu/kT$ for the two frequencies for a star of $T = 2 \times 10^5$ K. Confirm that $h\nu/kT < 1$ for both frequencies. (d) The fraction we want to find is given by the ratio

$$\int_{\nu_3}^{\nu_{10}} B_\nu d\nu \Big/ \int_0^\infty B_\nu d\nu.$$

To evaluate the denominator of this ratio, you will need the definite integral

$$\int_0^\infty \frac{u^3 du}{e^u - 1} = \frac{\pi^4}{15}.$$

To evaluate the numerator of the ratio, expand the denominator of the expression for $B_\nu(T)$ to the lowest possible order in a Taylor series, which will lead to a major simplification in the form of this quantity. Comment on why the ratio you find is considerably smaller than 1.

Chapter 4

Formation of Stars and Planetary Systems

4.1 Introduction

We have already looked at how stars in general, and our Sun in particular, function, and at how they develop through their lives. In this chapter we turn to the problem of how a star forms in the first place, and why this process is sometimes expected to be accompanied by the creation of a system of planets. This is one of the most complex and least well understood parts of the whole story of a star's life. The general picture presented below is widely accepted, and is very likely be correct overall, but probably a number of the details will turn out to be wrong.

Basically, we now know that stars form as condensations – dense places – in the cold giant molecular clouds. Such a condensation shrinks under the influence of its own gravity to become a distinct denser cloud within the large cloud. We call such dense regions **cores**. This shrinkage may be retarded or guided by the magnetic fields that permeate many giant molecular clouds. Each collapsing cloud core is rotating, and so instead of matter all falling inward onto a central point, the condensation forms a disk-like structure, a little like the form of the Milky Way galaxy. Because of various types of viscosity (friction) in the disk, gas and dust drift inward towards the centre of the cloud, and accrete to form a dense central region (a protostar) which gradually grows into a star. Much of the matter falling inward in the condensation passes through the disk before settling onto the star (or being ejected back into the surrounding molecular cloud). The disk is thus an essential feature of the protostar as it becomes a star. In many cases, some of the gas of this disk eventually becomes a system of planets.

Thus, we now believe that formation of planetary systems is an integral, common part of star formation; our picture of star formation also suggests the initial conditions in which planets form and which shape some of the general properties of the resulting planetary systems. In the following sections we look at the processes involved more closely.

4.2 How star formation occurs

Star formation takes place mainly in the giant molecular clouds that are found particularly in the spiral arms of our galaxy. These huge clouds of relatively dense gas and dust have masses of up to $3 \times 10^6 M_\odot$, and diameters of one or a few light-years. Much of the matter in interstellar space that is available for forming new stars is in such clouds. The high densities (a few million molecules per cubic m) and low temperatures (10 – 30 K) of these clouds makes them natural locations for star birth, since these conditions mean that the cloud is not easily able to provide enough pressure to hold up its enormous mass against its self-gravity. Thus the conditions in a giant molecular cloud favour the possibility that the self-gravity of a particularly dense region will be able to make the gas in that region contract spontaneously.

Such giant molecular clouds are in fact already too cold and dense in general to be held up against their internal gravity only by gas pressure due to internal temperature, as stars are. Instead, they seem to be prevented from shrinking by several other agents.

- One kind of support is due to weak pervasive magnetic fields that permeate the clouds and resist compression. The gas in the clouds is very slightly ionized, due to cosmic rays and ultraviolet radiation from hot stars (about one molecule in 10^7 has lost an electron), and the ionized molecules cannot freely move across the magnetic fields. The neutral molecules and dust grains feel a frictional drag from the trapped ions if they try to drift across the field, so the field keeps all the matter in the cloud from shrinking very rapidly, although the field cannot prevent shrinkage.

- A second kind of support comes from large-scale turbulent gas motions. These are more or less random motions of large blobs and streams of gas, and they provide a kind of support a bit like that provided by gas pressure – the random motions keep the gas in orbit around local gravitating centres rather than allowing the gas to simply fall into mass condensations. Large-scale turbulent motions are observed in dense clouds, but it is not clear how they are produced. Such motions would certainly die out rather quickly, due to collisions between gas clouds, if they were not constantly replenished. It is thought that the turbulent motions may be driven by the mass outflows that are observed to be produced by newly formed stars.

- Finally, the overall rotation of a giant molecular cloud also provides some support, similar to the support employed by solar system planets that keeps them from falling into the Sun. Gas and dust fall *around* the centre of the cloud rather than into it.

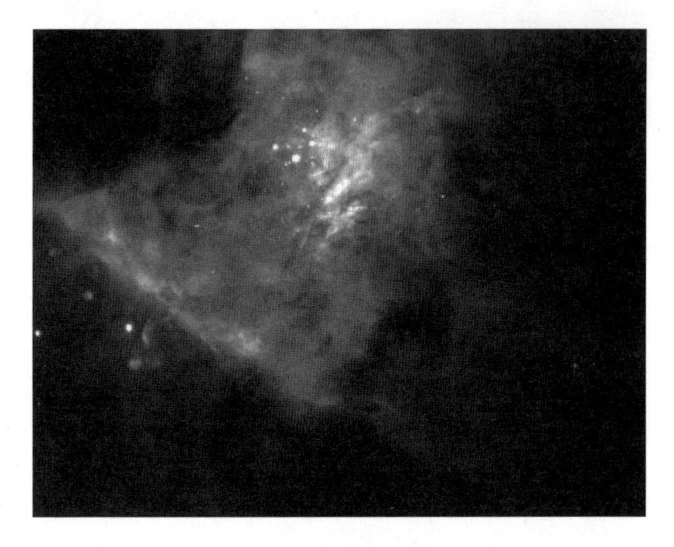

Figure 4.1: This image shows the famous Orion Nebula, an object visible with binoculars below Orion's belt. The nebula is an extremely active nearby region of star formation. This region is located (like a blister) on the near surface of a massive giant molecular cloud, which is not visible in the image. The four prominent stars near the brightest part of the cloud, close to the top of the image, are the most massive stars in a cluster of more than 3000 new stars that range in mass from 0.1 to 50 $M_{\odot}$. These hot stars are heating the surrounding nebular gas to a temperature of several thousand K, causing it to glow. Both the expansion of the heated nebular gas and the strong stellar winds from the massive stars are pushing in to the giant molecular cloud behind the visible nebula; this seems to have triggered the formation of another huge star cluster just inside the molecular cloud.

Nevertheless, from time to time some of the gas in a giant molecular cloud does begin to shrink slowly. Under the attractive influence of their self-gravity, blobs or **cores** of relatively dense gas (with densities 10 or 100 times higher than those of the larger cloud) form in the cloud and gradually contract. The magnetic field makes this contraction occur extremely slowly (it may take 10^7 or more years), but cannot prevent contraction entirely. Such cores are widely observed in giant molecular clouds; they seem to have masses of the order of a solar mass.

It may also happen that the compression of some cores is due to the action of an external trigger. One such trigger is mass *ejection* by previously formed stars that are within the cloud, for example by massive stars that quickly pass through their main sequence lives (in a few million years) and finally explode as supernovas. The expanding shell of debris from the supernova explosion could sweep up and compress molecular cloud gas until a large enough mass is accumulated that the swept-up gas can collapse to form a core (or perhaps a number of cores), again leading to star formation. Similarly, the powerful stellar winds from massive stars could locally compress nearby gas and trigger gravitational contraction. These processes seem to be at work in the Orion Nebula, seen in Figure 4.1. A third possible trigger is the passage of a giant molecular cloud through a spiral arm in the galaxy; this event is thought to lead to substantial compression of a giant molecular cloud, which sometimes may be enough to lead to contraction of cores.

As a core shrinks, it eventually becomes so dense that the gravitational attraction of one part of the core for other parts becomes stronger than the ability of gas pressure, turbulent gas motion, and magnetic field to resist the shrinkage. The core starts to collapse. This collapse occurs most rapidly near the centre of the core where the density is largest and the self-gravity is strongest; the outer parts of the core are less strongly attracted and fall inwards much more slowly. At the centre of the core a (relatively) small ball of gas forms, completely surrounded by a cloud of matter falling inwards towards the central ball.

As long as the central ball is not too massive or compact (until it reaches roughly the mass of Jupiter, about $10^{-3} M_{\odot}$), it remains transparent to infrared heat waves. Thus it can radiate away the gravitational energy released by shrinkage, and remain cool throughout. Once the central object becomes more massive than this critical value, it ceases to be transparent to infrared waves. Heat from the centre can no longer escape freely, and the central ball begins to heat up. This allows the central object to build up gas pressure with which to resist gravity, and the rapid collapse of the central object ceases. Instead, the object takes on roughly the same kind of internal structure that a star has, with pressure support (caused by the internal temperature, which has reached several hundred K) almost balancing gravity. Shrinkage occurs only as internal heat energy leaks out to the "surface" to be radiated away. At this point the shrinking central object may be referred to as a **protostar**; its radius is several AU. The central protostar steadily grows in mass as material from the surrounding cloud continues to fall onto it.

Now the infalling gas generally does not fall directly towards the protostar. Instead, it tends to fall *around* it. Typically the giant molecular clouds from which cores and stars form are rotating very slowly, if only because the galaxy in which they are found is rotating. Because of this fact, the gas falling in towards the new protostar tends to revolve in the same sense around the protostar. As the cloud of gas around a dense core shrinks, it tries to rotate faster, just as a figure skater spins faster by pulling in his arms. The general magnetic field, which links the gas to the surrounding matter in the giant molecular cloud, will impede this speeding up of rotation, but cannot prevent it entirely. By the time that the gas surrounding a core has shrunk enough to start falling freely towards the central protostar, it will also be free to spin faster as it shrinks.

The result is that by the time it shrinks to the dimensions of our solar system, some or much of the infalling gas is revolving fairly rapidly about the central protostar. This gas will form a dense and rather thick disk around the protostar, and much of the matter that falls towards the centre of the collapsing core will fall first onto the disk rather than directly into the accumulating protostar. The gas and dust in the disk are supported against falling directly into the protostar in exactly the way that planets support themselves against falling into the Sun: by falling around it instead. Much of the gas thus finds itself circling around the protostar at speeds which may be several km s^{-1}. In addition, because the disk is warm or hot (a lot of energy is released as clumps of gas crash into the main nebula) the gas will spread out vertically above and below the plane of the disk. This vertical extension will be supported by gas pressure, which counteracts both the component of the central star's gravity that attracts the gas towards the plane of the disk, and the self-gravity of the disk itself. Modelling shows that the thickness of the disk is expected to be quite significant, of the order of 20% of the distance to the central protostar, so the physical thickness increases with distance from the central star. At 1 AU from the proto-Sun, the disk of the solar nebula may have had a thickness of the order of 30 or 40 million km, some tenths of an AU; at 10 AU the disk was 1 or 2 AU thick.

However, since we hardly ever find disks around main sequence stars, the disks around protostars must be disposed of: the matter in the disk ends up in the star, in planets, or expelled from the system. One of the ways in which disk matter can finally fall into the central protostar is probably through various kinds of friction (viscosity) in the disk, which have the effect of slowing down material in the inner part of the disk so that is gradually spirals inward toward the central protostar, eventually falling onto it, while outer material moves farther out, carrying off excess rotation. The nature of the friction involved in this spiraling is not very clear. It has been suggested that the friction might involve magnetic fields, perhaps generated in the disk and linking various parts, which would tend to try to keep the disk rotating at the same angular speed at all distances from the central proto-Sun. Another possibility is that the temperature drop from mid-plane to the top and bottom surfaces of the disk, from which heat is radiated away, is large enough to lead to convective motions in the gas (see Chapter 10) which could lead to friction between adjacent parts of the disk. In any case, the disappearance of disks from stars by the time they reach the main sequence stage of life is strong indirect evidence that protostellar disks are not long-lived. Instead, they channel mass onto the growing central protostar, and in many cases leave some matter in orbit around the protostar which becomes a planetary system.

We return now to the story of what is happening to the protostar itself while gas is being accreted into the nebula. As gas flows down onto the growing protostar, its mass increases. The newly accreted gas releases much gravitational energy, heating the protostar. Some of this newly released energy is radiated away from the surface, but some goes into heating the growing central star. When the temperature in the interior of the protostar reaches about 2000 K, energetic collisions between H_2 molecules begin to break these molecules apart. (The technical term for this process is "dissociation" of molecular hydrogen.) Breaking H_2 molecules apart requires quite a lot of energy, which diverts the energy released from accretion of new gases away from raising the internal temperature. As a result, the internal temperature of the protostar falls below the value needed to support it against its own gravity, and the inner part collapses to a size not much larger than the present Sun, breaking up almost all the H_2 molecules in the process. The outer layers quickly fall onto the drastically shrunken central regions, also breaking apart their H_2 molecules. The result of this second collapse is that the protostar shrinks from a size of the order

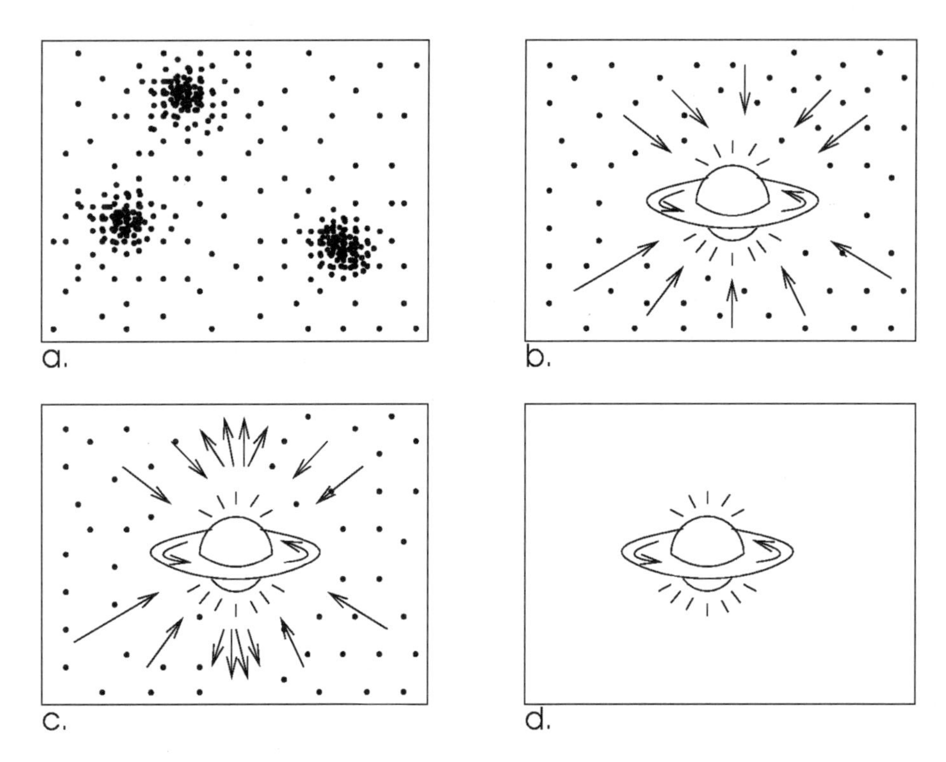

Figure 4.2: Stages of star formation are shown. (a) Dense cores form in a giant molecular cloud as gravity slowly shrinks blobs against the resistance of the magnetic field. (b) A proto star and its accretion disk form at the centre of a cloud core. Material from the outer part of the core falls in for some time after the central star collapses. (c) A stellar wind starts, breaking through the infalling matter first along the rotation axis. (d) Finally the infall is stopped by the stellar wind, leaving a newly formed star together with its accretion disk.

of some AU to a size only a few solar radii in size. At this point it might still have less than 0.1 $M_\odot$ of material, but it continues to accrete gas (mostly – somehow – through the nebular disk) from the surrounding gas cloud.

Soon after this point the protostar becomes hot enough at the centre (roughly 10^6 K) to start converting deuterium (^{2}H) to ^{4}He by the two reactions

$$^2\mathrm{H} + {}^1\mathrm{H} \rightarrow {}^3\mathrm{He} \quad (5.5 \text{ MeV})$$

and

$$^3\mathrm{He} + {}^3\mathrm{He} \rightarrow {}^4\mathrm{He} + {}^1\mathrm{H} + {}^1\mathrm{H} \quad (12.8 \text{ MeV}).$$

These two reactions stabilize the protostar's size while it continues to grow in mass as it accretes gases and dust from the surrounding gas cloud.

We now speak of the central object as a **pre-main sequence star**, since it has both reached dimensions resembling those of normal main sequence stars, and begun its career as an object in which nuclear burning replaces heat lost from the surface, stabilizing the size and structure. It is also at roughly this point that a low-mass star such as the Sun becomes optically visible, as the dust and gas surrounding the star is finally accreted or blown away.

Although there is not much ^{2}H in a star when it forms (only about 30 nuclei out of every million H atoms are deuterium), these reactions release enough energy to make the pre-main sequence star boil. It becomes strongly convective. The boiling motions within the star generate a stellar magnetic field, and this magnetic field bubbles out into the outer layers of the star where it reverts to simpler structure, releasing energy and heating the gas around it (as in solar flares) to such high temperatures that the gas begins to evaporate from the star. This evaporation of matter from the star creates a stellar wind, much like the solar wind evaporating from the top of the solar corona. In a pre-main sequence star this stellar wind is much more intense than in the Sun.

As gas evaporates from the star, at first it is confined by the infalling gas and the disk. After a while, the outflowing gas will burst through the weakest point in the infalling material, along the rotation axis, perpendicular to the disk. (This is the region where the nebula surrounding the star has the least mass.) Gradually the gas evaporating from the surface of the star stops the infall, and eventually begins to clear out the space around the protostar so that it becomes a visible young stellar object known as a **T Tauri star**, probably while it is still surrounded by a fairly extensive disk of gas and dust. Thus the onset of deuterium burning and the resulting occurrence of the stellar wind bring to an end accretion of gas by the young stars. The process of star formation is shown schematically in Figure 4.2.

The theory described above applies particularly to the formation of stars up to about 2 $M_{\odot}$. There are some significant differences in how more massive stars form. One important difference is that low mass stars often form without any massive stars developing while the opposite situation, massive star formation without formation of low mass stars, does not seem to occur. Special conditions, perhaps those found in a particularly massive or dense giant molecular cloud, are needed to insure that massive stars also form. Another difference is that in massive stars, deuterium burning does not stimulate convective motions to evaporate surface matter from the protostar. In fact, we don't properly understand what ends the accretion and growth process for a massive star.

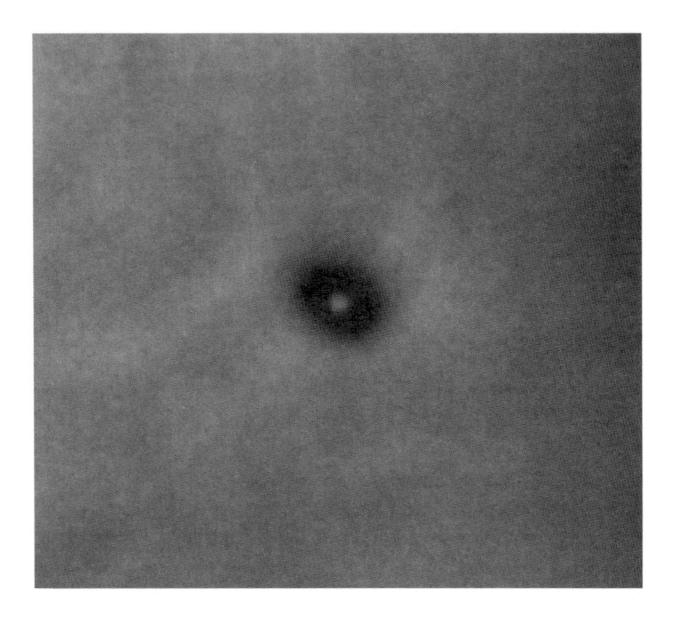

Figure 4.3: The image of a young star in the Orion star-forming region obtained by the Hubble Space Telescope. The star, the bright dot right at the centre of the image, is surrounded by an oval disk, which is dark as seen against the background light from the brightly glowing Orion Nebula. The disk is probably circular, but appears oval because it is seen obliquely. (Courtesy of NASA.)

4.3 Formation of planetary systems

From the point of view of our interest in planets and the solar system, the picture of star formation described above contains an exceedingly interesting feature, namely the accretion disk of gas and dust revolving around the new T Tauri star. It is from this disk that we believe that either a system of planets or perhaps a companion star will develop. We may call this disk a **protoplanetary disk**.

The radius of the protoplanetary disk at the time it stops shrinking in towards the Sun (when it reaches the size at which the rotation of the disk is able to balance the gravitational attraction of the growing protostar) is expected to be of the order of 10^2 AU in radius, not remarkably bigger than the present radius of our own solar system, in which Pluto orbits at about 40 AU from the Sun. There is also growing observational evidence that disks of dust and gas of roughly this size are actually present around a number of stars, including some young T Tauri stars. Direct images (Figure 4.3) show such disks around young stars in the Orion Nebula, the region of new star formation on the outer surface of a giant molecular cloud (Figure 4.1). Thus the formation of a protostar commonly appears to deposit quite a lot of matter into a structure from which a planet system of about the size of our own could form.

If we assume that planetary systems develop from such disks, we immediately have an explanation of one very striking feature of our own solar system, namely that the planets all move in essentially the equatorial plane of the Sun, and all revolve about the Sun in the same sense as the Sun's own rotation. This regularity is a direct consequence of the overall rotation of the initial gas cloud that contracted to form the Sun and the disk.

As we have already mentioned, this nebular disk is certain to be fairly warm throughout, particularly in the inner regions near the protostar. It is heated by radiation from the protostar, which is expected to be roughly as luminous as our own Sun. This heating alone would probably warm the disk of gas and dust to a temperature of roughly 500 K at 0.5 AU (about the same distance from the star as the orbit of Mercury is from the Sun), with correspondingly cooler temperatures farther out, dropping off to about 50 K at 30 AU (the distance to the orbit of Neptune). Further heating may be provided by the release of gravitational energy from matter that falls in onto the disk from the surrounding cloud, once the disk is formed, but the contribution from this source is hard to evaluate since it depends on the rate at which matter falls in; if blobs of gas fall in only infrequently, most of the heat released will be radiated away again rather than going to raise the temperature of the disk. Additional heat is also released in the disk from the same friction that allows gas in the disk to spiral into the central star. Finally, when the pre-main sequence star becomes magnetic, frequent and intense stellar flares may produce locally powerful heating. As a result of these various heat sources, parts of the accretion disk within two or three AU of the star are heated to temperatures of more than 1000 K during the accretion process, while farther out, at 5 or 10 AU, temperatures certainly exceeded 100 K.

We expect the disk to have essentially the chemical composition of the giant molecular cloud from which the star forms. This probably means that the chemical composition is close to that listed in Table 2.2 for the solar atmosphere. The disk is made up predominantly of H and He, but about 1% of the mass of the disk is made up of heavier elements, primarily O, C, N, Mg, Si, and Fe; about one atom in 10^3 will be something other than H or He.

Exercise: Explain why atoms of elements heavier than He make up roughly 1% of the *mass* of the disk, but only about 0.1% of the *total number of atoms*.

H and He, as far as they are in the form of molecules such as H_2 or single atoms, will certainly be in the gas phase. The temperatures everywhere in the nebula (50 K and up) are too high for either of these elements to condense in pure form even as liquid, and certainly not as solids.

The remaining 1% of the mass divides naturally into two groups whose behaviour is rather different from one another, and from that of H and He, as to whether they are in the gas, liquid, or solid phase. Most of the elements with nuclei heavier than those of H and He freeze out as solids (dust particles) at temperatures above 1000 K. These **refractory elements** include such common ones as Na, Mg, Al, Si, Ca, and Fe, as well as some O which combines with these materials. O condenses at high temperature in such minerals as olivine and pyroxene (see Table 2.2) but since there are about 20 times as many O atoms as Si atoms, at most about 1/5 of the O atoms will be combined in such refractory minerals. Except in regions where the protostellar disk is really hot (above 1500 K), we expect these refractory elements to be in solid form, mostly as minerals such as olivine and pyroxene (because Mg, Fe, Si, and O are the most common of the refractory elements), but with considerable impurities or inclusions to accommodate the many other refractory elements. This solid material, which we call the **rock component**, makes up an important part of the "dust" mixed in with the H and He gas.

However, the most abundant elements other than H and He, namely C, N, and O, remain largely unincorporated into the solids that condense from the nebula at high temperatures. Most of the atoms of these elements find themselves in compounds that only become liquids or solids at relatively low temperatures, though considerably higher than those needed to freeze out solid H. The principal compounds that these elements will form are those involving H and/or each other; which specific compounds predominate depends on the local temperature and pressure in the protoplanetary nebula.

- Even in parts of the nebula where temperatures are well above 1000 K, much of the O will be combined into H_2O (water) molecules.
- In regions where the nebular temperature is above 700 K, most of the C will be in CO molecules and the N will be in N_2.
- Between 700 K and 300 K, much of the C is expected to lose its O to H_2 molecules and become CH_4 (methane), while the nitrogen remains unchanged.
- Below about 300 K, the nitrogen molecules may be converted into molecules of NH_3.

However, the reactions that convert CO into CH_4 and N_2 into NH_3 go very slowly at low temperature, and it is not at all clear how much conversion is actually accomplished, or what the relative proportions of N_2 to NH_3, or of CO to CH_4 will be in the cooler parts of the nebula. However, all the common compounds formed from C, N and O freeze out to become solids only in the temperature range of roughly 50–300 K (recall Table 2.5); since they freeze out at temperatures lower than those common on Earth, we call them **ices** or **volatile substances**. In the inner part of a protoplanetary disk the substances which form ices are expected to be in gaseous form; in the outer part they are solids.

Sulphur is intermediate in behaviour; it reacts with Fe (if free Fe is available) to freeze out of the disk at temperatures below 700 K. The noble gases, such as Ne, Ar, and Xe, do not react to form compounds, but may be trapped in fairly large amounts as individual atoms caught in the crystal structure of the ices.

Thus although the protostar's disk is expected to have essentially the chemical composition of the new star, the elements will not be distributed among gas, liquid, and solid phases in the same way throughout the disk. In the inner part of the disk, where heating from the protostar and from infall is strong, the rocky component will probably be in the form of solid particles (probably quite small grains of dust), while the ice components will be gaseous. Farther away from the central star, where the disk temperature is lower, both the rock and ice components will be solid. H and He will be gaseous throughout the disk. We will see later, in Chapter 5, that meteorites provide us with much information about the details of how various elements were partitioned between dust and gas, and the sequence of formation of solids.

Another characteristic of the accretion disk that will have an important influence on its development is the total mass of gas that it contains. Unfortunately, we don't yet know enough about the details of how dense cores form in giant molecular clouds, or about how the forming star accretes mass from, and sheds angular momentum (rotation) into, the surrounding disk, to be able to predict the mass of matter in a typical disk (which certainly varies with time) with any certainty. However, from a rough calculation we may get a general idea of the mass that must have passed through the disk at the time when planet formation was under way, at least for our own solar system.

If we add up the masses of all the objects in the solar system (mainly Jupiter and Saturn), we find a present mass of about 2.6×10^{27} kg, or 0.0013 $M_\odot$. It is obvious that the disk from which these planets formed must have processed at least this mass. In fact, it must have had available a considerably larger mass than this value. In the Sun the ice component (including an appropriate number of H atoms) only makes up about 1.4% of the total mass, while the the rock component (which includes some O) constitutes only 0.44%. Now if we look at the four inner planets, which are composed almost entirely from elements of the refractory rock group, their present total mass is only about 1.2×10^{25} kg. However, the rocky material from which these planets are made was originally accompanied by a much larger amount of H, He, and ice material which was not incorporated into these planets but was somehow lost from the disk. Thus the present 1.2×10^{25} kg of the inner planets alone must originally have condensed from about $1.2 \times 10^{25}/.0044 = 2.7 \times 10^{27}$ kg of disk matter, an amount as large as the total present mass of all the planets of the solar system.

A similar calculation for the more massive outer planets is not so straightforward, since it requires an estimate of the mass of rock and ice that each contains. This can be only be done approximately, but it is thought that the present 2.6×10^{27} kg of the outer planets required at least 5.6×10^{28} kg, or about 0.028 $M_\odot$ of disk matter from which to form. Thus the disk from which our own planet system formed must originally have processed *at least* about 0.03 $M_\odot$ of matter. This is reassuring; we would be surprised to find that the disk was many orders of magnitude less massive than the Sun. It also is in accord with observations, which frequently reveal disks with masses of the order of 0.02 $M_\odot$ around protostars. Of course, it is probable that over the period during which the Sun accreted out of its molecular cloud, far more than 0.03 $M_\odot$ of matter passed through the nebula, leaving only a part of its condensible material behind in the planets.

4.4 Formation of planetary bodies

For planets to form, some of the dispersed gas and dust in the circumstellar disk must collect into gravitationally bound bodies. Two main kinds of processes could be at work. One method for condensing matter into larger aggregates is to start with the solid dust grains present in the gas. When these collide with one another, they will frequently stick together, gradually forming larger and larger objects. Any method in which such **solid body accretion** is an essential step will preferentially build planets out of the matter that is already solid in the disk. A second type of process is exemplified by the kind of **gravitational collapse** that occurs in the giant molecular cloud as the cores shrink. In such a process, the matter is somehow made dense enough that self-gravitation leads fragments or clouds to collapse rapidly to a much smaller size, at which either internal pressure or rotation can support the cloud.

The speeds of these two types of processes are quite different. Building objects by accretion or coagulation of solid particles is always a rather slow and patient business, taking thousands of years or even much more. In contrast, although the approach to gravitational collapse may be equally slow, once the brink of instability is reached, collapse goes almost as quickly as free fall, so that a collapse forming a solar system planet might need only a few years.

In the absence of a definitive theory, many combinations of the two processes discussed above have been proposed as operating to form planets. If we look at our own planetary system, we notice immediately that the inner four planets are made almost entirely of elements that are solids even at a temperature of more than 500 K, while the outer solar system has some bodies that are made almost entirely of matter that condenses above 100 K (moons of the outer planets) as well as some bodies that have large amounts of H and He (the outer planets themselves, especially Jupiter and Saturn). These facts suggest that only matter that went through a solid body accretion phase ended up in the inner planets and the moons of the outer ones, while the H and He of the large outer planets could probably only have been accumulated through gravitational collapse, perhaps onto smaller solid planetary cores originally formed by solid-body accretion.

These general ideas have stimulated a lot of calculations about how planets might form from a disk. The following sequence of events may be how the planets developed in our own solar system.

As we have seen, the collapse of a core in a giant molecular cloud is accompanied by the formation of a disk of gas and dust particles. Most of the matter that falls onto the protostar falls first onto the disk, and then slowly spirals in to the central star.

Both the gas and the dust in the disk, which has at any particular time in this process might have a total mass of the order of 0.01 $M_\odot$, circle the protostar in nearly circular (Keplerian) orbits. However, a small but important difference exists between the situation for the gas and that for the dust. The gas is mostly supported against falling directly into the protostar by its rotation about the protostar, but it is also supported to a small extent by the outward pressure exerted by gas closer to the central object. As a result, the gas at each distance from the central protostar orbits at a slightly slower speed than the speed which would just balance solar gravity. In contrast, the dust grains are *not* supported at all by this weak gas pressure. As a result, the dust grains and larger solid bodies are obliged to orbit the sun at almost exactly the speed which balances solar attraction. Consequently, at any particular distance from the Sun the orbital speed of the solid particles is a little larger than the orbital speed of the gas, by a few tens of m s^{-1}. The dust grains thus feel a strong headwind from the more slowly orbiting gas.

The effect of this headwind depends very much on the size of the solid body caught in it. The tiniest dust grains are forced to orbit at essentially the speed of the gas. Larger grains orbit a little faster, still larger grains still faster, since the surface area of a grain (which allows the headwind to drag on the grain) increases less quickly than its mass as we look at larger and larger grains. (For the same reason, a tiny chip of paper falls to the ground on Earth much more slowly than a tennis ball.) Because particles of different sizes orbit the protostar at somewhat different speeds, they have a strong tendency to collide with each other. When they collide, they will often stick together, leading to larger particle. It is estimated that bodies of the order of a km across (**planetesimals**) might grow by such collisions in roughly 10^4 yr. In the hot environment close to the central star, these planetesimals would be made mainly of rock; farther away from the proto-Sun planetesimals would be composed of both rock and ice.

The headwind also has the effect of causing planetesimals of a certain size to spiral into the central protostar. The smallest dust particles are so strongly affected by gas drag that they move essentially with the gas, and cannot drift inward significantly faster than the gas does. Really large planetesimals, one km or more across, are slowed so little by the headwind (because of their large masses) that they also spiral in only very slowly. Intermediate sized planetesimals, bodies whose dimensions are of the order of one m across, however, are greatly endangered by the headwind. They are large enough that they do not drift with the gas, but they do feel the wind, which is effective enough on bodies this size to slow them below the orbital speed necessary for an orbit at a constant distance from the central star. Planetesimals of this size would spiral into the central protostar in some hundreds or thousands of years! Since we now find the planets in the solar system that formed from such planetesimals, we conclude that the accretion process must have been fast enough to prevent the loss of all the solid bodies through this orbital decay. On the other hand, the strong orbital decay of meter-sized bodies probably insures that a significant amount of mixing occurred between the solid bodies in various parts of the solar nebula.

Once collisions between dust grains and small planetesimals led to the creation of bodies roughly a km across, another force came into play: mutual gravitational attraction among the planetesimals. This increased the ability of the larger planetesimals to sweep up smaller bodies, and most of the billions of small bodies rapidly became incorporated into some hundreds of larger objects, rather like the asteroids. The larger of these bodies had masses of the order of 0.001 or 0.01 $M_\oplus$ (recall that $M_\oplus$ is the mass of the Earth); they are sometimes called planetary embryos.

For these bodies to grow still larger, they must change from having nearly circular orbits to having orbits that cross one another. This probably resulted from mutual gravitational interactions (near collisions) among the planetesimals. As the orbits of the planetesimals became more eccentric, collisions between them also became more violent. Sometimes the collisions must have been so energetic that they led to destruction rather than to coagulation. Gradually, however, a few of the largest bodies, which we would now call **protoplanets**, swept up most of the other planetesimals and much of the smaller material. These were the bodies that eventually became the planets that we now see.

In the inner solar system, this sweeping up of small bodies by a few of the largest protoplanets was the final step in the formation of the terrestrial planets. The sweeping-up phase ended with some really spectacular collisions. The impact of a body of roughly the mass of Mars with Earth led to the creation of the Moon about 50 Myr after initial formation of the first solar nebula solids. Other enormous impacts produced Caloris Basin on Mercury, the maria basins on the Moon, and Hellas and Argyre on Mars (see Chapter 9). One mystery that remains from this era is the fact that today the orbits of the terrestrial planets, especially the largest (Earth and Venus) are nearly circular. Computer models of the period of final sweeping up suggests that usually the final planets in a system like ours should all have fairly eccentric orbits at the end of the accretion process.

The giant outer planets probably formed initially in a similar way, from planetesimals of rock and ice. It is thought that the period of mutual collisions and sweeping up produced rock-ice planets with masses 10 or 15 times larger than that of the Earth; such rock-ice cores appear to be present inside all four of the giant planets today (see Chapter 11). However, collisions of solid planetesimals does not explain the presence of massive outer layers rich in H and He in the giants. According to this theory, by the time that the protoplanets in the outer solar system had grown to masses of around 10 $M_\oplus$, their gravitational fields had become strong enough to essentially vacuum up the surrounding nebular gases and dust. Jupiter, which is about 80% H and He, was the largest and most successful of these gas collectors. When the gravitational collapse of disk matter onto the cores of the giant outer planets began, much unconsolidated dust and small bodies would have fallen in too; both this component and the gas would probably have had enough rotation to form small disks around the new giant planets. In these disks much of the same physics would have occurred as in larger solar nebula, with material spiraling in to the central protoplanet while leaving some solids behind as large planetesimals. It appears that it was from such protoplanetary disks that the large and regular moon systems of the giant planets formed.

We will look more closely at these processes in later chapters, as we examine individual types of bodies in the solar system.

We do not know very clearly what happened to the large fraction of the disk gas (at least 97%) that was not successfully accreted by the forming planets. It is suspected that when the stellar wind of the newly formed T Tauri star that became the Sun really turned on, this wind was able both to halt further accretion onto the central star and eventually to blow away uncondensed gas and small particles remaining in the accretion disk. This same wind may well have carried off much of the excess rotation.

We are still rather uncertain about a lot of the details of the processes that we have described above. Furthermore, we have not been able to proceed directly by making predictions from physical principles, but have had to let ourselves be guided strongly by observed features of the solar system. However, nothing in the theory described above seems particularly improbable or makes any very stringent demands on the precise physical characteristics of the initial gas cloud, the proto-Sun or its disk. It seems quite likely that if we have correctly described the general process by which our own planetary system formed, it is a process that probably occurs quite often during star formation. The fact that we frequently observe disks around pre-main sequence stars suggests that planetary systems like our own may be rather common in the Milky Way galaxy and elsewhere in the universe. We would not be surprised to find that other planetary system have all their planets orbiting all in the same sense in one plane, and with rocky planets close to the central star and much more massive giant planets formed around initial rock-ice cores further out.

4.5 Detection of planet systems around other stars

It would be a great help to our efforts to understand the origin and structure of our own solar system if we could actually observe and study other solar systems in various stages of development. In recent years this possibility, once remote, has become a serious area of research.

With current technology, two approaches leading in this direction are open. First, astronomers have used infrared-sensitive cameras and millimeter-wave radio telescopes to detect large, cool clouds and disks of gas and dust around very young stars. Such material is almost certainly a remnant of the collapsing cloud from which the star formed, and may be similar in form and structure to the solar nebula from which the planets of the solar system developed. Secondly, it has become possible in recent years to detect indirectly, through the wobbling movement of the visible star caused by the tug of one or more planets, the presence of companions of roughly the mass of Jupiter orbiting around stars similar to the Sun. It is not yet clear whether these companions were all formed physically by the initial gravitational collapse of the cloud, which is the process that forms binary star systems with two stars of normal mass, or whether some companions were formed by coagulation of small solid particles from a nebula, as the planets of the solar system formed. We suspect (and hope!) that some of the Jupiter-mass companions are the analogues of the giant planets of our own solar system.

The examination of other solar systems is essentially limited by the very great difficulty of simply detecting material, either in the form of gas and dust or in the form of planets, around a star. If we consider first the problem of detecting a cloud like the solar nebula around a young star, the essential problem is that we are trying to observed the radiation from a cloud of gas and dust at a temperature of some tens or hundreds of Kelvins in the glare of the light from a body with a temperature of some thousands of K. The brightness of a given surface area of the star is anywhere from 10^3 to 10^8 larger than the brightness of the same surface area in the surrounding cloud. Because the nearest stars young enough to still have their proto-stellar nebulas are at distances of a few hundred light-years from the Sun, a nebula 100 AU in radius would be only a couple of seconds of arc across on the sky, not much larger than the size of the disk into which the star image is spread out by the turbulent motions of our atmosphere. Furthermore, at visible wavelengths such a disk shines only by reflecting a tiny fraction of the starlight that falls on it. Thus the problem in detecting such a nebula on a visible image of a young star is to see a very faint fuzziness very close to the bright star image. This has been possible in a few cases using the Hubble Space Telescope, whose images are not degraded by the Earth's atmosphere. Such a nebula around a young star in the Orion star-forming region is visible in Figure 4.3.

However, a more powerful method for detecting such faint, small circumstellar clouds or disks is to make use of the fact that they are much larger than their stars, and radiate strongly at far infra-red wavelengths because they are cool. If we look for such a cloud with a camera sensitive to wavelengths around 100 μm, where heat radiation from a disk at a temperature of 30 K is strongest and the stellar radiation is far less than at visible wavelengths, the large size of the cloud relative to the central star makes it actually *brighter* than the star by a factor of 100 or more. Thus we have been able to indirectly detect disks or clouds around many young stars by the fact that such stars appear to emit far more long wavelength infra-red radiation than they would be expected to if the stars were not surrounded by dusty gas clouds. (Since the Earth's atmosphere is completely opaque to infra-red waves of wavelengths between about 20 μm and 1 mm, most such observations have been made from telescopes on orbiting satellites, although cool, large disks can also be detected by ground-based millimeter-wave radio telescopes.)

Infra-red and radio observations have now detected clouds around several dozen young (T Tauri) stars of masses similar to the Sun. The clouds have masses of the order of 10^{-1} or $10^{-2} M_{\odot}$, and typical temperatures of 100 or 200 K. The clouds are found around stars having ages estimated to be between about 10^5 and 10^7 years. These clouds appear to be flattened; if they were spherical and completely surrounding their central stars the stars themselves would not be visible because their light would be absorbed before it could leave the cloud, and so the fact that we do see the central stars indicates that such clouds are flattened and do not absorb much light leaving the central stars above or below the disk.

Such disks are probably similar to the solar nebula from which the planets of our own planetary system formed. However, we have not detected any planets in such systems. Instead, low-mass companions have now been found orbiting a number of middle-aged nearby main sequence stars very similar to our Sun. The companions probably include both real planets and stars of such low mass that they cannot even ignite H-burning nuclear reactions (known as **brown dwarfs**). These small companions are far too faint to be seen in the glare of the light from the large star in the system at any wavelength; instead, they are detected by their gravitational effect on the central star. In effect, as a planet orbits around a star, held in its orbit by the gravitational attraction of the star, the attraction that the planet exerts on the star causes the star to orbit in a small circle as well. Both bodies, in fact, orbit around their common centre of mass. In the Sun-Jupiter system, the gravitational tug of Jupiter, which has a mass close to $10^{-3} M_{\odot}$, causes the Sun to circle around a point about 10^{-3} of the distance from the centre of the Sun to Jupiter. Thus during one orbital period of Jupiter, about 12 years, the Sun makes one revolution around a point slightly above its surface. Although this centre of mass is not far from the centre of the Sun, and the orbital motion of Jupiter is slow, the Sun's velocity around this point as a result of Jupiter's gravitational attraction is still about 13 m s^{-1}. If we were to observe the Sun from a nearby star near the plane of the ecliptic, the Sun's line-of-sight velocity would vary around the average value by about 13 m s^{-1} either way over a period of 12 years. Although this is a tiny velocity change, it is within our ability now to detect such variations.

By looking for such tiny velocity variations in nearby stars, Swiss, American and other astronomers have now detected several dozen stellar companions of such low mass that some are probably planets. Most of the objects that are thought to be planets have masses of between about 1 and 10 times that of Jupiter. Typically, only one such object is detected orbiting a star (but other, lower-mass bodies would affect the star's motion even less and would be still harder to detect). Astonishingly, many of the objects have orbital radii of less than 0.1 AU, although a few are detected as far as 2 to 3 AU from their stars. The orbits are also frequently distinctly eccentric, and the distance between the star and its companion may be as much as three times larger at their greatest separation than it is when they are closest together, although much less eccentric orbits also occur.

Thus the lowest mass companions found around Sun-like stars generally do not seem to be much like the planets of the solar system, in which the large planets are at distances of several AU or more, the orbits are very close to circular, and none of the planets have more mass than Jupiter. The surprisingly small and eccentric orbits of possible planets found orbiting nearby stars have given astronomers a very substantial puzzle, since from our theories of the formation of the solar system we do not expect giant planets to be able to form close to their central star, where nebular temperatures would have been high, and only rocky planets formed in the solar system.

Two categories of explanation have been put forward for this surprising state of affairs. One is that the observed bodies are really planets, which means that they formed from a nebula around a young star by condensation of solids, which coalesced (as we have described in the case of the solar system) and then eventually, when they became massive enough, swept up much gas from the nebula to become giants. This must have occurred at several AU from the star, and so one must find some mechanism which then moves such planets in towards the central star. The most likely way in which this may have happened seems to be through gravitational interactions between the new planets and the residual disk of gas and dust still surrounding the young star. Such an interaction should lead the inwardly migrating planets to more and more circular orbits, suggesting that only those companions with nearly circular orbits are truly planets.

The other possibility is that the companions are actually simply very low-mass stars. In this case, one imagines that the companions formed, like the main star in the system, directly from the gravitationally collapsing proto-stellar cloud, in the same fashion that we think many binary pairs of normal stars are formed. This would normally lead to companions in fairly eccentric orbits, and so some astronomers think that the low-mass companions in highly eccentric orbits are probably very low-mass stars, not planets. In any case, the situation is far from clear at present, and the planets (if they are that) found orbiting nearby stars have not yet made the history of our own solar system much clearer!

Exercise: An astronomer on a planet orbiting α Centauri, a star quite near to the Sun in space, looks at our solar system through her telescope. Although Jupiter is far enough from the Sun that she could see it as a separate object (it is not blurred together with the Sun), she sees only the Sun, not Jupiter. What observation that you can make by eye explains why the Centaurian astronomer does not see Jupiter?

4.6 Mathematical aspects

Accretion of planetesimals

During the formation of the solar system we believe that many bodies grew to substantial size by a process in which the larger fragments found within the solar nebula swept up smaller pieces as they moved through the nebula. In this process, the accreting body would collide with other small bodies either simply because its motion carried it into the other bodies, or (once it got rather large) because of the effect of its gravity, which would attract other objects towards it.

For collisions of this sort to make a small body (such as a planetesimal) grow, the collisions must be relatively gentle. As long as almost all of the planetesimals in the nebula were fairly small (say less than ~ 1 km diameter), the initial circular motion of material in the solar nebula have been smooth enough that collisions were usually gentle, with relative speeds of less than, say, 1 m s^{-1}. Once some larger bodies formed by accretion, however, they would begin to exert substantial gravitational effects on the small bodies that passed near them but did not collide with them. These non-captured smaller bodies would be given larger random velocities relative to one another, and as a result their collisions with each other became less and less gentle, and eventually the majority of collisions between small bodies may actually have become destructive rather than leading to coalescence and further growth. We may estimate the rate of this process as follows.

Consider a test body moving through a collection of other bodies at a relative speed v. The other bodies have a space density or number density of n objects per unit volume. Our test body has a **(collision) cross section** σ, which is its effective area for collisions. If another body intersects this area, the two collide, as shown in Figure 4.4.

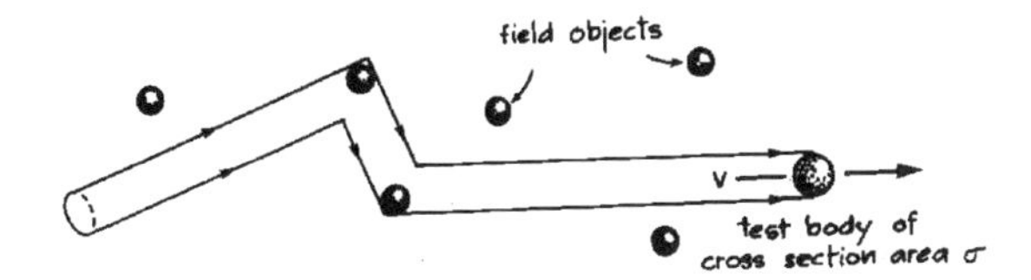

Figure 4.4: The path through space of a test body, which collides with other objects when the tube swept out by its cross section intersects the others.

As our test object moves through space relative to the other bodies, it will in effect carve out a tunnel in space. Any body which lies partly or wholly in this tunnel will collide with our test body. The test body sweeps out a volume of σv per unit time. Now the average volume per field object is $1/n$, so our test body has a probability $P = (\sigma v)/(1/n) = \sigma v n$ per unit time of colliding with a field object, and the mean time between collisions is

$$\tau = (1/P) = (\sigma v n)^{-1}. \tag{4.1}$$

The mean distance traveled by the test object between collisions, called the **mean free path** λ, is simply equal to the test object's speed times the mean time between collisions.

Exercise: At a certain time in the development of the solar nebula, the particles of dust have grown to a typical diameter of 0.1 mm. They have velocities of 0.1 m s^{-1}. Assume that the total average mass density of dust in the solar nebula is about 10^{-3} kg m^{-3} and that individual grains have mass densities of $\rho \sim 100$ kg m^{-3}. Calculate the number of dust particles per cubic meter, the mean time between collisions of a particular particle with any of the other particles, and the typical mean free path for a specific particle.

In many cases, the collision cross section will be the geometrical one. Thus if the test body is spherical, of radius R, and the field bodies are the same, collision will occur whenever the test body passes within a distance of $R + R = 2R$ of a field body, and $\sigma = \pi(2R)^2 = 4\pi R^2$.

An important case in which the capture cross section may be substantially larger than the geometrical cross section occurs when the test (or accreting) body exerts a significant gravitational force. Consider a gravitating body of mass m accreting much smaller objects. If a small body approaches the large one with an **impact parameter** a (the separation between its initial trajectory and a parallel line through the centre of the target) and initial velocity v, as shown in Figure 4.5, it will be deflected into a hyperbolic orbit of closest approach A. If A is smaller than the size of the accreting body of radius R, collision will occur. Thus there will be some critical $a_o(m, v, R)$ within which collision occurs, so that $\sigma = \pi a_o^2$. You can calculate A from a_o and v and m using conservation of energy and angular momentum only, and so work out a_o.

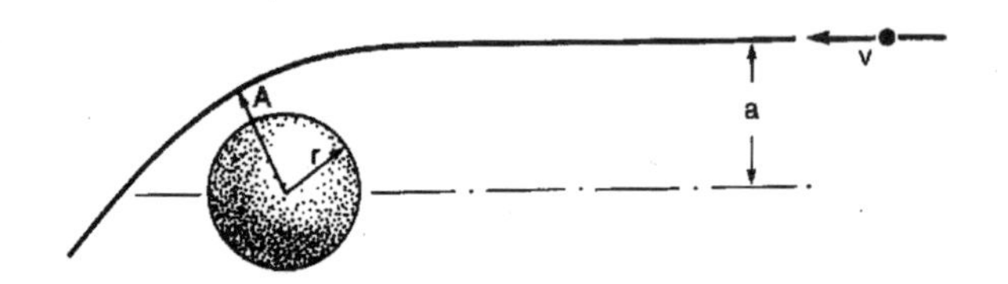

Figure 4.5: The minimum distance A between a small body gravitationally attracted to a larger one is less than its initial impact parameter a, so the gravitational collision cross section of the large body is bigger than πR^2.

Gravitational binding energy

Collisions do not always lead to accretion. Sometimes they disrupt a body already in existence. This will occur if the kinetic energy brought in by the approaching body exceeds the available binding energy of the target, whether this is gravitational or some other form. For the situation in which the binding energy is gravitational and the density of the "target" body is uniform, we can easily calculate exactly the binding energy, which is simply the total energy required to divide the body into small pieces and separate them by large distances against the attractive forces of gravity, or conversely the total energy released by gravity in assembling the body out of small pieces that are initially widely separated. To calculate the binding energy of a body, we consider the gravitational energy released as we construct it in a specific way.

We imagine building a body, of constant density ρ, by bringing in infinitesimally thin spherical shells of matter, one after another, to lay on top of the sphere already built. After some construction of this sort, the body built will have radius r and mass $m(r) = 4\pi r^3 \rho/3$. The next shell of matter put on will be dr thick and will have mass $dm = 4\pi r^2 \rho dr$. The gravitational energy released in adding this shell (or needed to remove it) will be

$$\begin{aligned} dE &= \frac{Gm(r)dm}{r} = \frac{G(4\pi r^3\rho/3)(4\pi r^2 \rho dr)}{r} \\ &= \frac{16\pi^2}{3}\rho^2 G r^4 dr. \end{aligned} \tag{4.2}$$

If we build up a body to radius R (or take it apart) the total energy released (or required) will be

$$\begin{aligned} E_g &= \int_0^R dE = \frac{16\pi^2}{3}\rho^2 G \int_0^R r^4 dr \\ &= \frac{16\pi^2}{15}\rho^2 G R^5 \\ &= \frac{3}{5}\frac{GM^2}{R}. \end{aligned} \tag{4.3}$$

Notice that in this particular case, the exact calculation of the binding energy gives a result that is different from that found using order-of-magnitude methods earlier in this chapter, in Equation (3.17), by less than a factor of two. This shows how such rough estimates can often give us valuable insight into the relative sizes of things and into what is happening.

Using this result, we conclude that if the kinetic energy of an impacting body of mass m and velocity v is larger than the binding energy of the target, so that the kinetic energy satisfies

$$\frac{1}{2}mv^2 > \frac{3}{5}\frac{GM^2}{R}, \tag{4.4}$$

we may be reasonably sure that the collision will be destructive, at least if the target body is large enough to be held together primarily by gravity rather than by solid body forces.

Exercise: (a) Show that the largest relative velocity that could occur between the Earth and any other body that is a bound member of the solar system is a little more than 70 km s^{-1}. (b) Estimate the mass of a body which would be large enough to shatter the Earth if it collided with Earth at a relative velocity of $v = 70$ km s^{-1}. Identify a body in the solar system of about the right mass to shatter the Earth if it impacted Earth at this velocity.

Structure of the solar nebula

It would be interesting to compute a rough model of the overall structure of the solar nebula as material was accreting onto the proto-Sun. Because we know very little about the conditions in the cloud from which the Sun formed (mass distribution, angular momentum, magnetic field, turbulence, presence of previously formed stars nearby, etc), it is very difficult to make a detailed description of the nebula. However, we can at least get an approximate idea of how the nebula might have appeared. Let's look at what plausible assumptions we might make that would allow us to develop a model of the nebula.

It will simplify matters a lot if we can neglect the nebula's own self-gravity, and consider only the gravity due to the proto-Sun, so we consider a time in the accretion process when the nebular mass was "small" compared to that of the Sun (we will see what "small" means later). We also want to avoid having to study the effects of infalling material, so we suppose that at the time we are considering there was a negligible rate of accretion from the surrounding nebula. It will simplify matters if we do not have to look at heating and cooling mechanisms that set the temperature of the nebular gas, so we will simply suppose that at each distance r from the sun (measured in the plane of the nebula) the nebular gas has a typical temperature $T(r)$, independent of z, which might vary from about 10^3 K near 1 AU to 10^2 K around 10 AU. We will ignore both inflow of new material into the nebula from the surrounding cloud, and losses from the nebula (by accretion onto the proto-Sun, for example).

With these simplifying assumption, it is possible to construct a simple model of the gas distribution in the solar nebula. Set up a system of cylindrical polar coordinates centred on the proto-Sun (which has mass M) with the z-direction normal to the nebular plane. Now at some point (r, z) in the nebula, suppose that the radial acceleration provided by the proto-Sun's gravity is just enough to keep the gas moving in a circular orbit (we neglect the effects of radial pressure gradients and of the drag that might be produced by turbulent viscosity). This implies that

$$\frac{GM}{r^2} = \frac{v^2}{r}. \tag{4.5}$$

Because we have assumed that the nebular mass is unimportant compared to that of the proto-Sun, the component of gravity acting on the gas in a direction perpendicular to the nebular plane is the z-component g_z of the proto-Sun's gravity. We assume the nebula is in a state of approximate equilibrium, so that the vertical component of the gravitational force, which acts to compress gas towards the nebular plane, is balanced by a vertical pressure gradient – that is, the gas pressure decreases away from the central plane of the nebula in just such a way as to balance the gravitational force from the proto-Sun towards the central plane. Using the same reasoning that we did to derive the equation of hydrostatic equilibrium, Equation (3.4), we find

$$\frac{dp}{dz} = -\rho g_z = \rho \frac{GM}{r^2 + z^2} \frac{z}{(r^2 + z^2)^{1/2}}. \tag{4.6}$$

Exercise: Verify Equation (4.6).

Now using the ideal gas law, Equation (2.5), we can replace ρ in the equation above and get an equation that can be integrated from the central plane ($z = 0$, where $p(0) = p_0$) up to some height z:

$$\int_{p_0}^{p(z)} \frac{dp}{p} = -\frac{\mu m_u GM}{kT} \int_0^z \frac{z\,dz}{(r^2 + z^2)^{3/2}}. \tag{4.7}$$

We could integrate Equation (4.7) exactly, but since we are really interested in conditions not too far from the nebular plane, we simplify the denominator to $1/r^3$. The integral is then trivial and the result is

$$\ln[p(z)/p_0] = -\frac{\mu m_u GM}{2kTr^3} z^2, \tag{4.8}$$

or

$$p(z) = p_0 e^{-z^2/H_n^2}, \tag{4.9}$$

where

$$H_n = \sqrt{\frac{2kTr^3}{G\mu m_u M}} = \sqrt{\frac{2k}{G\mu m_u M}} T^{1/2} r^{3/2} \tag{4.10}$$

is the *characteristic thickness* of the nebula. H_n is rather like a scale height, except that at a distance of more than H_n above or below the nebular plane, the gas pressure and density fall off much more rapidly than if they followed the usual barometric law.

This result provides us with a very interesting, if fairly rough, model of the gas in the proto-solar nebula. The gas is seen to be largely confined between the levels $z = \pm H_\mathrm{n}$. Now H_n decreases with increasing distance r from the proto-Sun because of the likely decline in $T(r)$ with r, but this variation is overwhelmed by the increase in H_n as $r^{3/2}$. Thus the prediction of this model is that the nebula is likely to be thicker at large distances from the proto-Sun than near it. And the thickness predicted is significant compared to the radial extent, of the order of 10%. Our simple model shows that the proto-solar nebula was a rather thick disk that flared out to even greater thickness as one went farther and farther from the proto-Sun.

Exercise: Show that by the time the mass of the Sun had approached its present value, H_n had a value of the order of 2×10^{10} m (about 15% of r) near 1 AU (assume $T \sim 10^3$ K), and a value about 10 times larger at around 10 AU (where $T \sim 10^2$ K).

Clearly on this model the central pressure in the plane of the disk, p_0, is determined by the total mass of the disk at a distance r from the proto-Sun. We define $\sigma(r)$ to be the total mass per unit area integrated from top to bottom of the disk; this useful quantity describes how much mass there is per m^2 of disk, at a given distance r, regardless of its vertical distribution. Now since at any r we have assumed that T is constant vertically, $p(z)$ and $\rho(z)$ are directly proportional (from the ideal gas law) and so

$$\rho(z) = \rho_0 e^{-z^2/H_\mathrm{n}^2}. \qquad (4.11)$$

Obviously $\sigma(r)$ is obtained by integrating $\rho(z)$ vertically through the entire nebula,

$$\sigma(r) = \int_{-\infty}^{\infty} \rho(z)\, dz = \frac{\sqrt{\pi}}{2} \rho_0 H_\mathrm{n}, \qquad (4.12)$$

so in terms of $\sigma(r)$, p_0 is given by

$$p_0(r) = \frac{\rho_0(r) k T(r)}{\mu m_\mathrm{u}} = \frac{2\sigma(r) k T(r)}{\sqrt{\pi}\mu m_\mathrm{u} H_\mathrm{n}(r)}. \qquad (4.13)$$

We would certainly like to know how $\sigma(r)$ varied with time and place (that would go a long way towards solving the whole problem of solar system formation!), but this is far more than we can expect to learn from such a simple model. However, we can at least specify how small $\sigma(r)$ needs to be for the solar gravity to dominate, so that the model is self-consistent.

To do this, we need to evaluate the gravitational acceleration produced by the nebula and compare this to the vertical acceleration due to the proto-Sun. This ratio certainly varied a lot over the nebula; the vertical component of gravity due to the proto-Sun varied by a factor of order 10^3 or more over the probable extent of the nebula from less than 1 AU out to more than 30 AU, and it certainly depended on the local mass surface density $\sigma(r)$ as well. We will limit ourselves to doing a useful order-of-magnitude estimate.

To get an idea of the sizes of the relevant quantities at a typical location, consider a point at 10 AU from the proto-Sun, and at a height of 2 AU above the nebular plane (and thus above most of the gas at that value of r). The vertical component of gravity due to the proto-Sun is about 10^{-5} m s^{-2}, assuming that the proto-Sun has most of its present mass. .

Exercise: Confirm the value of g_z.

But what is the vertical acceleration of gravity g_n due to the disk? To estimate it, we approximate the nebula as a thin, flat, very large ("infinite") disk of uniform mass surface density σ. Consider a point at a height z above this plane, and define cylindrical coordinates around the normal to the plane passing through the point. The thin ring of matter in the plane at a distance s from the axis, ds in width, has mass $dm = 2\pi s\, ds\, \sigma$. Its contribution to the vertical gravity at the point at z is

$$dg_\mathrm{n} = \frac{G\, dm}{s^2 + z^2} \frac{z}{\sqrt{s^2 + z^2}}. \qquad (4.14)$$

By symmetry, this ring will not exert any horizontal gravitational force; the horizontal force from each segment of the ring is balanced by an equal and opposite force from a segment on the opposite side of the ring. Only the vertical components from all the small segments of the ring will add constructively; the term $z/\sqrt{s^2 + z^2}$ evaluates the vertical component of the total gravitational attraction from each tiny segment.

The total gravitational acceleration due to the entire plane is obtained by summing the contributions from all the concentric rings around the z-axis:

$$g_\mathrm{n} = 2\pi\sigma G z \int_0^{\infty} \frac{s\, ds}{(s^2 + z^2)^{3/2}}. \qquad (4.15)$$

By making the substitution $u^2 = s^2 + z^2$ this integral can easily be evaluated, with the result

$$g_\mathrm{n} = 2\pi\sigma G z \int_z^{\infty} \frac{du}{u^2} = 2\pi\sigma G. \qquad (4.16)$$

Notice that the gravitational acceleration due to the plane is independent of the height z above the plane. For a real sheet of matter with a finite extent horizontally and finite thickness, this is still approximately true as long as the height above the plane is smaller than the lateral size of the plane, and we are located above or below most of the mass in the plane. Most of the attraction comes from the mass more or less directly below the point.

We can now combine these two results to find out how massive the nebula can be and still be consistent with our simple model. The contribution to the acceleration of gravity at the point from the proto-Sun is about 10^{-5} m s^{-2}, and this must be larger than the acceleration due to the nebula, Equation (4.16). This condition leads to the requirement that σ be much less than about 10^4 kg m^{-2}. This is not a very severe restriction; if σ were equal to this value the total mass of the nebula, assuming that it extended out to about 30 AU, would be of the order of 1 $M_\odot$.

Exercise: Confirm the numerical estimates above.

Thus for the model to be consistent, we simply require that the total mass of the nebula be substantially smaller than the mass of the proto-Sun. Observations of disks around other protostars suggest disk masses of the order of 0.02 $M_\odot$, consistent with our model; this disk mass would correspond to a surface mass density of a few hundred kg m^{-2}.

Exercise: Estimate the (volume) mass density ρ and the number density of H_2 molecules at mid-plane in the nebula at $r = 1$ AU, assuming $T = 10^3$ K there, total nebula mass 0.02 $M_\odot$, and uniform surface mass density $\sigma(r)$ out to 30 AU.

4.7 References

Boss, A. P. 1996, "Extra-solar planets", *Phys. Today*, Sept., 32. Boss describes how extra-solar planets are detected, and some of the first results that emerge from the recent discoveries.

Boss, A. P., Morfill, G. E. and Tscharnuter, W. M. 1989, "Models of the formation and evolution of the solar nebula", in *Origin and Evolution of Planetary and Satellite Atmospheres*, ed. S. K. Atreya, J. B. Pollack and M. S. Matthews (Tucson: University of Arizona Press), p. 35. This article reviews what is known about the processes that occurred during the formation of the solar nebula and the proto-Sun, emphasizing aspects that are still not well understood.

Cameron, A. G. W. 1988, "Origin of the solar system", in *Ann. Rev. Astr. Ap.*, 26, 441. This is an overview of the many processes involved in the formation of the solar system, with particular emphasis on how the planets and smaller bodies may have formed.

Doyle, L. R, Deeg, H.-J. and Brown, T. M. 2000, "Searching for the shadows of other Earths", *Sci. Am.*, Sep., 58. The transit of an extra-solar planet across the disk of its star, first observed in 1999, promises to provide valuable information complementary to that obtained from the observation of stellar radial motions.

Malhotra, R. 1999, "Migrating planets", *Sci. Am.*, Sep., 56

Sargent, A. I. and Beckwith, S. V. W. 1993, "The search for forming planetary systems", *Physics Today*, Apr., 22. The authors describe searches for and study of clouds and disks around young stars, and how we may learn more about the early solar nebula from such clouds.

Shu, F.H., Adams, F.C., and Lizano, S 1987, "Star formation in molecular clouds: observation and theory", in *Ann. Rev. Astr. Ap.*, 25, 23. The review of star formation presented in this article is mainly concerned with formation of low-mass ($M < 2M_\odot$) stars.

Stahler, S. W. and Walter, F. M. 1993, "Pre-main sequence evolution and the birth population", in *Protostars and Planets III*, ed. E. H. Levy and J. I. Lunine (Tucson: University of Arizona Press), p. 405. The successive steps in star formation, up to ignition of H, are reviewed from both a theoretical and an observational perspective.

4.8 Review questions

4.1 What observed characteristics of the current solar system suggest that this system formed from an accretion disk surrounding the early Sun? Fundamentally, why do we expect most protostars to have disks?

4.2 Why is a protostellar disk warm, or even hot near the forming protostar? Why is the disk temperature expected to vary a lot from near the protostar to far from it?

4.3 In the outer part of the solar nebula, before planet formation started, one would have found gases such as (a) H_2 and He, (b) H_2O, CH_4, and NH_3, and (c) CO, CO_2, and CN. Would you expect that molecules combining H with another element (the (b) gases) would have been as abundant (i.e. present in similar numbers of molecules per m^3) as H_2? Could the gases made up of molecules not involving H (such as the (c) gases) have been as abundant as H_2? Justify your conclusions.

4.4 What planetary formation processes are possible? What evidence helps us to decide where each of these processes may have occurred in the solar system?

4.5 What is the basic physical mechanism that led to the development of small, rocky planets in the inner solar system and giant, gas-rich planets with icy moons in the outer solar system?

4.6 The giant outer planets are all tens or hundreds of times more massive than the inner terrestrial planets. Describe how the giants may have become so much more massive than the inner planets.

4.7 What is the essential obstacle to detecting planets in other solar systems from direct images of such systems? What is the main technique currently used to detect extra-solar planets?

4.8 Some of the extra-solar planets detected are considered to be brown dwarfs while others are thought to be true planets. What is the meaning of this distinction? How might one discriminate between the two possibilities in a particular system where a low-mass object is observed?

4.9 Problems

4.1 Assume that a spherical gas cloud with a mass of 1 $M_\odot$ and an initial number density of $n_o = 3 \times 10^8$ H_2 molecules m^{-3} in a giant molecular cloud begins to contract under the influence of gravity. (a) What is its initial radius, in m and AU? (b) Suppose that the cloud contracts in such a way that each small element of mass conserves angular momentum, and that the cloud is initially rotating uniformly with the angular velocity of the galaxy, about $\Omega = 10^{-15}$ rad s^{-1}. (We don't know rotation rates for clouds well; this assumption just gives us a plausible initial rotation rate.) As the cloud contracts, it will spin faster. Consider now a small parcel of gas that remains at the outside edge of the cloud as the cloud contracts. Find an expression for the angular and transverse linear velocities of the parcel as a function of cloud radius. (c) At what cloud radius (again in m and AU) will the transverse motion of this parcel around the cloud roughly balance gravitational acceleration by the cloud mass, so that the parcel revolves in orbit around the main cloud? This is a rough way to estimate a possible size for the nebular disk around the proto-Sun.

4.2 Assume that the relative abundances in the solar nebula are the same as those given for the Sun in Table 2.2. (a) Calculate the mass fraction of the solar nebula mass that could condense as rocky material at high temperature ($T > 600$ K). Include Na, Mg, Al, Si, S, Ca, and Fe, and the amount of O that would condense with these metals, assuming that the main oxides would be Na_2O, MgO, Al_2O_3, SiO_2, SO_2, CaO, and FeO. (b) Calculate the mass fraction of the matter that could condense at $T \sim 100$ K as ices; include all metals from (a) as well as the C, N, and the remaining O in this component, together with an appropriate amount of H, assuming that H condenses in the ices CH_4, NH_3, and H_2O. Ignore Ne and Ar. What fraction of the mass (the H and He) would not condense anywhere in the solar nebula?

4.3 Suppose that the solar nebula has n_o dust particles per m^3, each of radius r_o, volume V_o and mass $m_o = 4\pi r_o^3 \rho/3$ at $t = 0$, where ρ is the density. Assume that the particles move about with relative velocities v and have essentially geometrical cross sections for collisions, and that whenever two particles collide, they stick together, keeping ρ constant. As a result, the average radius r of each particle will grow with time and the average number of particles per m^3 n will fall. (a) Assuming that at any time all the particles have the same radius r (a highly artificial assumption, but it allows us to solve the problem), and that the density of the particles stays constant, derive an expression relating the number density of particles to the radius r of the particles at any time, and to the initial values r_o and n_o. (b) Now derive an approximate expression for dr/dt. How does it depend on r? (Hint: approximate dt by one collision time τ_c, and estimate dr for that time interval from the fact that the volume of each particle is assumed to double in τ_c. Remember that both r and n are changing.) How does your expression depend on r? (c) For a particle mass density of 3000 kg m^{-3}, an average nebular mass density at $t = 0$ of 10^{-7} kg m^{-3}, and $v \sim 2 \times 10^{-2}$ m s^{-1}, what are the numerical values of n of dr/dt? (d) How long does it take to produce particles 0.1 m in radius?

4.4 Imagine a planetesimal sweeping up small particles from a dust cloud. Suppose the planetesimal, of mass M and radius R, is moving through the cloud at a velocity v. There are n_d dust particles per m^3, each of mass m_d. (a) Derive an expression for the number of collisions per second between the planetesimal and dust particles. Ignore the gravity of the planetesimal. (b) If all collisions result in the dust particles sticking to the planetesimal, derive an expression for the rate of change dM/dt of the mass of the planetesimal, and for the rate of change of the radius R of the planetesimal, dR/dt. Assume the planetesimal has constant density $\rho_{\rm p}$. (c) Assume that the planetesimal does not affect the dust cloud significantly, nor change its speed relative to the dust, so that v and $n_{\rm d}$ stay constant. Derive an expression for the time t required for the planetesimal to grow from a very small size to a particular radius R_1. (d) If the time required to make a body of $\rho_{\rm p} = 3000$ kg m^{-3} and $R_1 = 500$ km is 3×10^4 yr, the value of $m_{\rm d}$ is 10 gm, and the relative velocity v is 10^2 m s^{-1}, what is the number density $n_{\rm d}$ that must be present? What is the mass density $\rho_{\rm d}$ in the dust cloud?

4.5 Consider a large body ($R \sim$ the size of the Moon for example) accreting very small planetesimals ($r \sim 1$ m, for example); see Figure 4.5. (a) Use conservation of energy and angular momentum to evaluate the distance of closest approach A of a planetesimal originally approaching the large body with velocity v_∞ and impact parameter a. (b) From this expression, find an analytical expression for the cross section $\sigma = \pi r_{\rm A}^2$ (where $r_{\rm A}$ is the impact parameter for which $A = R$) for capture of planetesimals. (c) For sufficiently large mass M of the large body, show that σ increases as R^4. (Assume that the density of the large body stays constant, and remember that M depends on R.) (d) For $v_\infty = 10$ km/sec and the Earth's Moon, what is the ratio of capture cross section to geometrical cross section numerically? (e) At what mass and radius, for a body of the Moon's density, does σ change over from increasing approximately as R^2 to increasing as R^4, again assuming $v_\infty = 10$ km/sec?

4.6 Let's look at how difficult it would be to detect by direct imaging a planet like Jupiter if it were orbiting the nearby star α Centauri, a star very similar to the Sun. (a) α Centauri is at a distance of 1.3 pc (1 pc is equal to 3.26 ly; see Appendix B) from the solar system. Suppose a planet orbits this star with an orbit of 5 AU radius. How large would the maximum angular separation between star and planet be as seen from the Earth, in seconds of arc and in radians? Is this separation large enough that the two objects could be seen as separate bodies in spite of blurring of images by the Earth's atmosphere, which makes it difficult to separate objects that are less than about 1 second of arc apart on the sky? (b) Suppose that α Centauri has a radius of 1 $R_\odot$ and a surface temperature of 5800 K, and hence a luminosity of $1L_\odot$. If its hypothetical planet has the same radius as Jupiter (71,000 km), calculate the total power striking its surface. Now suppose that the planet reflects all the incident starlight striking it from α Centauri, and that this radiation is reflected uniformly into all directions. How much visible light energy is reflected per second from the planet? What is the ratio of the planet's reflected power to the power emitted by the star? (c) Now suppose that, like Jupiter, the hypothetical planet has an effective temperature for heat radiation of about 170 K. Find the wavelength (in m and μm) for which the black-body emission of the planet is maximum, and find and evaluate an equation giving the ratio of the monochromatic power output of the planet and the star at this wavelength. (Don't forget that α Cen and its planet have quite different surface areas.) (d) If you were going to try to detect the planet by direct imaging of the α Centauri system, would it be easier to do this using visible light or light in the infrared near the wavelength of the planet's black-body emission maximum, considering that your main problem would be to distinguish the faint planet in the glare of the star's light?

4.7 The aim of this problem is to appreciate the challenge involved in detecting extra-solar planets by observing the small radial velocity changes given to a star by a planet. Consider the effect of a single large planet orbiting a star. (a) Assuming at first that the mass m of the planet is negligible, derive the expression (Kepler's third law) relating the period P of a planet to the radius r of its circular orbit around the star of mass M at a velocity v, by equating the acceleration v^2/r of an object in a uniform circular orbit [see Equation (1.1)] with the gravitational acceleration produced at r by the central star. (b) Now recall that the two bodies will actually orbit around their common centre of mass. Find a simple expression for the distance $r_{\rm c}$ of the centre of mass from the centre of the star. (c) Assuming (correctly) that the period is given by the expression that you have derived with the substitution of $(M + m)$ for M, write an equation for the circumference of the orbit of the planet *about the centre of mass*, and the circumference of the orbit of the star about this same point. Use these expressions, and the one for the period for the system that you have derived, to obtain equations for the orbital velocities of the planet and of the star as functions of r, M, and m. (d) Now assume that the star has one solar mass (2.0×10^{30} kg) and the planet has the same mass as Jupiter (1.9×10^{27} kg). Compute the orbital velocity in m s^{-1} of the *star* for a separation of 0.1, 1, and 5 AU. (d) Assume that you are observing the line-of-sight component of velocity v_z of the star in this system from the plane of the orbit. Calculate and plot the variation of the v_z as a function of orbital position of the planet for some points through the orbit, for the case of part (d) that will be easiest to detect. Normal measurements of line-of-sight (radial) velocity of a star have precision (standard error) of the order of 500 m s^{-1}. Should it be easy to detect the effect of the planet on the star's radial velocity?

Chapter 5

Meteors, Impacts, and Meteorites

5.1 Overview

Almost everyone has had the experience of seeing a 'shooting star': a point of light that suddenly streaks across a portion of the visible sky, briefly leaving an incandescent trail, and then vanishes. The whole event lasts only a couple of seconds. Normally a person watching the sky steadily on a clear dark night, far from city lights, would see a few of these in an hour. Most such events, which are correctly called **meteors**, appear fairly similar in brightness and duration. However, very rarely, a meteor will be far brighter than most. It will flare brightly enough to read by (momentarily, of course). It may briefly leave a track with wider and narrower parts; it may also split into two or more pieces that pursue slightly different trajectories across the sky. Such a bright meteor is called a **fireball**. Still much more rarely, so rarely that relatively few people ever have the experience of seeing one, a particularly brilliant fireball will be followed by a noise like thunder, perhaps accompanied by a sharp report like a gun being fired, and pieces of stone, or even iron, will fall to the ground, apparently from the sky.

These extremely rare events, in which a particularly brilliant meteor is followed by a fall of rocks from the sky, give us an essential clue to understand the nature of all meteors. A meteor occurs when a piece of stray space debris, which we call a **meteoroid**, enters the Earth's atmosphere, typically at a speed of 10 $\mathrm{km\,s^{-1}}$ or more, and air friction heats it to incandescence as it is rapidly slowed to a speed of less than 1 $\mathrm{km\,s^{-1}}$. The visible meteor phenomenon is simply the light given off by the extremely hot surface of the object, and by the momentarily heated air in its wake. If the object is large enough (say at least some kg before it enters the atmosphere), part of it may survive the fiery descent, and arrive at the Earth's surface. The surviving fragments, once found, are called **meteorites**.

The meteorites that are found following a fireball can be of several different substances. Many are a kind of nondescript grey rock, which on close inspection usually appears to have tiny spherical pebbles, roughly one mm across, embedded in it. These pebbles are known as **chondrules**, and so the meteorites having them are known as **chondritic meteorites**, or simply **chondrites** (pronounce the 'ch' as 'k'). Other meteorites resemble terrestrial volcanic rocks, and are called **achondritic meteorites**, or **achondrites**, a term which simply says that they lack chondrules. Still other meteorites appear to be chunks of more or less pure iron; these are simply called **iron meteorites** or **irons**. Finally, a few objects in which veins or blobs of iron are mixed in between large ragged pieces of stone are known as **stony-irons**.

Once people began to understand that rocks, and in fact quite distinctive rocks, do indeed sometimes fall from the sky, it became possible to recognize other such rocks on the ground which had not been seen to fall, either because the region where they fell is not densely inhabited (forest or field or mountainside), because they fell at a time when no one was looking (early in the morning), or because they fell long ago. In fact, the majority of the meteorites now in the collections of universities and museums were not seen to fall, but have been simply found. It is useful to distinguish between meteorites seen to fall (**falls**), and found ones (**finds**), because if we want to estimate what fraction of all meteorites are of a particular type, observed falls may give us a reasonable indication of relative proportions, while finds, which are much more readily noticed on the ground if the meteorite is iron than if it is stony, furnish a very biased sample.

Meteorites are of course interesting in themselves, as a natural phenomenon. However, these objects have a special importance for planetary science which is considerably more general than simply being one more kind of solar system object. These pieces of stone or iron are actual physical samples of interplanetary material that are delivered to us free of charge, without any of the huge costs of a space exploration programme, and which can be examined and dissected in the laboratory. As we shall see later in this chapter, most meteorites are samples of the materials out of which the planets formed, from the period when this matter was first incorporated into asteroid-like bodies. Meteorites thus provide us with enormously valuable clues about conditions in the solar system at the time when the planets were forming. Such information is particularly precious because the material of the planets from which we have so far obtained samples (only terrestrial and lunar rocks, and a few meteorites from Mars, have been studied in terrestrial laboratories; rocks on Venus and Mars have been analyzed — much less thoroughly — on site by robot space probe landers) has been greatly modified by processes that occurred in and on these planets once they formed (volcanic activity, mountain building, erosion, metamorphism, etc). As a result, planetary matter no longer carries very much information about the conditions that prevailed when the planets were forming. Meteorites provide us with our primary method of looking into the past to the time when the planets were first growing out of much smaller objects.

5.2 Collisions of the Earth with space debris

A little history

The extreme rarity of witnessed meteorite falls meant that until about two centuries ago, their nature was generally unknown. At a place where a fall of rocks was actually witnessed by many people, it might be widely understood, quite correctly, that these rocks came (somehow!) from the sky. This was clearly the case for a fall of rocks that occurred in 1492 near Ensisheim, in Alsace, France; this fall was widely described in a printed broadsheet, and is one of the oldest recorded falls from which material is still available for study (the meteorite is preserved in the Ensisheim town hall). However, after a couple of generations such an event would recede into the mythical past, and in any case people elsewhere who had not themselves witnessed the fall would usually be very sceptical of the reality of such an apparently impossible event. Thus it was still possible late in the eighteenth century for scientifically educated people to dismiss the very possibility of rocks falling from the sky as completely unbelievable, in spite of several widely witnessed falls.

The tide began to turn in 1794 when E. F. F. Chladni (1756–1827) published a small book in which he assembled a number of historical reports of bright meteors which had led to meteorites. He also discussed two large iron objects that he argued are ancient meteorites, and he correctly concluded that these objects had fallen from the sky. Most scientists of the day remained skeptical about this idea, but in the next few years, several meteorite falls were clearly documented, and the tide of scientific opinion began to change. The very careful study by J.-B. Biot (1774–1862) for the Académie Française of a fall that occurred in April, 1803, at L'Aigle, France, when some 3000 stones fell to the ground in broad daylight in the presence of hundreds of witnesses, convinced most of the remaining skeptics of the reality of meteorite falls. Since that time, these rocks from the sky have been widely sought, collected, and studied in the laboratory.

By now, several hundred falls have been documented, and several thousand meteorites have been found and collected. These objects are in collections all over the world, both public and private. The collections have been considerably augmented in recent years by systematic searches for meteorites in such normally rock-free areas as the plains and prairies of North America and Australia, and large deserts such as the Sahara.

A particularly interesting reservoir of meteorites was discovered in Antarctica in 1969 by Japanese scientists, which has now yielded thousands of meteorites. Meteorites that fall on this continent become buried in snow and ice. Much of the ice that covers Antarctica is part of huge moving glaciers that spread toward the sea as they are made deeper and deeper by successive snowfalls. Where such glaciers must climb over buried hills or mountains as they move towards the coast, scouring by high winds leads to net evaporation of the moving and rising ice front, and buried meteorites are gradually brought to the surface, where they accumulate and can be found in large numbers. This source of meteorites has greatly enriched the world's collections, and in particular provided the first meteorite known to be of lunar origin—a tiny piece of rock blasted loose from the lunar surface by a large (meteoroid!) impact, which eventually fell to Earth. Antarctica has also yielded a number of a rare meteorite type known as SNC meteorites, believed to have been ejected from the surface of Mars less than 1.3 Gyr ago by the impact of another meteoroid.

5.3 Meteors

It is now clearly understood that meteorites fall from the sky, that is, that they come to Earth from outer space, and if they are seen to fall, they produce a spectacular meteor display. But what are their sources? Could they mostly be objects from outside the solar system entirely, or fragments of comets, or of asteroids? Do they somehow come from our Moon, or from another planet? These questions have been addressed by deducing the orbits in space (before collision with the Earth's atmosphere) of the meteoroids that produce fireballs and fainter meteors. This may be done by carefully observing the track through the sky followed by such a body as it enters the Earth's atmosphere and reveals its presence – and the direction and speed with which it is moving – by analyzing the meteor display. In effect, the atmosphere is used as a giant meteoroid detector.

Meteor trails have been observed by photographic sky patrols that were set up in a number of countries such as Canada, the U. S. A., and the (former) Soviet Union. Such a sky patrol typically consists of a network of automatically operated cameras, perhaps 200 or 300 km apart on the ground and distributed over an area hundreds of km across, that survey the sky night after night. Each station (which may have several cameras pointed in different directions) has a sensor that electronically opens the camera shutter(s) when the light of a bright fireball is detected. Each camera is also equipped with a special secondary shutter (in addition to the one that opens when a fireball is seen); this shutter consists of a rotating disk with alternate open and covered sectors, so that in effect the camera shutter is opened and closed a number of times per second as the fireball streaks across the sky. The appearance of a fireball is recorded on one or more photographs at each station that detects it, as a dashed streak of light on a photograph. Since the camera orientation at each station is fixed and known, study of such a photograph allows scientists to determine the direction in the sky from the camera towards the fireball (that is, to deduce the orientation of the plane containing the camera and the fireball's trajectory).

Frequently the fireball would be recorded by cameras at two or even several stations in the network. Since each photograph is taken at a known time, photos of the same meteor taken from different locations can be paired up. Combining the recorded tracks from two or more stations, it is possible to deduce the trajectory of the meteor in the sky (it is simply the track where the two planes, one from each camera, containing the fireball's trajectory, intersect). The interruption of each exposure by the rotating disk at a known rate permits the speed of the fireball at various points in its track to be established. From these data, the orbit of the meteoroid as it enters the Earth's atmosphere may be established. The final trajectory of the object as it fades and vanishes from the photographs can be used to deduce where the meteorite, if it survives atmospheric entry, should land. Furthermore, the way in which the object is slowed down by atmospheric drag may be studied and its brightness can be measured. Using these data, it is possible to determine approximately the mass, size and density of the incoming meteoroid.

From studies with such photographic networks of thousands of meteor trails, much valuable information has been obtained. It is found that visible meteors, the kind we see by eye at night, generally enter the Earth's atmosphere at speeds of between about 11 km s^{-1} (essentially the escape velocity from Earth, and thus the lowest possible infall speed), and about 72 km s^{-1} (the speed of an object barely bound to the solar system that is moving in a retrograde orbit in the ecliptic plane). For the more rapidly moving incoming meteoroids, the visible meteor display begins somewhere around 120 km above the ground and ends perhaps 100 km up. For slower objects, the display may start around 100 km altitude and end about 75 or 80 km above the ground. A particular meteor is thus generally visible from a region on the ground of the order of 200 km in diameter.

Exercise: A meteor that appears at an altitude of 100 km above the ground, and that occurs 300 km away from where you are standing, will be seen at 17° above the horizon. Are there any reasons that this meteor would be less likely to be visible to you than an identical meteor occuring 100 km directly overhead?

When we watch meteors carefully over several years, we find that meteors arrive in two somewhat different ways. The meteors that are seen on most nights are **sporadic meteors**. The meteoroids causing these meteors arrive singly, and make trails on the sky that are randomly orientated. On a dark, clear night without moonlight, a dark-adapted person watching the sky will typically see a few such meteors per hour. When the orbits in space of the meteoroids causing the trails are deduced from the speed and direction of the meteor in the Earth's atmosphere, it is found that sporadic meteors strike the Earth from all directions. However, like the orbits of comets, essentially all of the meteoroid orbits before their arrival at the Earth are confined to the solar system. There is no evidence for an origin of a significant number of these sporadic meteors from outside the solar system, either in excess velocities, or in an excess coming from the direction of the Sun's motion through the local stars.

However, the deduced space orbits do not completely clarify what kinds of bodies the sporadic meteors are related to. The sporadic meteors that have the highest arrival velocities in the atmosphere are produced by meteoroids having orbits that resemble those of long-period comets, with large inclination to the ecliptic and large semi-major axes. Since comets are known to shed small pieces of solid material, it is natural to assume that these high-velocity meteors are probably produced by comet debris. However, there is also a population of meteoroids that strike the Earth with relatively (!) low velocity, of the order of 10 or 20 km

s^{-1}. In order to reach the Earth's upper atmosphere with such a low velocity, the meteoroid must be travelling in an orbit in which its speed and direction at 1 AU from the Sun is fairly similar to that of the Earth. This requires that the low-velocity meteoroids are in direct orbits, roughly in the ecliptic plane, with orbital semi-major axes that are not too large, a few AU or less. The meteor-producing bodies could be either the short-period comets, whose orbits have this character, or near-Earth asteroids, whose orbits typically reach from an aphelion somewhere in the asteroid belt to a perihelion around 1 AU, and lie approximately in the ecliptic plane. Probably both sources contribute to the observed meteors.

On particular calendar dates, during one or a few consecutive nights, a second type of meteor, known as **shower meteors**, may be seen. These meteors can be substantially more numerous than sporadic meteors; up to some tens of meteors may be seen per hour, or in really exceptional cases known as meteor storms, even thousands. They appear to originate in a particular spot in the sky, called the radiant, from which all of the trails of meteors associated with the shower radiate outwards. The existence of the radiant is a perspective effect; in fact the meteoroids of a meteor shower are travelling through space on parallel tracks, and thus appear to come from a single point in the sky, just as the two parallel rails of a straight railroad line appear to come from a single distant point. (Meteor showers are named after the constellation – or a particular bright stars – from which they seem to radiate.) When the orbits of a particular shower are studied in detail, it is found that not only are the motions through space of the various meteoroids parallel as they arrive at the Earth, but their velocities are also very similar – thus all the meteoroids of a particular meteor shower have very similar orbits in space.

The orbits in space of the meteors of a particular shower turn out in a number of cases to be very similar to the orbit of known comets, and it is this association that led nineteenth century astronomers to deduce that the nucleus of a comet might simply be a swarm of small meteoroids. We now understand that a meteor shower is produced by the cloud of solid fragments of rocky material that are lost from the associated comet as it outgasses during it passage through the inner solar system. The tiniest fragments of solid comet debris, those that produce the comet tails, are not responsible for shower meteors; these microscopic dust grains (they are typically only about 1 μm in size) are affected strongly enough by solar radiation that they quickly separate from the parent comet and are generally shifted, within a single perihelion passage, into orbits that carry them completely out of the solar system. The shower meteoroids are much larger fragments, 0.1 mm or more across. They are part of the swarm of larger particles that are blown off the comet nucleus as it loses gases, sometimes gently, sometimes rather explosively. These larger grains and particles, too large to be significantly affected by the Sun's radiation pressure, drift slowly away from the comet nucleus and form a part of the coma.

These fragments of solid matter are ejected from the comet nucleus in various directions at speeds of a few tens or hundreds of m s^{-1}. As a result they no longer follow exactly the orbit of the nucleus. They are transferred by the ejection process into orbits that are similar in shape and orientation in space to the orbit of the nucleus, but may differ significantly in size and period. For example, if a particle is ejected at a speed of 100 m s^{-1} near perihelion from a comet nucleus in an orbit of semi-major axis $a = 5$ AU, which has a period of about 11 years, the fragment may be placed in an orbit which has a semi-major axis as much as 6% larger or smaller, and which differs in period by as much as a year from the orbit of the nucleus. As a result, these larger dust particles gradually spread around the entire cometary orbit as they get ahead of the nucleus or fall behind it. Later, if the Earth passes close to the orbit of the comet, even though the nucleus may be far away, there is likely to be a swarm of particles through which the Earth passes, causing a meteor shower.

Some of the more prominent meteor showers are listed in Table 5.1. This table gives the name of each shower; the typical date on or around which it occurs each year; the duration D of the shower in days; the zenith hourly rate ZHR, which is the normal maximum rate which could be seen under exceptionally clear and dark conditions by an experienced observed in one hour; the velocity v with which the meteoroids strike the atmosphere; and the associated comet if one is known (compare to Table 7.2).

Entry of a meteoroid into the atmosphere

Let's look more closely at what happens as a meteoroid (any meteoroid, not just fragile, tiny bits of comet debris) collides with the Earth's upper atmosphere. The meteor display that we see from the ground results from this high-speed collision. As a rapidly moving piece of solid material enters the upper atmosphere, it strikes one individual air molecule after another, so violently that an electron of the air molecule may be lifted into an upper energy level or even detached. Furthermore, one or more atoms of the meteoroid will probably become highly energized, effectively heating the surface, but rather slowly at first, since the air molecules

Table 5.1: Some important meteor showers

Shower	Date	D (d)	ZHR	v (km s^{-1})	Comet
Quarantids	Jan 3	0.8	85	42	
η Aquarids	May 4	14.	30	65	Halley
β Taurids	Jun 30	14.		31	Encke
δ Aquarids	Jul 28	12.	20	41	
Perseids	Aug 12	5.	100	60	Swift-Tuttle
Draconids	Oct 9	2.		24	Giacobini-Zinner
Orionids	Oct 21	8.	20	66	Halley
Leonids	Nov 17	4.	60	71	Tempel-Tuttle
Geminids	Dec 14	3.	95	35	(asteroid) Phaethon
Ursids	Dec 22	2.	20	34	Tuttle

Sources: K. R. Lang 1992, *Astrophysical Data: Planets and Stars* (New York: Springer-Verlag); *Observer's Handbook 1997* (Toronto: Royal Astr. Soc. of Canada)

are very far apart in the outermost atmosphere of the Earth. As the meteoroid continues on into the atmosphere, the air rapidly increases in density; the density doubles roughly with every 6 km decrease in altitude. One collision with an air molecule follows another, until at an altitude of roughly 100 km the air is dense enough that individual collisions between the meteoroid and air molecules are replaced by the formation of a sheath or plasma of very hot swept-up air molecules mixed with molecules vaporized from the meteoroid. Air molecules now collide with this sheath, and the energy they transfer to it is carried in to the meteoroid, further heating it. Within a second or so, the surface of the meteoroid heats up to a temperature of between 2000 and 3000 K, causing the surface of the meteoroid to rapidly melt and then evaporate. The cloud of heated atoms evaporated from the meteoroid has many atoms in which an electron is lifted to an upper energy level, both because of the initial evaporation process and because of collisions with other atoms, and as these electrons drop down to lower energy they create an emission spectrum (see Chapter 2), producing the brilliant incandescence that we see from the ground.

As the meteoroid speed drops below 3 km s^{-1}, energy dissipation ceases to be sufficient to maintain the meteoroid surface in a state of incandescence. If any of the mass of the original meteoroid remains, it cools rapidly and continues to fall in **dark flight**. Within a few tens of seconds, all but the largest meteoroids slow down to a speed of a few hundred m s^{-1} or less. If only a tiny mass is left, it drifts downward through the air at a very slow speed; because of its small size, it will not be recognized as a meteorite even when it does finally reach the ground. If the remaining mass is larger, say a few hundred gm or more, it will continue to fall for several minutes, and might be recognized as a meteorite after it strikes the ground.

The ionization of air molecules by the incoming meteoroid also makes possible the observation of meteors, by radar. If a powerful radio transmitter sends a burst of radio waves upwards, a tiny fraction of this radio emission will be reflected by the free electrons in the ionized trail of the meteor and can be detected by a radio receiver back on the ground a fraction of a second later. By this means, meteors can be studied even in the daytime, and meteoroids even smaller than those that make visible trails can be detected.

The process of meteor deceleration is reasonably well understood now, and enables us to learn more about the incoming meteoroid in addition to the direction of its initial orbit. If the diminishing speed of a meteor at various points along its track is determined from photographic observations from two or more stations, we can apply the theory of meteoroid motion in the resisting atmosphere to deduce both the initial mass of the incoming body and the final (usually much smaller) mass that may remain after the deceleration is complete. By measuring the intensity of the radiation emitted by the meteor at various points along its track, we obtain further information about the meteoroid (for example its density). One result is particularly surprising: a meteoroid with a mass of less than 1 gm and a radius of a few mm, moving at 30 or 40 km s^{-1}, can produce a meteor trail that is easily visible from the ground 100 km below! An object like this emits many kilowatts of radiation during the second or so that it takes to slow down. In fact, most of the meteors we see, both sporadic and shower meteors, are due to particles of roughly this size. It is thus hardly surprising that meteors almost never lead to recoverable objects, since after losing most of their mass to vaporization as they slow down, the vast majority reach the ground as no more than tiny grains or small clusters of atoms. In fact, shower meteors, due to debris from comets, never seem to reach the Earth as meteorites. These bodies are so small or fragile, and strike the atmosphere at velocities that are so large (see Table 5.1) that no significant solid object survives to reach the ground. No meteorite whatever is known to have been produced by a cometary meteor shower.

The incoming meteoroids detectable by radar (which can detect the ion trail of a meteoroid of a particle with a mass of the order of 10^{-12} kg), by "patrol cameras (networks of cameras specially set up to watch for Meteors), the eyes – and amateur video cameras – of observers, and orbiting satellites (which frequently observe objects having masses of tonnes striking the atmosphere) cover a huge range of mass. It should come as no surprise that this general picture of the interaction of a "typical" meteoroid with the Earth's atmosphere actually depends substantially on the mass and size of the incoming object. In fact, four rather different situations occur.

- The smallest meteoroids, those with sizes of less than about 0.01 mm and masses of less than roughly 10^{-11} kg, have such a large ratio of surface area to mass that they are slowed down to speeds of a few km s^{-1} or less by collisions with isolated single air molecules above 100 km altitude. Their surface temperatures never rise to the evaporation point at all, no hot vapours are produced, and *no meteor phenomenon is observed.* Such a tiny meteoroid, not much altered from its state before colliding with Earth, simply drifts slowly downwards through the atmosphere. These particles can be collected and studied using sounding rockets (small rockets that do not leave the atmosphere) and very high-flying planes, and studied in the laboratory.

- Typical meteor particles detectable by the eye (or at least by radar) have sizes ranging from about 0.01 mm to perhaps 20 cm, and masses in the range of 10^{-11} kg up to a few kg or tens of kg. These objects are still travelling at nearly their original speed as they plow into the denser air below 100 km altitude. They heat up very rapidly and lose mass by sublimation, by loss of tiny fluid droplets, and by fragmentation. Most of the kinetic energy carried by the incoming meteoroid is used to erode the object. Such meteoroids radiate intensely, and constitute almost all the meteors that we see at night. However, after some km or tens of km of flight, such a body ceases radiating because *all of its mass has been lost.* Objects in this size range do not in general produce meteorites, even if the meteor display is truly spectacular.

- Meteoroids with sizes between some tens of cm and several meters in size (masses between tens of kg and hundreds of tonnes) also enter the denser atmosphere below 100 km altitude while still travelling at hypersonic velocity. They too are intensely heated and lose much of their surface mass, but because the kinetic energy of the incoming meteoroid is not transferred efficiently into heating the surface of the meteoroid (more goes into heating the air blasted out of the way by the meteoroid), if the meteoroid remains intact, it reduces its speed below about 3 km s^{-1} *before its mass is completely sublimed.* Below this speed, the falling body no longer is heated intensely enough to continue to lose mass or to radiate, and so the remaining mass of the meteoroid falls as a rapidly cooling, dark object. However, the majority of meteoroids in this size range will explode high in the atmosphere as a result of the intense heating and pressure, and the smaller pieces will also lose mass as they quickly decelerate. The result is that one or many small remnants of the original body (usually a few percent of the original mass or less) drop though the atmosphere at speeds determined by the resistance of the air (this is called "free fall"). This last, dark flight takes several minutes. These small survivors strike the ground at speeds of some tens or hundreds of m s^{-1}, digging pits not much larger than the falling bodies themselves, and leaving meteorites on the ground that may be recovered.

The possibility of some remnant meteorites surviving the violent deceleration and heating depends strongly on the initial velocity of the meteoroid and on its mechanical strength. The faster the body is moving when it strikes the atmosphere, the more intense the **ablation** (sublimation by intense heating) of material, and the tinier the fraction of the original mass that survives. Objects that enter the atmosphere at speeds in excess of about 30 km s^{-1} have little chance of having a remnant large enough to produce a meteorite. Similarly, mechanically weak objects (stones, particularly the relatively fragile carbonaceous ones) are likely to be fragmented into many small pieces that individually are largely vaporized before landing, while a stronger object (a solid mass of iron or a strongly cohesive stone) may withstand the tremendous pressure that occurs during deceleration and end as a single meteorite or a small number of large fragments on the ground.

- The largest (and rarest) meteoroids, with masses of thousands of tonnes or more, and sizes of tens of m or more, contain more mass than is present in the entire column of air through which they pass as they fall to the Earth. As a result, they are not slowed appreciably by their passage through the atmosphere, even though they produce enormous meteor displays. Such a body strikes the ground with essentially its original hypersonic velocity. The instantaneous release of almost all of the meteoroid's initial kinetic energy on impact produces an enormous explosion. This explosion vaporizes the entire incoming body (except for fragments that may have broken off during its passage through the atmosphere), excavates an enormous crater, sends shock waves throughout the Earth, and lofts many tonnes of pulverized rock and Earth high into the atmosphere where it may remain for months or years. Examples on the Earth of such impacts are discussed in the next section, and the topic is explored in more depth in Chapter 9.

Not all of these different sizes of meteoroids fall equally often, of course. The smallest particles are by far the most common, and as one looks for larger and larger objects, they become rapidly rarer. Thus, most of the meteors we see are produced by the smallest objects capable of producing a visible display; really spectacular fireballs are also extremely rare. Impacts of bodies with sizes of the order of some tens of meters (and masses of order 10^5 tonnes) occur only roughly once per millennium; bodies ten times larger in dimensions (masses of order 10^8 tonnes) strike the Earth only every million years or so. An overview of the frequency of impacts of various sizes of bodies is given in Table 5.2.

When we add up the total mass of material striking the Earth's atmosphere over all sizes of impacting bodies, we arrive at a rough total of about 70 tonnes per day, or about 30,000 tonnes per year.

Table 5.2: Impacts of small bodies on Earth

Mass of meteoroid	Result of impact	Approximate impact rate, hits per yr
10^{-6} gm	vaporize particle invisibly	
10^{-4} gm	faint visible meteor, no meteorite	
10^{-2} gm	visible meteor, no meteorite	
1 gm	bright visible meteor, no meteorite	10^7
10^2 gm	fireball	10^5
10 kg	fireball, meteorites	3×10^3
1 tonne	brilliant fireball, meteorites	50
10^2 t	brilliant fireball, meteorites	0.2
10^4 t	1 Mton TNT explosion, few meteorites	0.01
10^6 t	100 Mton TNT explosion 2 km diameter crater	10^{-4}
10^{10} t	K-T event, global catastrophe	10^{-8}

Source: Brown, P. et al. 2002, *Nature* 420, 294.

5.4 Impact craters on the Earth

A very, very small fraction of meteoroids are much larger than the rest. As we shall see later, early in the Earth's history (roughly during the first 0.5 Gyr of its 4.5 Gyr present age), the Earth must have been struck repeatedly by objects having diameters of tens of km; the largest of these impacts, which we now believe led to the formation of the Earth's Moon, probably involved a collision with an object roughly the size of the planet Mars! During the past billion years, however, the largest impacts have been with objects only(!) 10 or 20 km in diameter, typical sizes of relatively small asteroids or of comet nuclei, the two sources of bodies that currently are colliding with Earth.

Such enormous collisions, or even collisions with meteoroids only a few tens or hundreds of m in diameter, do far more than simply leave a sprinkling of space debris on the ground. As we have seen, an object with a mass of more than a few tons is more massive than the column of air it must push out of the way as it descends to the ground, and is hardly slowed at all by its passage through the atmosphere (although it does make a spectacular display, both as a brilliant fireball and as a source of a powerful sonic boom). Unless this body fragments completely as it pushes through the atmosphere, it strikes the ground with almost its original velocity.

The kinetic energy carried by a such a **hypervelocity** body is enormous. There is more than enough energy to vaporize the meteoroid; the conversion of the meteoroid's kinetic energy into heat at the instant of impact will certainly vaporize the incoming body, but plenty of energy will be left over for other effects. The impacting body will excavate a large crater, typically ten to twenty times the diameter of the meteoroid itself. A meteoroid with a diameter of a few km thus excavates a hole of the order of one hundred km across, that is momentarily tens of km deep. The crater floor will rebound within seconds or minutes, mainly because of the high pressure exerted on the walls and floor of the crater by the surrounding Earth. (Try to visualize this compared to the place where you live.) The impact produces a huge fireball and blast wave, like that generated by a gigantic nuclear bomb, capable of burning and flattening trees and structures in a region tens, hundreds, or even thousands of km across. This blast will send out powerful earthquake waves through the Earth. The impact will also loft a huge mass of very tiny particles of rock and soil high into the atmosphere (the mushroom cloud of a nuclear bomb explosion is due to this effect). This dust cloud will spread out over a significant part of the globe, only very slowly falling to the ground again, typically during several years, and, if the cloud is dense enough, producing an extended period of darkness on the ground, a "nuclear winter". (The largest terrestrial volcanic eruptions produce similar long-lived dust clouds in the upper atmosphere, as do the largest forest fires.)

An impact on deep water (recall that 70% of the Earth's surface is covered with deep oceans) produces similar phenomena, except that the crater also creates a huge hole in the water which quickly fills, generating enormous "tidal waves" (tsunamis) hundreds of meters in height that sweep across the ocean surface and wash up on coastlines around the world. The mushroom cloud is full of steam as well as dust from the ocean floor.

Only one major hypervelocity impact has been recorded in historical times. Early in the morning on June 30, 1908, a brilliant fireball was seen streaking north-westwards through the sky over southern Siberia. Less than a minute later, more than 600 km from where the meteoroid first entered the atmosphere, a huge explosion occurred over the region of the Podkammenaya Tunguska River in central Siberia, at a point about 500 km north of the town of Bratsk (the position of the final explosion was at 60° 55′ N, 101° 57′ E). The sound of the detonation was audible several hundred km away, and was registered on recording barometers all over the world. The explosion was detected by seismographs 1000 km away. Because the region was (and is) almost uninhabited, the only known fatalities were some reindeer, although houses were damaged in Vanovara, the nearest village, some 70 km away.

The region of the Tunguska impact is so remote (the nearest towns of any size – and the railroad lines – lie hundreds of km to the south) that it was not until 19 years later that the first expedition to the blast site was led by L. A. Kulik of the Russian Academy of Sciences. Kulik reported that although there was no crater, and no sign of any fragments of the impacting object, the forest near the site of the explosion had been completely destroyed and burned. Further away from the centre of the explosion, pine trees in the forest, many with trunks 50 to 75 cm in diameter, had been knocked over (falling radially away from "ground zero") and burned, out to a distance of 20 or 30 km away from the blast centre. Some 2000 km^2 of forest was destroyed. Figure 5.1 reproduces a photograph of the devastated forest.

Figure 5.1: A photograph of trees knocked over and burned by the blast and fireball of the Tunguska meteoroid impact some 8 km away. The photo was taken by the third expedition to the site in 1929, more than 20 years after the impact.

It is now believed (both from mathematical modelling of the entry and explosion of such an object, and from tiny fragments reportedly found in trees near ground zero) that the impacting body at Tunguska was a chondritic asteroid, perhaps 50 m in diameter (the size of a typical university building), that entered the atmosphere almost horizontally over southern Siberia and finally fragmented and vaporized at an altitude of 5 to 10 km above the ground. The energy release of the explosion has been estimated to have been 5×10^{16} to 10^{17} Joules. This is equivalent to the explosion of a hydrogen bomb with an energy yield of 10 to 20 *megatons* of TNT. Clearly, if this explosion had occurred over a city such as Moscow or Toronto, the results would have been devastating for thousands or millions of people. Fortunately, such densely populated areas cover only a tiny fraction of the Earth and thus are very unlikely to be struck by impacting meteoroids.

Exercise: If the Tunguska event had occurred (in Siberia) in the year 1600, do you think we would know about it?

Figure 5.2: An aerial photograph of Barringer Crater, near Winslow, Arizona. This crater is about 1.2 km in diameter and about 100 m deep. It was produced by the impact 49,000 years ago of a massive iron meteorite. The lip, made of some of the material ejected during the impact, can still be seen around the rim of the crater. (Courtesy of the Geological Survey of Canada)

To find traces of earlier impacts, we search for the most durable record produced by such an event, the crater. A number of craters have been identified on the Earth's surface which were produced by meteoroid impacts. Some of the smaller and more recent ones, having diameters that range between 100 m and 1 km, are still littered with fragments of the impacting meteoroid (often an iron meteoroid). Such small craters are eradicated by erosion within roughly a million years, so the known ones are relatively young. The largest and best preserved of these craters, shown in Figure 5.2, is the well-known Barringer Meteor Crater in northern Arizona, in the U.S. This crater was excavated approximately 49,000 years ago by an iron meteoroid roughly 30 m in radius, with a mass of about 10^5 tonnes, from which several tonnes of meteorites have been recovered. The crater is about 1.2 km in diameter, and is presently (after many millennia of erosion) about 100 m deep.

Exercise: Both the Barringer and the Tunguska meteoroids have been estimated to have had masses of roughly 10^5 tonnes. Explain why the Barringer object left a crater that 50 000 years later is still over 1 km in diameter, while the much more recent Tunguska meteoroid left no crater at all.

Some tens of older and usually larger craters are also recognized, even without any obvious remnants of the impacting body, by their distinctive bowl shapes, by changes produced in the mineral structure of underlying rocks by the explosion, and by lack of any obvious evidence of volcanic origin. Many of these are found in areas of the Earth where very old rock formations come to the surface, as in the Canadian shield region, and were protected by a covering of sediments until their recent excavation by erosion, often by glacial action during the ice age of the last million years. Some of these craters have diameters of 100 km or more, and must have been produced by truly catastrophic impacts. The New Quebec Crater, in Quebec, Canada, which is 3.4 km in diameter and 1.4 million years old, is seen in Figure 5.3. This impact would have been roughly comparable to the one that produced the Barringer Crater. The crater is still relatively well preserved. The 214 million year old Manicouagan Crater (Figure 5.4), now just a roughly circular trench in the shield rock of northern Quebec, is about 100 km in diameter. The impact responsible for this structure must have been catastrophic on a vast scale. The even larger and older Sudbury basin in northern Ontario, a structure about *1.85 Gyr* old and some 250 km long, is now known to be of meteoric origin. (The famous nickel deposits resulted when magma from beneath the impact area seeped into the crater, depositing the ore; they are not remnants of the actual impactor.)

Figure 5.3: The New Quebec Crater, on the Ungava Peninsula in northern Quebec, near the entrance to Hudson Bay. This 3.4 km diameter crater, 1.4 Myr old, is now a circular lake (Courtesy of the Geological Survey of Canada)

Sufficiently large impacts may have a really devastating global effect on terrestrial life. At the end of the Mesozoic era about 65 million years ago, about 60% of all species of living plants and animals, including every single species of dinosaurs (except for the forerunners of today's birds), became extinct almost simultaneously. It has long been argued that this may have been due to some kind of global catastrophe, such as the explosion

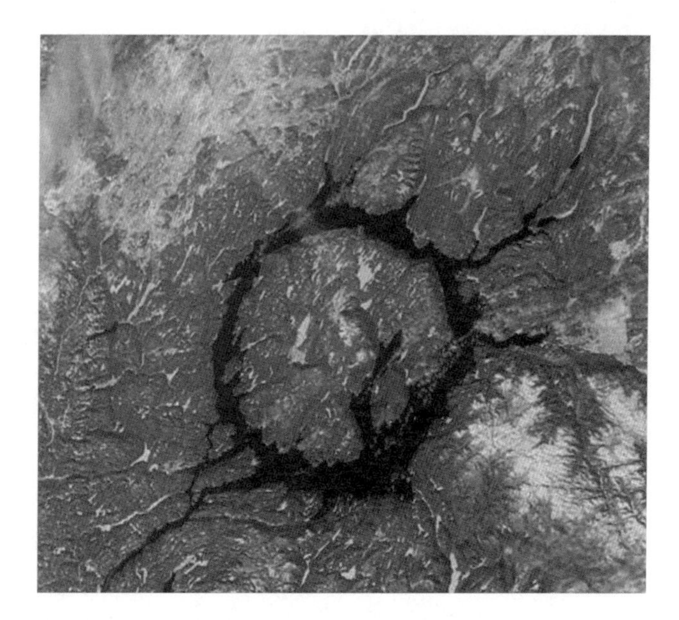

Figure 5.4: Manicouagan Lake, north of the mouth of the St. Lawrence River in Quebec. Most of this 214 million year old impact scar has been eroded away, leaving only a roughly circular trench as the visible remnant of the 100 km diameter crater. (Courtesy of NASA.)

of a nearby supernova, a world-wide epoch of extraordinary volcanic activity, or some kind of far-reaching plague. It is now generally believed that the extinction of so many species was caused by the impact of an asteroid or comet nucleus with a diameter of 10 or 20 km onto the Earth.

The first important piece of direct evidence for this idea was discovered by the father and son team of Luis and Walter Alvarez. They found that in a rock layer in Italy that was laid down as sediments at the end of the Mesozoic era, a thin layer of clay relatively rich in the rare element iridium is present. (The excess iridium is found between a rock layer from the Cretaceous period and a layer from in the following Tertiary period; this boundary is often referred to as the "K–T boundary".) Iridium makes up only a tiny fraction of the solid material in the inner solar system; in the solar atmosphere and in primitive meteorites only about 5 atoms of iridium are present per million Si atoms. Iridium is even less abundant in the rocks of the Earth's crust; most of the Earth's iridium has become concentrated in the planet's metallic core. Its exceptionally high abundance in this layer of sediment, about 10^2 times higher than in other similar rocks, is taken to be an indication of contamination of the soil in this layer by a vast amount of meteorite debris. If we assume that this iridium-enriched layer exists all over Earth (it has now been identified in many locations), it is possible to estimate the mass of an impacting body large enough to provide the necessary quantity of iridium at about 5×10^{11} tonnes, about the mass of a comet nucleus or a small asteroid. This evidence shows that a huge meteoroid impact occurred at the end of the Cretaceous period, an impact large enough to leave easily discernible traces all over the Earth.

The coincidence in time with the extinction of so many species suggests that that meteoroid was the cause of the world-wide catastrophe. A body large enough to leave an easily found chemical trace in rock layers all over the world must have had a diameter of 10 or 20 km. Its impact somewhere on Earth would have produced a crater more than 100 km in diameter, a blast wave and fireball that would have devastated and incinerated the land and living creatures for thousands of km in all directions, and huge tsunamis if the impact had occurred in or near water. Devastation would have been total for a distance of thousands of km around the impact site in all directions, and the rain of stones falling back into the atmosphere from the impact all over the Earth would probably have briefly produced oven-like conditions, setting fires everywhere and broiling many land creatures.

Furthermore, the detonation would have lofted billions of tonnes of dust high into the atmosphere, from where the dust would have taken months or years to drift back to the ground. This could have reduced the incoming sunlight to the Earth's surface by such a large factor as to practically stop all photosynthesis, perhaps for several years. This would have killed off a substantial fraction of the organisms that depend on photosynthesis. In turn, this would have created a food crisis for larger creatures that survived the initial impact. Conversion of atmospheric nitrogen into nitrates could have led to years of poisonous acid rain, killing off many further species of plants and smaller animals, for example fish. The catastrophe would thus have been truly global. A meteoroid impact of this size would have been quite capable of leading to the vast destruction of animal and plant life that occurred at the end of the Mesozoic era.

But if a meteoroid impact extinguished the dinosaurs, some trace of the crater produced by this event should exist. Geologists have searched eagerly for a suitable crater. The most likely candidate is a crater discovered in geological data obtained for the Mexican state petroleum corporation, which has led to the identification of a huge buried basin in the Gulf of Mexico, off the coast of the Yucatan peninsula near Chicxulub. The Chicxulub crater has a diameter of at least 180 km, so that it is one of the largest craters known on Earth, and is large enough to have been associated with a global catastrophe. It is buried beneath one km of sediments, but from rock cores drilled from deep in the crust, it appears that its age is about 65 million years.

Fortunately, impacts on Earth of this magnitude are exceedingly rare. From the known crater record, and from observations of (far smaller) events that lead to observable fireballs, we can estimate – very roughly! – the frequency of impacts of bodies of various sizes on the Earth. The probability or frequency of impact decreases sharply as we look at larger and larger masses. From Table 5.2 above, we see that the Earth is showered continuously with tiny objects, and that tens of thousands of objects large enough to result in meteorites hit the Earth every year (although only a few dozen of these are found). Objects large enough to devastate a town, like the Tunguska event, fall perhaps once per century (but fortunately mostly fall in the oceans or in uninhabited land). Impacts as powerful as the Barringer Meteor Crater event probably only occur about once per millennium. Impacts on the scale of the one that is thought to have ended the Cretaceous era are (fortunately for us!) typically separated by a hundred million years. But stop and think for a moment – if Comet Hale-Bopp had collided with Earth (fortunately, it did not even come close), it would have led to devastation on the scale of the K-T event.

5.5 Meteorite types and parent bodies

Meteorite classification

We now survey what is known about the meteoroids that did make it to the ground as meteorites, and try to discover what information they contain about other solar system bodies and about conditions in the early solar system.

A close examination of a good collection of meteorites, for example at a museum of natural science, reveals a bewildering variety of objects. To understand how they were produced, and what they can tell us about the physical and chemical processes that modified them, we must start by classifying – sorting – these objects to see if they fall into recognizable families. For this purpose, we have two major kinds of characteristics that turn out to be really useful sorting parameters. The first is the details of the **chemical composition** or **chemical abundances**: ratios of the numbers of atoms of various chemical elements to the number of atoms of some reference element (such as silicon or hydrogen) in a given volume. (Of course, measurements of chemical composition may be made either for a meteorite as a whole, or for individual mineral grains within it.) The second characteristic is the nature and texture of the mineral grains and other structures within the body of the meteorite. Other features, such as the mass or shape of a meteorite, turn out to provide less useful information about its origins. Let us therefore survey what is known about the chemistry and the physical structure of meteorites in various groups and families into which meteorites are generally sorted.

All meteorites consist primarily of combinations of a few abundant chemical elements that are refractory or that form refractory compounds. (Recall that the term **refractory** means that the element or compound, for example iron or olivine, remains a solid up to rather high temperature; the opposite is **volatile**, which describes a substance that becomes a vapour at a low temperature, for example helium, methane, or water.) The main elements found in meteorites are oxygen, silicon, magnesium, and iron. In addition to the major elements, many other chemical elements such as calcium, sodium, chromium, manganese, potassium, phosphorus, nickel, and titanium are also present in small quantities, either mixed through the major mineral crystals of the meteorite as impurities or trace elements, or isolated in small crystals of uncommon minerals such as apatite [$Ca_5(PO_4)_3$].

Exercise: Explain why one would expect meteorites to be composed *primarily* of O, Mg, Si and Fe rather than, say, Ca or Al.

Study of meteoritic chemistry reveals that the meteorites separate naturally into two fundamentally different classes on the basis of their chemical compositions. One class is the **chondritic** meteorites, all stones, that have overall chemical compositions that (apart from a lack of light volatile elements such as H, He, N, and Ne) are closely similar to the chemical composition of the atmosphere of Sun (see Table 2.2). The other basic class we call collectively the **differentiated** or **igneous** meteorites. This class includes several obviously different meteorite types, including the achondrites (which resemble terrestrial igneous rocks), the stony-irons, and the irons (both of which are distinguished by having large amounts of metallic iron and nickel).

We shall see in more detail below that both of these basic classes of meteorite are fragments of planetesimals that have avoided incorporation into planets or ejection from the solar system for billions of years. This surviving population of planetesimals, mainly in the asteroid belt, contains a great variety of bodies, some only a few km across, others hundreds of km in diameter. These asteroids have had rather diverse histories. Some have clearly never been heated to temperatures much above the melting point of water, while other asteroids have been heated enough to drive out any water and soften mineral grains, but without becoming hot enough for even partial melting to occur (they have always had $T < 1250$ K). These asteroids are the bodies from which we have chondritic meteorites, the meteorites with almost solar proportions of refractory elements.

Other asteroids at one time became so hot inside that iron and rock were able to melt and separate. Some melted only partially ($T \approx 1400$ K), allowing low melting point basalt to separate from denser (mafic) minerals by floating towards the surface under the action of buoyancy. Such partial melting also led in some asteroids to crystal fractionation. (Both processes were discussed in Chapter 2.) Other asteroids became hot enough inside (reaching temperatures of at least 1600 K) to melt iron and soften the rock minerals with which it was mixed. In these asteroids, blobs of dense iron (with density of nearly 8000 kg m^{-3}) were able to sink through the rock (density about 3000 – 3500 kg m^{-3}), forming a metallic core surrounded by a lower density rocky mantle. The iron that sank to the core generally carried with it a number of trace chemical elements, such as Cr, Ni, and S, that have a chemical affinity for iron (the **siderophiles**), leaving the silicate rocky minerals, together with a sprinkling of trace chemicals, such as Sc and Al, that are more easily accommodated in these minerals (the **lithophiles**). All of the differentiated types of meteorites originated as a result of such fractionation processes.

(A warning: in the literature on heating of meteorite parent bodies, it is usual to quote temperature in degrees C rather than degrees K. If you don't notice this, considerable confusion may result.)

These two main meteorite families are divided into a number of more specific classes on the basis of chemical and mineral composition and the presence of such inhomogeneities as chondrules. The classification scheme has two important values. The first is to reduce our confusion as we try to make sense of information about many individual meteorites, by sorting these meteorites into a manageable number of classes. The second use is to help us to identify the basic processes that were involved in forming the meteorites. The classes into which meteorites are usually sorted are listed in Table 5.3. For each class, the "% of falls" column gives the percentage of all witnessed meteorite falls which belong to that class; there is also a brief description of the main mineral components of members of the class.

We now look in a little more detail at the nature of the main types of meteorites.

5.6 Chondritic meteorites

Chondrites are by far the commonest meteorites that are found after being seen as meteors or fireballs during their passage through the atmosphere, making up about 85% of the known falls. The common characteristic of these meteorites is that when their bulk chemical compositions are determined, it is found for most elements that the ratio of the number of atoms of a particular element (say Mg or Ge or Pb) in a particular sample or volume to the number of atoms in the same sample or volume of a suitable reference element such as Si (the **relative abundance** of the particular element) is very similar to the relative abundance of that element in the Sun. There are only about a dozen elements for which chondritic meteorites and the Sun have very different relative abundances; these are invariably elements which vaporize at low temperatures, such as H, He, C, N, Ne, and Ar (see Table 2.2). The very close agreement between the relative abundances of a large number of common and uncommon elements in a particular class of chondrites, the CI chondrites, and the Sun, is illustrated in Figure 5.5.

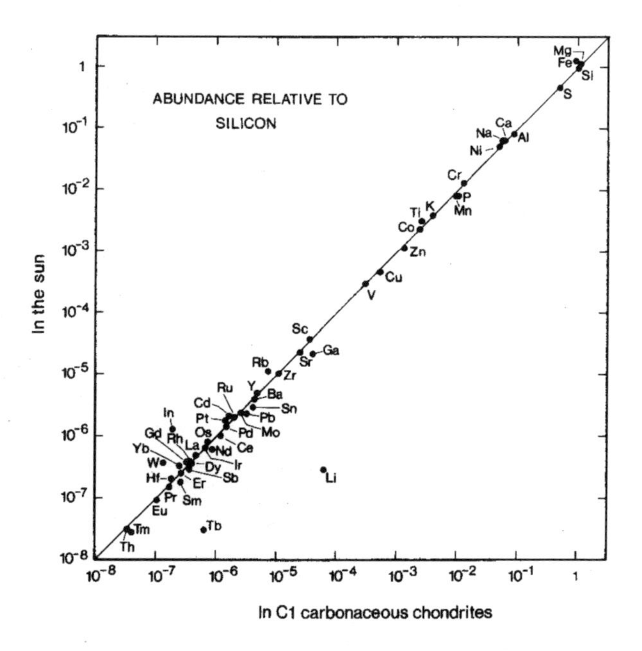

Figure 5.5: Abundances relative to Si of a number of different chemical elements as measured in CI chondrites are compared to the relative abundances found in the Sun. The diagonal line corresponds to equal abundances. Note that the scales are logarithmic. Essentially the same relative abundances are found in the Sun and in CI chondrites both for elements with roughly the same abundance as Si and for elements that are far less abundant. Data from N. Grevesse & A. J. Sauval 1998, Space Sci. Rev., 85, 161

Table 5.3: Common classes of meteorites.

Family	Group name or symbol	% of falls	Density (kg m^{-3})	Main minerals and characteristics
Chondrites				
Volatile-rich	CI=C1	0.7	2200	Hydrated silicates, magnetites, ~30% volatiles. No chondrules.
Mini-chondrule	CM=C2	2.0	2500 – 2900	Hydrated silicates, olivine, ~20% volatiles. Some chondrules.
	CO=C3	0.8	3400 – 3800	Hydrated silicates, olivine, ~5% volatiles. Small chondrules, some Ca-Al-rich inclusions.
Refractory-rich	CV=C3	1.1	3400 – 3800	Hydrated silicates, olivine, ~5% volatiles. Many large chondrules & Ca-Al-rich inclusions.
Ordinary	LL chondrite	7.2	3300 – 3600	Olivine with some low-Ca pyroxene [LL=low Fe, low ratio of (metallic Fe)/(total Fe)].
	L chondrite	39.3	3300 – 3600	Olivine with low-Ca pyroxene (L=low Fe).
	H chondrite	32.3	3400 – 3900	Low-Ca pyroxene & olivine, FeNi (H=high Fe).
	E=Enstatite	1.6	3450 – 3650	Mg in enstatite, Ni-poor FeNi, FeS.
Differentiated meteorites				
Enstatite	Aubrites	1.1	3350	Nearly pure enstatite.
Achondrites	Ureilites	0.4	3050 – 3250	Olivine & clinopyroxene, carbon, FeNi.
	Diogenites	1.1	3200 – 3400	Mg-rich pyroxene (from asteroid Vesta?).
	Howardites	2.5	average 3250	Hypersthene & anorthite (from asteroid Vesta?).
	Eucrites	2.8	2950 – 3350	Pigeonite and anorthite (from asteroid Vesta?).
	Others	1.0		Varied.
Stony Irons	Mesosiderites	0.9	4850	Olivine &/or pyroxene matrix with some plagioclase, FeNi nodules.
	Pallasites	0.3	average 4800	FeNi matrix enclosing olivine grains
Irons	Hexahedrites	1.0	7900	FeNi with Ni$<$7% (kamacite).
	Octahedrites	4.7	7800	FeNi with 7%$<$Ni$<$14% (kamacite & taenite).
	Ataxites	0.1	7850	FeNi with Ni$>$14% (taenite).

Sources: J. T. Wasson 1985, *Meteorites* (New York: W. H. Freeman), Table A-1.
H. Y. McSween 1999, *Meteorites and their Parent Bodies* (Cambridge: Cambridge Univ. Press).

Most of the chondritic meteorites not only show approximately the abundance pattern of Figure 5.5, but also contain chondrules, millimeter-sized spherical spherules embedded in the rocky **matrix** of the remaining material. (As mentioned earlier, this is the origin of the name chondrite.) Chondrules appear to have formed as liquid droplets from material that was flash-heated (perhaps by massive lightning discharges in the protoplanetary nebula, or the high temperature regions briefly produced in various parts of the nebula by the impact of infalling cloud fragments). The chondrule droplets cooled quickly (in hours or days) and were later incorporated into the bodies from which meteorites come. However, some chondrites lack chondrules. We shall see later that the characteristic of nearly solar relative chemical abundances, which is true of chondrites both with and without chondrules, is much more fundamental than the presence or absence of chondrules, and so we group all the meteorites which show the characteristic chemical abundance pattern of the Sun in the chondrites class regardless of whether they actually have chondrules.

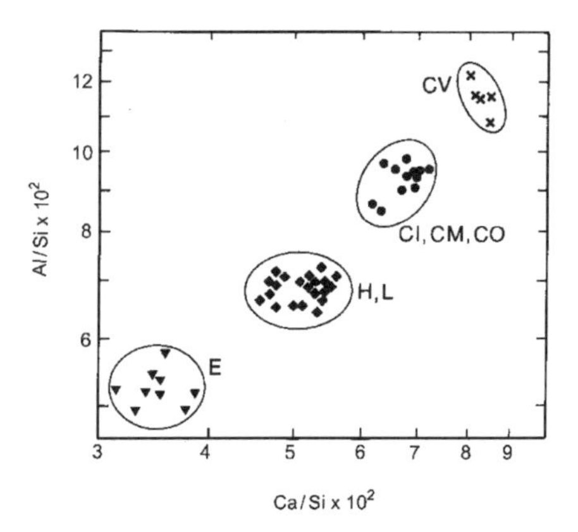

Figure 5.6: The variations in abundance (relative to Si) of the two refractory elements Al and Ca in several chondrite groups are illustrated here. Different symbols enclosed in ovals distinguish the various groups into which we classify chondrites. The CV group has overabundances of both of the elements shown here with respect to what is found in CI chondrites, while the H, L and E groups have systematically lower abundances of these elements. Adapted from J. T. Wasson 1985, *Meteorites* (New York: W. H. Freeman), Fig. II-3.

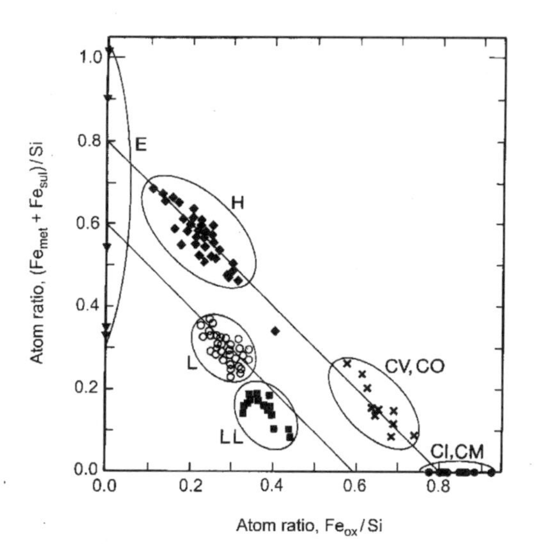

Figure 5.7: Iron abundance in metallic plus sulphide form is plotted against iron abundance in oxidized silicates. Letters and associated symbols grouped inside oval lines indicate the various meteorite groups. Diagonal lines are lines of constant total iron abundance, with lower total iron towards the lower left of the diagram. The H chondrites and all the carbonaceous types have similar total iron content, while the L and LL chondrites have only about 75% as much as the other groups. However, although the total iron does not vary drastically, there are great variations in the form of this iron: in the various carbonaceous meteorites the iron is almost totally oxidized, while in the H and E chondrites the iron is largely in sulphide or metallic form. Adapted from J. T. Wasson 1985, *Meteorites* (New York:W. H. Freeman), Fig. II-4.

However, although all the chondritic meteorites have approximately solar abundances, there are significant differences between different meteorites. It is found, when abundance tables of different meteorites are compared, that the meteorites fall into a small number of more or less discrete groups, each having a distinctive abundance pattern. Some differences between these various groups within the larger family of chondrites are illustrated in Figure 5.6, which shows that the elements Ca and Al occur in approximately the same proportions (about 3 Al atoms for every 2 Ca atoms) in the various chondritic meteorites, but that various objects have significantly different amounts of these elements relative to Si. The chondritic meteorites are found to fall into a few distinct clusters in this figure, giving us a basis for classifying them into several groups, which are labelled on the figure. (Differences between groups that overlap in this figure, for example various types of E meteorites, or the CM, CI, and CO types, occur when other chemical elements are examined.)

A second important respect in which chondrites differ from one another, besides small general abundance differences, is in the degree to which the various elements found in the meteorite are *oxidized*. In some chondrites, such as the CI and CM types, everything that will combine with oxygen to form an oxide is completely oxidized, while in others, such as the E chondrites, some metals such as iron are present almost entirely as either pure metal or as sulphides; the degree of oxidation of these meteorites is much lower. (Note that even in very unoxidized meteorites, strongly reactive substances such as Mg occur in completely oxidized form; the O abundance varies from one chondrite group to another, but all chondrites are at least somewhat oxidized.) Variations in the degree of oxidation are displayed in Figure 5.7, which shows the abundance of iron (relative to Si) in metallic or sulphide form to the iron abundance in oxides (i.e. in silicate minerals such as olivine or pyroxene). Diagonal lines in this figure correspond to constant total Fe abundances. The total Fe abundance in chondrites varies rather little even though the degree of oxidation varies a lot. Notice also again the existence of little clusters of points that encourage us to classify the chondrites into discrete groups, which we guess must have different histories.

Still another difference among chondrites is in the abundance and sizes of chondrules. In the chondrites that have chondrules, these can make up 50 – 80% of the volume, while chondrules are generally absent from carbonaceous chondrites. Chondrules therefore furnish another potential classification parameter. Related to this point is the fact that the crystalline texture of the chondrites varies both within one composition group and from one composition group to another. In some chondrites, the minerals found are not in equilibrium; for example, in many chondrites the chondrules and the matrix of minerals in which they are embedded clearly formed at different temperatures. At the other extreme, the matrix may have the appearance of a rock that has been held at fairly high temperature (about 1100–1300 K) for a long enough time that atoms could diffuse from their original places in small crystals into neighboring crystals, so that the original crystals have been able to equilibrate with one another and the matrix has recrystallized. This variation in crystal texture is recognized by appending to the group classification of each chondrite a **petrologic type** number between 1 and 6 or 7, with small numbers 1 – 3 describing crystal structure strongly out of equilibrium (and thus meteorite material that has not been strongly heated since accumulating into parent bodies, although types 1 and 2 have been warmed enough for water to become incorporated into the mineral structure, while in type 3 the temperature has at one time been warm enough to drive off almost all the water), and large numbers indicating more equilibration (thus, meteorite material that has been subjected to relatively high temperatures after combining in the parent body). Generally, the more equilibrated a chondrite is, the less C and H_2O it contains. Thus, a chondrite could have a type such as CV3 (a highly unequilibrated carbonaceous chondrite with a little water in its minerals) or L6 (a strongly equilibrated ordinary chondrite with relatively low Fe content).

One very interesting feature of some chondrites (particularly some CV's) is the presence of large (a couple of mm across) irregular white rocky fragments that are found to be composed of unusual, and highly refractory, minerals containing aluminum, calcium, and titanium as well as silicon and oxygen. These white crystals are called **Ca-Al-rich inclusions** or **CAI**s. The CAIs are very much out of equilibrium with the other minerals found in the same meteorites. We will see later that these crystals have a very interesting story to tell.

From the preceding discussion, it is clear that a number of distinct groups or types of chondrites exist, whose differences form the basis for the classification names and/or letters as indicated for the most common groups in Table 5.3.

The numerous types of chondrites may be separated into two basic groups. These two families are known as the **carbonaceous chondrites**, which include the CI, CR, CM, CO, and CV types, (often just called C1 through C3 in older articles, using the petrological classes without distinguishing the chemistry), and the **ordinary chondrites**, which include the types H, L, LL, and E. The basic chemical and mineral difference between these two large families is that the carbonaceous chondrites, unlike all other meteorites, have important amounts of such volatile substances as water, carbon, and sulphur incorporated into their minerals. All the carbonaceous chondrites have minerals formed by **aqueous alteration**. This means that the minerals are the result of some extended period of heating to temperatures in the range of about 300 – 600 K, allowing water trapped in the material to be incorporated into the mineral structure, for example as serpentine. The amounts of H_2O, C, and S present also provide one of the essential discriminants between the different carbonaceous types; the CI meteorites typically are composed of as much as 20% water by weight, the CM's have around 13%, while the CO and CV's have only about 1% water. Similarly, the fraction by weight by carbon varies from about 3.5% in the CI's to 0.5% in the CO and CM's; of course, it is compounds of carbon that gave rise to the term "carbonaceous".

The ordinary chondrites, on the other hand, are completely **anhydrous** (without water). They all contain chondrules, and differ somewhat from one group to another in the abundances of major elements, for example in the ratio of iron to silicon, and the degree to which the iron is oxidized or reduced, as seen in Figure 5.7. The H, L, and LL chondrites all have similar abundances of trace elements, but differ from the E (enstatite) chondrites and from the carbonaceous meteorites in this respect (see Figure 5.6). The enstatite chondrites are rather different from other ordinary chondrites; they have fully oxidized Mg (in enstatite, $MgSiO_3$), but the iron in them is completely unoxidized, and is present either in metallic form or as iron sulphide, FeS (troilite).

The extent to which mineral equilibrium exists in chondrites varies systematically from carbonaceous to ordinary chondrites. The carbonaceous meteorites often show great deviations from chemical equilibrium: high-temperature minerals, such as those found in the Ca-Al-rich inclusions of the CV meteorites, may coexist with other minerals that seem to have formed at temperatures 1000 K lower, such as hydrated silicates. In the carbonaceous meteorites the chondrules (if present) are usually sharply defined and may be glassy. Some of the ordinary chondrites of types H, L, and LL are considerably nearer to chemical equilibrium of the minerals found in individual crystals than are the carbonaceous chondrites. The texture of the material between the chondrules, called the matrix, is also coarser in these more equilibrated chondrites. Equilibrated mineral structure in an ordinary chondrite is the result of thermal alteration or metamorphosis, produced by heating up to a temperature of between about 700 and 1225 K shortly after the formation of the asteroid in which the meteorite originated. The chondrules may be poorly defined because they have partly recrystallized into the matrix minerals during the heating episode, or may even be absent altogether. The level of heating experienced by the ordinary chondrites was sufficient to drive out most of the water that was originally trapped as the parent bodies formed; the thermal alteration was responsible both for the dryness and the level of equilibration reached in such meteorites.

If we include all the unique and unusual chondrites, altogether about 27 clearly different abundance, metamorphism and isotopic composition patterns are found among the chondrites (only the most widely found types are listed in Table 5.3). If we guess that each of these distinct compositions represents a distinct parent body, then the evidence suggests that the Earth has recently taken delivery of samples of more than two dozen different undifferentiated planetesimals.

5.7 Differentiated meteorites

The differentiated meteorites, which include the achondritic meteorites, the irons, and the stony irons, are radically different from the chondrites. Some appear to be igneous rocks or pieces of iron that formed directly by the differentiation of the parent body of the meteorite (now an asteroid) that became hot enough to allow separation of a predominantly nickel-iron core from the rocky mantle by melting of the iron through the bulk of the asteroid. Other differentiated meteorites formed by still further processing of the mantle of an asteroid which had already developed a core and mantle, for example by partial melting of the mantle followed by extrusion of basaltic lava onto the surface, with the resulting separation of basalt from denser mafic rock. As a result, the differentiated meteorites are very different from the chondritic meteorites. Because of the separation of the siderophile metals in the metallic core from the mantle lithophiles, the differentiated meteorites all have chemical compositions which differ greatly from the approximately solar proportions found in chondrites; they show no traces of chondrules, all presumably destroyed during the first major melting episode; their crystal structures are relatively coarse following the period at rather high temperature; and mineral assemblies created in the interiors are in equilibrium, the result of slow cooling from a temperature of 1500 K or more.

The achondrites

The division of the differentiated meteorites into the families of achondrites, irons, and stony-irons is based simply on the observation that some contain only rock, some only metal, and some both. Although we will retain this division, which is firmly entrenched in the terminology of meteorites, it is not a very useful division from the point of view of understanding the origins of these objects.

There are several main groups of achondrites, such as the eucrites, diogenites, howardites, aubrites, and ureilites (Table 5.3), named either after their composition, or after prominent meteorite specialists. The **eucrites**, **diogenites**, and **howardites** form a particularly interesting and closely related family of achondrites. The eucrites are basaltic rocks, similar to terrestrial lava. If a pocket of rock in the mantle of an asteroid (that had already separated out a core and mantle) were heated enough to produce partial melting of the rock, the first part of the mantle rock to melt (a lava containing roughly equal amounts of plagioclase and pyroxene) would have a composition very similar to that of the eucrites, and the mafic material that remained unmelted (rich in olivine or in pyroxenes, poor in calcium-rich minerals such as plagioclase) would closely resemble the diogenites. The eucrites are clearly samples of a basaltic lava that made its way to the surface of an asteroid, and the diogenites are samples of mantle rock that was left behind by the partial melting. Both of these types of meteorites, and the howardites, are **breccias**, rocks formed from splinters and fragments of pre-existing rocks. Close similarities among these three types of meteorites strongly suggest that they actually all originate on the same asteroid, very possibly the third largest, Vesta (see Chapter 6). This is the only case in which a fairly secure identification of the specific parent body of a family of meteorites has been possible.

In general, the achondrites are understood as fragments of the mantles of asteroid-like bodies that have been heated enough to differentiate into a core-mantle structure.

Iron meteorites

These pieces of more or less pure nickel-iron (Fe-Ni), clearly different from normal terrestrial rocks, form an important part of the world collection of meteorites. They are readily noticed, and have even been used as raw material for tools until recent centuries. Because Fe-Ni is mechanically very strong, rather large pieces of meteorite can survive impact with the Earth's atmosphere and surface; one single piece of meteoric iron in Southwest Africa weighs about 60 tonnes. At least some of the large impact craters on Earth (such as the Barringer Crater) were produced by iron meteorites, judging from the fragments found around the impact sites.

The chemical composition of the iron meteorites is principally Fe and Ni. The Ni normally makes up between 4 and 20%, but in rare cases can go as high as 60%. In addition, small amounts (up to about 2% of the total weight of the meteorite) may be made up of the siderophile elements Co, S, P, Cu, Cr, and C. The melting process that segregated the Fe-Ni and the siderophiles from other chemical elements during the formation of a core in a differentiated asteroid clearly separated elements with reasonably high efficiency.

The iron meteorites are classified into three large families on the basis of the Ni/Fe ratio and the resulting crystal structure of the alloy. Meteorites of less than 6% Ni are mainly large crystals of the kamacite (body centred cubic iron). Because of the cubic (hexahedral) orientation of planes of weakness (cleavage planes) in the crystals, such meteorites are called hexahedrites. Meteorites with more than 14% Ni are made up of taenite (face centred cubic iron), and are called ataxites. With an intermediate composition, crystals of both kamacite and taenite are intermixed in a distinctive pattern, called Widmanstätten structure, that is revealed if a surface of the meteorite is polished and lightly etched with dilute nitric acid. More than 80% of the known iron meteorites have Ni/Fe ratios in the appropriate range to display this type of structure, and it is an excellent test for meteoric origin of a piece of iron. These meteorites are called octahedrites.

Close examination of the Widmanstätten structure crystals in an octahedrite reveals that all the iron meteorites cooled very slowly between about 875 and 675 K. To understand the evidence for this, imagine an initially molten mixture of, say, 90% Fe and 10% Ni cooling. As the melt cools, it will solidify at a temperature of about 1700 K as a block of pure taenite. The metal will remain pure taenite as it continues to cool, until a temperature of about 975 K is reached. Below this temperature, taenite is not stable (not in equilibrium) with a Ni fraction as low as the 10% that the mixture started with. In fact, as the temperature falls below 975 K, the taenite crystals require a steadily rising fraction of Ni in order to remain stable.

The cooling metal solves this problem by concentrating much of what Ni is available in some regions, leaving others with Ni abundance even lower than 10%. This concentration of Ni atoms occurs by atomic diffusion. In a hot metal, the atoms all vibrate around their fixed positions vigorously, and sometimes two neighbouring atoms spontaneously trade places with each other. In this way, Ni atoms can migrate slowly through a solid crystal, as long as the metal is hot enough for atomic place exchanges to occur frequently.

The regions of the metal from which Ni is removed are not able to remain taenite. Instead, they spontaneously change to the other crystal structure possible for NiFe, kamacite. Since the kamacite crystals are stable with only a few percent of Ni present, this transformation allows the metal to achieve stable structure everywhere, with crystals of high-Ni abundance taenite alternating with crystals of low-Ni kamacite. (The crystals of kamacite prefer to grow in the taenite along particular directions defined by the lattice structure of the taenite. This is what leads to the distinctive pattern of the Widmanstätten structure).

As the temperature drops, the Ni fraction required for the taenite phase steadily rises. This requires further concentration of Ni atoms into taenite regions. Increasing the Ni concentration in the taenite requires that larger and larger regions of the metal be reduced in Ni, so as the temperature drops, the fraction of the metal that is in the form of taenite decreases, while the fraction that is kamacite grows.

But as the temperature drops, the exchange of atoms becomes less frequent as the thermal vibrations decrease in amplitude. The speed at which Ni diffusion can occur decreases. Eventually a point is reached at which the Ni atoms are not able to diffuse all the way into the centre of taenite crystals, but are trapped near the edges. Further cooling, to about 675 K, virtually stops all diffusion, and the solid metal is left with taenite crystals that have higher Ni fractions near their boundaries with the kamacite than in their interior.

The final Ni abundance in the taenite crystal, and its distribution across an individual crystal from edge to edge, depend on the rate at which the cooling of the metal occurred between about 875 and 675 K. From observed Ni profiles found in octahedrites it is possible to calculate that these meteorites must have cooled at a rate of between 1 and 10 K per million years. This is a very slow rate. It means that the cooling metal mass must have been very well insulated. It is estimated that the observed cooling rates could occur in the deep interior of a body with a radius of between 70 and 200 km. This is very direct evidence that the melting, differentiation, and subsequent cooling of the NiFe must have gone on deep inside a body of asteroidal size. Iron meteorites are thus samples of core material from differentiated and later disrupted, rather large asteroids.

Stony-iron meteorites

These objects contain about half FeNi and half silicate material. They occur in two quite different forms. **Pallasites** contain fragments or crystals of olivine in a matrix of FeNi. **Mesosiderites** reverse the structure of pallasite: they are formed of chunks of kamacite or taenite embedded in a matrix of pyroxene or plagioclase, sometimes with olivine.

These two types of objects were probably formed in quite different ways. It is widely agreed that the pallasites formed at the interface between the iron-nickel core and the silicate-rich mantle of an asteroid, where the unmelted rocky fragments were not completely separated from the sinking molten iron. The fact that for every pallasite originating in a witnessed fall, only about 20 irons are seen to fall, indicates that the separation of mantle and core in at least some meteorite parent bodies was far from neatly finished; there must apparently be a fairly thick layer over the fully metallic core where iron and rock are mixed together. In contrast, the mesosiderites, whose silicates resemble those in eucrites, may be breccias formed from the impact of an iron meteoroid onto the surface of an asteroid with a surface composition like that of the eucrites.

Altogether over 100 different chemical and mineralogical families of differentiated meteorites are known. This appears to mean that we have samples from more than 100 different parent objects, each of which was heated intensely enough for sinking of molten iron to lead to the formation of a Ni-Fe core and a rocky mantle.

5.8 Information about the solar nebula from chondrites

Condensation of solids in the solar nebula

We now return to chondrites to see what clues they carry about the processes that occurred in the solar nebula at the time that they formed. To start, we review some of the characteristics of the solar nebula that are relevant to the formation of the meteorites, and that may have left traces in the mineral or chemical structure of the chondrites. We pick up from the account that was started in Chapter 4.

The disk of gas and dust that was left orbiting the Sun as it shrank to its present size, out of which the planets developed, must have processed *at least* about 0.02 or 0.03 $M_\odot$ of material. We estimated this value in Chapter 4 from the requirement that the nebula had to furnish the mass of rocky material needed for the observed planets, and of course this rocky stuff was accompanied by a considerably larger mass of gas, mostly H_2 and He. It seems probable that a much larger total mass, probably a large fraction of all the mass eventually accreted by the proto-Sun, passed through this disk.

The matter in the pre-planetary cloud was certainly hot. It was heated in part by radiation from the forming Sun, in part by the gravitational energy released by material falling onto the disk, and in part by whatever internal friction the disk had that allowed material to gradually spiral in toward the proto-Sun, releasing more gravitational energy as it got closer to the central mass. We can estimate from the total gravitational energy available for release that the temperature could have risen to a value of 1000 K or even more at one AU from the proto-Sun. However, the heat which was released (all of which came ultimately from gravitational contraction until the start of nuclear reactions in the proto-Sun) would also have been radiated away, at a rate which must have increased rapidly as the protoplanetary disk became hotter. Thus the actual temperature achieved in the disk in any particular region, at any particular time in the contraction process, would have depended both on how rapidly heat was being released by contraction, and how fast it was being lost again by heat radiation. (We will come back to this particular competition again several times in this book.)

Since we do not understand yet very clearly the conditions during the contraction of the proto-solar cloud to become the Sun, and we also do not really know how strong the friction in the disc was, it is very hard to estimate theoretically just how hot the protoplanetary disk became. However, theorists tend to conclude that temperatures might well have reached 1000 K or somewhat more in the inner part of the disk (say within 2 or 3 AU from the proto-Sun).

We can also get some help from astronomical observations on this question. Observations of young (T Tauri) stars with disks, stars which seem to be in the final stages of accretion (and probably of planet system formation) suggest disk temperatures of 200 to 800 K at 1 AU from the central star, and 100 to 400 K at 2.5 AU (the distance from the Sun where the asteroid belt formed). Still younger protostars, with more rapid accretion, appear to have still hotter envelopes, with temperature up 1200 K near 1 AU and close to 1000 K at 2.5 AU.

In our own solar system, one of the most fundamental features of the planet system is closely connected with the question of how hot the protoplanetary nebula became. Recall that the four inner planets have such high densities that they must be essentially composed of chemical elements that are solid even at temperatures of 1000 K or more (rocks and minerals, metallic iron), while the moons of the outer planets, with much lower overall densities, must be made up of both rocks and of ices that only become solids at 1–200 K. In both cases, to produce bodies with these compositions from a nebula in which H and He made up almost all the available atoms, we have to suppose that the planets originally formed from elements that froze out of the solar nebula as *solids*, and then coagulated to become planetesimals and eventually planets. In order to have refractory elements form dust grains which did not include ices (or much of the sulphur), we have to suppose that the temperature in the inner solar system where the terrestrial planets formed had (for a while at least) a temperature of the order of 1000 K, while solids in the outer solar system formed under conditions where the temperature was at most about 150 – 200 K.

Chondritic meteorites can help us to get a clearer idea of the history of the protoplanetary nebula. In a simple way, we could imagine two different possible situations.

- We could suppose that the inner part of the nebula never became much hotter than 1000 K. In this case, the solids that formed the terrestrial planets would be dust particles already present in the solar nebula. In the inner nebula, the temperatures would have become hot enough to cause all volatiles to become gaseous and to escape from the dust, leaving behind refractory dust grains to become planets.

- Alternatively, we could equally well suppose that the nebular temperature in the inner disk rose above 1500 K and then cooled. In this case, all the dust would be vaporized, and then the more refractory material would re-condense as solids to form the terrestrial planets at a time when temperatures were still too high for incorporation of volatile elements into the dust, or the planets.

Let's try out the low temperature hypothesis first. Suppose that the temperature through the part of the solar nebula that produced the bodies whose fragments are the meteorites that we find today never got much above 1000 K. Then the chondrites, which as we have seen were incorporated into bodies that also never got much hotter than 1000 K inside, should be formed of more or less unaltered interstellar grains of dust. This is because most of the refractory atoms in the interstellar medium (and particularly in the massive, cool and dense gas clouds from which new stars form) are not isolated as single free atoms mixed in with the gaseous H_2 and He, but incorporated into tiny dust grains. These dust grains certainly have a variety of compositions, depending on where they were formed; some are probably rich in silicates, others in carbon compounds, and others may be basically dirty ice crystals. However, in the nebula around the forming Sun, these various grains would have been vigorously mixed together by the turbulence of the collapse process, and the volatile grains at least (those containing mainly water, for example) would have been evaporated or disrupted. If the part of the nebula which produced our meteorites was never hotter than about 1000 K, the silicate-rich grains and many of the carbon-rich ones would have been left intact. These grains would have been accreted to form planetesimals directly, and then subsequently modified by partial or complete melting in the asteroids that became hot enough for core separation. In other cooler asteroids, the grains would simply have been cemented together by moderate heat and by the shocks of impacts onto the asteroidal surface during further accretion. Thus, if the solar nebula never got much hotter than 1000 K, we should expect that the chondrites, which originate on asteroids that never really melted (although some did reach temperature of 1200 K), would be formed of aggregates of interstellar grains.

But this idea does not seem to be consistent with the observation that chondrites of different types, although they have relative chemical abundances of refractory elements that are *similar* to the abundances in the Sun, actually also show clear chemical differences from one group to another. If all chondrites were simply formed out of aggregated, and well-mixed, interstellar grains, they should all have exactly the same relative abundances of refractory chemical elements. The fact that they certainly do not all have the same abundances, even of the most refractory elements, means that the refractory elements in the solar nebula were segregated from the gas by some process which was capable of giving somewhat different chemistry to the solid material at different sites in the solar nebula. This appears to require that the interstellar grains in the inner solar system reached temperatures of roughly 1300 K or more, and were largely vaporized Then the refractory atoms recondensed into solid grains before being combined into planetesimals. The chemistry of the newly condensed grains probably varied from place to place in the nebula because of locally varying temperatures and other conditions. Some such sorting in the nebula must have occurred in order to produce grains for planetesimals with mildly different chemistry in different regions.

So we deduce that the nebula must have gotten hot enough to evaporate interstellar grains before recondensing them into solids. It must have reached a temperature of at least 1300 K in the inner parts where most meteorites originate. The only kinds of chondrites for which we cannot make this argument are the

CI chondrites, whose abundances are almost exactly the same as those of the Sun; it is possible that they formed in a region where nearly complete evaporation of the interstellar grains did not occur.

Now if the mineral grains that make up chondrites were formed by vaporization followed by condensation in a cooling nebular gas cloud, perhaps they carry some information about the sequence of events that occurred at that time. To get some idea of how these grains might carry information about their condensation from the nebular gas, we must look at the process of condensation theoretically. This has been done by a number of scientists. It is found that if we start with a volume of gas of solar chemical composition at, say, 2000 K and a pressure of perhaps 10^{-4} atmospheres (plausible conditions for a typical region in the inner solar nebula), and then slowly cool the gas, different elements condense out as crystalline grains at different temperatures. Elements with large abundances form their own minerals (silicates form olivine or pyroxene, for example), while atoms of low relative abundance are incorporated one at a time into these dominant minerals as impurities.

- As our theoretical nebula cools, the first minerals to be condensed out into solid form are ones containing the particularly refractory elements Ti, Ca and Al, which freeze out as the minerals corundum (Al_2O_3), perovskite ($CaTiO_3$), melilite ($Ca(Al,Mg)(Si,Al)_2O_7$, and spinel ($MgAl_2O_4$) at temperatures somewhat above 1500 K.

- If we assume that these elements form into tiny grains that remain mixed into the surrounding gas as the temperature continues to fall, the next stage is that the grains begin to accrete other less refractory elements which, because of their higher abundances, gradually take over, converting the first mineral grains into other minerals such as diopside ($CaMg(SiO_3)_2$) and forsterite (Mg_2SiO_4 plus impurities) at around 1400 K. At about the same temperature, near 1400 K, iron and nickel begin to condense as metallic grains, perhaps in the same solid particles as the silicates, but as separate mineral grains.

- The minerals formed at 1400 K then gradually change in part into anorthite ($CaAl_2Si_2O_8$) and enstatite ($MgSiO_3$) at around 1300 K as more and more of the very abundant element Mg condenses, along with approximately one atom of O for each Mg atom. Since there is only one atom of Ti for every 300 atoms of Mg, the Ti gradually becomes an impurity in these minerals.

- As the temperature drops further, below 1000 K, the anorthite collects relatively volatile sodium atoms to become plagioclase, $(CaAl, NaSi)AlSi_2O_8$.

- Between 900 and 600 K the iron is gradually oxidized by extracting further O from the gaseous surrounding material, and incorporated into olivines and pyroxenes of mixed Mg and Fe. At about this temperature sulphur also condenses, combining with iron to form troilite (FeS).

- Still further changes may happen if the grains are able to remain in contact with the remaining gas as the temperature continues to drop; eventually water and carbon are incorporated into the mineral grains.

So far, we have assumed that the grains and the gas remain in contact throughout the cooling process, and that it goes as slowly as necessary for minerals to convert from one form to another as the temperature drops (and of course this happens more and more slowly as the atoms vibrate less and less vigorously about their normal places in their minerals). In fact, of course, we expect that the process of collecting grains into planetesimals (as discussed in Chapter 4) will be going on at the same time as the nebula is cooling, so that some of the first new grains, formed at the highest temperatures, may actually be separated out of the cooling nebula and isolated from the gas that would condense at lower temperatures. They might thus retain their identity as high temperature condensates. One tracer of the condensation process might be grains which retain a composition characteristic of the early stages of condensation. The refractory white Ca-Al-rich inclusions (CAIs) that are found in CV chondrites seem to be exactly such escapees. These grains consist entirely of the very minerals that the cooling calculations suggest should condense first in the solar nebula. Presumably these crystals were incorporated into larger solid bodies before the temperature had fallen enough to condense more abundant elements onto them, changing their mineral nature. The existence of the CAIs is clear evidence that parts of the protoplanetary nebula reached temperatures of well over 1500 K.

Another remnant of this condensation sequence is the metallic nickel-iron. At low temperatures, if the iron remains in the gas, it is oxidized to become part of various silicate minerals. However, even in many chondrites we find iron at least in part not in oxidized form but as little metallic flakes (Figure 5.7). This is iron that has escaped transformation into an oxide as the temperature lowered, presumably because it was separated from most of the gaseous oxygen before the temperature had dropped too far. (Note that the metallic iron in *differentiated* meteorites is related indirectly to the survival of metallic iron flakes; only the *metallic* iron melted and sank to the centre of the differentiated asteroids when they were heated. Iron already incorporated into olivine and pyroxenes would remain in the mantle.) The enstatite meteorites (type E) are one extreme of the spectrum of possibilities; they were evidently segregated from the nebular gas at a high enough temperature that, although they have roughly solar abundances of iron, none of the iron was able to combine with oxygen before the grains were incorporated into a planetesimal. The CI and CM chondrites are the other extreme; they seem to have reached a low enough temperature for the iron to combine completely with oxygen before the grains were separated from the gas (Figure 5.7).

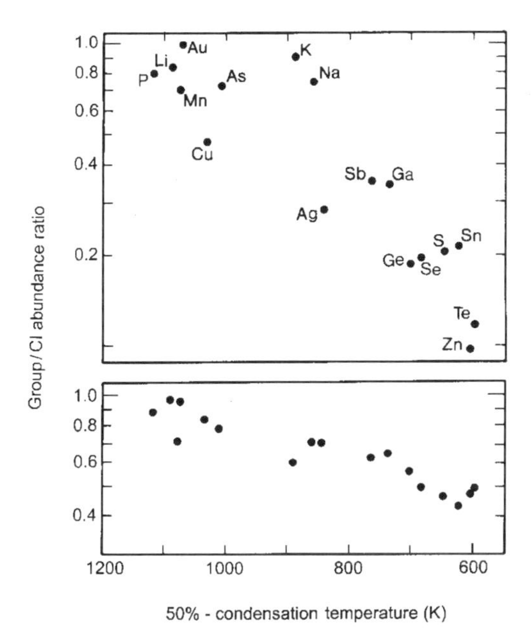

Figure 5.8: The abundances of somewhat volatile elements in a number of ordinary H chondrites (upper panel) and in some CM carbonaceous chondrites (lower panel), normalized to the abundances of the same elements in CI carbonaceous chondrites, are plotted against the temperature at which 50% of each element should be condensed from the nebula. (Thus refractory elements are on the left, more volatile ones on the right.) Individual elements are identified only in the upper panel. Clearly, the more volatile the element is, the less of it ends up in these chondrites. Adapted from J. T. Wasson 1985, *Meteorites.* (New York:W. H. Freeman), Fig VIII-5.

Another fairly direct result of the nebular condensation process is seen in Figure 5.8, where the abundances of a number of trace elements in a normal H chondrite, and in a CM carbonaceous chondrite (relative to the abundances of the same elements in a CI chondrite) are plotted as a function of the temperature at which nebular cooling calculations indicate that half of the element would be condensed into solid grains. Thus for example, gold (Au) is half condensed at a temperature slightly below 1100 K, while zinc (Zn) condenses around 650 K. What this figure shows clearly is that the more volatile the element is, the less of it succeeds in condensing before the grains are swept up into the forming planetesimals that ultimately produced these meteorites.

It thus seems clear that the process of vaporization of solar nebula solids, followed by recondensation into solid grains in a cooling nebula, did occur in a manner resembling the picture we have described above. We do not yet understand very clearly how, at any particular distance from the Sun in the nebula, the detailed history of heating, cooling, condensation, and accretion of grains into planetesimals led to the particular types of meteorites we now find. However, it appears that these processes left behind many clues that we hope to use to eventually understand the important processes. And in fact, since we have meteorites from more than two dozen rather different parent bodies, it seems that we actually have the very good luck to have samples of the condensation and accretion process from a number of different distances from the proto-Sun, and probably also from different times in the condensation process.

Meteorite sources

We have seen that the objects which survive entry into the Earth's atmosphere to arrive as findable objects at the ground must be fairly tough. The rather loosely compacted silicates in comets, for example, seem never to survive entry (although tiny fragments of comet dust have been collected by experimenters using high-flying airplanes). Essentially all of the meteorites in the world's collections are thought to be fragments of objects, like asteroids, that have been substantially compacted before being (at least partially) disrupted into the bits and pieces that we find. So it is reasonable to ask if we can identify the particular bodies, or at least the group of bodies, that furnish the meteorites that we find.

A strong hint is furnished by the fact that the orbits of all the meteorites that were found after being sighted by the photographic networks, or for which orbits could be determined from amateur videos or satellite observations, as well as many other fireballs whose orbits have been determined, have orbits with aphelia (recall that aphelion is the most distant point from the Sun in an orbit) that occur in or near the asteroid belt. This strongly suggests that most meteorites are fragments of asteroids. The cooling histories of iron meteorites, which suggest that they were formed in bodies with radii of the order of 100 km, support this hypothesis.

The simplest method by which we might imagine that meteorites could reach us from the asteroid belt is as fragments blasted off large asteroids during high speed collisions. Images of asteroids (see Figure 1.5 and Chapter 6) show that they are covered with impact craters, large and small, and theoretical estimates also agree that any particular asteroid is likely to have suffered many collisions in its lifetime. Such collisions must frequently eject rocks, boulders, and larger pieces from the main asteroid. Because these fragments leave the parent body at speeds of hundreds of m s^{-1}, they will go into somewhat different orbits around the Sun than that of the parent.

However, for such a fragment to go directly into an orbit that carries it in to 1 AU from the Sun, it would have to leave the parent body at extremely high speed, at more than 6 km s^{-1}. This is *very* improbable, as most debris from a collision escapes from the impact site with much smaller velocity than the speed of the impacting projectile (which should be of order 1 – 2 km s^{-1}); what little high speed debris is produced is fragmented to fine dust, not left in big pieces. (Direct experimental evidence for the difficulty of blasting big pieces off a surface at high speed by impact is provided by the fact that only about a dozen tiny meteorites have so far been found that come from the Moon. If impacts could easily knock off large bits of debris with speeds of more than 2.3 $\mathrm{km\,s^{-1}}$, the escape velocity from the Moon, far more meteorites should reach Earth after being blasted off our neighbour.) Thus we cannot expect meteorites to be delivered to the Earth directly as a result of asteroid collisions.

Instead, delivery seems to follow a more indirect route. Once smaller pieces have been broken off a large asteroid and gone into independent orbits around the Sun, they are subjected to influences that were not important to the larger parent body. The most significant of these is an effect due to heating by the Sun. An asteroid is only heated by sunlight on the side facing the Sun. The incoming sunlight exerts a very small force outwards on the asteroid, but this only enlarges the orbit very slightly compared to its size if there were no sunlight. However, the incoming sunlight also heats the asteroid, which then radiates away the heat it receives. Because the asteroid is almost certainly rotating, the "afternoon" side of the asteroid will be warmer, and radiate more strongly, than the "morning" side. This radiation will continue for a while on the "early night" side of the asteroid, as the surface cools off after the sun has set. Because of this lack of symmetry, the radiation from the asteroid will usually exert a small force *along* the orbit, either speeding the asteroid up or slowing it down. The importance of this force is greater for small asteroid fragments than for large asteroids, because the amount of surface area (and hence radiation force) per kg of mass is larger for small asteroids. This effect, known as the *Yarkovsky effect*, is sufficiently strong to cause the orbits of objects meters or tens of meters in diameter to change size significantly.

The resulting slow changes in orbit size are what make the delivery of some of asteroid fragments to Earth possible. As the orbit of an asteroid fragment changes size, the asteroid can move into an orbit that has a resonance with one of the planets. For example, if the meteoroid is knocked off an asteroid having an orbit with a semi-major axis a in the range between 2.3 and 2.7 AU, the fragment could eventually (after tens of Myr) reach $a = 2.5$ AU. In an orbit of this size, it would circle the Sun exactly three times for every single orbit executed by Jupiter. Thus it would meet Jupiter at the same points in its orbit each time the two were closest together.

Exercise: With a sketch, show why an asteroid circling the Sun with a period exactly 1/3 of that of Jupiter would always pass closest to Jupiter at the same two points in its orbit.

It is found that such an orbit, one that resonates in a certain way with the orbit of Jupiter (or Saturn), is very unstable. The repeated encounters with the large planet at the same point(s) in the fragment's orbit cause the orbit of the asteroidal fragment to change chaotically. The fragment's orbit will usually become highly eccentric, leading it to cross the orbit of the Earth (and in many cases actually end up plunging into the Sun). Of the order of 1% of the fragments that evolve into the 3:1 resonance (or into another important resonance with Saturn known as the ν_6 resonance) end up striking the Earth. This seems to be the main route by which meteorites are delivered to the Earth.

An important consequence of this mechanism is that the meteoroids currently striking the Earth are derived from a fairly broad sample of asteroids that have orbits reasonably near one of the important delivery resonances. It appears that the Earth's meteorite collection provides an interestingly diverse sample of the bodies in the inner asteroid belt.

5.9 Dating meteorites: the age of the solar system

Radioactive isotopes and dating

Dating rocks – which in geological terms means essentially determining the time since the rock was last heated intensely, or when it condensed from a vapour –

gives us very useful information on when various events occurred, and in what order. We shall find that dating of terrestrial and particularly of Moon rocks greatly helps us to understand the early history of these bodies. Dating of meteorites also turns out to yield some very interesting results. We first look briefly at how dating of rocks is possible using **radioactive isotopes** of particular trace elements, and then see what results have been found from dating experiments.

Recall (Chapter 2) that most chemical elements occur naturally in several different isotopes: that is, the nuclei of a particular element (all of which have the same number Z of protons) occur with various numbers N of neutrons and hence with various total atomic mass number $A = Z + N$. Frequently, especially for atomic nuclei heavier than iron ($Z = 26$), some of the naturally occurring isotopes of a particular element spontaneously change, very slowly, from one nuclear form to another by ejecting one or several particles, such as (positive or negative) electrons, protons or helium nuclei (alpha particles). Thus, for example, an isotope of rubidium, ^{87}Rb (the 87 is the atomic mass number A of the isotope) slowly and spontaneously changes to an isotope of strontium, ^{87}Sr, by emitting a positive electron and a neutrino. Decay by emitting a positive or negative electron is called **beta decay**. We write the equation describing the beta decay of ^{87}Rb as

$$^{87}\mathrm{Rb} \rightarrow {}^{87}\mathrm{Sr} + \mathrm{e}^{+} + \nu.$$

Another example of beta decay is the transformation of an isotope of potassium, ^{40}K, into an isotope of the gas argon, ^{40}Ar, via

$$^{40}\mathrm{K} \rightarrow {}^{40}\mathrm{Ar} + \mathrm{e}^{+} + \nu.$$

The rate at which such radioactive decays occur for any particular isotope follows a very simple law. Each kind of decay has a characteristic time for occurrence, which we call the **half-life** of the decay, which is the time it takes for half of a sample of the radioactive material to decay. No matter how many or how few atoms we have of a particular radioactive isotope at any particular moment, approximately half of them will decay during a time equal to one half-life. If we start with, say, 10000 atoms of a particular substance, after one half-life about 5000 of them will have decayed, leaving about 5000. After one further half-life, half of these, or 2500, will have decayed, leaving about 2500. A third half-life brings the remaining sample down to about 1250, and so on. After a few half-lives, only a small fraction of the original sample of radioactive elements will still be left. (Half-lives ($t_{1/2}$) of a few radioactive decays of interest are given in Table 5.4.)

Exercise: The half-life of ^{40}K is 1.3 Gyr. If a particular crystal in a rock that formed 3.9 Gyr ago originally contained 20000 atoms of ^{40}K, how many of these ^{40}K atoms are still left in the crystal?

Radioactive decays may be very useful for dating major heating events in the history of a particular rock, such as when the material in the rock last solidified from a melt. This is possible because melting often leads to the partial or complete chemical separation of the radioactive element from the element to which it decays. In the simplest situation, the decay product is completely removed by the heating event, as argon may easily be if a rock containing argon atoms melts: the non-reactive gas atoms simply evaporate from the rock when its crystal structure dissolves. Thus, when the rock solidifies, it has at first no Ar atoms at all. However, the radioactive decay of ^{40}K atoms will immediately start to replenish the supply of ^{40}Ar atoms. These newly created Ar atoms will be locked into the mineral structure of the solid rock. If we then examine the rock at some long time after the melting, we will find some of both the radioactive isotope and its decay product. The longer the time that has passed since the last melting, the more of the radioactive substance that will have been converted to the decay product. Thus by measuring the amounts of the radioactive isotope and the decay product isotope, we can determine the time that has passed since the rock solidified. This procedure is most practical if the amount of time since the last melting is comparable to the half-life of the decay, so that significant numbers of both the radioactive isotope and of the decay product are present. Thus more rapid decays are useful for dating recent events, while slower decays are useful for dating event far in the past.

Exercise: Explain why some of *both* the original radioactive isotope (the "parent" isotope) and the resulting stable isotope produced by the decay (the "daughter" isotope) must be present in order to determine the time elapsed since the system became "closed" (became able to retain the decay product). (Hint: consider how you would measure the age if there were *none* of the parent isotope left.)

Dating measurements based on radioactive decays, both of radioactive ^{87}Rb and of various isotopes of uranium and thorium that slowly decay to lead, have been carried out for a fairly large number of chondrites and also for a number of differentiated meteorites. What we find is that most chondrites have ages very close to one another, generally between 4.4 and 4.6 Gyr. It is very hard to see why most would have essentially the *same* ages if the last melting of most chondrites occurred at any time since the condensation of solids from the solar nebula, and in fact (as discussed above) we do not think that the chondrites were ever melted after they accreted. Thus, we conclude from this result that almost all chondrites were formed at the same time, about 4.5×10^9 years ago, and that *this age is actually the age of the Sun and of the solar system.* The dating of chondrites provides us with the most accurate value for the age of the solar system.

Dating has become astonishingly precise in recent years. The most unaltered Ca-Al-rich inclusions (CAIs) have very similar ages of 4566 ± 2 Myr, and these are the oldest ages found for components of meteorites. This number is essentially a precise value for the length of time that that has passed since the first high-temperature condensates formed in the inner protoplanetary nebula, and from the agreement of a number of such measurements, it appears that most of the CAIs formed within a period of no more than 2 or 3 Myr.

With dating precision now reaching a couple of Myr at a distance of 4.5 Gyr in the past, it is interesting to ask if the sequence of events as matter solidified can be detected in the measured ages. This is now becoming possible. The oldest ordinary chondrite known has an age of 4563 ± 1 Myr, and is thus formed slightly after the CAIs. The oldest achondrite age is 4558 ± 1 Myr, definitely younger than the CAIs. These date strongly suggest that at least some of the planetesimals were formed within a few Myr of the time when the CAIs first condensed from the hot solar nebula, and that the melting and separation of core and mantle in the differentiated meteorites was underway within less than 10 Myr. The whole process of planetesimal formation and evolution may well have occurred in a time span of only ten or twenty Myr.

Short-lived radioactivities

It is not surprising that radioactive nuclei with half-lives of Gyrs were present in the solar nebula. Many such nuclei are formed during the later stages of stellar evolution, and some are blown back into the interstellar medium during periods of strong mass loss and particularly during supernova explosions (Chapter 3). Even if such nuclei were created long before the solar system, their slow decay would allow some radioactive atoms to still be present Gyrs later, so that they could be incorporated into the solar nebula. However, we also find evidence in the isotope composition of meteorites that there were some radioactive nuclei present that have half-lives of a few million years or less.

As an example, consider the radioactive isotope ^{26}Al, which decays to ^{26}Mg with a half-life of only about 0.7 Myr. Because its half-life is extremely short compared to the age of the solar system, essentially none of the ^{26}Al is now present in planets or meteorites. However, in some of the CAIs we find excess amounts of its daughter ^{26}Mg compared to other isotopes of Mg. When we measure the relative numbers of the various isotopes of Mg on Earth, or in ordinary chondrites, we find that ^{26}Mg makes up about 11% of all Mg; the rest is ^{24}Mg and ^{25}Mg. However, in some CAIs we find that ^{26}Mg makes up a larger fraction of the total Mg present than this. Furthermore, the amount of excess ^{26}Mg found is proportional to the amount of Al found in the CAI. This result is strong circumstantial evidence that ^{26}Al was present along with normal, stable ^{27}Al in the aluminum that was incorporated into these CAIs. The radioactive isotope then quickly decayed to become magnesium. Assuming that the magnesium originally incorporated into the CAI had a normal mix of isotopes, the decaying ^{26}Al would have then contributed the excess ^{26}Mg that is now found. Thus we have strong evidence that when the earliest CAIs solidified in the solar nebula, the Al in the gas included a small fraction (about 5×10^{-5} of the total) in the form of ^{26}Al.

The inferred presence in the solar nebula of ^{26}Al was a very surprising discovery. If the solar nebula had formed from gas that included nuclei of ^{26}Al that had been created, say, 100 Myr before the solar system, essentially all of these nuclei would have decayed in the 150 half-lives since their creation, and none would be left in the gas at the time the solar system formed. The decay product, ^{26}Mg, would simply have mixed with other Mg and contributed to the Mg isotope ratio we observe in the Earth. There would not be any excess ^{26}Mg in CAIs.

To understand the presence of "live" (radioactive) ^{26}Al in the solar nebula when the CAIs formed, we have to assume that it was synthesized inside a stars only one or two half-lives earlier and then mixed into the gas that became the solar nebula. This is actually possible; the Sun probably formed in a large cloud from which other stars also formed (as in the Orion star-forming region today; see Chapter 4). If this region included massive stars that could synthesize heavy elements and inject them back into the gas of the giant molecular cloud, then some of this newly modified gas could be incorporated into the solar nebula. In fact, the strong wind from high-mass giant stars, or the blast wave from a supernova, might have precipitated the collapse of the actual cloud from which the Sun formed.

Alternatively, the ^{26}Al might have been produced by bombardment of stable ^{25}Mg in the solar nebula by protons accelerated in the frequent and very powerful flares that all young solar-type star produce.

There is also evidence in the CAIs and other components of chondrites that other short-lived radioactive isotopes were present in the solar nebula. These include

^{10}Be, ^{41}Ca, ^{53}Mn, and ^{129}I as well as several other isotopes. Some of these, such as ^{10}Be, were probably produced by particles emitted by flaring on the proto-Sun, but others such as ^{129}I appear to require injection from nearby massive star evolution.

These now extinct radioactive isotopes, which go under the general name of called **short-lived radionuclides**, can be used to look at the sequence of events in the early solar nebula. That is, these radioactive nuclei can help us to establish relative dating of events that occurred close together in time during the formation of the planetesimals and planets. Again we can see roughly how this may be done by considering a simplified example, that of ^{129}I (iodine). This isotope decays with a half-life of 15.7 Myr to ^{129}Xe (the noble gas xenon). The ratios of the various stable isotopes of Xe (there are nine of them) are well known from the Earth's atmosphere. ^{129}I is one of the radioactive isotopes that was apparently created shortly before the solar nebula formed (this isotope can only be created in supernova explosions) and mixed into the gas of the protoplanetary disk. When we measure the proportions of Xe isotopes in CAIs and chondrites (although Xe does not freeze out at any solar nebula temperature, a very small amount of the gas, with whatever isotopic mixture is available, is incorporated into mineral lattices) we find that the fractions of the total composed of various isotopes are normal – except for ^{129}Xe, which often shows a substantial excess. This is taken as evidence for presence in the early solar nebula of radioactive ^{129}I.

Now we have no way of knowing exactly what fraction of the total I was made up of ^{129}I at the time the solar nebula formed. However, suppose that the radioactive I was created before the nebula formed, was well mixed in with any other I (which would all be ^{127}I, the only stable isotope), and incorporated into solids in the solar nebula the same proportion as its proportion in the gas. Then a solid that condensed early in the solar nebula's history would have some particular ratio of ^{129}I to ^{127}I; a different solid that condensed 15.7 Myr later would have only half as much ^{129}I relative to ^{127}I; one that condensed 31.4 Myr after the first solid would have only one-fourth as large a ratio of ^{129}I to ^{127}I; and so on. In fact what is found is that all the chondrites have ratios of excess ^{129}Xe (which is a direct measurement of the original amount of radioactive ^{129}I), relative to ^{127}I, that vary by less than about a factor of two from the values found in CAIs.

Other radionuclides tell a similar story for the differentiation (core–mantle formation) of parent bodies of igneous meteorites. Apparently the formation of solids in the solar nebula, their incorporation into planetesimals, and heating and differentiation of some of the meteorite parent bodies all occurred within roughly a period of 15 or 20 Myr. Considering the short interval of time between the formation of the CAIs and the subsequent development of the meteorite parent bodies, it appears reasonable to regard the age of 4.56 Gyr as, quite simply, the age of the solar system.

Exercise: Explain why it is possible to obtain *relative* dates of events far in the past using radionuclides that have completely decayed away, even though (see the preceding Exercise) you cannot get *absolute* dates for these events unless you can measure the amount of both a parent isotope and its daughter isotope.

Dating of events that occurred during the formation of the solar system is a rapidly developing field. Using both live and extinct radioactivity, the sequence of events that led to the formation of meteorite parent bodies – and of the planetary system generally – is gradually becoming clearer. There are still many puzzling and confusing aspects in our efforts to understand this story, but a lot of progress is currently being made.

5.10 Mathematical aspects

Physics of meteors

The theory of meteors provides a number of opportunities to try out familiar physics in a new setting. Let us look first at the braking of a meteor by interaction with the air. This occurs basically by a transfer of momentum from the meteoroid to the air it pushes out of the way, which by its resistance to being accelerated and shoved aside effectively exerts a (drag) force on the meteoroid. We cannot determine the precise strength of this force without quite detailed computations, but its general size is easy to estimate.

Let's make the simple assumption that as the meteoroid pushes into the atmosphere, it *evacuates* a tube of air by accelerating the air molecules in front of it to its own current speed. These molecules will soon move out of the way of the onrushing body, and fill in the empty tube behind it, but each molecule will carry away from the meteoroid an amount of momentum which is of the order of its own mass times the velocity of the meteoroid. This is a rather rough approximation for the momentum transfer to the air (and hence for the drag force exerted on the meteoroid), but it is found that in practice it is accurate to within about a factor of two.

With this simple assumption, as a (spherical) meteoroid of radius R, density ρ_M and mass $M = 4\pi R^3 \rho_M/3$ moves though air of local density ρ_a at a speed v, in time dt it will sweep up a mass of air m_a equal to $m_a \approx \rho_a \pi R^2 v\, dt$, which will acquire a momentum of about $p_a \approx m_a v \approx \rho_a \pi R^2 v^2\, dt$. This momentum transferred to the air is lost to the meteoroid, which thus loses $dp_M = d(Mv) \approx M\,dv$. Equating this lost momentum to the momentum gained by the air, we find

$$\frac{dv}{dt} = \frac{-\Gamma\pi R^2 \rho_a v^2}{M} = \frac{-3\Gamma\rho_a v^2}{4\rho_M R}, \tag{5.1}$$

where the factor Γ is a number of order 1 into which we collect the details we have ignored. In detailed studies, it is found that generally $0.4 \le \Gamma \le 1.5$.

Exercise: Suppose that a meteoroid of density 3000 kg m^{-3} has a mass of 1 gm at the time it reaches an altitude of 75 km, where it is moving with a velocity of 20 km s^{-1}. The meteoroid is moving roughly horizontally, and the local air density is 5×10^{-5} kg m^{-3}. Use Equation 5.1 to obtain an order-of-magnitude estimate of how much time is required to reduce the meteoroid's speed to a small fraction of its initial value.

Equation (5.1) has a very interesting direct consequence. If we use data from patrol camera networks to *measure* both the altitude $h(t)$ and velocity $v(t)$ for a meteor, so that we can determine v and dv/dt at various points along the meteor trail, and estimate the density of air ρ_a which we know as a function of h, we can derive from the equation the value of R^2/M for the meteor. If we go a little further and assume a value for the density ρ_M, we can determine approximate values for R and M separately. Thus, the dynamics of the meteor flight tell us about the size and mass of the body. Determination of the meteoroid's mass from observation of its rate of deceleration is possible because at a particular altitude a small meteoroid sweeps up a more significant mass of air relative to its own mass than a large meteoroid does, and therefore slows down more. A meteoroid mass determined in this way is called a **dynamical mass**, and is thought to be accurate to roughly a factor of three. Such measurements are a basic source of information on the masses of meteor-producing bodies.

To look at energy transfers during meteor flight quantitatively, it is convenient to express energies in a form that makes comparison with atomic energies easy, so here we will express these energies in units of electron volts (eV). Recall that one eV is the energy gained by one electron (of charge $e = 1.602 \times 10^{-19}$ C) falling through a potential of one volt. Thus one eV = $1.602 \times 10{-}19$ J, a very small amount of energy indeed. This is a convenient energy unit to use because it is about the right size for characterizing individual atoms. (Recall that we have already met electron volts in Chapter 3, where we described the energy release in nuclear reactions in MeV.) For example, the energy required to remove the outermost (valence) electron from an atom is between about 4 and 25 eV. The energy needed to split up a diatomic molecule such as NaCl is also a few eV.

We now look at the energy transfers on and around the meteoroid. It arrives with a very large amount of kinetic energy e_k per atom or per unit mass, of the order of $e_k \approx 0.1v^2$ electron volts (eV) per atom, where v is measured in km s^{-1}. The energy required to detach an atom from the meteoroid is roughly 2 or 3 eV, so a meteoroid travelling as slowly as 10 km s^{-1}, with about 10 eV per atom, has more than enough kinetic energy to completely evaporate itself, if most of this energy is used in ablation. In faster meteoroids the available energy is even more adequate.

Of course, as the meteoroid plows through the ever denser air, it does not simply dissipate its kinetic energy $E_k = Mv^2/2$ through surface heating. Some part of this energy does heat the surface, causing both heat radiation and sublimation. (In this respect the situation is very much like that of a comet entering the inner solar system, on which solar heating of the surface causes both emission of infrared radiation and evaporation of volatile gases.) The dissipated energy may even lead to enough melting to cause the meteoroid to shed molten droplets of matter. However, part of the kinetic energy lost by the meteoroid also goes into heating and ionizing air molecules struck by it, and into producing an atmospheric shock wave (a sonic boom) that travels outwards from the meteor path.

We may most easily estimate the effects of heating on the meteoroid by going to the meteoroid's frame of reference and looking at the kinetic energy dissipated by the air impacting the object. Suppose that the energy required to ablate a mass dM is $Q\,dM$. (Q generally has a value of about 0.8–2×10^7 J kg^{-1}, or about 2-4 eV per sublimed atom.) Now assume that a fraction Λ of the kinetic energy available from the deceleration causes ablation. Then in dt the kinetic energy dissipated by the mass $\pi R^2 v \rho_a\,dt$ of air striking the meteoroid is $dE_k \approx (1/2)\pi R^2 v \rho_a v^2\,dt$. If a fraction Λ of this energy removes mass from the meteoroid, the mass dM lost in dt is

$$Q\,dM \approx \Lambda\,dE_k \approx (1/2)\Lambda\pi R^2 v^3 \rho_a\,dt,$$

or

$$\frac{dM}{dt} \approx \frac{\Lambda\pi R^2 \rho_a v^3}{2Q}. \tag{5.2}$$

This is known as the **vaporization equation**.

The efficiency Λ of ablation depends rather strongly on instantaneous conditions. Well above 100 km altitude, where the air is so thin that the mean free path λ of molecules is larger than the meteoroid (and so a molecule of air is likely to recoil out of the meteoroid's path before hitting another molecule), the efficiency of ablation is relatively high. Each impacting molecule strikes the surface of the meteoroid, usually ejecting one or several atoms from the incoming body as it recoils. As the meteoroid penetrates into denser air where $\lambda \approx R$, colliding molecules of air and evaporated molecules form a plasma cloud around the body which partly screens it from direct impacts with molecules. These molecules instead collide with the surrounding vapour cloud, and the inefficiency of transfer of energy in through the cloud to the surface of the meteoroid reduces the ablation efficiency from $\Lambda \approx 1$ to as low as 10^{-2}. (This decrease in heat transfer efficiency is the main reason that an object with not too large an initial velocity can survive deceleration and produce meteorites.)

Equations (5.1) and (5.2) allow us to determine roughly how much of the original meteoroid may survive as a meteorite. Divide Equation (5.2) by (5.1) to eliminate t and express M as a function of v, and integrate from the initial mass M_0 and velocity v_0 to the final values M and v. We find

$$M = M_0 \exp[-\sigma(v_0^2 - v^2)/2] \approx M_0 \exp[-\sigma v_0^2/2], \quad (5.3)$$

where the second equality applies if the final velocity is much smaller than the initial value. Here $\sigma = \Lambda/2\Gamma Q$ has a value of roughly $10^{-7} - 10^{-8}$ s^2 m^{-2}, and so a meteoroid with an initial velocity of much more than 10 km s^{-1} will lose most of its mass to ablation. This equation shows that there is a very strong tendency for meteoroids with the large values of v_0 to be completely destroyed by ablation; only the slowest will deposit significant meteorites.

Exercise: Carry out the integration to obtain Equation (5.3).

Some part of the kinetic energy given to the sublimed atoms and the excited air molecules will appear as emitted light. If we call the efficiency factor for conversion of the kinetic energy of this ablated material into radiation τ, we may write an equation for the luminosity L of the meteor:

$$L \approx \tau \frac{dM}{dt} \frac{v^2}{2}. \quad (5.4)$$

Because the radiation emitted from the meteor is a combination of emission lines from the gas surrounding the body with black-body thermal radiation from the meteoroid surface at 2-3000 K, and much of this radiation occurs outside the visible wavelength band, the efficiencies τ for conversion of ablation energy into visible radiation are usually rather small, of the order of a few percent or less. For a meteor whose luminosity and velocity are measured by patrol network observations, it is possible to integrate Equation (5.4) to determine the initial mass of the meteoroid. Such a mass estimate is called a **photometric mass**.

If one has good measurements of $v(t)$, $h(t)$, and $L(t)$, it is possible to solve the braking, vaporization, and luminosity equations simultaneously to determine M, dM/dt, and R, assuming that all the other quantities in the problem (Γ, Λ, Q, τ, and the density of air ρ_a as a function of height) are known.

Of course, the theory of meteors as sketched above is quite simplified. The equations assume that the meteoroid is spherical, and that it does not fragment as it decelerates. Furthermore, much interesting physics is hidden in the coefficients Γ, Λ, Q, and τ, which must be included (approximately) in a more complete treatment of meteor flight. However, even the simple theory described here is enough to reveal much of the basic behaviour of meteors.

Radioactive decay and dating

We next look at how the law followed by nuclei of atoms as they decay allows us to use radioactive decay as a "clock", making it possible to determine how long ago a mineral sample was last strongly heated.

Radioactive decay of an atomic nucleus is observed to obey a very simple law. Essentially, the *probability per second* λ that an unstable nucleus will decay is a *constant*, independent of time. Therefore, if we start with $n(0)$ atoms of the radioactive isotope in a box at time $t = 0$, after a short time dt we find that the decrease dn in the number of nuclei, that is, the number that have spontaneously changed to the decay product, is simply equal to the current number of nuclei n times the probability $\lambda\, dt$ that any one of them will decay in dt

$$dn = -\lambda\, n\, dt. \quad (5.5)$$

The constant λ is a known as the **decay constant**. That is, the number of decays per second is simply proportional to the number of radioactive atoms present, regardless of their past history. Equation (5.5) may easily be integrated from time $t = 0$ when there are $n(0)$ nuclei to a later time t to yield

$$n(t) = n(0)\, e^{-\lambda t}. \quad (5.6)$$

This is the fundamental equation of radioactive decay.

The constant λ is sometimes given directly (since it is a probability per unit time, its units are s^{-1} or yr^{-1}), or the decay rate may be specified in terms of the half-life $t_{1/2}$ of the isotope, the time required for half of a given sample to decay. From (5.6), we see that the half-life satisfies

$$e^{-\lambda t_{1/2}} = \frac{1}{2}, \quad (5.7)$$

or

$$t_{1/2} = \ln(2)/\lambda \quad (5.8)$$

Table 5.4: Decay constants and half-lives of radioactive decays used for geological dating.

Decay reaction			λ (probability yr^{-1})	$t_{1/2}$ (yr)
^{40}K	$\rightarrow$	$^{40}Ar + e^+ + \nu$ (12.4%)	5.93×10^{-11}	11.9×10^9
	$\rightarrow$	$^{40}Ca + e^- + \bar{\nu}$ (87.6%)	4.72×10^{-10}	1.47×10^9
		all decays of ^{40}K	5.30×10^{-10}	1.31×10^9
^{87}Rb	$\rightarrow$	$^{87}Sr + e^- + \bar{\nu}$	1.43×10^{-11}	48.5×10^9
^{147}Sm	$\rightarrow$	$^{143}Nd + \alpha$	6.54×10^{-12}	106×10^9
^{232}Th	$\rightarrow$	$^{208}Pb + 6\alpha + 4e^-$	4.99×10^{-11}	13.9×10^9
^{235}U	$\rightarrow$	$^{207}Pb + 7\alpha + 4e^-$	9.72×10^{-10}	0.713×10^9
^{238}U	$\rightarrow$	$^{206}Pb + 8\alpha + 6e^-$	1.54×10^{-10}	4.50×10^9

Source: S. Moorbath, in *Understanding the Earth*, ed. I.G. Gass et al (Cambridge, Mass: MIT Press), chap. 2.

Decay constants and half-lives vary enormously from one radioactive substance to another. The half-life may be much less than a second or much more than a billion years. This range in decay constants makes it possible to use radioactive decays to date events with a large variety of typical time scales. Decay constants and half lives are tabulated in Table 5.4 for a few substances that have long enough half-lives to be useful for geological dating.

The practical use of Equation (5.6) to measure the time since a rock was last molten (or strongly heated, or vaporized, etc.) involves measuring the total numbers of nuclei of the radioactive isotope and of the decay product in a sample. These are usually measured relative to some reference isotope of the decay product element that is not produced by any radioactive decay, using a device called a mass spectrometer. Suppose we call the ratio of the radioactive isotope to the reference isotope r, and the ratio of the decay product isotope to the reference isotope s. Both are functions of time, and once the rock has solidified, they change in accordance with (5.6). The radioactive isotope decreases as

$$r(t) = r(0)\, e^{-\lambda t}. \qquad (5.9)$$

The decay may produce only a single daughter isotope, or may have several channels (e.g. ^{40}K in Table 5.4). If several decay products are produced, let us call α the fraction of decays that go to the decay product that we want to measure. Then the decay product at the time t is made up of the amount $s(0)$ present at $t = 0$, plus the fraction of the total decay, $\alpha[r(0) - r(t)]$, that ends up as the decay product being studied. The decay product ratio $s(t)$ thus increases as

$$\begin{aligned} s(t) &= s(0) + \alpha\,[r(0) - r(t)] \\ &= s(0) + \alpha r(0)\,[1 - e^{-\lambda t}] \\ &= s(0) + \alpha r(t)\,[e^{\lambda t} - 1]. \end{aligned} \qquad (5.10)$$

When a melting event has completely separated the radioactive isotope from the decay product, as normally happens in the decay of ^{40}K, whose decay product ^{40}A is easily outgassed during melting, then the initial value $s(0) = 0$. In this case, if we measure $s(t)$ and $r(t)$, and know α ($= 0.124$ for $^{40}K \rightarrow {}^{40}A$), the only unknown in equation (5.10) is t, and we may solve for the age of the rock:

$$t = \ln\{[s(t) + \alpha r(t)]/\alpha r(t)\}/\lambda. \qquad (5.11)$$

In this equation, λ is the total decay constant for all decay paths for the radioactive isotope; in the case of ^{40}K, $\lambda = 5.30 \times 10^{-10}$ yr^{-1}.

Exercise: You have a crystal grain from an ancient lava. When you analyze its potassium and argon content, you find that there is 1 atom of ^{40}K present for every 8000 atoms of ^{39}K (the principal stable isotope of potassium), and that the crystal contains 1 atom of ^{40}Ar for every 7.25×10^4 atoms of ^{39}K. How long ago was the lava molten? At the time when the lava melted, what was the ratio of ($^{40}K/^{39}K$)?

The situation if the decay product is already present in the rock to be analyzed when the heating event is finished is a little more complex. This is the situation for the decay of ^{87}Rb, since some ^{87}Sr is usually present in the rock before heating and may not be completely separated out even by complete melting. In that case, we have two unknowns in Equation (5.10), $s(0)$ and t. With only one equation, we cannot solve for both, which is to say that we can't tell from one sample how much of the observed decay product was produced by the decay and how much was there to begin with. However, it often happens that when a rock crystallizes from a melt it forms grains of various minerals that interlock, as in granite, where the small white or pink specks are grains of quartz (SiO) and the dark grains are usually plagioclase and orthoclase. When this happens, the initial ratio of the radioactive element to the decay product element will usually vary from one grain or type of grain to another. Rubidium, which is chemically similar to potassium, will tend to concentrate in K-rich grains, while strontium will concentrate in grains rich in its chemical counterpart, Ca. However, this separation usually does not alter the ratios of the isotopes of a single element found in various grains.

In that case, we get an Equation (5.10) for each grain that is studied. Since the initial ratio of the decay product isotope (^{87}Sr in this case) to another isotope of the same element not produced by any common radioactive decay (usually ^{86}Sr) does not vary from one mineral to another, $s(0)$ is the same for rocks poor in the decay product and for rocks rich in it. Then if we study two grains, we have two equations with measured values of $r(t)$ and $s(t)$, and two unknowns, $s(0)$ and t or $[e^{\lambda t}-1]$:

$$s_1(t) = s(0) + \alpha r_1(t)\,[e^{\lambda t} - 1] \qquad (5.12)$$

and

$$s_2(t) = s(0) + \alpha r_2(t)\,[e^{\lambda t} - 1], \qquad (5.13)$$

where the $s_i(t)$ and $r_i(t)$ are the isotope ratios measured in grains 1 and 2, and $\alpha = 1.0$ for the Rb-Sr decay. This is a system of two linear equations in the two unknowns $s(0)$ and $\alpha\,[e^{\lambda t} - 1]$, and may be solved to determine the initial isotope ratio $s(0)$ and the age t.

Mass spectrometry of a larger number of individual grains offers another common means of solving for $s(0)$ and t. In that situation, we have a number of equations like Equation (5.10), all with the same (unknown) values of $s(0)$ and $\alpha\,[e^{\lambda t}-1]$, and all with individual measurements of $s(t)$ and $r(t)$. If we plot a graph with $r(t)$ along the x-axis and $s(t)$ along the y-axis, the relationship between these two variables as given by Equation (5.10) is a straight line of y-intercept $s(0)$ and slope $\alpha\,[e^{\lambda t}-1]$. If the assumptions above are satisfied by the rock under study, the observed pairs of points should plot along a straight line from which $s(0)$ and $\alpha\,[e^{\lambda t}-1]$ may be determined easily.

5.11 References

Alexander, C. M. O'D., Boss, A. P. and Carlson, R. W. 2001, "The early evolution of the inner solar system: a meteoritic perspective", *Nature* 293, 64. This is a clear, brief review of the processes involved in forming the terrestrial planets, and particularly of the evidence furnished by meteorites.

Alvarez, W., Asaro, F., and Courtillot, V. E. 1990, "What caused the mass extinction", *Sci. Am.*, Oct., 76. These authors argue the case for a giant impact as the cause of the catastrophe that ended the age of dinosaurs.

Brown, P. et al. 2002, "The flux of small near-Earth objects colliding with the Earth', *Nature* 420, 294. This article provides a clear, recent overview of the rate of impact of bodies of various sizes on the Earth.

Boss, A. P. 1998, "Temperatures in protoplanetary disks", in *Ann. Rev. Earth Planet. Sci.*, 26, 53. This review discusses the various kinds of evidence that inform us about temperatures in the disk in which the solar system formed, and how theories describing this disk try to account for the observations.

Ceplecha, Z. et al. 1997, "Big meteoroids and meteors", in *Interplanetary Dust*, eds. S. Dermott, B. Gustafson, E. Grün (Tucson: Univ. of Arizona Press). This is a comprehensive technical review of the whole subject of meteors and their parent bodies.

Gehrels, T. 1996, "Collisions with comets and asteroids", *Sci. Am.*, Mar., 54. Gehrels argues that we should make a greater effort to discover the space hazards that may endanger us.

Gibson, E. K. et al 1997, "Relic life on Mars", *Sci. Am.*, Dec., 58. A meteorite from Mars might contain fossil evidence of life on the Red Planet. (This is disputed, however; see *Sci. Am.*, Apr 1998, 18 for another view.)

Grieve, R. A. F. 1990, "Impact cratering on the Earth", *Sci. Am.*, Apr., 66. This article describes the sequence of events that occur to form a crater during a large impact on the Earth, and how we can recognize such craters later.

Grossman, L. 1975, "The most primitive objects in the solar system", *Sci. Am.*, Feb, 30. This rather old article clearly explains the mineral and chemical evidence found in carbonaceous chondrites about conditions in the cooling solar nebula.

Hartmann, W.K. 1977, "Cratering in the solar system", *Sci. Am.*, Jan., 84. Hartmann describes the effects of collisions between asteroid-size objects and the larger planets and moons in the solar system.

Keil, K. 2000, "Thermal alteration of asteroids: evidence from meteorites", *Planet. Space Sci.* 48, 887. This is an extensive technical review of the meteoritic evidence for heating of asteroids, with lots of journal references.

McSween, H. Y 1999, *Meteorites and their Parent Bodies*, 2nd edition (Cambridge: Cambridge University Press). This is an easy to read, elementary, but up-to-date introduction to meteorites, with a lot of detail particularly on the chemical and mineral nature of these bodies.

McSween, H. Y. and Stolper, E. M. 1980, "Basaltic meteorites", *Sci. Am.*, Jun., 54. The authors discuss the eucrites, igneous meteorites probably from the asteroid Vesta, and the shergottites, which are almost certainly samples of the crust of Mars.

Wasson, John T. 1985, *Meteorites: Their Record of Early Solar System History* (New York: W.H. Freeman). This very interesting book concentrates on discussing how details of the chemistry and mineralogy of meteorites offer clues to their origins and to how the solar system formed.

5.12 Review questions

5.1 What effects make it unlikely that neither very low mass nor very high mass meteorites will survive arrival at Earth to be found?

5.2 Very large meteorites are not much slowed by the Earth's atmosphere. Why not? What determines how large a meteorite has to be not to be slowed very much?

5.3 How can we recognize major ancient terrestrial impact craters?

5.4 What kinds of effects can a major impact on Earth have?

5.5 What chemical elements do we expect will be most abundant in meteorites? Why?

5.6 What are the two fundamentally different families of meteorites? What distinguishes these two families? Why is this distinction so important in understanding meteorites?

5.7 Why do we put such emphasis on whether a meteorite is equilibrated or not? What does information about equilibration tell us about a meteorite's history?

5.8 What evidence from chondrites suggests that the inner solar nebula was at one time hot enough to evaporate most dust grains?

5.9 How do we understand the occurrence in some chondrites of grains rich in the particularly refractory elements Ti, Ca, and Al?

5.10 Some chondrites have iron mostly in metallic form, while in others it is mainly oxidized. How might some meteorites have acquired metallic iron while others acquired oxidized iron?

5.11 Do meteorites contain unaltered interstellar grains? How do we recognize such grains if they are present?

5.12 How is it possible to date a meteorite? What physical event does the age of a meteorite refer to?

5.13 Problems

5.1 The rate at which large meteorites (ones with masses larger than 0.5 kg) reach the surface of the Earth is about one impact per 10^6 km^2 per year. Such meteorites undergo almost all of their deceleration, while making a spectacular meteor display in the sky, at an altitude of about 100 km. Because the meteorites that survive entry into the Earth's atmosphere are typically travelling at about 20 km s^{-1} relative to the Earth when they begin to slow down in the atmosphere, the actual meteor display lasts only a few seconds. Assume that if you were looking in the right direction, you could see such a meteor at any time of day or night. Make reasonable (very approximate) assumptions about the amount of time you spend on average each day in places where you can see the sky, about the surface area of sky near 100 km altitude that you can survey at once, etc, estimate the probability that you might see the meteor display of one such meteorite in your lifetime.

5.2 Suppose a piece of asteroid debris with a mass of 10^{-4} kg (about 3 mm in radius) enters the Earth's atmosphere directly towards you at a velocity of 20 km s^{-1}, and that it loses its 5% of its kinetic energy as optical radiation at a uniform rate in 1 s. (a) If the meteor event occurs at an altitude of 80 km above you, what is the optical radiation flux $\mathcal{F}$ (in W m^{-2}) that you will see? (b) Estimate the "apparent magnitude" of the meteor, using the fact that stellar magnitude m is defined by $m = -2.5\ log \mathcal{F} + C$, where C is a constant, and that a $m = 0$ star is one that delivers a radiation flux $\mathcal{F}$ of about 1×10^{-8} W m^{-2} at the surface of the Earth. Stars of $m \leq 6$ are visible by eye. Will the meteor be visible?

5.3 A large meteorite will be slowed substantially before striking the Earth's surface only if the mass of atmospheric gas that must be displaced as it passes through the atmosphere is larger than the mass of the meteorite itself. The total mass of terrestrial atmosphere above each m^2 is about 10^4 kg (i.e., about 1 kg per cm^2). (a) Consider a spherical meteorite of mass M, radius R and density ρ entering the Earth's atmosphere vertically. Find approximate expressions for the limiting values of mass and radius of such a meteorite above which it will not be greatly slowed by the atmosphere (b) What are the limiting values of M and R if the meteorite is an iron with $\rho = 9000$ kg m^{-3}? If it is a chondrite with density $\rho = 2700$ kg m^{-3}? (c) Compare your limiting masses with the masses of the iron meteoroid that produced the Barringer Meteor Crater, and the chondritic meteoroid responsible for the Tunguska explosion (both has masses of about 10^5 tonnes).

5.4 A meteorite small enough to be completely decelerated by atmospheric drag as it falls to the Earth's surface will finally fall with a nearly constant (terminal) speed. The force of gravity downward will be just balanced by the upward drag force exerted by the atmosphere on the meteorite. (a) Consider a spherical meteorite of radius r and density ρ falling vertically through air of density ρ_A with this terminal velocity. Estimate the upward drag force F_d on the meteorite by assuming that each second the meteorite accelerates to its own velocity the air in the cylinder that it passes through in one second; the force exerted on this air to accelerate it (and therefore the force exerted on the meteorite by the air) is simply equal to the momentum p per second given to the accelerated air (i.e., $F_d = dp/dt$). (b) Now assume that the meteorite has reached equilibrium, and is falling at a speed such that the drag force balances gravity. From this equality, derive an expression for the velocity at which the two forces balance. (c) Evaluate this expression for a stony meteorite of $\rho = 2700$ kg m^{-3} and $m = 20$ kg, at an altitude where $\rho_A = 1$ kg m^{-3}.

5.5 The Richter scale of earthquake magnitude is defined in terms of the amplitude of the ground wave rather than in terms of energy released, and the relationship of the magnitude on the Richter scale to the energy release is somewhat uncertain. One recent version of this relationship is

$$\log E = 2.57\, m - 2.22,$$

where m is the magnitude on the Richter scale and E is the energy release in Joules. Use this relationship to estimate the magnitude of the earthquake generated by the impact of the asteroid that made the Arizona Meteor Crater. Assume that the meteorite making the crater was a block of iron of total mass 4×10^9 kg, and that it had a direct elliptical orbit in the plane of the ecliptic, with aphelion at 3.5 AU and perihelion at 1.0 AU, at the time it struck the Earth. Calculate (a) the velocity of the meteoroid when it is at aphelion, (b) the velocity difference between the Earth and the meteoroid before the Earth's gravity has accelerated the meteoroid very much, (c) the velocity of the impact with Earth (hint: use conservation of energy, with the initial kinetic energy estimated with the velocity from the previous part), (d) the energy release on impact, and (e) the magnitude of the resulting earthquake on the Richter scale. (f) An earthquake of magnitude 4.5 can cause local damage, one of magnitude 6 is quite destructive over a limited area, one of magnitude 7 is major and can easily be detected all over the world. The San Francisco earthquake of 1906 was magnitude 7.8; the largest earthquakes (e.g. Honshu 1933, Assam 1950, Alaska 1964) have magnitudes of about 8.5. How does the Arizona Meteor Crater event rate on this scale?

5.6 When a massive meteoroid strikes Earth at a speed of tens of km s^{-1}, conversion of the kinetic energy of the body into a massive explosion will vaporize the incoming body, excavate a large crater, and lift a large amount of dust high into the atmosphere. Only detailed computations can reveal precisely how the incoming energy is distributed among these and other results of the impact. However, we can get some idea of the consequences of a large impact by computing what would happen if, say, 20% of the available energy goes into each of these effects. So: consider a iron meteoroid of $M_m = 100$ tonnes striking the Earth with an impact velocity of $v_{im} = 20$ km s^{-1}. (a) Estimate the number of atoms in the meteoroid, and assume $C_v = 3k$ per atom. Calculate the temperature rise ΔT of the body resulting from conversion of 20% of the available energy into internal energy. If iron vaporizes at about 3300 K, what should happen to the material of the meteoroid? (b) Assume that the crater excavated by the meteoroid is a cylindrical hole of radius r_{cr} and depth $d_{cr} = r_{cr}$, and that the energy required to dig this crater is what would be needed to raise the material in the crater to form a crater wall of height d_{cr} (i.e. that all the material in the crater is simply raised by an amount d_{cr}). If the density of the Earth where the impact occurs is $\rho_e = 3000$ kg m^{-3}, and the available energy is again 20% of the incoming kinetic energy, estimate r_{cr}. Compare r_{cr} to the radius of the initial meteoroid, taking this to be a sphere of density $\rho_m = 7850$ kg m^{-3}. (c) If 20% of the available energy is used to lift tiny dust fragments from the crater to an altitude of 200 km, what is the mass of dust that might be deposited into the upper atmosphere of the Earth?

5.7 The following table contains measured $^{87}Sr/^{86}Sr$ and $^{87}Rb/^{86}Sr$ ratios for a number of individual grains in the Guareña H6 bronzite chondrite (adapted from G.J. Wasserburg, D. A. Papanastassiou & H. G. Sanz 1969, *Earth Planet. Sci. Letters*, 7, 33). Examine the table, and note

$^{87}Sr/^{86}Sr$	$^{87}Rb/^{86}Sr$
0.70189	0.0304
0.70225	0.0345
0.70234	0.0344
0.70261	0.0425
0.70283	0.0427
0.70416	0.0647
0.72155	0.334
0.75240	0.808
0.75435	0.845
0.75665	0.873
0.75680	0.864
0.75710	0.869
0.75827	0.875

that although grains with a small $^{87}Rb/^{86}Sr$ ratio have high $^{87}Sr/^{86}Sr$, the $^{87}Sr/^{86}Sr$ ratio is larger in grains with high $^{87}Rb/^{86}Sr$. Now, use these data calculate the initial $^{87}Sr/^{86}Sr$ ratio and the age of the meteorite. Use both (a) the graphical method using all the data, and (b) the algebraic method involving two suitably chosen grains. For the graphical method try to estimate the uncertainty in the age of the meteorite by estimating the uncertainty in the fitted slope and intercept of the line through the data points. For the algebraic method, chose two grains that have reasonably different positions on the graph; don't just use the first two points in the table!

Chapter 6

Asteroids

6.1 Overview

The **asteroids** (or **minor planets**) make up a large family of small bodies, most of which orbit the Sun between the paths of Mars and Jupiter. They range in size from a maximum diameter of about 1000 km on down to diameters of a kilometer or less, and there are probably many, many objects in the **asteroid belt** quite a lot smaller still. The orbits of most asteroids lie more or less in the ecliptic plane with the planets, and most of these orbits are no more elongated and off-centred than that of Mercury. Studies of the way asteroids reflect light of various colours suggest that they are composed of minerals similar to those found in several common classes of meteorites, and most meteorites are almost certainly samples of some asteroids. We believe that some asteroids have undergone rather little chemical or physical change since the era when the planets of the solar system formed, and thus these small objects (together with the comets) contain important clues about the process of planet formation. In fact, they seem to be essentially a group of primordial planetesimals that never succeeded in accumulating to form a major planet.

6.2 Discovery

In the 1770's, Johann Bode (1747–1826) discovered and popularized an empirical "law" of planetary orbits (also found earlier by J. D. Titius, and now known as the **Titius-Bode law**). This law describes approximately the spacing of the orbits of the known planets, and predicts that there should be a planet between Mars and Jupiter at about 2.8 AU from the Sun. The Titius-Bode law led to the suspicion that there might be a planet there that had not yet been discovered. The discovery of the planet Uranus by William Herschel (1738–1822) in 1781 made it clear that new planets could indeed be found. In 1800, Franz von Zach, Director of the Ducal Observatory at Gotha, in Germany, began to organize a systematic search for the missing planet. However, on January 1, 1801, before serious work had begun on von Zach's programme, an object not shown on star charts was found by the Sicilian astronomer Giuseppe Piazzi (1749–1826) at Palermo. He observed the new "star" on the following nights and within three nights was sure that it moved. At first Piazzi thought he had discovered a new comet. He measured its position relative to the background stars as often as possible until early February 1801, when he fell seriously ill.

At the end of January, Piazzi had written to report his new "comet" to other astronomers, including Bode at Berlin. The report created some stir among the Germans, and von Zach even speculated that the new object might be the missing planet. However, the letters travelled slowly enough to Northern Europe that by the time the German astronomers heard of Piazzi's discovery, the new body was too close to the Sun to observe. In fact, by summer, Bode and Piazzi realized that it was lost—the methods of calculating orbits in use at the time were simply too crude to yield a useful orbit from position measurements spread over only a few degrees of sky.

The situation was saved by the brilliant young German mathematician Karl Friedrich Gauss (1777–1855), who read about the new object in the newspaper. He put aside his other work and set to devising a better method of determining an orbit from limited observations. By November of 1801 he was successful, and on December 31 von Zach recovered the body almost exactly where Gauss had predicted that it would be. Gauss won such fame from this work that in 1807, at the age of only 30, he was appointed the director of the Göttingen Observatory, where he remained for the rest of his life. The orbit calculated by Gauss clearly showed that the new body follows a nearly circular orbit at 2.8 AU from the Sun, rather than a cometary orbit, and it was generally agreed that the missing planet predicted by the Titius-Bode law had been found. Following Piazzi's proposal, the new planet was named Ceres, for the patron goddess of Sicily.

Since the "missing" planet had now been found, it

came as a great surprise when, in March 1802, Wilhelm Olbers (1758–1840), a busy Bremen physician and an active amateur astronomer, discovered a *second* small planet near Ceres, about as bright as Ceres, moving in an orbit of about the same size as that of Ceres, but rather strongly inclined to the ecliptic. The new body, soon named Pallas, naturally fueled searches for other similar objects, and in 1804 Juno was discovered, followed in 1807 by Vesta. And so the gap in the spacing of the planets between Mars and Jupiter was filled, but in a completely unexpected way: by four tiny planets, rather than one large one. Because of their star-like appearances (they are so small that they show no detectable disks when viewed through a telescope), they soon were called asteroids (from Greek *aster*, star).

No more new minor planets in the zone between Mars and Jupiter were found until 1845, but after that fainter asteroids were found with increasing frequency until more than 300 were known by 1891. In that year, the German astronomer Max Wolf (1863–1932) at Heidelberg first used long time exposure photography to find asteroids; on a photograph taken with a telescope that faithfully follows the fixed stars, the stars appear as dots but slowly moving asteroids make small dashes which are readily noticed. This technique is so powerful that by now many thousands of asteroids have been detected; more than 2×10^4 have computed orbits.

6.3 Orbits

For most of the two centuries that asteroids have been known, interest has centred on discovering them and determining their orbits. Only since about 1960 has a major effort been made to understand their physical nature.

When an asteroid is discovered and then frequently observed for some weeks or months as it moves through the sky, an orbit may be computed from which future positions can be predicted. Once the asteroid has a securely known orbit, so that it can be found again, it is officially recognized as a known asteroid, and is given a serial number, and a name chosen by the discoverer. Thus the full designation of an asteroid would be a name like 1 Ceres, 2 Pallas, 3 Juno, or 324 Bamberga. With many thousands of asteroids already named, you can imagine that finding a "suitable" name not already in use can be a challenge.

The physical and orbital characteristics of some of the largest asteroids (mostly with diameters of 200 km or more) as well as of a number of smaller but individually interesting bodies are listed in Table 6.1. In this table, two or more numbers in the "diameter" column indicate that the asteroid is known to be non-spherical; the numbers give approximate diameters measured along the main axes of the body. The columns describing orbital characteristics should be familiar from earlier chapters; the last two columns (albedo and spectral class) will be described later in this chapter.

Most asteroids are found to have orbits with semi-major axes of between 2.2 and 3.5 AU. These orbits are normally somewhat elliptical (not quite circular), with eccentricities e of the order of 0.1 or 0.2. All asteroids circle the Sun in the same sense as the planets, and their orbits lie in planes that are mildly inclined to the plane of the ecliptic, usually by no more than 15° or 20°. (Recall the description of elliptical orbits in Section 1.3.) The asteroid orbits are a little more eccentric than those of most planets, which have orbital eccentricities of 0.1 or less, except for Mercury with 0.21 and Pluto with 0.25. The orbits of asteroids are also somewhat more varied in inclination than those of most planets, all of which have orbit planes within 4° of the ecliptic, again except for Mercury (at 7°) and Pluto (at 17°). However, the eccentricities and inclinations of asteroids are much smaller than those of the comets. The great majority of asteroids are thus located in a wide belt that starts somewhat outside the orbit of Mars ($a = 1.5$ AU), but does not reach as far as the orbit of Jupiter ($a = 5.2$ AU). Because of the inclinations of the asteroid orbits, this belt also extends to roughly 1 AU above and below the ecliptic plane.

An overview of the orbital characteristics of several thousand numbered asteroids is shown in Figure 6.1, which plots for each of about 5000 numbered asteroids the orbital semi-major axis a and the orbital eccentricity e. Each asteroid is represented by a dot in the figure; you can clearly see the inner and outer edges of the main asteroid belt at about 2.2 AU and 3.2 AU, and the relatively small number of asteroids with orbital eccentricity of more than 0.2.

Within the asteroid belt, a remarkable feature of the orbits is that certain values of the semi-major axis seem to be virtually forbidden. This phenomenon is visible in Figure 6.1 in the obvious existence of lightly populated vertical bands in the swarm of points at a values of 2.5, 2.8, 2.9, and 3.3 AU. The tendency to avoid certain orbit sizes (or periods) is still more clearly seen in Figure 6.2, which plots the total number of numbered asteroids having orbital periods P within small intervals. Definite gaps in this histogram are clearly visible, for example around periods of 3.95, 4.75, and 5.1 yr. These "forbidden" orbits are found to correspond to orbital periods that are in resonance with Jupiter, which means that an asteroid in such an orbit would pass closest to Jupiter at the same place(s) in many successive orbits. For example, if the orbital period of Jupiter (11.86 yr) is exactly three times longer than

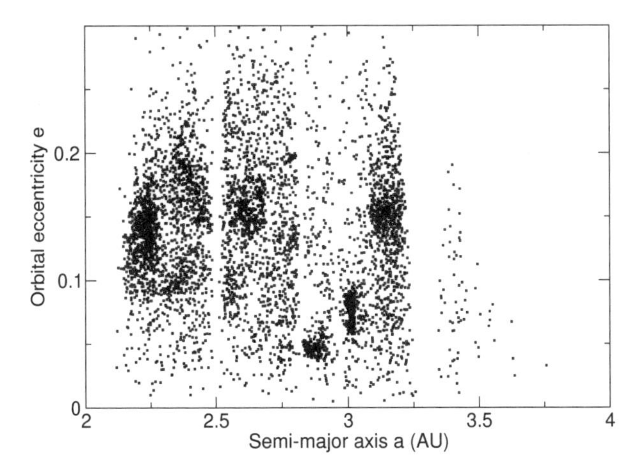

Figure 6.1: This diagram summarizes orbital properties of about 5000 numbered asteroids. Each point represents the orbit of a single asteroid; its horizontal position gives the semi-major axis a, while the orbital eccentricity e is plotted vertically. A position in the upper part of the diagram thus indicates an asteroid with a rather eccentric orbit. The Kirkwood gaps are visible as narrow vertical regions with few points. (Figure based on data made available by Dr Andrea Milani.)

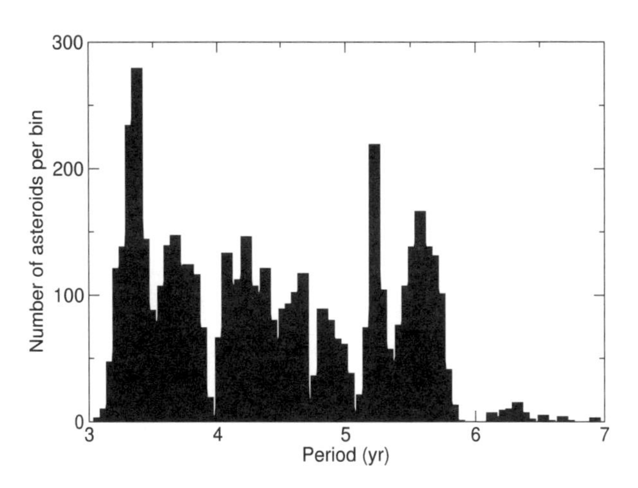

Figure 6.2: A histogram showing the numbers of asteroids having various orbital periods. The Kirkwood gaps at the 2:1, 3:1, 5:2 and 7:3 resonances with Jupiter (respectively at 5.93, 3.95, 4.74 and 5.08 yr) are quite obvious in the figure. (Figure based on data made available by Dr Andrea Milani.)

that of an asteroid (which thus has a period of 3.95 yr, one of the gaps noted above), Jupiter and the asteroid will always pass close to one another at two points on opposite sides of Jupiter's (and the asteroid's) orbit. Such repeated close encounters at the same points in the orbit will eventually result in Jupiter being able to change substantially the orbit of the asteroid by its extra gravitational effect on the asteroid at the positions of close encounter.

Exercise Sketch the orbital motions of Jupiter and of an asteroid having an orbital period one-third that of Jupiter over two Jupiter years (24 earth years) and find the points in the two orbits where the two bodies repeatedly pass one another.

The "forbidden" orbits are known as the **Kirkwood gaps** after their discoverer; they occur for orbits having period ratios P(Jupiter) : P(asteroid) with Jupiter of 2:1, 3:1, 4:1, 5:2, 5:3, and 7:3. Note that the Kirkwood gaps are forbidden values of period of revolution (or of semi-major axis), not of distance from the Sun; a map of actual asteroid positions at any moment shows no gaps at all. A very strange situation occurs for a period ratios of 3:2, 4:3 and 7:2, however, where there are actually accumulations of asteroids!

Astronomers who study orbital motions have begun to understand the logic of where Kirkwood gaps appear and where they do not. In the gaps, the effect of the resonance with the orbital period of Jupiter is to change the orbit parameters (eccentricity and semi-major axis) of the asteroid steadily in an unpredictable direction, so that these orbits become chaotic. The orbits of asteroids in these resonances become more and more eccentric, and they may end by crossing the orbit of Mars. In such a planet-crossing orbit, the asteroid is likely to be ejected from the solar system or to impact the Sun or a planet. In contrast, the resonances where asteroids are still present seem to be where the perturbing effect of Jupiter is to make orbit parameters vary up and down around some average values. In the long term the orbits of these asteroids are not changed substantially, and so these orbits remain populated.

A number of asteroid families (**Hirayama families**) have been identified. These are groups of between roughly 10 and 80 asteroids that have almost identical orbits. The asteroids of a given family are not actually particularly close to one another in space; they are spread along their common orbital track in much the same way that comet debris spreads out along the cometary orbit. What they have in common is nearly identical values of a, e, and i. A few of the most populous families show up on Figure 6.1 as clusters of points, for example the Themis family at $a = 3.14$, $e = 0.15$, Eos at $a = 3.01$, $e = 0.08$, and Koronis at $a = 2.88$, $e = 0.04$. Perhaps as many as half of all asteroids are members of one of roughly 100 Hirayama families that have been identified; some 10% belong to the three largest families. Some of these families are very probably made up of the debris from a single asteroid disrupted by a violent collision with

Table 6.1: Orbital and physical characteristics of some interesting asteroids.

Number & Name		Diameter (km)	Distance from Sun (semi-major axis, AU)	Orbital period (yr)	Orbital eccentricity e	Orbital inclination (°)	Albedo	Spectral class
Near-Earth asteroids								
2062	Aten	1.0	0.966	0.95	0.200	19.3		S
433	Eros	$30 \times 19 \times 7$	1.46	1.76	0.219	10.8	0.18	S
1862	Apollo	1.6	1.47	1.78	0.549	8.9		Q
1866	Sisyphus	10	1.89	1.893				
Main Belt asteroids								
4	Vesta	$566 \times 531 \times 437$	2.36	3.63	0.090	7.1	0.38	U
13	Egeria	215	2.58	4.13	0.121	16.3	0.099	C
15	Eunomia	270	2.64	4.30	0.143	13.3	0.19	S
3	Juno	267	2.67	4.36	0.255	13.0	0.22	S
324	Bamberga	240	2.68	4.39	0.285	13.3	0.057	C
45	Eugenia	215	2.72	4.49	0.115	6.1	0.048	C
1	Ceres	959×907	2.77	4.60	0.077	10.6	0.10	C
2	Pallas	$570 \times 525 \times 482$	2.77	4.61	0.233	34.8	0.14	U
16	Psyche	265	2.92	4.99	0.138	3.1	0.10	M
704	Interamnia	335	3.06	5.36	0.153	17.3	0.064	C
451	Patientia	230	3.06	5.36	0.068	15.2	0.073	C
52	Europa	280	3.10	5.45	0.109	7.5	0.057	C
48	Doris	225	3.11	5.49	0.064	6.7	0.064	C
24	Themis	230	3.13	5.55	0.159	1.2		C
10	Hygeia	430	3.14	5.57	0.118	3.8	0.075	C
31	Euphrosyne	250	3.15	5.61	0.228	26.3	0.070	C
511	Davida	$417 \times 333 \times 292$	3.18	5.67	0.172	15.9	0.053	C
Asteroids beyond the Main Belt								
65	Cybele	245	3.43	6.35	0.110	3.6	0.057	C
87	Sylvia	270	3.48	6.51	0.093	10.9	0.040	C
153	Hilda	175	3.97	7.91			0.060	P
279	Thule	135	4.29	8.90			0.060	D
Trojan asteroids								
624	Hektor	150×300	5.20	11.86			0.02	D
Centaurs								
944	Hidalgo	50	5.86	14.19	0.66	42.4		
2060	Chiron	220	13.65	50.43	0.383	6.9	0.08?	C
5145	Pholus		20.30	91.43	0.572	24.7		
Trans-neptunian objects								
	1992 QB1		44.01	292.0	0.071	2.2		

Sources: R. P. Binzel, T. Gehrels & M. S. Matthews (eds.) 1989, *Asteroids II* (Tucson: Univ. of Arizona Press), Parts II &VI; and C. T. Kowal 1996, *Asteroids: Their Nature and Utilization* (New York: John Wiley & Sons)

another asteroid. Since the ejection velocity of most debris from a violent collision is typically in the range of 0.1 to 1 km s^{-1} (relative to the centre of mass of the colliding bodies), and this is small compared to orbital speeds of around 18 km s^{-1}, the fragments continue to follow almost the same orbit that the parent body did, gradually spreading around the orbit.

Not all asteroids are found in the main asteroid belt, however. A small number have orbital semi-major axes that are near one AU. These near-Earth asteroids, although relatively rare, are of particular interest to us because they may be able to collide with Earth (recall Sec. 5.2). Such asteroids are usually assigned to one of three families on the basis of orbit size. The Aten group have semi-major axes a of less than 1.00 AU, and thus orbit the Sun more quickly than the Earth does. The Apollo group have Earth-crossing orbits with $a > 1.00$ AU. Still further out, the Earth-approaching Amor asteroids move in orbits which do not at present cross that of Earth, but which have perihelion distances from the Sun of less than 1.3 AU. These three groups of objects are usually lumped together and called **near-Earth asteroids (NEA's)**. Roughly 200 such bodies are now known, and it is estimated that about 700 Apollo asteroids have diameters greater than 1 km. The probability of a collision between Earth and one of these bodies within the next 1000 years is about 0.4%. They are probably the source bodies for many of the meteorites that fall to Earth.

A little further out, not far outside the orbit of Mars, the small Hungaria group orbits between 1.8 and 2.0 AU, substantially closer to the Sun than the inner edge of the main belt at about 2.2 AU.

Beyond the main asteroid belt, which ends at about 3.2 AU, we have the Cybele family at about 3.4 AU, the Hildas at 4 AU, and the **Trojan** asteroids, which revolve around the Sun in orbits of $a \approx 5.2$ AU, essentially the same as the orbit of Jupiter. The Trojans occupy particularly interesting orbits; they are found in two clusters on Jupiter's orbit, equidistant from the Sun and from Jupiter. One group is about 5 AU ahead of Jupiter on its path, and the other is about 5 AU behind. These orbits are two of the so-called **Lagrange points**, after the great French mathematician Joseph-Louis Lagrange (1736–1813), who in 1772, more than one century before the discovery in 1906 of the first Trojan asteroid, showed that bodies in these particular positions relative to Jupiter would be kept gently in position by the gravitational "shepherding" of the planet.

A few really remote small bodies have been found in recent years orbiting among the outer planets. It is not clear whether these objects are physically more similar to the main belt asteroids or to the nuclei of comets, but with one exception they show no cometary outgassing, so we can conveniently look at them along with the asteroids. These bodies have much more distinctive orbits than the main belt asteroids, both in their much larger distances from the Sun and in their much larger eccentricities. Three are listed in Table 6.1. 944 Hidalgo travels from a perihelion at 2 AU, inside the inner edge of the main asteroid belt, out to 9.7 AU, just beyond the orbit of Saturn. Its highly inclined orbit resembles that of a short-period comet, but it shows no cometary activity. 2060 Chiron, farther out, ranges from 8.5 AU from the Sun, somewhat inside Saturn's orbit, out to 18.9 AU, near the orbit of Uranus, in an orbit not far out of the plane of the ecliptic. For ten years after its discovery, Chiron looked like a normal asteroid, but in 1988 it was observed to flare up in brightness, and the next year it showed a faint coma, like a comet. Unlike objects in the main belt, bodies at such large distances from the Sun may well contain considerable amounts of ice, so they may be physically closely related to comet nuclei even if they show no comas.

Finally, recall the bodies discovered in the Kuiper belt (Sec. 4.5). The objects so far discovered in this broad region outside the orbit of Neptune are typically of order 200 km or more in diameter (smaller bodies are mostly still too faint to be detected from the Earth). They are thus very similar to the larger asteroids in size, although they are very probably made of a mixture of ice and rock, like comet nuclei. Like the asteroids, most Kuiper belt objects orbit the Sun in orbits that are mildly eccentric and moderately inclined. In many ways, the Kuiper belt appears to be a second asteroid belt beyond the region of the giant planets. Because it is so much more difficult to detect and especially to study Kuiper belt objects, we still know rather little about this outer family of small bodies. The first object discovered in the Kuiper belt, 1992 QB1, is included in Table 6.1. The few large "asteroids" like Chiron and Pholus that are found among the giant planets could well be bodies brought in from the Kuiper belt by the perturbing action of Neptune, as described later in Chapter 7.

6.4 Physical nature of asteroids

Asteroids are mostly so small that it is very difficult to obtain accurate measurements of size or mass for them by the kinds of direct methods useful for large planets. Hence a variety of indirect techniques are employed. As only one asteroid has ever been landed upon, and only a few have been observed close up by spacecraft, much of what we know about them still comes from Earth-based observations.

Sizes

Even the largest asteroids are somewhat less than one second of arc in diameter as seen from Earth, an thus are not seen as disks in a telescope, but simply as fuzzy points of light. Direct measurements of diameter are therefore difficult and inaccurate except for rare measurements from space probes. However, several methods provide asteroid diameters indirectly. The simplest method is to assume a reflectivity (the fraction of light reflected is usually called the **albedo**) for an asteroid (one might reasonably guess from comparison with terrestrial rocks that perhaps 10 or 20% of the light is reflected), and then to use the measured brightness at a known distance from the Sun and Earth to calculate the size the asteroid must have to reflect as much light as it does. Clearly a (spherical) asteroid with a diameter of 100 km and a projected surface area of $\pi D^2/4 = 7850$ km^2 will reflect roughly 10,000 times more light, and be about 10,000 times brighter, than an asteroid of only 1 km diameter with a projected surface area of 0.8 km^2; even if the albedos are not known exactly, the enormous difference in reflecting surface between large and small asteroids allows one to derive a rough size for an asteroid as soon as its orbit is determined and its brightness is measured. The biggest source of uncertainty in measuring sizes by this method is the assumed albedo. Terrestrial rocks actually vary in reflectivity from around 3% (coal) to 50% (limestone); if we assume a corresponding range in asteroid albedos, the derived asteroid diameters are uncertain by a factor of more than three!

The situation can be greatly improved if the albedo can be measured. There are several methods for doing this. One is to recognize that the fraction of the sunlight that falls onto an asteroid but is *not* reflected must be absorbed. This warms the asteroid up to a temperature at which the heat radiation from the surface just balances the heating from absorbed sunlight. Now if the asteroid has a high albedo, and reflects most sunlight so that little warming takes place, it will be *cooler* than another darker asteroid at the same distance from the Sun, which reflects less light and absorbs more. The darker asteroid will have a higher surface temperature than the lighter asteroid, in order to radiate away the larger amount of absorbed heat. Now an important difference between the incoming sunlight and the radiated heat is due to the fact that the asteroid surface is far cooler than the surface of the Sun. Because the Sun's surface is at about 6000 K, most of the heat it radiates comes out between about 2,000 and 20,000 Å (0.2–2.0 μm), essentially in the (visible) band of wavelengths to which the eye is sensitive. The *reflected* light from an asteroid will therefore also be in this wavelength range. In contrast, an asteroid normally has a surface temperature of less than 200 K, and hence emits mainly in the wavelengths band between 6 and 100 μm, in the infrared. Thus a measurement of an asteroid's brightness in visible light measures the amount of reflected light, while an infra-red brightness measurement determines the amount of absorbed and re-radiated energy. A highly reflective asteroid will be brighter in reflected light than in re-radiated light, while a dark asteroid will be brighter in the infra-red than in visible light. Calculating the ratio of these two brightnesses allows us to determine an asteroid's albedo, and then to use the observed infrared brightness to deduce a reasonably accurate (±10%) diameter. The idea is illustrated in Figure 6.3.

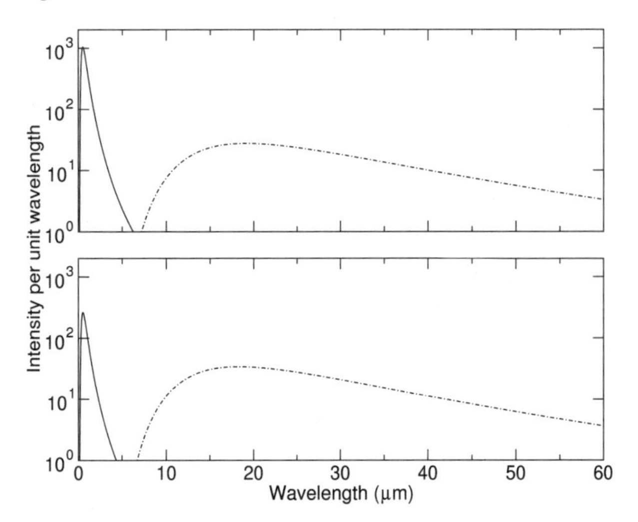

Figure 6.3: This figure shows approximately the reflected visible light (solid lines) and the infra-red heat radiation (dot-dash lines) for two asteroids at 3 AU from the Sun. The asteroid of the upper panel has (visual) albedo $A = 0.20$, and the lower has $A = 0.05$. Notice, first, that the reflected visible light and the radiated IR light virtually do not overlap, so it is easy to identify which is reflected light and which is thermal radiation. Then notice that the ratio of visible to infra-red radiation (the ratio of the areas under the two curves in the panel) is higher for the more reflective asteroid of the upper panel than is for the less reflective body in the lower panel. By comparing the *relative* amounts of visible and infra-red light from an asteroid, you can deduce its albedo.

A much more accurate method of measuring asteroid sizes takes advantage of the fact that an asteroid will occasionally pass in front of a star and eclipse it. If the event has been predicted, astronomers can set up portable telescopes along the path of the asteroid's shadow on Earth, and measure the time and duration of the eclipse. (Amateur astronomers have been of great help to professionals in a number of such campaigns.) From several such observations of the same event (called an occultation), one can easily calculate how large the asteroid's shadow is on the Earth while it eclipses the star. The eclipsed star is so far away that all the light rays from it striking the asteroid are parallel, and the asteroid's shadow is a cylinder with the same diameter as the asteroid. Thus, knowing the shadow diameter gives directly the asteroid size. This technique has yielded quite accurate (±10 km) diame-

Figure 6.4: The asteroid 951 Gaspra was imaged from a distance of 5300 km by the Galileo space probe in 1991. It is about 19 x 12 x 11 km in size. The smallest features visible in the image are about 100 m across, about the size of a football field. Some 600 small craters are visible in images of this body. The very irregular shape of the asteroid suggests that it may be a piece of a larger asteroid fragmented by a violent collision. (Courtesy of NASA.)

Figure 6.5: The asteroid 253 Mathilde, which is 56 km across its largest dimension, was observed by the NEAR spacecraft in 1997. This view, from about 2400 km away, clearly shows a huge crater comparable in size to the asteroid itself. The asteroid is almost black, reflecting only about 3% of the sunlight striking it, in contrast to Ida and Gaspra, which are about as reflective as gray rock. (Courtesy of NASA.)

ters for a few of the larger asteroids. The largest, Ceres, has had not only its diameter but its shape measured by this method. Due to its rather rapid rotation (one rotation every 9 hours), it has the shape of a slightly flattened sphere (like the Earth), with an equatorial diameter of 959 ± 5 km and a polar diameter of 907 ± 9 km.

Sizes have been determined by one method or another for a large number of main belt asteroids by now. Estimated sizes are available for almost all the asteroids listed in Table 6.1. Ceres is by far the largest. The next two largest in size are Pallas and Vesta, with diameters of a little over 500 km. More than 10 asteroids have diameters exceeding about 250 km. As one goes down in size, the number of asteroids increases rapidly. About 100 are larger than 150 km in diameter; almost 1000 exceed 40 km. And there are certainly hundreds or thousands of bodies more than 100 km in diameter in the Kuiper Belt.

At still smaller sizes, there must be many thousands of asteroids, but such small bodies are very faint and hard to study, and only a small fraction have known orbits. However, on the basis of the number of asteroids found in surveys, it is possible to estimate their total numbers, at least of those with sufficiently large diameters (of the order of hundreds of m) to be detected. There are probably around 40,000 bodies in the asteroid belt with diameters of 1 km or more, and perhaps one million bodies if we count everything more than 100 m across. (Note that such a statistic, to be meaningful, must specify the lower size limit of objects included in the count!) Although this seems to be an enormous number of objects, the volume of space occupied by the asteroid belt is huge, and the typical separation between asteroids with diameters of 100 m or more is of the order of 3 million km. The familiar image from the movies of a space ship maneuvering madly to avoid one asteroid after another is certainly not appropriate for the solar system's asteroid belt!

Three asteroids have been viewed from distances of only a few thousand km by passing space probes, and a fourth has been studied in detail by its own orbiter. The asteroids Gaspra (in 1991) and Ida (in 1993) were imaged by the Galileo spacecraft during its long trip to the Jupiter system. Ida and its tiny moon Dactyl are seen in Figure 1.5. Gaspra is shown in Figure 6.4. Asteroid Mathilde (Figure 6.5) was observed by the NEAR (Near Earth Asteroid Rendezvous) space probe in 1997 (now called the NEAR-Shoemaker mission). The NEAR probe then went into orbit around Eros (Figure 6.6), from which it has sent back an enormous amount of fascinating information, finally *landing* (Figure 6.7) on the asteroidal surface at the end of the mission!

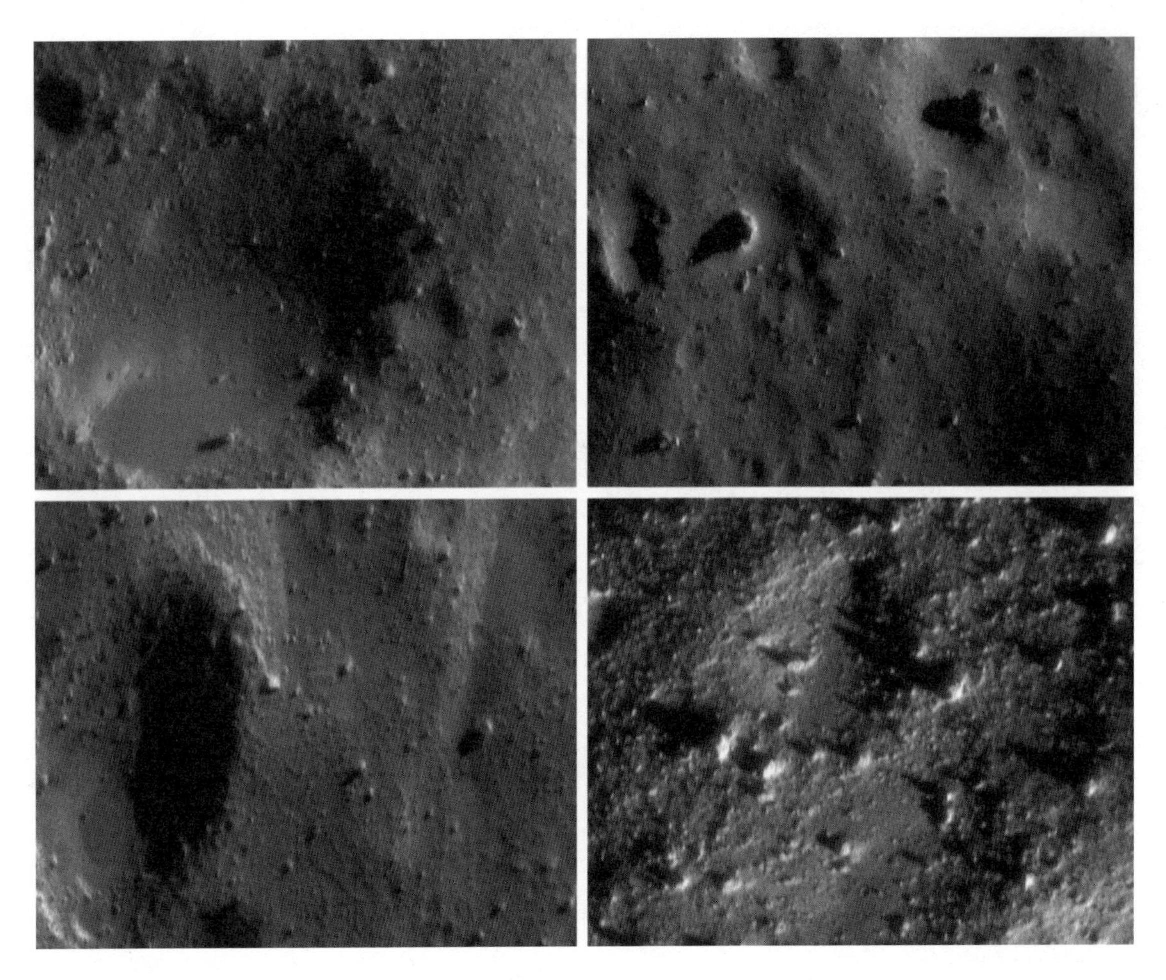

Figure 6.7: Four views of the surface of asteroid 433 Eros taken during the last few days of the mission before the NEAR spacecraft settled in to land on the surface of the asteroid. The top images were taken from about 12 km above Eros, and show regions about 500 m across; the two lower images are from about 5 km up and show regions about 250 m across. The surface of Eros is dotted with small craters and covered with boulders. (Courtesy of NASA.)

Spins and Shapes

Careful observations of the brightness of most asteroids show changes in brightness that repeat regularly with periods that are usually between about six hours and 2 days. This effect is caused by rotation, combined with non-spherical shapes and/or perhaps non-uniform surface reflectivity (darker and light regions). Variations in reflectivity or colour over the surface ("spots") probably dominate the brightness changes for the largest asteroids (with diameters of $\sim$ 300 km or more), which are massive enough that their own gravities force them to be roughly spherical. The much more common smaller asteroids are often markedly non-spherical. Ida (Figure 1.5), Gaspra (Figure 6.4), and Eros (Figure 6.6) all have longest dimensions roughly twice as large as their smaller dimensions. The small near-Earth asteroid 4179 Toutatis has been imaged by radar, and it is found that it has a shape like a peanut, smaller around the waist and larger at both ends. As such a small irregular body spins, usually around an axis roughly perpendicular to the longest dimension, the light it reflects towards Earth varies strongly as we see the asteroid broadside on and then end on.

Such close-up views are not possible for most asteroids. However, we can still obtain information about the shapes of asteroids that we see only as points of light by studying closely the light variations. As an asteroid and the Earth move around their respective orbits, we are able to observe how the light reflected from the spinning asteroid varies when seen from various directions. At one moment, we might be looking at the asteroid (let's assume that it is elongated like Eros, and rotating around an axis perpendicular to its long dimension) from its equatorial plane. We would then observe large variations in the brightness of reflected sunlight as we see first the full length of the asteroid and then its smaller end-on profile. At another time,

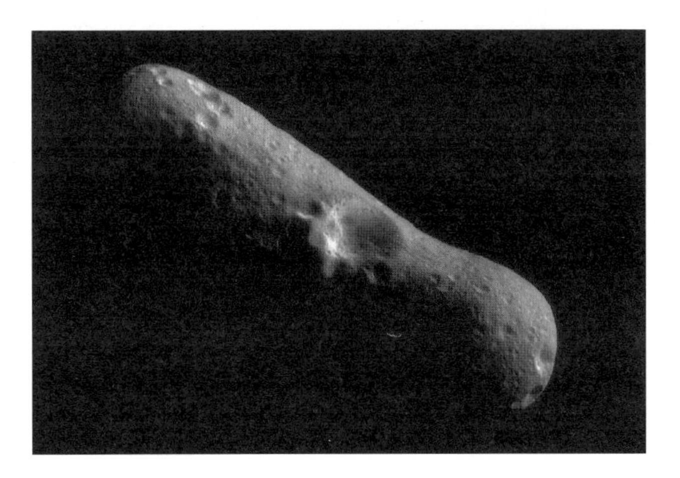

Figure 6.6: The asteroid 433 Eros, viewed in a mosaic of images obtained by the NEAR spacecraft shortly after going into orbit around the asteroid in February 2000, from a distance of about 300 km. The many high resolution images sent back to Earth from NEAR will help space scientists to understand the details of Eros' history. Notice how remarkably non-spherical this small body is (the longest dimension is about 30 km), and that the largest visible crater is more than 15% of the asteroid's length in diameter! (Courtesy of NASA.)

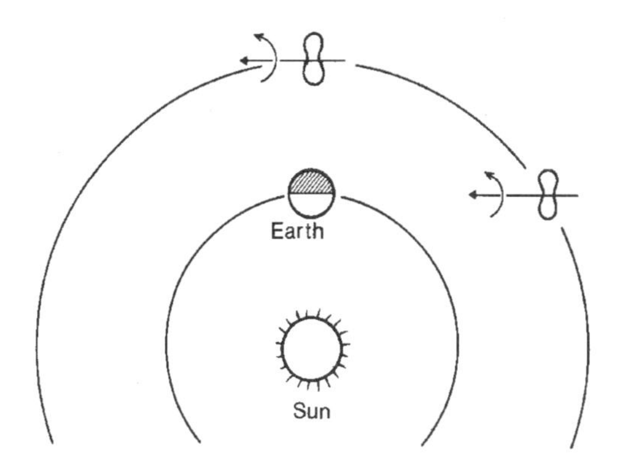

Figure 6.8: This sketch shows an elongated asteroid (like Gaspra or Eros) that is rotating around an axis perpendicular to its long axis, as seen from the Earth at two different places in its orbit. At one location, its rotation is seen from the side, and the apparent area and brightness of the asteroid vary considerably as it is seen first end on and then side on. In the other position, its rotation is seen from along its rotation axis, and although its orientation on the sky changes, its projected surface does not, so that its brightness variations are quite small.

we could be looking roughly along the rotation axis; in this case, we would hardly see any variations. These possibilities are sketched in Figure 6.8. By observing a particular asteroid a number of times from various directions, it is possible to deduce – very approximately! – its overall shape and the direction in space of its rotation axis. The bodies in Table 6.1 for which the diameters are given as three numbers are mostly bodies for which observations of light variations have allowed astronomers to infer shapes. Other techniques (such as occultations, use of radar, and "speckle interferometry") provide valuable additional information. It appears that the very bizarre shapes seen in the images of asteroids are typical enough of the great majority of small asteroids which have never been seen from close up.

Masses and densities

The masses of the three largest asteroids, Ceres, Pallas, and Vesta, have been determined observing the tiny attractive effects these bodies have via gravity on smaller asteroids in similar orbits, and on each other. The attractive forces of even these largest asteroids on other bodies are so small that the effects to be observed require extraordinarily precise position determinations, and the deduced masses still differ somewhat from one investigation to another. Table 6.2 lists masses that have been determined in this way, as well as three others that have been observed from nearby spacecraft. The masses given for Ceres and Vesta are probably still uncertain by about 10%, and that of Pallas by 20%. Ida's mass is derived from observations of its moon Dactyl, and is accurate to about 15%; Mathilde was weighed by observing the deflection of the NEAR space probe and is uncertain by about 4%. The mass of Eros was measured with enormous precision (±0.05%) by the NEAR craft, which orbited the asteroid for months before actually landing on it on 12 February 2001.

Both mass and mean radius are well enough known for the large asteroids Ceres, Pallas and Vesta to obtain approximate mean densities, which provide valuable clues about the overall chemical composition of these small bodies. The density of Ceres is significantly lower than the density of almost any kind of terrestrial rock, but similar to the densities of carbonaceous chondrite meteorites. The densities of Pallas and Vesta are considerably larger; their densities are comparable to the densities of ordinary (not carbonaceous) chondrites, or to the typical densities of achondritic meteorites or those of stony-irons (see Table 5.3). It seems probable that Ceres is made of material similar to that in carbonaceous chondrites, while Pallas may be related to ordinary chondrites. Vesta is clearly related to a family of igneous (differentiated) meteorites.

As we have seen, spacecraft passed quite close to the asteroids Ida and Mathilde, and actually orbited

Table 6.2: Masses, mean radii and mean densities of some asteroids

	Name	Mass (kg)	Mean diameter (km)	Mean density (kg m^{-3})
1	Ceres	9.54×10^{20}	933	2230
2	Pallas	2.4×10^{20}	524	3200
4	Vesta	2.8×10^{20}	508	3900
243	Ida	4.2×10^{16}	31	2600
253	Mathilde	1.03×10^{17}	53	1300
433	Eros	6.687×10^{15}	16.8	2670
	All others	3×10^{20}		

Sources: Viateau, B. & Rapaport, M. 1998, *Astr. Ap.* 334, 729; Yeomans, D. et al. 1997, *Science* 278, 2106; Yeomans et al. 2000, *Science* 289, 2085.

Eros. Those close encounters changed the probe orbits enough to allow determination of the masses of these small bodies, and since the detailed shapes were also observed, volumes and mean densities could be computed. The densities of Ida and of Eros are typical of carbonaceous chondrites or terrestrial rock, so from this information we would suspect that they are parent bodies of such meteorites. However, they are not nearly as dark as carbonaceous meteorites. Mathilde's density turned out, to everyone's great surprise, to be only 1300 $\pm$ 200 kg m^{-3}, less than half the density of any normal rock. Mathilde is probably a loose aggregate of boulders, with much empty space inside between rocks; even if Mathilde's boulders have the relatively low density of carbonaceous chondrites, which is consistent with the nearly black colour of the asteroid, some additional effect such as internal voids must be lowering the both densities still further. This discovery makes it seem likely that densities of other small asteroids are probably lower than the densities of the rocks of which they are composed. (Of course, for asteroids near the outer edge of the asteroid belt, a significant mineral could be water ice, with its density of about 900 kg m^{-3}, but this is not possible for the asteroids observed up to now from space probes, because they are too close to the Sun and hence too warm.)

If we estimate the total mass of all the smaller asteroids by assuming a reasonable typical density, it turns out (see Table 6.2) that Ceres contains about half the mass of the asteroid belt, and that the total mass of all the asteroids only adds up to about 1/40th of the mass of the Earth's Moon.

Chemical and mineral composition

To understand the nature and history of asteroids, we need to know not only about their orbits, sizes, shapes, and masses, but also about their chemical and mineral compositions. These compositions are the result of the processes that formed and altered them, and thus contain extremely valuable clues about these processes. How can we learn something about the minerals present in an asteroid?

The first broad hint about asteroid chemistry comes from the fact that asteroids are mostly quite dark (they have relatively small albedos); furthermore, among the larger asteroids there seem to be some, like Mathilde, that are almost black, like coal or soot (albedos of 3 or 4%), while others, such as Gaspra and Ida, are merely dark, like dark grey rocks (albedos of 10 to 20%), and a few are actually rather bright, like limestone (albedos approaching 50%). This fact strongly suggests that there are at least two or three kinds of asteroids that probably have rather different minerals and chemistry.

Further differences among asteroids can be found when we look into how well they reflect various colours – that is, we measure the brightness at several wavelengths. This has been done for more than a thousand asteroids using a photometer (a device that measures the brightness of light, like the light meter in a camera). In the simplest version of this kind of measurement, the brightness of the asteroid is measured through three standard coloured glass filters, which pass yellow, blue, and near ultraviolet light. When the brightness of the asteroid as measured through the three filters is compared, we obtain information about the colour of the asteroid. For example, a grey-coloured asteroid would reflect all three colours about the same, and so would have the same brightness as measured through all three filters. On the other hand, and asteroid that has a reddish colour, like some sandstones – or bricks – reflects more yellow than blue light, so the brightness as measured through the yellow filter would be brighter than measured thorough the blue filter. Notice that since this type of measurement relies on *ratios* (for example the ratio of brightness through the blue filter to the brightness through the yellow filter), it does not depend on whether the asteroid is bright or faint, large or small, or near or far.

Using both albedo measurements and this sort of colour measurement, we find that the asteroids group into several large, more-or-less distinct classes. Each of the larger classes is found to have albedo and colour that is characteristic of a family of meteorites. It was natural to guess that the similarity of albedo and colour of each large class of asteroids to the characteristics of one type of meteorite hints that the asteroids of that class are actually similar in mineral composition to

Table 6.3: Asteroid types, meteorite analogues, and mineral identifications

Type	Number	Albedo	Meteorite analogue	Possible mineral identifications
A	4	high	olivine-rich achondrites, pallasites (stony-irons)	olivine, olivine-metal
B, C, F, G	6, 88, 13, 5	low	CI and CM carbonaceous chondrites	hydrated silicates, carbon, organic materials
D, P	26, 23	low	organic-rich CI and CM carbonaceous chondrites?	carbon- and organic-rich silicates?
E	8	high	aubrites (enstatite-rich achondrites)	enstatite or other iron-free silicates
M	21	middle	irons, perhaps also enstatite chondrites	iron-nickel, perhaps metal and enstatite
Q	1	high	ordinary (not carbonaceous) chondrites	olivine, pyroxene, and metal
R	1	high	pyroxene-olivine achondrites	pyroxene and olivine
S	144	middle	pallasites, olivine-rich stony-irons, ureilites (olivine-rich achondrites), CV and CO carbonaceous chondrites	combinations of metal, olivine, and pyroxene
T	4	low		similar to types P and D?
V	1	high	basaltic achondrites	pyroxene and/or feldspar

Source: M. J. Gaffey, J. F. Bell & D. P. Cruikshank 1989, in *Asteroids II*, ed. R. P Binzel, T. Gehrels & M. S. Matthews (Tucson: Univ. of Arizona Press), p. 98.

the corresponding meteorites, and the asteroid classes have been named accordingly. Thus, asteroids that are nearly black but reflect all colours about equally well (or poorly), and are similar to the carbonaceous chondrites (recall Table 5.3), were placed in the C class. The more reflective asteroids with A values of 0.1 or 0.2 break into two distinct groups, one with colour similar to iron meteorites which were called M asteroids, and a redder group with colours like those of some stony-iron meteorites, thus labelled S asteroids. A few really reflective, neutral coloured asteroids are similar in colour and reflectivity to the enstatite meteorites and have been assigned to the E class. The strong similarities found between meteorites and asteroids supports the idea that most meteorites are derived from asteroids.

However, colour measurements using only three filters are not sufficient to discriminate among the large number of meteorite types described in the previous chapter, or, one assumes, among a similarly large number of kinds of asteroids. Thus asteroid scientists have developed still more powerful methods of observation that yield more information. One of the main ways this has been done is to measure brightness of a larger number of colours at both visible and infrared wavelengths. Substantial differences in brightness observed in the infrared are found among various meteorites – and among the asteroids. With more colours, more asteroid classes are identified, and in recent years the classification system has grown to include more than a dozen different types. For reference, the main classes in use are summarized in Table 6.3. The various types have been tentatively identified both with specific classes of meteorites that have similar reflectance properties, and with the kinds of minerals that can lead to the various colour properties observed. From the table, you can see that some classes (S, C, M, D, P, etc.) have a large number of members, while others (Q, R, V, etc.) have few or even only one known representative. (Of course, the numbers in this table are large for types of asteroids that are found near the Earth than for types far out in the solar system.) These are the asteroid types used to describe individual asteroids in Table 6.1.

The natural next step after measuring the brightness of an asteroid at several wavelengths is to measure the brightness of reflected or emitted radiation at many wavelengths – that is, to observe the spectrum of the body. From the ground, this is most practical in the visible and near infrared, between about 0.3 μm and 2.5 μm, where the reflected sunlight is relatively bright (see Figure 6.3) and the Earth's atmosphere does not present too much absorption. Asteroid (and mineral) spectra in this wavelength region are found to contain a lot of information about the chemical and mineral nature of the material(s) observed.

Unlike gases, solids do not show sharp spectral emission lines (Figure 2.3) or absorption lines (Figure 3.7).

Instead, mineral – especially iron-rich ones – show broad regions of relatively poor reflectivity whose position and width in the spectrum allow one to identify with reasonable certainty particular mineral species (such as olivine or pyroxene), and to determine which metal (iron, magnesium, etc.) is the main one present in the mineral. The way in which reflectivity varies with wavelength is shown for several common minerals in Figure 6.9. Clearly each of the minerals shown exhibits a distinctive signature in its reflection (or reflectivity) spectrum.

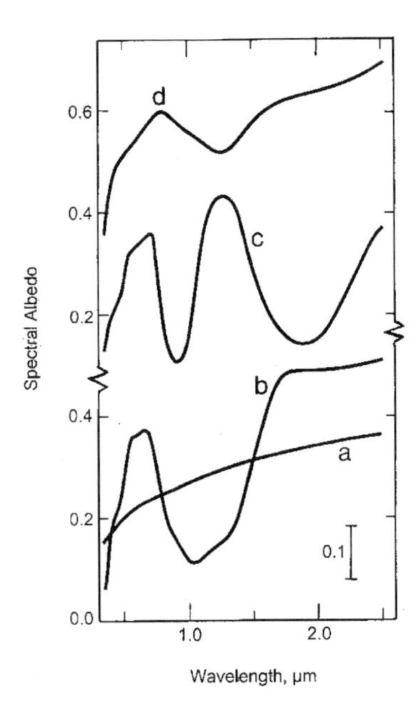

Figure 6.9: Reflectivity spectra of common silicate minerals and iron. From bottom to top they are (a) metallic nickel-iron, (b) olivine, (c) pyroxene, and (d) plagioclase feldspar (anorthite). Notice that the vertical scale makes a sudden change about half-way up the figure. (Adapted from M. J. Gaffey, J. F. Bell, and D. P. Cruikshank 1989, in *Asteroids II*, ed. R. P. Binzel, T. Gehrels and M. S. Matthews (Tucson, AZ: Univ. of Arizona Press), p. 101.)

Several important kinds of absorption patterns are found in the reflectivity spectra of the kinds of substances that seem to be common in asteroids. First, there are opaque, very poorly reflecting materials. These include various forms of carbon such as graphite, various tarry organic materials, and the iron oxide magnetite (Fe_3O_4). All are black – that is, they reflect almost no light of any colour; they simply have albedos that are very low (around 0.03) throughout the visible and near infrared spectrum. Next, there are the abundant metals, such as iron, perhaps mixed (alloyed) with nickel. These metals have no distinctive features in their reflection spectra, but rather show a moderate reflectivity (of order 0.30) that rises steadily towards longer wavelengths, from the near ultraviolet into the infrared. Sunlight reflected from a metal is more depleted in blue light than in red, and so the reflected light has a somewhat reddish colour (Figure 6.9 (a)).

Another type of spectrum is the family of silicate minerals containing iron. The two most prominent families in asteroids are the olivine series (Mg_2,Fe_2)SiO_4 and the pyroxenes (Mg,Fe)SiO_3. The olivines (Figure 6.9 (b)) show a single deep absorption between 0.7 and 1.5 μm (and the strong peak of reflectivity between 0.5 and 0.7 μm is responsible for the pronounced green colour of this mineral). The pyroxenes have a pair of regions of poor reflectivity, one around 1 μm and the other centred near 1.9 μm (Figure 6.9 (c)). The shape and width of an observed absorption near 1 μm, and the presence or absence of the 1.9 μm depression, are key indicators of the relative importance of these two mineral families. The plagioclase feldspars ($NaAlSi_3O_8$ – $CaAl_2Si_2O_8$), which normally contain trace amounts of iron, show a weak, broad absorption near 1.2 μm (Figure 6.9 (d)).

A final spectral family of importance in asteroids is that of water and ice. H_2O molecules can be present as ice, or H_2O or OH can be bound into hydrated minerals such as serpentine, $(Fe,Mg)_3Si_2O_5(OH)_4$, which can be formed by reaction of pyroxenes with water. Substances containing water or OH will typically show fairly narrow absorption bands at 1.4 and 1.9 μm, and also between 2.9 – 3.3 μm.

The spectrum of reflected sunlight has now been observed for several hundred of the brighter – larger and/or nearer – asteroids (this is not yet practical for the fainter ones). In these spectra we immediately see many of the same regions of poor reflectivity as are found in the albedo spectra of laboratory mineral samples and meteorites. Several examples of asteroid reflectivity spectra are shown in Figure 6.10. It is obvious that some of the same features seen in Figure 6.9 are present in the the spectra of these asteroids, and it is thus possible to identify one or more major minerals present at the surfaces of these small bodies. In a few cases, spectra have been obtained from several directions as the asteroid rotates, and it is possible to deduce which are the dominant minerals on various sides of a single body. The results of such investigations are summarized for a number of asteroids in Table 6.4. It is from such studies that the mineral identifications in Table 6.3 have been derived.

Note that the detailed investigations, which require fairly bright asteroids to be possible, are very incomplete both in not sampling asteroids of less than about 20 km diameter, and not sampling well the darker asteroids, particularly in the outer asteroid belt. Never-

Table 6.4: Mineral nature of asteroid surfaces

Asteroid (type)	Surface minerals and probable nature
1 Ceres (G)	Iron-poor phyllosilicates containing water molecules, magnetite or opaque carbonaceous material. Produced by aqueous (water) alteration of CI/CM material.
2 Pallas (B)	Similar to Ceres.
4 Vesta (V)	Strong pyroxene absorption, weaker plagioclase. Surface is mostly similar to certain basaltic achondrites, with regions of feldspar-poor basalt. The surface of Vesta is the nearly intact crust of a differentiated planetesimal.
8 Flora (S)	Metal, olivine, and some pyroxene present, and quite variable over the surface. The present surface might be the core-mantle boundary of a differentiated asteroid that has lost its crust.
15 Eunomia (S)	Metal and olivine, with some pyroxene. This asteroid is quite elongated, and may expose the interior of a differentiated body from core-mantle boundary to crust.
16 Psyche (M)	No Mg or Fe-rich silicates; surface dominated by metals. Psyche reveals the iron-rich core of a differentiated body.
44 Nysa (E)	Highly reflective surface is apparently iron-poor enstatite. The surface is the crust or exposed mantle of a differentiated body similar to the enstatite chondrites.
113 Amalthea (S)	Olivine with some pyroxene and metal. This might be the lowest part of the mantle of a very differentiated parent object.
349 Dembowska (R)	Spectrum shows strong pyroxene absorption and some evidence of olivine, but no metal. Dembowska's surface is probably the iron-poor silicate residue in the upper mantle of an incompletely differentiated body.
354 Eleonora (S)	Olivine and metal. Perhaps the core-mantle boundary layer of a completely differentiated parent object.
446 Aeternitas (A)	Essentially pure olivine, the mantle of a strongly differentiated parent object.
1866 Apollo (Q)	Olivine and pyroxene, indistinguishable from the spectrum of an ordinary chondrite. Apollo is the only known probable source of this common meteorite type.

Source: M. J. Gaffey, J. F. Bell & D. P. Cruikshank 1989, in *Asteroids II*, ed. R. P Binzel, T. Gehrels & M. S. Matthews (Tucson: Univ. of Arizona Press), p. 98.

theless, spectral studies like those discussed in Table 6.4 reveal that asteroids, like meteorites, range from almost unaltered primitive solar nebula material similar to the carbonaceous chondrites, to highly differentiated, thermally processed bodies analogous to the igneous meteorites.

Many of the same spectral features are seen in meteorites. In fact, the spectra of some asteroids and some meteorites match extremely well, as shown in Figure 6.11. The strong olivine-pyroxene absorption is clearly visible in Vesta, while the increase in reflectivity of iron is obvious in the spectrum of Amantis.

One of the very puzzling points that emerged from the study of the minerals on the current surfaces of asteroids is the realization that the meteorites held in collections on Earth show very important differences from the asteroids. Although plausible asteroidal sources have been identified for essentially all meteorite classes, the relative proportions of various kinds of known meteorites are *very* different from the proportions of various types of asteroids. The worst problem concerns the ordinary chondrites. Only a *single body*, the tiny Earth-crossing asteroid Apollo, is known to have reflection characteristics closely similar to those of the ordinary chondrites, although these are by far the most common type of meteorite seen to fall. At the other extreme, the very common S asteroids display spectra that match roughly those of the rather rare stony-iron meteorites. One possible resolution of this dilemma is that the surface spectra of the S asteroids is somehow altered by exposure to cosmic rays or impacts with other asteroids (this effect is called space weathering) so that the spectra of such bodies are not really representative of their composition. This idea has received strong support both from the low densities measured for the S asteroids Ida and Eros, and from the x-ray and γ-ray experiments on board the NEAR orbiter, which observed essentially chondritic ratios of major chemical elements for Eros. Thus it appears that the S asteroids, in spite of have spectra reminiscent of stony-iron meteorites, may be the parent bodies of ordinary chondrites. (Note that the conclusions of Table 6.4 were drawn at a

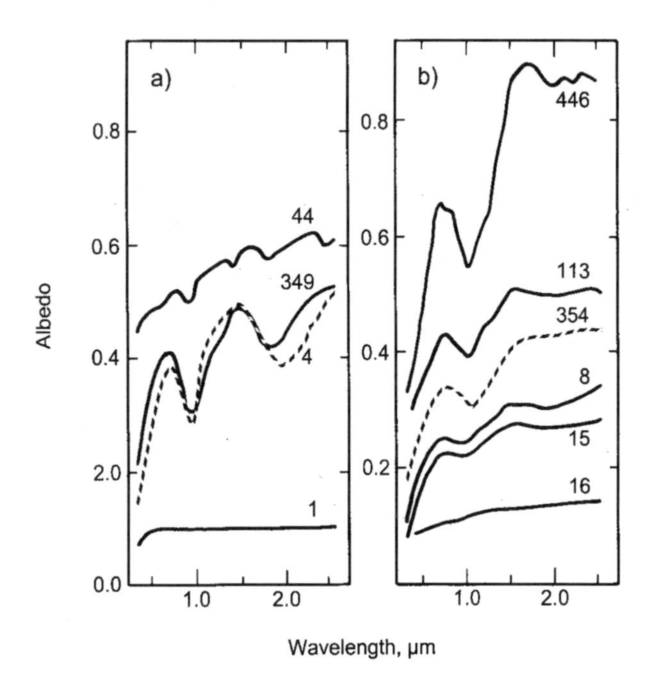

Figure 6.10: Reflectivity spectra of several bright asteroids, labeled by asteroid number. A plausible interpretation of these spectra is described in Table 6.4. (Adapted from M. J. Gaffey, J. F. Bell, and D. P. Cruikshank 1989, in *Asteroids II*, ed. R. P. Binzel, T. Gehrels and M. S. Matthews (Tucson, AZ: Univ. of Arizona Press), Figs. 3 and 4.)

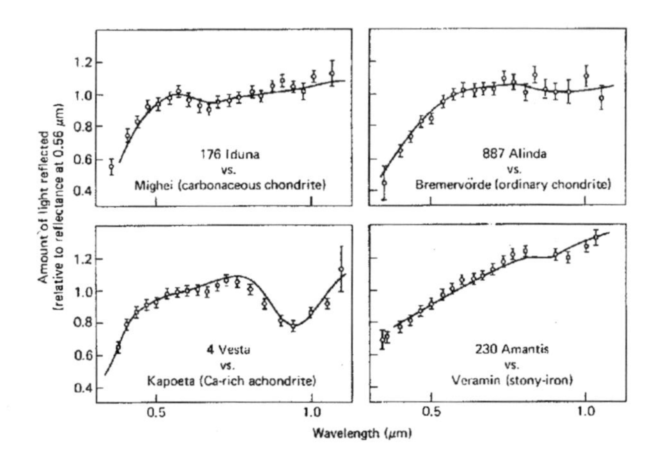

Figure 6.11: These four panels compare the fraction of light reflected by individual asteroids at a number of wavelengths (colours) between about 3500 Å (in the near ultraviolet) and 1.1 μm (in the near infrared), shown as points with error bars, to the reflectivity of powdered meteorite rock samples, shown as solid curves. The two upper curves show asteroids similar to carbonaceous and ordinary chondrites; both have very low reflectivity (albedo). The lower left panel shows the strong pyroxene absorption band near 0.9 μm in Vesta and a basaltic achondrite. The lower right panel shows the relatively poor blue reflectivity of a stony-iron meteorite and an S asteroid. (Source: C. R. Chapman 1976, Geochim. Cosmochim. Acta, 40, 701.)

time when it still seemed that S asteroids are stony-iron rather than ordinary chondrites.)

Another problem occurs for the achondrites. Basalt-rich achondrites are about 100 times commoner among meteorite falls than olivine-rich achondrites, but among the asteroids that may be the sources of these meteorites, the A types (olivine-rich surfaces) are roughly four times as common as the V types (basalt surfaces). Where are all the olivine achondrites?

It appears that the meteorites that fall to Earth at any one time (almost all those currently available have fallen within the past 1 Myr) are dominated by source bodies which sample the main asteroid belt very unevenly. Thus, although almost all meteorites certainly come from the asteroids, they may provide a rather non-representative sample of the larger bodies.

The numerous classes of asteroids, which are essentially distinguished by having different spectra, can be grouped into a small number of **superclasses** on the basis of broadly common history concerning the extent of heating during their formation. The dark, organic and carbon-rich asteroids of classes of types C, D, P and Q, which are related to carbonaceous and ordinary chondrites, we may call **primitive** meteorites. These objects, like the carbonaceous chondrites, appear to be almost unaltered from the small fragments that originally accreted to form planetesimals; they may have been strongly heated, but they never melted. The asteroids whose minerals have been altered by liquid water (types B, F, G and T) may be called **metamorphic**. These asteroids seems to have been mildly heated, enough to melt water ice and form hydrated minerals, but not enough to differentiate rock and metal. (The least processed meteorites in our possession, the carbonaceous chondrites, probably come from this group of asteroids.) Finally, many asteroids seem to have been differentiated by partial or complete melting of their rocky minerals (types A, E, M, R, S and V), so we call these bodies **igneous** asteroids (but recall that the membership of the S asteroids in this class is now very questionable).

When the number of members of each superclass is plotted for various orbital semi-major axis bins, it is found that the relative proportions of the three superclasses change dramatically with increasing distance from the Sun, as shown in Figure 6.12. Near the inner edge of the asteroid belt around 2 AU, almost all the asteroids are igneous (this is reflected in the large number of igneous asteroids described in Table 6.4). By

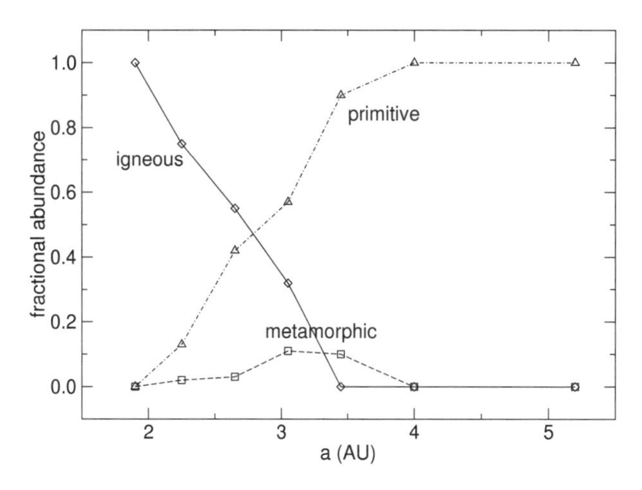

Figure 6.12: Variation of the relative numbers of the three asteroid superclasses with distance from the Sun. Igneous asteroids (squares) diminish rapidly in numbers with increasing a and are no longer present beyond 3.5 AU. Metamorphic asteroids (circles) are a minor type around 3 – 3.5 AU. Primitive asteroids (diamonds), minor in the inner asteroid belt, dominate beyond about 3 AU. (Data from J. F. Bell et al. 1989, in *Asteroids II*, ed. R. P. Binzel et al. [Tucson: Univ. of Arizona Press], p. 921.)

3.5 AU from the Sun, such asteroids have completely disappeared. The metamorphic asteroids, always rare, are concentrated around 3 AU. The primitive asteroids rise rapidly in importance with increasing a values, until beyond 3.5 AU where they completely dominate the composition of the asteroid belt. Thus the degree of alteration experienced by an asteroid is very closely connected with its distance from the Sun. This dramatic change in asteroid mineral properties with distance from the Sun may be a very important clue about the origin and history of the asteroid belt.

Exercise: A small space probe is put into orbit around an asteroid. Because of budget limitations, the probe is only able to send back black-and-white visual images of the asteroid. In addition, from the radio signals the size and orientation of the probe's orbit around the asteroid can be determined. Can anything be deduced about the chemical composition or internal structure of the asteroid from such data?

6.5 Origin and evolution of asteroids

It was natural in the past to imagine that the asteroids are remnants of an exploded planet, since they are small, they occupy similar orbits in a region of the solar system where the Bode-Titius "law" predicts a planet, and many meteorites (long thought to be possibly asteroid fragments) seem to have come from a geologically differentiated planet. In recent years, this theory has been discarded. In the first place, the *total* mass of the present asteroid belt is more than 100 times smaller than that of any of the terrestrial planets (see Table 6.2), and no source of energy is known which would be able to disrupt a terrestrial-sized planet. Furthermore, it is clear that none of the minerals found even in the igneous meteorites requires high pressure (such as would be found in the deep interior of a full-size terrestrial planet) for formation. Finally, we now can imagine some plausible ways of heating bodies too small to have been much heated internally by gravitational energy during accretion or by the kind of long-lived radioactivity that powers geological activity in the Earth: quick heating might have been produced, for example, by short-lived (and now extinct) radioactivities, or by induction heating due to interaction with an early, powerful solar wind carrying a magnetic field.

Instead, it has seemed more reasonable recently to observe that the asteroid belt as it now exists is rather reminiscent of the planetesimal stage of development of the solar system, with swarms of small bodies that collide from time to time, sometimes sticking together by gravity and sometimes disrupting one another. Thus, much effort has recently been given to understanding the asteroid belt as a natural part of the process that built all the planets. Furthermore, the asteroid belt is probably also the best remaining source of clues about conditions in the inner solar nebula at the time of planet formation, and so study of its origins should shed much light on the more general problem of formation of the planets.

To follow this line of thought, we must try to see, first, how a structure like the asteroid belt might have been formed, and why it should have failed to produce a planet. Then we have to look at processes that have affected the belt since it was created to try to find out to what extent it really is a fossilized relic of early solar system history, and what kinds of important changes may have taken place since that time, both in the orbital organization of the asteroid belt, and in the asteroids themselves.

Formation

According to the view of the development of planets discussed in Chapter 4, the accretion disk of the solar nebula that surrounded the forming Sun contained much matter that solidified as dust grains. These dust grains apparently accumulated by collisions into larger and larger bodies until eventually they formed planetesimals with sizes that we estimate may have been of the order of a km across. We now look in more detail at what may have happened next. As we do so, we will discover a great many parts of the picture which are still very unclear or even contradictory. This is a field of solar system research that is still very much under construction.

A first major uncertainty, as we pick up the story of the newly formed small bodies in the region of the asteroid belt, is that it is unclear just how large a mass of solid material was deposited there. Was there only a few times the total mass of the present asteroid belt bodies, say around 10^{22} kg, of the order of 10% of the mass of the Earth's Moon? Or was the mass in this region at one time perhaps 10^3 times larger than that, comparable to the mass of the Earth? The history of the solar system is not well enough understood to be at all certain on this point. If we look at the amount of mass that ended up in planets both in the inner and the outer solar system, we realize that the asteroid belt is at present particularly deficient in mass. Closer to the Sun, enough solid matter was available to form the massive planets Venus and Earth. However, going outwards, there is already a shortage of mass apparent in the fact that Mars has so much less mass than its two big inner neighbors, even though it had a bigger swath of orbital space than they did from which to accumulate material. In the (present) asteroid belt the shortage of mass is several powers of ten more severe than at the distance of Mars. And then we come to Jupiter, and suddenly there is a lot of mass again. On this argument, we would perhaps expect that originally the asteroid belt had far more mass than today. On the other hand, it may be that the original solar nebula had a pronounced ring structure, with a large gap in the asteroid belt.

We do have some constraints derived from calculations carried out to try out various possible initial conditions and see where they lead. It is found that at a minimum at least several times the mass of the present asteroid belt should have been present; without this much, the accretion of a single body as large as Ceres would have taken the age of the solar system or longer. At the other extreme, a mass many hundreds of times larger than the present total mass of asteroids would have quickly led to the **runaway growth** of a single planet-sized body like Mars or the Earth. If such a body once formed, where is it now? We have already discounted the possibility that it was somehow disrupted. On balance, it seems preferable to assume that the original mass of the asteroid belt was only a few times more than the present mass.

We believe that in the early stages of the solar nebula, the orbital motions of newly formed planetesimals around the Sun were in nearly circular orbits of very small eccentricity and inclination. That is, at each distance from the Sun, all the planetesimals had nearly the same speed. They thus had very small speeds relative to one another; when they collided, their relative speeds were usually less than 1 km s^{-1}. This is certainly no longer the case in the asteroid belt. At some point in the early history of the solar system, *something* substantially changed the speeds of most asteroids, to such an extent that now collisions occur at speeds of roughly 5 km s^{-1}. While relative speeds were small, collisions mostly resulted in coalescence and the gradual construction of larger and larger planetesimals. Today, with the much larger relative speeds found at each distance from the Sun, collisions occur at such high speed that the impact fragments are not left bound to either asteroid. Collisions mostly lead to material fragmenting and splashing off into space. The current collisions are mostly destructive rather than constructive. If the relative speeds had remained small, eventually practically all the planetesimals *would* have been swept up by the largest one. (This is what is meant by runaway growth.) What stopped the gradual sweeping up of small bodies by the largest ones, and left the asteroid belt as a big collection of small bodies rather than as a single small planet, was most probably the change from relative speeds of hundreds of m s^{-1} to relative speeds of several km s^{-1}.

We do not know precisely what caused the great increase in eccentricities and inclinations of the orbits of the asteroids, but it is usually supposed that it was due to Jupiter. This seems likely because, first, the fact that the only asteroid belt in the interior of the solar system is directly adjacent to Jupiter is a strong hint; secondly, the existence of the Kirkwood gaps shows directly the powerful influence that Jupiter can have on asteroid orbits; and finally, a very powerful perturber is needed to stir up the asteroid orbits to their present level of disorder.

However, this hypothesis still leaves a number of questions to answer. First, we need to be reasonably sure that Jupiter was able to form quickly enough out of the planetesimals at its distance from the Sun that it was already able to influence the orbits of the planetesimals in the asteroid belt as they began to to accumulate into larger and larger bodies. It is not clear yet that this was the case; calculations of the formation of the planets are still on very shaky ground because we know so little about the start-up conditions, and because the processes were so very complex.

Let's suppose that Jupiter did form quickly enough to have a major influence on the development of the asteroid belt. Two main ways have been suggested for the giant planet to affect the asteroids. First, as the planets formed there must have been a number of rather large bodies (even the size of small planets such as Mars) orbiting the Sun that had not yet been swept up into the present planets or ejected from the solar system. By near collisions, Jupiter could have altered the orbits of such bodies to send them sweeping through the asteroid belt. As these objects passed back and forth through the asteroids, near collisions with planetesimals there would have altered the planetesimal orbits, increasing inclinations and eccentricities. The main weakness with this idea is that a number of fairly large bodies (Mars-sized) are required. It is not at all clear that enough bodies that big would have been available, and one wonders what has become of them since – where are they now? Perhaps they too ended up being incorporated into Jupiter (or Earth) or being expelled, but it is surprising that none are left.

The second way in which Jupiter might have greatly altered orbits in the asteroid belt is if the giant planet itself has not always been at the same distance from the Sun as at present, but had a changeable orbit size early in its history, perhaps from tidal effects produced by the solar nebula or due to Saturn. In this case, the period resonance which today cause the Kirkwood gap would have affected asteroids with many different orbit sizes as Jupiter's orbit changed, perhaps again with the effect of greatly increasing inclinations and eccentricities among the forming asteroids. (This effect is known as **resonance sweeping**.)

In any case, it seems plausible that it was the increase in orbital disorder, and the consequent rise in collision speeds, that changed the situation in the asteroid belt from one of the larger bodies gradually sweeping up and incorporating the smaller ones, to a situation in which most collisions led to fragmentation and destruction. It is the increase in orbital speeds that probably prevented Ceres from becoming essentially the only body in the asteroid belt. The fact that most collisions are destructive has kept the asteroid belt full of small bodies, and even today infrequent collisions between the larger asteroids are gradually reducing their sizes and contributing orbiting debris to the asteroid belt.

However, there are observational features of the asteroid belt that indicate that the degree of orbital disorder introduced by Jupiter was not so extensive that the entire region of the belt became mixed. The observation that igneous and primitive asteroids each dominate a part of the belt (see Figure 6.12) clearly shows that the asteroid belt has never been completely mixed, since we are pretty sure – from meteorite ages, for example – that the heating of some asteroids occurred very close in time to the period of formation of these objects.

Thus, our overall picture of the early evolution of the asteroid belt is roughly the following. We guess that the belt started off as a huge swarm of small planetesimals, containing at least several times as much mass as the present asteroid belt, in which initially small relative velocities made it possible for collisions to lead to gradual growth of a few large bodies by accumulation of many smaller ones. This process was probably only part way to producing a single final asteroid when Jupiter pumped up the orbital eccentricities enough to change collisions from occurring at hundreds of m s^{-1} to occurring at several km s^{-1}. This ushered in the era of destructive collisions, and the asteroids have mostly been slowly decreasing in size since this time, breaking down into smaller and smaller fragments as they collide with one another.

Heating

The condensation process that deposited solids in the central plane of the solar system certainly deposited a mixture of chemical elements that depended on distance from the Sun, as already discussed in Chapter 4. Near the Sun, only the most refractory elements and compounds froze out as solids; this would probably have included metallic iron, oxides of magnesium and silicon, and oxides of a number of less abundant elements such as Ti, Al, and Ca. Further out, the more volatile metals such as Na, K and Fe condense in oxide form, and still further out carbon compounds, then water ice, and finally even CO_2 and perhaps NH_3 and CH_4 freeze out. Thus, the chemical composition of the dust grains that gradually accumulated to form planetesimals would have varied rather strongly with distance from the Sun (and also somewhat with time). Even within the region that was to become the asteroid belt, a fairly strong composition variation would have been found.

Now from the fact that many meteorites clearly solidified from molten rock or metal, while others seem never to have been much heated at all, and from the igneous minerals detected in some, but not all, asteroids by spectroscopy, it is clear that some asteroids were heated strongly enough to melt iron and sometimes rock, while others were only mildly heated, just enough to incorporate water into mineral structure. From the variation of asteroid superclasses with distance from the Sun (Figure 6.12), it appears that this heating must have depended quite strongly on distance from the Sun, diminishing rapidly with increasing distance. However, the strong overlap of the igneous, metamorphic, and primitive superclasses between about 2 and 3 AU also suggests that the heating mechanism, whatever it was, was not simply dependent on distance from the Sun, but depended as well on something else. At a particular distance from the Sun, some asteroids were strongly heated, while others were hardly affected. What was it that heated some, but not most, of the asteroids?

One obvious possibility is the heat energy released by gravity as the various planetesimals collide and stick together, as discussed in several previous chapters. Small bodies are accelerated towards a larger object that they collide with and that sweeps them up, and as they strike the surface of the larger object their speed of infall is converted instantly into heat energy. Some of this heat is radiated back into space, but often much will be deposited into the crust of the larger body, and as more material is swept up, this heat is trapped in the interior of the growing object.

For objects as large as the terrestrial planets, this is a powerful source of internal heating, as we will see in Chapter 9. However, the total heat per kilogram released by accumulation increases with the mass of the larger body, and although it is very important for terrestrial planets, it is only capable of heating a body as large as Vesta, the largest differentiated asteroid, by some 50 K. This is not a large enough heat release to be a significant means of melting asteroids.

Another possible heat source is radioactivity, the spontaneous splitting of unstable atomic nuclei. The basic idea of this process has been discussed in Chapter 2. In a **radioactive decay**, the nucleus of an atom spontaneously breaks into two (or more) pieces because of an imbalance between the number of protons and the number of neutrons in the nucleus. Some of the nuclear reactions that occur in stars, as described in Chapter 3, involve the spontaneous decay of nuclei that are produced during these reactions, for example by expelling a positron (e^+) particle, and changing from one element to another. Other examples were found when we looked at dating meteorites by using radioactive atoms, in Chapter 5. When an atomic nucleus decays, one of the effects is that a large amount of energy is released along with the fragments, in the form of gamma rays, high speed electrons or positrons, or as kinetic energy of the separating fragments. Usually some millions of electron volts of energy are released from each decay, as compared to the few electron volts released when two atoms combine chemically. Radioactive decay is thus potentially a source of energy that can release millions of time more energy from a given mass than is available from chemical reactions involving the same amount of matter; this is why fission reactors have come into use for generating electricity.

Radioactive nuclei, like other nuclei, are produced in the nuclear furnaces of stars. Such radioactive nuclei display a huge variety in the average time it takes for half the nuclei in a particular sample to decay into something else; this time is known as the **half-life** of that type of nucleus, and is a definite time for each kind of radioactive nucleus. Some nuclei decay within microseconds of the instant that they are created, while others take thousands or even billions of years. Radioactive nuclei with very short half-lives will hardly escape the place where they are formed before falling apart. Other, longer-lived isotopes will be able to travel far from their places of origin before decaying. We therefore expect that the atomic nuclei that found their way into the solar nebula would include hardly any isotopes that decay with much shorter half-lives than the time that elapsed between the last supernova explosion to blast into the interstellar cloud from which the Sun formed, and the collapse of that cloud to form the solar system. On the other hand, isotopes with half-lives longer than this interval would be incorporated into the solar nebula, and many of these would certainly end up as trace elements in the solids that froze out of this cloud to become planetesimals. When such radioactive nuclei end up incorporated into planets or asteroids, where they finally undergo radioactive decay, they provide a potential source of heat.

However, only the relatively slowly decaying nuclei are left by this time. Because they decay very slowly, during millions or even billions of years, and also because they make up only a tiny fraction of the total number of nuclei, such radioactive nuclei are quite weak heaters except in bodies large enough that the heat takes even longer to leak out than it does to be released. In bodies the size of the Earth, the time it takes for heat released by radioactivity (or heat released by gravity as the planet accumulates) to leak out of the planet is billions of years, and for these objects even very slowly released radioactive energy is a powerful heat source. An example is provided by the element potassium (symbol K), which has $Z = 19$ protons in each atomic nucleus. In the Earth's crust at present, 93.26% of naturally occurring potassium has 20 neutrons and an atomic mass number $A = 39$, while 6.73% has 22 neutrons and $A = 41$. Both ^{39}K and ^{41}K are stable. However, about 0.01% of naturally occurring potassium is ^{40}K, which is naturally radioactive. ^{40}K can decay either by converting a proton into a neutron, a positive electron, and a neutrino and thus becoming an argon nucleus,

$$^{40}\mathrm{K} \rightarrow {}^{40}\mathrm{Ar} + \mathrm{e}^+ + \nu,$$

or it can convert a neutron into a proton to become a calcium nucleus,

$$^{40}\mathrm{K} \rightarrow {}^{40}\mathrm{Ca} + \mathrm{e}^- + \overline{\nu}.$$

In both decay modes little more than 1 MeV is released per event. As it takes about 1.3×10^9 years for half the ^{40}K atoms initially present in an asteroid to decay, this process can provide an important source of heat inside planets over a geologically long time. Other isotopes that provide substantial heat to the solid bodies of the solar system at present are ^{232}Th (thorium) and ^{238}U (uranium), both of which also have half-lives measured in billions of years.

However, asteroids are far smaller than the big terrestrial planets, and so the time required for heat to leak out to the surface and be radiated into space is much smaller. For these small bodies, the slowly released radioactive energy of the main current radioactive heat sources can raise the internal temperature by only a couple of hundred degrees. This is not enough to melt anything much more refractory than water ice. Furthermore, the radioactive ages of igneous meteorites show that the asteroids were heated very shortly after the formation of the solar system, not much later in its history.

But we have not yet excluded all possible radioactive heat sources. In our study of meteorites, we found evidence that the last polluting supernova before the collapse of the solar nebula may have occurred less than a million years before that collapse – perhaps the collapse was even caused by that last explosion. If the supernova created an important number of radioactive nuclei with half-lives so short that they have long since disappeared, but long enough to have still been present in the solar nebula, such nuclei could perhaps have been an important heat source. Because they would heat the asteroid quickly and briefly, such nuclei might overcome the problem of rapid heat leakage from small bodies by releasing their heat even more quickly than it could escape. They would also have done their heating right at the beginning of the solar system, as the meteorite ages demand. We need to look for hints of the brief presence of such short-lived isotopes.

One radioactive nucleus that might have functioned in this way is ^{26}Al. This isotope decays to ^{26}Mg by emission of a positron and a neutrino, with a half-life of 726,000 yr. It appears to be produced in significant amounts in supernovae, and there is evidence from excess ^{26}Mg in the refractory inclusions of oxides and silicates of Ti, Al, and Ca found mainly in CV meteorites (see Chapter 5) that a high enough percentage of ^{26}Al was once present in these grains to completely melt a body of this composition if it was at least some km in diameter. However, there is no evidence that the km-size bodies of this composition were ever present in the solar system – the grains that were once enriched in ^{26}Al are all very small. Furthermore, this excess ^{26}Al is only known to have been present in some unusual grains in one particular kind of meteorite; there is no clear evidence that excess ^{26}Al was more widely distributed in the solar system. Thus it not clear whether this short-lived radioactivity was an important heat source in any asteroids. However, the increasing number of meteorite sites which have yielded evidence of a number of short-lived radioactivities has encouraged many researchers to favour this explanation of the rapid initial heating of some asteroids.

Yet another possible heat source that may have melted some of the early asteroids is due to the interaction of the growing asteroids with the outflowing solar wind from the growing Sun. As the Sun settled down to become first a T Tauri star (Chapter 4) and then a main sequence star, it probably went through a phase of producing a very strong stellar wind, as we now observe in many current T Tauri stars. This T Tauri wind would probably have included a weak magnetic field. Because of this magnetic field, as the wind flowed past forming planets and asteroids, electrical currents would have been induced in the solid bodies by the effect known as "electromagnetic induction". These electrical currents could have heated the interiors of bodies that were sufficiently strongly affected.

Evolution

We now come back to the main thread of our effort to understand the evolution of asteroids. From the discussion above, we expect that the composition of the planetesimals in the present asteroid belt initially varied with distance from the Sun. Planetesimals were probably made of fairly refractory compounds near the orbit of Mars, but the further out one looked, the more volatile material such as water ice and various compounds of carbon would have been incorporated into these small bodies. These planetesimals collided with one another and so gradually become asteroids, also with composition that varied systematically with distance from the Sun. In the inner belt, we probably would have found asteroids with composition similar to that of the enstatite (EH and EL) chondrites, with Mg in the form of pyroxenes but iron still in metallic (unoxidized) form. Somewhat farther out, the composition could have been appropriate for ordinary (H, L, LL) chondrites, with both Mg and Fe in oxidized form in silicates. Beyond that, the planetesimals could have had a composition like the CO and CV chondrites, with fully oxidized metals and small amounts of water and carbon compounds. Still farther out we would have found the asteroid sources of the most primitive meteorites, the CI and CM carbonaceous chondrites. At even greater distance from the Sun, in a region not sampled by the meteorites in our collections, we imagine that the planetesimals had a composition still more primitive and rich in organic compounds. If we had any meteorites of this material, we might call them ultra-carbonaceous.

As we have seen, some – but not all – of the asteroids formed from this material were heated. Some of the enstatite-rich bodies melted to produced rock like the enstatite-rich achondrite meteorites. Asteroids with composition like the ordinary chondrites melted to produce the minerals found in the igneous meteorites. Farther out in the forming asteroid belt, some bodies were heated enough to incorporate water into their mineral structures and produce serpentine, but not enough to melt any of the metal or rocks. Still farther out, little heating of importance occurred.

The strong heating of some asteroids in the inner belt led to such high temperatures (around 1600 K) that the metallic iron in these bodies, probably present initially in the form of small grains like those found in chondritic meteorites, melted. This melting led to the separation of some asteroids into layers of different density. Because iron is much denser than the surrounding rock, the iron sank towards the centre of the asteroid under the pull of gravity, while the less dense rock tended to float above the iron, like oil on top of vinegar in a salad dressing. This separation occurred whether the temperature rose high enough to completely melt the rock or not; the liquid iron could have flowed downward through cracks and fissures in solid (but somewhat flexible) rock, or if the rock melted, the liquid rock floated on top of the liquid iron core. A thin veneer of particularly low density material, similar to terrestrial basalts, could have been separated – again by buoyancy – from the main layer of olivine-rich rock and formed the surface of such fully melted bodies. Thus the heating episode led to some asteroids developing a structure with a metallic core (mainly iron but including minor elements with an affinity for iron, such as nickel), a thick middle layer (a mantle) of dense rock with an olivine-rich composition, and perhaps a thin surface crust of basalt. Probably the boundary between one layer and the next was not sharp, but formed a thick zone of mixed composition. As the heat source that had stimulated the melting waned, the asteroids froze, rapidly at the surface and more slowly in the interiors. The larger bodies, with greater distances for heat to travel before it could radiate away into space, and a larger mass of interior material to radiate heat away through each square meter of surface area, cooled more slowly than the smaller objects.

During the same period when the heating and melting of some asteroids was happening, collisions continued to occur. As we have seen above, at first these collisions involved rather low speeds, and mostly led to smaller bodies growing by coalescence. This process gradually led to one dominant asteroid, Ceres. However, before the collisions had allowed Ceres to sweep up all its competitors, something (probably Jupiter)

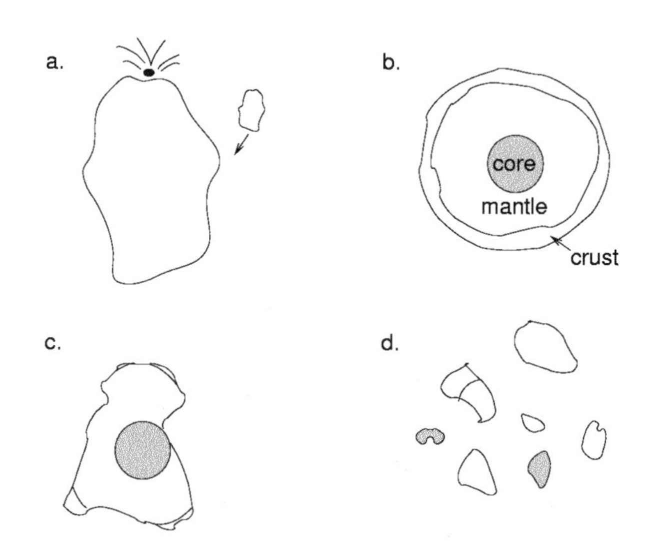

Figure 6.13: An asteroid forms by accretion of planetesimals. As it originally develops (a) it may be uniform throughout, with approximately the chemical composition of ordinary or carbonaceous chondrites, depending on where in the solar system it forms. As a result of strong internal heating (b), which did not occur in all asteroids, it may develop a layered structure, with a core of composition similar to an iron meteorite, a thin region around the core where iron is mixed with overlying rocky layer, as in stony iron meteorites, a mantle of rock similar to ordinary chondrites or achondrites (depending on how hot it got) and perhaps a basalt-rich crust. Further violent collisions (c) may disrupt the asteroid enough to reveal one or more of the inner layers, and perhaps eventually (d) fragment it entirely into an asteroid family.

increased the inclinations and eccentricities of asteroid orbits to the point that most collisions became destructive rather than constructive. Further impacts between asteroids led to blasting off pieces rather than continued growth of even the largest bodies. A few asteroids such as Vesta avoided really destructive collisions (although even Vesta has a large impact crater near one pole), but most asteroids were at least shattered and many were broken into smaller pieces that continued in separate orbits as members of one of the asteroid families. This evolution is sketched in Figure 6.5.

This era of destruction would have blasted the rocky shells off some of the asteroids that had developed a structure with a metallic core surrounded by a rock mantle. Because rock is considerably weaker than iron, many of the rock mantles were probably shattered into big boulders and ejected by successive collisions from the layered asteroids. The stronger iron cores would have been more resistant to disruption and probably mostly remained largely intact. As a result, it appears that iron cores make up a relatively high proportion of the large inner-belt asteroids, the ones that can easily be studied from the Earth, while their rocky mantles have become small, hard-to-detect bodies. Selective destruction of rocky bodies may be the reason that the population of larger, well-studied asteroids of the main belt appears to differ greatly from the proportions of different types of chemical composition found among meteorites, although we should not forget that the study of Eros suggests that asteroid spectra may not be infallible guides to asteroid chemistry.

Many of the smallest fragments of collisions have gradually been lost to the asteroid belt. This could occur, for example, through interaction between sunlight and small (mm- or cm-size) objects, which experience the flood of photons from the Sun as a kind of fluid through which they must move in their orbits around the Sun. The drag from sunlight is strong enough to have caused such small particles to spiral into the Sun in a time less than the age of the solar system. This and related effects may have reduced the mass of the asteroid belt by a factor of several since it was formed.

As we discussed in Chapter 5, delivery of a small fraction of the asteroids and fragments from the main belt to Earth-crossing orbits, and eventually to the Earth's surface as meteorites, probably occurs through a series of interactions. Initially, we think that asteroids suffered collisions among themselves, knocking off pieces a few km or smaller across. These spinning fragments found their orbits changing slowly as a result of the very weak force of re-radiated heat, which is more strongly emitted on the evening side than the morning side. Some of these pieces eventually came to have orbital periods near one of the unstable resonances with Jupiter's or Saturn's period, and soon their orbits were perturbed to more and more eccentric form. Some of these are eventually shifted into orbits so eccentric that they cross the orbit of Mars or even Earth. The largest fragments are seen by us as Apollo, Aten or Amor asteroids. Some near-Earth asteroids and many smaller fragments eventually collide with Earth or the Sun; many others are ejected from the solar system by close misses. The amount of time a near-Earth asteroid or meteoroid can spend in an Earth-crossing orbit before it is swept up by the Earth or ejected from the solar system is only a few million years.

We thus have a provisional picture of how asteroids have formed and developed, and how they are may be related to the various kinds of meteorites that we have in collections here on Earth. This picture still leaves many points unclear, and will certainly change significantly during the coming years, but much of it is undoubtedly already basically correct.

6.6 Mathematical aspects

Orbital properties

Exercise: Radar observations have revealed that the small near-Earth asteroid 1999 KW4 is has a satellite (i. e., this is a binary system). The larger body in the system has a diameter of about 1.2 km. Assuming that the density of the larger asteroid is about 2 kg m^{-3}, estimate its mass. The small body orbits around the larger with a period of about 16 hours. Assume that the orbit of the smaller body around the larger is circular, and use the orbital period to estimate the semi-major axis of the orbit. (You may be surprised at how small it is.)

Exercise: At one point the NEAR–Shoemaker space probe orbiting the asteroid 433 Eros was in a circular orbit with radius 200 km. The mass of Eros is about 7.2×10^{15} kg. How long did the probe take to orbit Eros once?

Reflection and radiation from an asteroid

As we have discussed above, the size and albedo of an asteroid may be estimated if the radiation coming from it can be measured in both the visible part of the spectrum and in the infrared. Let's see more exactly how that works, making whatever approximations we need to in order to get a reasonably simple result.

Consider a spherical asteroid of radius R at a distance r from the Sun. You know from the images you have looked at that most asteroids are really not spherical, so this is a fairly rough approximation. Consider R as a typical dimension of a real asteroid. Now the flux $f_\odot$ of solar energy (the amount of energy falling on a square meter each second, in W m^{-2}) at r is

$$f_\odot(r) = L_\odot/(4\pi r^2), \qquad (6.1)$$

where $L_\odot$ is the luminosity of the Sun. Let's assume (again an approximation; see Figure 6.10) that the average albedo in visible light has the value A_v. The total energy reflected from the projected surface πR^2 of the asteroid per second, which we may think of as the asteroid's visible "reflected luminosity" ℓ_ref, is

$$\ell_\mathrm{ref} = A_\mathrm{v} f_\odot(r) \pi R^2, \qquad (6.2)$$

while the energy absorbed per second, and then re-radiated as long wavelength infrared thermal radiation (see Figure 6.3), which we think of as the asteroid's "thermal luminosity" ℓ_th is

$$\ell_\mathrm{th} = (1 - A_\mathrm{v}) f_\odot(r) \pi R^2. \qquad (6.3)$$

The visible sunlight is not reflected uniformly into all directions. If you are between the asteroid and the Sun, you will see the fully illuminated asteroid, like the full Moon, and the flux of reflected light from the asteroid will be relatively large. If you are looking at the asteroid from the side, as you see the first or third quarter Moon, only half of the asteroid will appear lit, so it will appear fainter than when you see only the lit side. In addition, reflection tends to be more efficient when light is returned back towards the direction from which it comes, while the efficiency for reflecting in other directions is less; this effect will also make the asteroid less bright when viewed from a direction in which it appears only partly illuminated. The extreme case is when you view the asteroid from the side facing away from the Sun: you do not see any reflected light at all. Thus we need to describe or approximate the way in which reflected light is distributed in angle around the line joining the Sun and the asteroid. We use a very simple approximation: we assume that the asteroid is in opposition to the Earth (we are on the line joining the Sun and the asteroid), and that the reflected sunlight is reflected uniformly but only into half of the full 4π steradians of possible directions. On the Earth we are at a distance $r_\oplus$ from the Sun, and so our distance d at opposition from the asteroid is $d = r - r_\oplus$. Since we assume that the asteroid's luminosity ℓref is reflected uniformly into 2π steradians, the flux we will detect at Earth is approximately

$$f_{\rm ref} \approx \ell_{\rm ref}/(2\pi d^2) = A_{\rm v} f_\odot R^2/(2d^2). \qquad (6.4)$$

From this expression you can easily see that the brightness of the reflected light from an asteroid increases as R^2, so the difference in brightness between an asteroid of $R = 1$ km and that of an asteroid having $R = 100$ km, both at opposition and at the same distance from Earth, is a factor of the order of 10^4. This is why a simple brightness measurement allows us to estimate the size of an asteroid at a known distance from Earth, even if $A_{\rm v}$ is fairly uncertain.

Similarly, the re-radiated sunlight, which is emitted from the asteroid as long wavelength infrared radiation, is not emitted uniformly into all directions. If the asteroid always keeps one face pointed towards the Sun (if it is spinning, its rotation axis would need to be aligned with the Sun-asteroid line), only one side will be heated, and even that will not be heated uniformly, any more than the equatorial and polar regions on Earth are heated equally intensely by the Sun. We nevertheless assume, as a rough approximation (which will allow us to follow the basic reasoning that we use in this problem), that the asteroid is spinning fairly quickly in such a way that it is heated on all sides, and assume that the thermal radiation is also emitted uniformly in all directions. Then the flux of thermal infrared radiation received at Earth is

$$f_{\rm th} \approx \ell_{\rm th}/(4\pi d^2) = (1 - A_{\rm v}) f_\odot R^2/(4d^2). \qquad (6.5)$$

Now if we *measure* both the reflected flux $f_{\rm ref}$ and the thermal flux $f_{\rm th}$ that reach the Earth, and then take the ratio of these two measurements, most of the factors in each of the expressions above cancel out and we find

$$f_{\rm v}/f_{\rm th} \approx \frac{A_{\rm v}/2}{(1 - A_{\rm v})/4} = 2A_{\rm v}/(1 - A_{\rm v}), \qquad (6.6)$$

which can easily be solved for $A_{\rm v}$.

Once $A_{\rm v}$ has been determined, either of the two flux expressions can be inverted to allow determination of R, again showing that a brightness measurement allows an estimate of the asteroid size to be made. (Note that in practice we cannot measure the whole visible and whole infrared fluxes; we measure brightnesses at one or two wavelengths in each spectral region and use these to estimate the total fluxes that are needed.)

Exercise Verify the equation above, solve it for $A_{\rm v}$, and find an even simpler expression valid when $A_{\rm v}$ is much smaller than 1.

Exercise Solve the equations above to determine R, expressing the result as a function of r, d, $L_\odot$, and the two measured fluxes $f_{\rm v}$ and $f_{\rm th}$.

Internal heat sources

The pressures and densities found inside asteroids are almost independent of the internal temperature of the asteroid, provided that it is not too hot inside. That is, for typical asteroid internal pressures the equation of state is essentially $\rho =$ constant, independent of p and T. This holds as long as p satisfies $p \leq 10^{10}$ Pa (10^5 atm) and T satisfies $T \leq 1 \times 10^5$ K, both of which are certainly valid inside asteroids.

However, the internal temperature of an asteroid or planet can be quite important even if it does not significantly affect the internal density. If the temperature is high, rock will deform slowly even under rather low pressure. A still higher temperature can cause part or all of the interior of a body to melt, allowing separation of an iron core from the silicate component. Temperatures near melting in the interior of an asteroid or planet can lead to occurrence of surface volcanic activity, and to slow internal convective motions (circulation of material like that observed in thick soup on the stove just before it boils). The mantle of the Earth is believed to flow – very slowly – in this way. Thus, even if the hydrostatic equilibrium in an asteroid is not affected much by a high internal temperature, it is still of considerable interest to study the resulting effects.

Table 6.5: Heat released by radioactive decay of elements important in heating planets.

Isotope	Half-life $t_{1/2}$ (10^9 yr)	Isotope fraction x	Element abundance C	Heating rate (isotope) ($\mathrm{J\,yr^{-1}\,kg^{-1}}$)	Heating rate (chondrite) ($\mathrm{J\,yr^{-1}\,kg^{-1}}$)
^{40}K	1.25	0.00011	5.60×10^{-4}	9.20×10^{2}	5.7×10^{-5}
^{87}Rb	50.0	0.293	2.20×10^{-6}	5.44×10^{-1}	3.51×10^{-7}
^{232}Th	13.9	1.00	2.9×10^{-8}	8.37×10^{2}	2.4×10^{-5}
^{235}U	0.71	0.0072	8.2×10^{-9}	1.80×10^{4}	1.1×10^{-6}
^{238}U	4.50	0.993	8.2×10^{-9}	2.97×10^{3}	2.4×10^{-5}

Sources: G.H.A. Cole 1984, *Physics of Planetary Interiors* (Bristol: Adam Hilger Ltd.), Table 5.1. *CRC Handbook of Chemistry and Physics, 1982–83 Ed.* (Boca Raton, Fla: CRC Press, Inc.), B-255. J.T. Wasson 1985, *Meteorites* (New York: W.H. Freeman and Co.), Appendix D.

Several internal energy sources have been identified that could be important in most asteroid or planetary-sized bodies. The first of these is the gravitational energy released in forming the body from planetesimals or diffuse matter. The gravitational energy released in forming a body by accretion (or required to completely disrupt it) has already been calculated for a body of constant density in Chapter 4 (Equation 4.3); recall that the result is

$$E_{\mathrm{g}} = -\frac{3}{5}\frac{GM^2}{R}. \tag{6.7}$$

Now in fact, not all this energy will actually be available to heat the forming asteroid. The infall of new material onto an accreting body will heat the surface of the body, using the freshly released gravitational energy. If accretion is very slow, and the infalling bodies are small, much of this energy will be radiated away into space as it is released rather than being stored inside the forming object. Only if accretion is fairly rapid, or the impacting objects large, will most of the energy released by gravity be retained in the interior of the body as internal energy. On the other hand, the loss by radiation of some of the energy released by infall will be partly compensated by the fact that collisions will usually occur with velocities somewhat larger than the escape velocity of the accreting body. Thus it is not unreasonable to use Equation 4.3 to estimate the heat energy available from gravitational energy release.

A quite different heat source is due to the natural radioactivity of a few unstable isotopes that are present in a solar or CI carbonaceous chondrite mixture of refractory chemical elements. These elements are individually rather powerful energy sources, but all are present only in minute amounts in the original mixture of elements (although geochemical processes have concentrated some of them into particular ore bodies in the terrestrial crust). The principal radioactive energy sources of greatest importance in the context of planetary heating are listed in Table 6.5. For each radioactive isotope (an isotope is a nucleus of a particular chemical element which also has a definite number of neutrons), the table lists the half-life $t_{1/2}$ of that isotope, the fraction x of the element that normally occurs *at present* in the form of the radioactive isotope in question, the fractional concentration C (by weight) of all isotopes together of the element in a carbonaceous chondrite, the energy release (heating rate) in Joules per yr per kg of the isotope in question, and the heating rate in Joules per yr per kg of carbonaceous chondrite.

Most of the heat energy supplied by radioactivity in geological circumstances today comes from ^{40}K, ^{232}Th, and ^{238}U; the total is about 1.1×10^{-4} $\mathrm{J\,yr^{-1}}$ for each kg of carbonaceous chondrite-like matter. This value was higher in the past because abundances of the radioactive isotopes were higher; the abundance of ^{40}K was about 12 times larger 4.5×10^9 years ago than it is now, the abundance of ^{238}U was 83 times larger then than now, and the abundance of ^{238}U was 2.0 times larger than now (note that the half-life of ^{238}U almost exactly equals the age of the solar system). When the solar system formed, the total radioactive heating rate would have been about 8.5×10^{-4} $\mathrm{J\,yr^{-1}\,kg^{-1}}$, almost ten times higher than at present, mainly due to the large abundance then of ^{40}K.

Specific Heat

An important effect of energy release inside an asteroid or planet by any of the mechanisms just discussed is to raise the internal temperature. To assess the significance of this effect we must know how much a given energy input to a unit mass of material raises the temperature: that is, we must know the specific heat $C_v = dU/dT$, where U is the (thermal) internal energy.

The simplest system in which to study the dependence of U on T is an ideal gas of monatomic molecules (for example a noble gas such as Ne or Ar). It is well known that in such a gas, the specific heat depends on how energy is added to the gas. If heat is added at *constant volume*, so that the gas does not use any of the added energy doing work on its surroundings, the specific heat of a monatomic gas is $3R_g/2$ per mole, where R_g is the gas constant, or $3k/2$ per atom, where k is Boltzmann's constant (see Equation 2.8). If heat is added at *constant pressure*, so that the gas can do work on its surroundings, the specific heat of a monatomic gas is increased by roughly half again, and has the value $C_p = 5R_g/2$ per mole, or $5k/2$ per atom.

The specific heat may also depend on atomic structure. This is immediately clear when you recall that the specific heat at constant volume of a diatomic gas such as N_2 is $5R_g/2$ per mole, or $5k/2$ per molecule ($5k/4$ per atom) at room temperature. Thus we can expect specific heats of different substances to vary from one to another.

Table 6.6: Specific heat at constant volume for various substances.

Substance	c_v (J K^{-1} kg^{-1})	$\mu m_u c_v$ (J K^{-1} atom^{-1})	$\mu m_u c_v / k$
Argon (Ar)	3.12×10^2	2.07×10^{-23}	1.50
Hydrogen (H_2)	1.04×10^4	3.45×10^{-23}	2.50
Nitrogen (N_2)	7.42×10^2	3.45×10^{-23}	2.50
Water (H_2O)	4.19×10^3	4.18×10^{-23}	3.03
Ice (H_2O)	2.1×10^3	2.1×10^{-23}	1.5
Mercury (Hg)	1.38×10^2	4.60×10^{-23}	3.33
Iron (Fe)	4.6×10^2	4.3×10^{-23}	3.1
Basalt (typical rock)	8.4×10^2	3×10^{-23}	2

Table 6.6 lists a few representative specific heats for several substances. These are given as specific heats at constant volume per kg (c_v), as well as per atom in solids and liquids and per molecule in gases ($c_v \mu m_u$). Notice that although the specific heats per kg vary by almost a factor of 100 between H_2 and Hg, the specific heats per molecule or atom of the substances in the table are all between $1.5k$ (A) and $3.3k$ (Hg), regardless of the molecular weight of the substance, and regardless of whether it is solid, liquid or gas. In fact, this behaviour is quite general, and specific heats differ strongly from about $3k$ per atom only at temperatures near absolute zero, where they fall below this value. For reconnaissance purposes, or when one is in ignorance of the true specific heat, $c_v \approx 3k/(\mu m_u)$ per kg is usually a reasonable estimate for any solid or liquid if the temperature is well above $T = 0$ K, while for gases a good estimate is $c_v \approx 3k/(2\mu m_u)$ per kg for monatomic gases, or $c_v \approx 5k/(2\mu m_u)$ per kg for diatomic ones.

Exercise: By equating the available gravitational energy to the change in internal energy, show that the maximum average temperature increase that could be achieved in an accreting rocky body of mass M and radius R, composed of atoms having a typical molecular weight μ, as a result of release of gravitational energy is approximately

$$\Delta T \approx \left(\frac{m_u G}{5k}\right)\left(\frac{\mu M}{R}\right). \qquad (6.8)$$

Evaluate this expression for an asteroid with a radius of 200 km and a mean density of 3500 kg m^{-3}that is made of atoms with a typical molecular weight of about 35. Could gravitational energy contribute in a significant way to heating this forming asteroid?

Heat transfer by conduction

If the interior of an asteroid or planet is hot, the heat will gradually leak to the surface and be radiated into space. There are three general ways in which heat may leak from one place to another inside a hot object. These are conduction (the effect by which the outside of a metal pot becomes hot when you pour hot water into the pot), radiation (the means by which the direct radiation of the Sun warms your skin on a cool, sunny day), and convection (when heat is transferred physically from one place to another by boiling motions in which hot blobs of liquid move to cool regions, exchanging places with cooler blobs, as above a hot room radiator). In fact, in an object like an asteroid which is not too hot inside (say $T < 1000$ K), so that the rock is much too solid to slowly flow as it probably does inside the Earth, only conduction is important.

Conduction is described by an equation known as the heat flow equation. Imagine a slab of material of thickness dx, with temperature $T(x)$ on one side and temperature $T(x+dx) = T(x)+dT$ on the other. Then the heat energy flowing across the slab from the hot side to the cool side, per unit time, is

$$\frac{\Delta Q}{\Delta t} = -k_c A \frac{dT}{dx}, \qquad (6.9)$$

where A is the area of the slab. The amount of heat flowing across a *unit* area per unit time, $q = \Delta Q/A\Delta t$, is often called the **heat flux**. The quantity k_c may be measured empirically and is known as the **thermal**

conductivity of the material in the slab (the usual symbol for this quantity is k, but we use k_c here to avoid confusion with Boltzmann's constant, also called k). Thermal conductivities of some common materials are listed in Table 6.7.

Table 6.7: Thermal conductivities of common substances.

Substance	k_c ($\mathrm{W\,m^{-1}\,K^{-1}}$)
Air	2.5×10^{-2}
Water	6.7×10^{-1}
Ice	2
Iron	8.0×10^{1}
Copper	4.0×10^{2}
Sheet insulation (e.g. corkboard)	4×10^{-2}
Limestone (typical rock)	2
Granite (typical rock)	3

Source: *CRC Handbook of Chemistry and Physics*, 1982–83 edition (Boca Raton, Fla: CRC Press Inc.), Sec E.

It may be seen that conductivities range over about four orders of magnitude. For rocky material such as might be found in the mantle of an asteroid or planet an appropriate value is probably around 2 $\mathrm{W\,m^{-1}\,K^{-1}}$; for an iron core the conductivity is about 40 times larger.

Heat loss from asteroids

The internal temperature of an object such as an asteroid that has – or had – a significant internal heat source is the result of a competition between internal heat production and the rate at which the heat leaks out into space. A familiar form of this competition occurs when you get into bed on a cold night – the heat production of your body (roughly 25 W) keeps you warm all night if you have thick covers over you, which insure slow heat loss, but if you try to sleep under just a sheet the heat loss rate is high enough that your heat production does not keep you at a comfortably warm temperature.

When we look at how the competition between heat production and heat loss determines internal temperature in asteroidal or planetary bodies, we find two extreme cases where the result is fairly easy to calculate. At one extreme, consider a body which has a brief but intense heating episode (from heat released by accretion, for example, or a short-lived radioactivity) which quickly dies away. In this case, once the heat source has run down or switched off, the heated object slowly cools back towards equilibrium with its surroundings: its internal temperature gradually approaches that of the surroundings (typically the internal temperature approaches the surface temperature set by solar heating of the surface). The other extreme is the case where the heated object has a heat source which does not change substantially during the characteristic time required for the body to lose most of its internal energy once the internal heating switches off. This is the case for small bodies heated by long-lived radioactive heat sources such as ^{238}U. In this case the asteroid settles into an equilibrium in which the heat production internally essentially balances the heat loss to the surroundings. Situations intermediate between these two also occur, of course, but are more difficult to evaluate.

Let us first estimate the **cooling time scale** for a solid body of radius R from an initial hot state, assuming that there are no continuing internal heat sources. (This is also an estimate of the time required for the body to come into approximate equilibrium with a very slowly changing internal heat source.) Suppose the internal temperature T is much higher than the surface temperature, so that $dT/dx \sim T/R$. If the material has specific heat c_v per kg, the total internal energy is roughly $U \sim 4\pi R^3 \rho c_\mathrm{v} T/3$. The total heat flow out of the body is of order

$$\begin{aligned} \frac{\Delta Q}{\Delta t} &\sim -k_c 4\pi R^2 (T/R) \\ &\sim -4\pi R k_c T \end{aligned} \tag{6.10}$$

and so the characteristic time for cooling (i.e., the time required for heat flow to carry to the surface – or redistribute – most of the initial heat content) is

$$\begin{aligned} \tau &\sim -\frac{U}{(\Delta Q/\Delta t)} \\ &\sim (R^2/3)(\rho c_\mathrm{v}/k_c) \end{aligned} \tag{6.11}$$

The quantity $\kappa = k_c/\rho c_\mathrm{v}$ is often called the thermal diffusivity, and for rocky planetary material it has a size of roughly $1 \times 10^{-6}\ \mathrm{m^2\,s^{-1}}$. Then Equation (6.11) shows that the characteristic time to cool an initially hot rocky body is of order

$$\tau_\mathrm{yr} \sim 1 \times 10^4\ R_\mathrm{km}^2 \tag{6.12}$$

where R_km is the size in km and τ_yr is measured in years. A body as small an asteroid ($R_\mathrm{km} < 500$ km) would lose any initial internal energy in a time short compared to the age of the solar system, but a body as large as any inner planet ($R > 2400$ km) should still be hot inside if it was initially formed hot, even without any radioactive internal energy sources!

Exercise How does the estimated cooling time scale change if the surface temperature of the body is T_s rather than being taken to be essentially zero as in the discussion above?

Now consider the opposite limit, in which a body has an internal heat source that changes slowly compared to the time in which most of the current internal energy can leak out. In this case the heat production in the interior gradually (in about the characteristic cooling time) settles into an equilibrium with the heat loss, and the internal temperature of the body comes to a steady state that changes only as the internal heat sources change. We will look at this case through the example of Ceres. The basic idea is that the asteroid reaches an equilibrium in which the rate of heat release in the centre approximately balances the loss of heat through leakage to the surface. Ceres is small enough ($R =$ 470 km) that its cooling time scale is less than the age of the solar system, and so this approximation may be roughly valid. Let's see what temperature would result from this equilibrium. The surface temperature T_s of Ceres, set by solar heating, is about 200 K (see Section 4.4). As a rough approximation, assume that the temperature drop from centre (at temperature T_c) to surface occurs roughly uniformly over the radius of the asteroid, so that the temperature gradient is

$$dT/dx \approx (T_c - T_s)/R. \tag{6.13}$$

The surface area of Ceres is $A = 4\pi R^2$, so the heat loss to the surface (Equation 6.9) is approximately

$$\frac{\Delta Q}{\Delta t} \approx (4\pi R^2)k_c(T_c - T_s)/R. \tag{6.14}$$

Assume a heat production typical of a carbonaceous chondrite, about $L \sim 4 \times 10^{-12}$ W kg^{-1}, and a mass $M \approx 9.5 \times 10^{20}$ kg. We now equate the total heat production rate LM with the rate at which heat is lost from the surface, and solve the resulting equation for T_c, which leads to

$$T_c \approx T_s + ML/(4\pi k_c R). \tag{6.15}$$

With the values appropriate to Ceres, we find $T_c \approx 520$ K. As long as the internal radioactive heat production does not change greatly, Ceres will maintain a central temperature of about 500 K, which drops steadily with distance from the centre towards the surface, reaching about 200 K at the surface.

Note that reradiation of incident sunlight, which provides roughly 10^2 W m^{-2}, is much larger than the internal heat leakage rate, about 2×10^{-3} W m^{-2}, and so the surface temperature of Ceres is not altered significantly by the leakage of internal heat.

Exercise Confirm the internal heat leakage rate given above for Ceres, and estimate the increase in surface temperature caused by the leakage of internal heat to the surface.

Exercise Apply the reasoning above to estimate the present surface and central temperatures of the asteroid 511 Davida, assuming equilibrium (see Table 6.1).

6.7 References

Asphaug, E. 2000, "The small planets", Sci. Am., May, 46. The Galileo and NEAR mission have brought us fascinating close-up images of several asteroids, and have led to the realization that most large asteroids are loosely consolidated rubble piles.

Binzel, R., Barucci, M. A. and Fulchignoni, M. 1991, "The origin of the asteroids", *Sci. Am.*, Oct., 88. This clear article focuses particularly on the physical and mineral nature, and shapes, of asteroids.

Bottke, W. F. et al. 2002, *Asteroids III* (Tucson, AZ: Univ. of Arizona Press). The latest in a series of comprehensive volumes on the subject of asteroids, this book has more than 50 review articles by specialists on all aspects of the subject. The introductory article provides a guide to the subjects covered and how they are divided among the various articles.

Kowal, C. T. 1996, *Asteroids, Their Nature and Utilization*, 2nd edition (New York: John Wiley and Sons). Kowal's small and recent book presents a clear overview of the subject at about the level of this book, with many illustrations and interesting details about individual objects.

Millis, R. L. et al, 1987, "The size, shape, density, and albedo of Ceres from its occultation of BD+8° 471", *Icarus*, 72, 507-518. The description of how the size and shape of Ceres were actually measured from Earth is very interesting, and even the technical parts of this journal article should be mostly intelligible to physics and astronomy undergraduate students.

Wetherill, G. W., 1979, "Apollo objects", *Sci. Am.*, Mar., 54. This article describes the small asteroids (or perhaps degassed comet nuclei) that inhabit the inner solar system and occasionally collide with Earth.

6.8 Review questions

6.1 Why are certain orbital periods apparently not allowed for asteroids?

6.2 How can the dimensions and masses of any asteroids be determined?

6.3 Could the asteroids of the main belt have been created by the disruption of a large terrestrial planet originally formed between Mars and Jupiter?

6.4 What information do we have about the chemical composition of asteroids?

6.5 How do we know that some asteroids have been differentiated into a structure with a metallic core and a rocky mantle? How could this differentiation have occurred?

6.6 What evidence shows that some meteorites originate in asteroids of the main belt? How are such meteorites transported to Earth?

6.7 Where and how did most most meteorites originate? What evidence helps us to answer this question?

6.8 What information do we have to estimate the fraction of various types of meteorite that occur in the region from which these meteorites originate? How is this information altered by the process of recovering meteorites on Earth?

6.9 Is it possible to identify specific source bodies for particular meteorites? If so, how?

6.10 What kinds of bodies in the current solar system are capable of catastrophic impact with the Earth? How do they get into orbits which can lead to Earth impact?

6.9 Problems

6.1 Two asteroids orbit the Sun in virtually identical orbits. One has a radius of 40 km and a density of 3300 kg m^{-3}. The other has a radius of only 100 m, and the same density. Because of a tiny initial difference in speed, the larger asteroid eventually comes close enough to the small one to capture it gravitationally, and the small asteroid crashes into the large one. (a) With what velocity does the small body hit the larger one? (b) Assume that all the energy released in the impact is retained in the immediate neighborhood of the impact, in an amount of matter equal to twice the mass of the smaller asteroid. Making reasonable assumptions about the specific heat of asteroidal material, how much would the temperature of the heated matter rise?

6.2 Assume that Jupiter and an asteroid are moving in circular, coplanar orbits, and that the ratio of orbital periods if $P(\text{Jupiter}) : P(\text{asteroid}) = 5 : 3$. (a) Sketch the two orbits to scale. (b) Show that the time from one close approach and the next of the two bodies is equal to xP_{Jupiter} and also equal to $(1+x)P(\text{asteroid})$, where x is some number. (c) Calculate how long an interval of time elapses between one close approach of the asteroid to Jupiter and the next. Give the result in Jupiter revolutions and in years, (d) On your sketch, show the places in the two orbits where the giant planet and the asteroid (repeatedly) pass closest to one another.

6.3 On Earth, a vigorous person can jump vertically to a height of roughly 0.3 meter (i.e. raise her centre of mass by that much). Suppose an astronaut tries to launch herself into a hyperbolic (escape) orbit from a small asteroid of mean density $\rho =$ 3000 kg m^{-3}, radius R, and mass $M = 4\pi\rho R^3/3$. From how large an asteroid could the astronaut escape? Make your assumptions and reasoning clear.

6.4 Consider an asteroid in a circular orbit around the Sun at 2.8 AU. (a) What is its velocity? (b) Suppose it were slowed down enough to drop into an elliptical orbit with an aphelion of 2.8 AU and perihelion of 1.0 AU. What would its velocity at aphelion then be? (c) Calculate the change in the kinetic energy per kg of the asteroid for this orbit change, at aphelion. (d) Calculate the mass of the asteroid and the gravitational binding energy per kg, for an asteroid of density $\rho = 3000$ kg m^{-3} and radius $R = 10$ km. (e) Calculate the number of atoms per kg, assuming a composition of $(MgFe)SiO_4$. (f) Calculate the crystal binding energy per kg, assuming that it is of order $E_b \sim 3nkT_b$, where n is the number of atoms per kg and T_b is the boiling point of the rock, roughly about 3000 K (note that this estimate ignores latent heats). (g) Is it likely that an asteroid could be shifted from the circular orbit into the elliptical one as a result of a collision without being completely fragmented or vaporized?

6.5 With what rotation period would Ceres have to rotate so that the rotational velocity of material at the equator of the asteroid would just be equal to the speed of a small body orbiting just above the surface? Could Ceres rotate with a period any shorter than this? Explain your conclusion.

6.6 Assume that the asteroid belt extends between 2.2 and 3.2 AU, and extends to 0.5 AU above and below the ecliptic. (a) If we estimate that there are about 10^6 asteroids of $R > 0.1$ km within this volume of space, what is the average space density of such asteroids (in asteroids per km^3), and an estimate of their typical separation (in km and in AU)? (b) When Voyager 1 passed through the asteroid belt, it had a speed of about 22 km s^{-1}, and its trajectory (which was confined essentially to the plane of the ecliptic) made approximately a

45° angle with the radius vector to the Sun. Ignoring the motion of the asteroids, use the space density calculated above to estimate (c) the probability P(100) of passing within 100 km of an asteroid of $R > 0.1$ km, and (d) the distance of closest approach to an asteroid of $R > 0.1$ km (that is, find the distance at which the probability of interaction at that distance would be about 1 for Voyager 1's track through the asteroid belt). (e) From a closest approach to an asteroid of $R \sim 10$ km equal to the distance estimated in (b), how large an angle would the asteroid subtend from Voyager? Would Voyager have been able to send back a detailed photo of this asteroid if the smallest detail its cameras could detect was about $3''$ across on the sky?

6.7 Suppose you discover an asteroid. You decide to observe it intensely, and you name it after your childhood pet, Gloop. You find that Gloop is in opposition (directly opposite the Sun as seen from Earth) every 1.25 years. (a) Assuming that Earth has a circular orbit, how far from the Sun is Gloop, what is its orbital period and what is the shape of its orbit? How far from the Earth is Gloop at opposition? (b) You also measure the total visible and near infrared light reflected from Gloop at opposition, finding a flux of about 1.0×10^{-13} W m^{-2}. Similarly, the total flux of heat radiation received from Gloop at infrared wavelengths longer than about 5 μm is 1.0×10^{-12} W m^{-2}. Assume for simplicity that Gloop rotates rapidly, and that it reflects light uniformly into 2π steradians and reradiates heat uniformly into 4π steradians. What are the albedo and radius of Gloop?

6.8 Consider an asteroid with an iron core ($\rho_c = 8000$ kg m^{-3}) covered by a thin silicate mantle ($\rho_m = 3400$ kg m^{-3}) with a thickness of 20% of the radius R of the asteroid. Assume that the internal temperature $T_i = 600$ K is constant throughout the core because of the high thermal conductivity of iron. Take the thermal energy of the core to be $3kT_i$ per atom, and assume that the thermal conductivity of the silicate mantle is about $k_c = 2$ W m^{-2} (K m^{-1})$^{-1}$. Ignore the heat capacity of the mantle. If the surface of the asteroid has a temperature of $T_s = 200$ K, find the value of the radius R for which the cooling rate is about 1 K per 10^6 yr. (You are estimating the size of the asteroid which could be the parent of an iron meteorite).

6.9 Consider an asteroid that forms by accretion in a very short time and that traps in its interior almost all the heat released by gravity during the formation. The resulting asteroid has uniform density $\rho = 3000$ kg m^{-3} and constant chemical composition throughout. Assume that the internal energy per atom is given by $E_{th} = 3kT$, that the mean molecular mass is $\overline{m} = 25m_u$, and that the melting point of iron is $T_{melt} = 1800$ K. Assume also that the accreting matter starts with $T_0 = 200$ K before accretion. (a) Suppose that the accretion occurs in a time short compared to the time required for heat to be transported away from the level at which it is deposited. Derive an expression for the temperature as a function of radius, $T(r)$, inside the asteroid of radius R. How large must the R grow for the local temperature to exceed the melting point anywhere? (b) Now make a different assumption, namely that mixing is effective enough that as the body accretes, the whole interior stays at about the same (increasing) temperature $\overline{T}(R)$. How large must R be in this case in order for enough heat to be supplied to melt the entire object? (c) Does it appear that accretion heating is a plausible mechanism for explaining how asteroids can differentiate?

6.10 Suppose that the asteroid 52 Europa is chemically homogeneous throughout, and that the radioactive heat sources are uniformly distributed through the asteroid's volume. Let the heat energy released per unit mass per unit time due to radioactive decay be E. From Table 6.5 the value at present of E for carbonaceous chondrite-like matter is about 1.1×10^{-4} J kg^{-1} yr^{-1} $= 3.5 \times 10^{-12}$ J kg^{-1} s^{-1}. Now suppose that E changes so slowly that the asteroid has been able to reach a state of equilibrium in which the total heat produced inside a radius r is just balanced by the heat carried out of that volume by thermal conduction. (a) For an arbitrary value of r, write down the expression for L_r, the total radioactive energy release per second inside of r. Write down a corresponding expression for the total energy flux carried outward by conduction at r; this expression will involve dT/dr. The condition of equilibrium is that these two expressions are equal. (b) Assuming that E and the conductivity k_c are independent of r, integrate the resulting equilibrium equation to get an equation relating $T(r) - T_c$ to r, where T_c is the central temperature $T(0)$. (c) Assume that $T(R)$ is known to be about 200 K, that E has the value above, and that k_c is about 2 W m^{-1} K^{-1}. Solve for the value of T_c. Graph the resulting temperature profile $T(r)$.

Chapter 7

Comets

7.1 Overview

From time to time, roughly every few years, a comet will be visible in the evening or morning twilight. To the unaided eye, it is usually a faint diffuse smudge of light smaller than the full Moon. Sometimes a wispy tail may be seen extending a few degrees across the sky from the smudge. The smudge moves from night to night relative to the pattern of fixed stars, and after a few weeks or months vanishes into the sunlit sky or fades from visibility.

Time exposure photography (or imaging with a CCD camera) makes possible a more interesting view. The smudge is revealed as the core of a large bright round or oval structure called the **head** or **coma** of the comet, from which a long **tail** extends. The tail may contain wisps and knots, like threads of illuminated smoke, or it may be almost featureless. Some comets even have two tails. Both coma and tail as photographed are likely to be several times larger than the structures visible to the eye. Photography also makes it possible to find comets earlier, to follow them longer than is possible by eye, and to detect many comets too faint to be seen by eye alone.

Occasionally a comet will be really bright, with a tail that visibly stretches across a third of the sky. Such a show was put on during the 1910 apparition of Halley's comet. Unfortunately, such awe-inspiring apparitions are rare, occurring only a few times a century. The only really spectacular comets in recent years have been Comet Hyakutake in 1996 and Comet Hale-Bopp in 1997. An amateur's photograph of Comet Hyakutake is shown in Figure 7.1.

Since most comets appear irregularly, they must be discovered. The bright ones, of course, are widely seen while they are bright, but most comets are never bright enough to be seen by eye. The fainter comets are sometimes found by professional astronomers who are photographing the sky for other reasons, but they are often found by amateurs who sit out at night specifically to search for comets, usually with small telescopes or huge binoculars. Such discoveries require a good bit of hard work; one estimate is that discovery of a comet requires on average more than 1000 hours (about 100 full nights) of observing the sky.

Once discovered, a comet is officially named for its discoverer (e.g. Comet Kohoutek, found by a professional) or discoverers (e.g. Comet Ikeya-Seki, found independently by two Japanese amateurs). It is also given a catalogue designation. This name contains the category letter P if the comet is known to return to the inner solar system more frequently than once every 200 years, C if it returns less often than every 200 years, X if its orbit is unknown, and D if it disappears. The category letter P is preceded by a serial number which recognizes the order in which the comet's periodic behaviour was clearly established. The other categories are followed by the year of discovery and a combination of a letter and a number which encodes the date of discovery. Thus Halley's comet is now known as 1P/Halley, since it was the first comet whose periodic returns were recognized, while comet Hale-Bopp is C/1995 O1, and comet Shoemaker-Levy 9, which crashed into Jupiter in 1994, is D/1993 F2.

7.2 Orbital behaviour of comets (and a little history)

Comets were of course known before any systematic astronomy began, and their physical nature was discussed by philosophers during the Greek and Roman periods in antiquity. Some people suggested that comets are indeed astronomical objects analogous to planets that move independently through the sky, but the most widely accepted view was that of Aristotle, who argued that because comets appear unpredictably, and because they are not confined to the plane of the ecliptic (as planets are), they cannot be truly celestial objects. Instead, Aristotle suggested that a comet is a kind of gaseous combustion high in the Earth's atmosphere, which was usually assumed in classical times to extend to the orbit of the Moon. Comets were therefore

Figure 7.1: A photograph of Comet Hyakutake, taken in March 1996 by an amateur astronomer. The bright ball of (reflected) light at the bottom of the image is the coma of the comet, and its tail stretches out over many degrees on the sky upwards, away from the Sun. At the time this photo was taken, the comet was about 20 million km from the Earth, and easily visible with unaided eyes and with binoculars. This image appears in colour on the front cover of the book. (Courtesy of Dominique Dierick)

assigned by Aristotle and many of his successors (e.g., the great astronomer Claudius Ptolemy in the 2nd century A.D.), to meteorology rather than astronomy.

During the first half of the European middle ages, science almost ceased to exist. When classical works – at first those of the Latin popularizers and encyclopaedists, but later the original writings of Aristotle, Plato, Ptolemy and others – gradually became available in the 11th and 12th centuries, Aristotle's view was again accepted. Serious study of comets only began in the 15th century, when position measurements of several comets (including the body later known as Halley's comet, in 1456) were made by Paolo Toscanelli (1397–1482). During the 15th century the first attempts were also made by Georg Peuerbach (1423–1461) or Regiomontanus (1436–1476) to measure the distance to a comet.

The Danish astronomer Tycho Brahe took the first major step towards establishing the modern view of comets with his observations of the comet of 1577. He measured the position of the comet relative to the fixed stars with large instruments of his own manufacture with an error of only about 4 minutes of arc. His main objective was to determine the distance (or parallax) of the comet by observing it when it was near the horizon and when it was high in the sky. If the comet was closer to the Earth than the Moon, as argued by Aristotle, Brahe expected to see a shift in its position relative to the background stars by a degree or more between observations near the horizon and near the zenith (see figure 7.2). Of course, the comet drifts steadily across the field of background stars, but the average rate of drift can be established by observations at the same time on several successive nights. The shift in position due to the movement of the observer with the rotating Earth would be superimposed on the average drift.

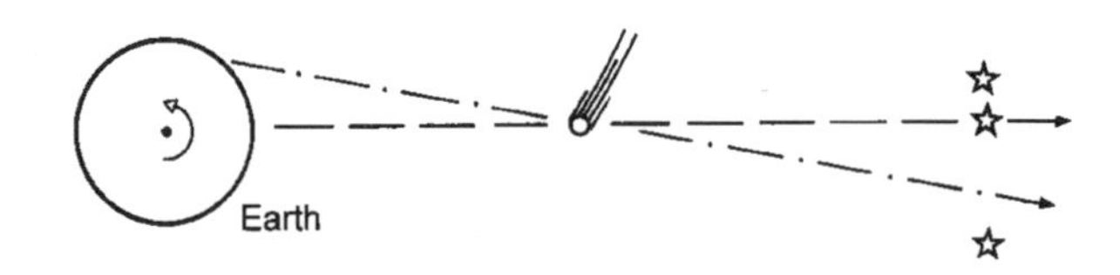

Figure 7.2: Lines of sight towards a stationary comet from Earth as the comet crosses the zenith (dashed line) and as it sets (dot-dash line). This is the shift that was *not* seen by Brahe. The figure is not to scale!

Tycho found no detectable effect due to his position on the Earth, and cautiously concluded that the comet was at least four times as far from the Earth as the Moon is, and therefore is definitely a planetary rather than a meteorological phenomenon. He suggested that comets move in oval orbits around the Sun.

During the 17th century great progress was made in understanding the nature of planetary orbits, first by Johannes Kepler and then by Isaac Newton, who worked out the complete solution to the orbit problem for the motion of a body in the gravitational field of the Sun. Newton's friend Edmund Halley encouraged Newton in his research, helped him to publish his great work, the *Mathematical Principles of Natural Philosophy*, and stimulated his interest in comets. Newton concluded that "comets are a sort of planet revolved in very eccentric orbits around the Sun". Halley applied Newton's orbit theory to observations of comets, and in

1705 published a catalogue of orbits worked out from observations made over the preceding three centuries (by other astronomers!) for two dozen comets. He noted that the orbits in space of the comets of 1531, 1607, and 1682 were nearly the same, and suggested that all three were repeated appearances of one comet at intervals of 75 or 76 years. In 1716 he discussed this comet again, noting that it may also have been the comets seen in 1378 and 1456, and predicting its return in 1758. This comet is the most active one presently returning regularly to the inner solar system, and has been named in Halley's honour.

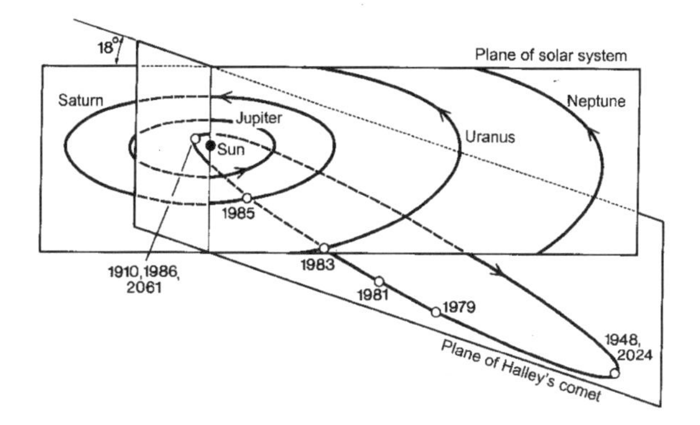

Figure 7.3: The orbit of Halley's comet relative to the planets of the solar system. The plane of the cometary orbit is only mildly inclined to that of the planets, but the comet orbits the Sun in the opposite sense from the motions of the planets. During its 76-year orbit, the comet passes inside the orbit of Venus and then recedes to a distance from the Sun greater than the orbital radius of Neptune. Dated points on the orbit show several of P/Halley's positions during its most recent return to the inner solar system.

Calculations of orbits of comets that include the gravitational effects of the planets as well as the Sun are quite complicated. However, the effects of the planets can be quite important for a comet, especially if its orbit takes it near one of the giants. During the 18th and 19th centuries, mathematicians and physicists gradually became more proficient at these difficult computations. In 1758, French mathematician Alexis-Claude Clairaut (1713–1765) worked out the effects of planetary perturbations on the motions of comet Halley (with six months of calculations from morning to night!) just in time to predict that the comet would pass perihelion on April 15, 1759, give or take a month. The comet was first seen on Christmas night 1758 by a German amateur astronomer; it passed perihelion on March 13, 1759. Its predicted return was widely hailed as a clear demonstration that Newton's law of gravity is not true only for planets, but applies to other objects as well. Halley's comet has since returned on schedule in 1835, 1910, and 1986, and historical records have been found of every return since 240 B.C., including an illustration of the comet on the Bayeux Tapestry, a long cloth documenting the Norman conquest of England in 1066, a year in which the comet appeared. Table 7.1 lists the years for which historical records of the return of Halley's comet have been found, and the shape of the orbit is shown in Figure 7.3.

Table 7.1: Returns of Halley's Comet

Date		Date	
B.C.	240	A.D.	912
	164		989
	87		1066
B.C.	12		1145
A.D.	66		1222
	141		1301
	218		1378
	295		1456
	374		1531
	451		1607
	530		1682
	607		1759
	684		1835
	760		1910
A.D.	837	A.D.	1986

The next returning (periodic) comet to be identified was found by Johann Encke (1791–1865), who realized that comets seen in 1786, 1795, 1805, and 1818 were the same comet returning every 3.3 years. This comet, now called Encke's comet, orbits between 0.34 and 4.08 AU from the Sun. By 1838 it had become clear in addition that this comet's orbital period was decreasing. Encke proposed that the solar system is filled with a very tenuous fluid that resists the motion of bodies through it, causing a small, light object like a comet to spiral in towards the Sun with a decreasing orbital period. As an alternative, it was also suggested that a belt of meteoric particles orbiting the Sun might accomplish much the same effect. A third possibility was suggested by Friedrich Bessel (1784–1846), who noticed a sunward plume of matter (in addition to the tail) on Halley's comet at its 1835 return; Bessel suggested that gas ejected from the comet might act as a rocket engine to change the orbital period.

Some typical comets are listed in Table 7.2. This table includes examples of comets with short periods (less than 200 years) many of which are associated with Jupiter, and of comets having long (more than 200 years) periods. Some comets listed are sources of meteor showers, while others are well-known comets that have been widely visible in recent years. The columns

Table 7.2: Orbital properties of some interesting comets

Comet name	a (AU)	q (AU)	e	i (°)	P (yrs)	Peri-helion	Comments
Short-period							
1P/Halley	17.9	0.587	0.967	162	77	1986	η Aquarid, Orionid showers
2P/Encke	2.22	0.341	0.846	12	3.28	2000	Taurid meteor shower
6P/d'Arrest	3.44	1.291	0.625	19	6.38	2002	
21P/Giacobini-Zinner	3.51	1.028	0.708	32	6.61	2005	Draconid meteor shower
26P/Grigg-Skjellerup	2.96	0.989	0.666	21	5.09	2002	
27P/Crommelin	9.1	0.735	0.919	29	27.4	2011	
55P/Tempel-Tuttle	10.3	0.982	0.904	163	32.9	1998	
109P/Swift-Tuttle	24	0.963	0.960	114	135	1992	Perseid meteor shower
Long-period							
Ikeya-Seki C/1965 S1	91.8	0.008	1.000	142	880	1965	
Bennett C/1969 Y1	141	0.538	0.996	90	1678	1970	
Kohoutek C/1973 E1	large	0.142	1.000	14	large	1973	
West C/1975 V1	6830	0.197	1.000	43	large	1976	
Hale-Bopp C/1995 O1	250	0.914	0.996	89	4000	1997	Bright comet of 1997
Hyakutake C/1996 B2	large	0.230	1.000	125	large	1996	Bright comet of 1996

Source: K. R. Lang 1992, *Astrophysical Data: Planets and Stars* (New York: Springer-Verlag), Table 7.4

of the table start with the comet name, followed by the semi-major axis a of the orbit in AU, the distance q of closest approach of the comet to the Sun in AU, and the eccentricity e (recall the discussion in Chapter 1 of how these quantities describe an elliptical orbit), the inclination i of the plane containing the orbit of the comet to the plane of the ecliptic (an angle of more than 90° means that the comet moves in the opposite sense around the Sun from the direction of planetary motion), the period P in years that it takes the comet to complete one orbit, the year of the next perihelion passage or of a recent passage, and some comments.

7.3 Comet nuclei, comas, and tails

Some observational clues

Up to this point we have only discussed how comets move through space. We must now turn to the problem of what a comet is, and how the phenomena that we observe are produced.

The observation that comet tails point away from the Sun, already well known in the 16th century, suggests that the visible comet head and tail are formed of material ejected somehow from a small central body, and then repelled by the Sun. This view was given added plausibility by the detailed shapes seen in comets. Bessel and others observed jets, fans, and rays emanating from the bright centre of comet Halley in 1835; in one case, a bright cone of light extended towards the Sun but was observed to curl back away from the Sun at a short distance from the comet centre, as though strongly repelled by the Sun. Donati's comet in 1858 and Comet Morehouse in 1910 showed parabolic envelopes on the side of the head towards the Sun, again suggesting matter that was spraying outward from the centre like a fountain and then being blown backwards into the tail by some repulsive force from the Sun. It was natural to suppose that at the heart of these phenomena lies a small nucleus, a solid object containing or covered with some easily vaporized material such as water ice or dry ice (frozen carbon dioxide). The comet nucleus was thus visualized as a kind of iceberg travelling through space. As such a nucleus approaches the Sun, increased heating causes strong vaporization of the solid ice (sublimation) directly into a gas cloud that expands away from the nucleus. The observed hazy cloud of the comet's head is due to light scattering from the molecules in this expanding gas cloud. This **iceberg theory** was accepted by Pierre-Simon de Laplace (1749–1827), Bessel and others during the 18th and early 19th centuries.

However, the iceberg theory was called into question late in the 19th century by studies of meteor showers (see Chapter 5). In 1866 Giovanni Schiaparelli (1835–1910) showed that the shower of meteors emanating from the constellation of Perseus in August of each year (the Perseids) is produced by small particles all moving through space along essentially the same orbit as that of Comet Swift-Tuttle. The next year it was shown that the particles causing the Leonid meteor shower travel in the same orbit as Comet Tempel-Tuttle, and soon other identifications between comets and meteor showers were made. This discovery suggested that the tiny stones causing the meteor shower might actually constitute the solid body of the comet, and by early in this century it was common to visualize a comet core as a loose swarm of small particles moving together through space in separate but nearly identical orbits, rather than a solid object like an iceberg. The comet nucleus was thus hypothesized to be a kind of flying gravel or sand bank. The particles were thought to be small (diameters of mm or cm, perhaps), and separated by some meters from one another. The vapour released to form the coma and tail was thought to be frozen onto the surface of the small grains, so that it could sublime as the swarm of stones approaches the Sun. We call this model of comet nuclei the **gravel bank** theory.

Spectroscopic observations using visible light began to reveal more clues to the nature of comets late in the 19th century, when William Huggins (1824–1910), one of the pioneers of spectroscopy, identified spectral lines due to the C_2. Most comet comas show strong spectral lines that are produced by small molecules (molecules made from two or three atoms). Typically as a comet nears the Sun, its coma begins to display spectral lines of CN at about 3 AU, C_3 and NH_2 at 2 AU, C_2 at 1.8 AU, and OH, HN, and CH by about 1.5 AU. If the comet gets very close to the Sun, it may begin to show spectral lines due to sodium or even iron. It seems quite clear that the source of the comet's gas cloud is rich in the light elements, H, C, N, and O, which may combine chemically to make simple compounds such as water, (H_2O), carbon dioxide (CO_2), methane, (CH_4), and ammonia (NH_3) that may be frozen at low temperatures but vaporize below or near room temperature.

These various molecules and molecular fragments make themselves visible by producing **emission lines** and **bands**. That is, they emit brightly at certain specific wavelengths (colours) or at a large number of individual wavelengths near one another that become distinguishable when the light from the comet coma is spread out into a spectrum (see Figure 2.3). As we have discussed in Chapter 2, specific patterns of such bright lines enable us to identify the various gases emitting the light as CN, NH, C_2, etc. For most comets nearer the Sun than about 3 AU, the largest part of the observed light from the coma is due to such emission lines and bands: the coma is visible mainly because it can emit these spectral lines, as seen in the spectrum of Comet P/Tuttle 1980 in Figure 7.4.

The emitted colours are produced by a very simple mechanism known as resonance fluorescence, which was described when we discussed absorption and emission

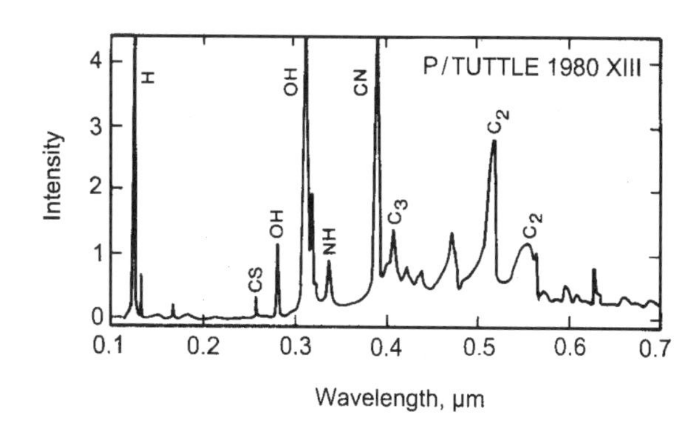

Figure 7.4: The emission line spectrum of the coma of Comet P/Tuttle (1980 XIII). The spectrum only distinguishes features more than about 40 Å apart. The coma is very bright (high intensity of light) at colours emitted by H at 1216 Å, by OH near 3100 Å, by CN near 3883 Å, and by C_2 near 5100 Å. Each of the bright emission bands produced by a molecule is actually made of of many closely spaced emission lines. Adapted from W. F. Huebner, ed. 1990, *Physics and Chemistry of Comets* (Berlin: Springer-Verlag), p. 92.

of radiation by an isolated atom (see Figure 2.4). The main difference from the situation described there is that a molecule has a very large set of energy levels, many more than most kinds of atoms have. In the physical conditions found in the gas of the coma, each molecule is usually in one of the lowest lying energy levels, because if the molecule is raised to one of the high energy levels by a collision or by absorbing a photon, it will drop back spontaneously to a low energy almost instantaneously. Now as sunlight passes through the coma, a photon of one of the many specific wavelengths that carry exactly the right energy to raise the molecule from a low-lying level to a higher one is absorbed by the molecule. The molecule then quickly drops back to a low energy level, usually either the original one or one very close to it, emitting a second photon of almost the same wavelength as the original. However, the emitted photon may be sent off in any direction, so *some of these photons will reach Earth* (unlike the original stream of photons from the Sun that passes through the comet's coma). Thus, the process by which a cometary coma produces most of its visible light is that it traps photons of visible light streaming from the Sun through the coma, absorbs them, and then re-emits photons of the same or almost the same wavelengths in all directions.

In addition to the coma, many comets show tails when they get to within about 1.5 AU of the Sun, as seen in Figure 1.6 and in Figure 7.1. Two quite different types of tails are recognized now; one is rather straight and quite complex in appearance, with rays, streamers, and knots (this is the type seen in both comet images); the other type is fairly smooth, broad and featureless. Many comets have one type of tail or the other, but some comets have both kinds.

Again spectroscopy comes to our aid in understanding the nature of these two types of tails. When we obtain spectra of the straight, complex tails, the spectra are rather similar to those of the coma, and are also dominated by molecular emission lines. However, in the tail the molecules are all ionized (that is, they have lost one electron), in contrast to the molecules of the coma, which are all neutral! For this reason, such tails are usually called **ion** (or **plasma**) **tails**. Typical molecules found in ion tails are CO^+, N_2^+, CH^+, and OH^+. Again, the spectra reveal the presence of the light chemical elements that appear to be fragments of volatile ices.

The smooth, featureless tails reveal quite a different kind of spectrum, one that is essentially identical to the spectrum of the Sun. As we discussed in a previous chapter, this spectrum is an **absorption line** spectrum; that is, it is bright at most wavelengths, but certain wavelengths are fainter (see Figure 3.7). The fact that the light we see coming from a comet tail of this type is essentially the same as the spectrum of the Sun reveals that the matter in such a tail simply reflects sunlight at all wavelengths without much altering it, in much the same way that light is reflected from a ping-pong ball, from the water droplets in a terrestrial cloud, or from the small ash particles in a column of smoke. The spectrum in such a situation is simply that of the original light source, in this case the Sun. Observations reveal that the particles in a smooth tail reflect blue light more efficiently than they reflect red light, and this implies that they are not much bigger than the wavelength of visible light. Probably they are typically somewhat less than 1 μm in diameter, so that the particles that reflect most of the light tail are much smaller than those involved in meteor showers. The larger particles undoubtedly also reflect sunlight, but there are not enough of them to produce a visible effect. These small particles, which we often call dust particles, (though some of them are probably tiny ice fragments) make it reasonable to call this kind of comet tail a **dust tail**.

Evidence of small dust particles is also often seen within the comas of comets, especially in comets that are entering the inner solar system for the first time. That is, some comas show the molecular emission bands produced by fluorescence superimposed on a spectrum of reflected sunlight. We believe that in such comas the fluorescing gas is intimately mixed together with small reflecting dust particles.

Gravel bank or iceberg?

We now look more closely at the evidence supporting the two competing hypotheses for the nature of comet nuclei, the iceberg theory and the gravel bank theory, to see how observations of cometary behaviour from Earth enabled us to make a choice between them. Although we now have direct observations of the nucleus of Halley's comet from a spacecraft, the reasoning used to deduce that comets are icebergs, not gravel banks, helps us to understand these objects and their behaviour better.

The gravel bank theory naturally explains the association of meteor showers with cometary orbits. The explanation offered by this theory for the source of the gas that flows into the coma and ion tail is that the gas is produced by sublimation of ices *adsorbed* onto the surfaces of the bits of rock making up the core of the comet. This view seems plausible for a comet making its first trip into the inner solar system. However, the gravel bank theory has a real problem in accounting for the fact that a periodic comet such as 1P/Halley, which has returned to the inner solar system at least 28 times, can continue to release gas at a high rate. (It has been estimated that Comet Halley has sublimed at least 1 km^3 of ice in its historical apparitions.) The thin skin of ice adsorbed on a small stone should be evaporated away on the first pass near the Sun, leaving little or nothing for further returns. On the other hand, the iceberg theory, in which the ice makes up the bulk of a large (diameter $\sim$ 1 km or more) solid nucleus, can easily account for the large amount of gas needed for many successive apparitions of a periodic comet.

The gravel bank theory has other problems. It does not readily account for the tiny dust particles that appear to be steadily released to form a dust trail as a comet moves into the inner solar system. On the iceberg theory, these are tiny bits of rocky material (perhaps similar chemically to the material of carbonaceous chondrites) trapped in the body of the iceberg. When sublimation eats away the surface to the point that a particular dust particle is exposed, that particle is carried away by the breeze produced by the outflowing gas molecules if it is small enough. Larger pieces of rock are left on the surface of the eroding iceberg as a kind of crust, although some these are also lost to the comet nucleus (broken off by impacts with other space debris, ejected when pockets of trapped gas blow out, or dispersed when finally all the ice is sublimed away). The dust particles that escape the nucleus gradually spread around the comet orbit, and some may be swept up by the Earth in a meteor shower.

A third problem concerns what are called non-gravitational accelerations. Some periodic comets, such as Encke's comet, return later or earlier than expected, even after the gravitational influences of the planets have been accounted for. Such accelerations are not readily explained for a loose swarm of particles, but can be accounted for on the iceberg theory by a kind of rocket effect, like that proposed by Bessel. The rocket effect probably mainly occurs because the side of the comet nucleus facing the Sun is where most of the sublimation is occurring; the dark side cools quickly enough that sublimation is weaker there. If a comet always kept one side facing the Sun, it would have a kind of permanent rocket operating on the bright side that would oppose and slightly reduce the acceleration towards the Sun due to solar gravity (see Figure 7.5). However, the comet is very likely rotating, and this has an important influence on the rocket effect. Because of rotation, the warmest part of the comet is not on the centre of the sunlit side, and maximum rocket thrust is not directed straight towards the Sun, but off to one side somewhat. The rocket can thus accelerate or decelerate the comet, especially during its perihelion passage (see Figure 7.5 again). If the comet rotates in the same sense that it orbits the Sun, the rocket will increase its speed past the Sun near perihelion and increase the size and period of the orbit. Rotation opposite to orbital motion slows the comet and causes its orbit to decrease in size an period. It turns out that it is the rocket effect directed along the orbit that is most important in changing the orbital characteristics, even though it is estimated that the rocket effect towards the Sun is usually several times stronger.

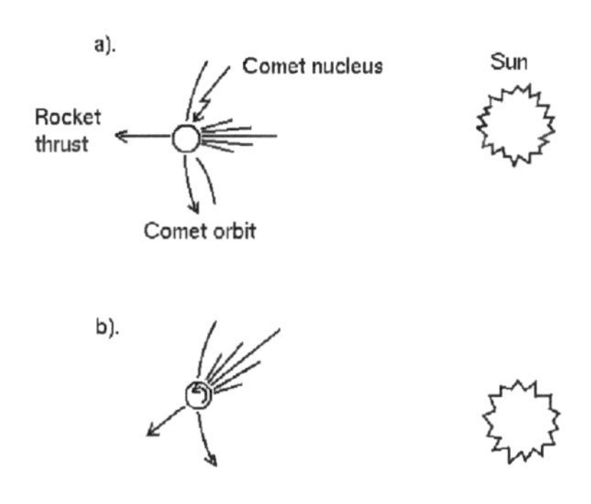

Figure 7.5: The rocket effect produced by subliming gas from a comet nucleus is shown. In the upper part of the figure the nucleus always keeps the same side towards the Sun, resulting in a force that diminishes solar gravity somewhat. The nucleus in the lower part of the figure is rotating so that the rocket effect acts along the orbit (accelerating the nucleus in the situation shown) as well as reducing the pull of solar gravity.

Still another comet observation that the gravel bank theory has trouble explaining is the fact that some comets pass very close to the Sun without disruption or destruction. Comet 1843 I, for example, passed within 0.1 solar radius of the solar photosphere (it thus went through the corona) without apparent damage. Since this distance is well within the Roche limit of the Sun for a gravitationally bound heap of ice cubes of density 920 kg m^{-3} (about the same as the mean density of the Sun, which is 1420 kg m^{-3}), the nucleus of the comet must be held together by a force considerably stronger than simply gravity. In the iceberg theory this cohesive force is the tensile strength of the ice of the nucleus (it isn't easy to break a snowball, and an ice cube can be positively frustrating). The gravel bank theory, on the other hand, has no obvious way to keep the rocky pieces of the swarm together when they pass near the Sun, and a close passage by the solar surface should spread out the comet greatly. Furthermore, the small rocks of the gravel bank should be completely de-iced in a close pass, and perhaps vaporized entirely, so that the comet should cease to appear at all after perihelion passage. An iceberg sweeping by the Sun, on the other hand, may lose material off its surface even to a depth of many meters, but if it has a diameter of a kilometer or so, there is still lots of matter left to continue to generate the coma and tail.

It should be clear that the gravel bank theory of comet nuclei is no longer accepted. It is now understood that a cometary nucleus is typically a large block of (very dirty) ice or snow, although some comets probably do resemble icy rubble piles with rather loose cohesion.

Comet nuclei

It is normally not possible to observe the nucleus of a comet directly from the Earth. When the comet is near the Earth, it is also near the Sun, and there is almost always a bright coma that completely obscures the nucleus. Rarely, a comet passes close enough to Earth that the nucleus may be visible; observations of Comet Pons-Winnecke in 1927, when it passed within 0.04 AU of the Earth, suggested a maximum nuclear diameter of about 5 km. Such observations cannot usually be made, however. A more promising technique for determining the size of a comet nucleus (without obtaining much other useful information, however) is to observe the brightness of the comet when it is far (more than 4 or 5 AU) from the Sun. If it is assumed that the coma is not very important (though it may well be that there is always some coma), and that the reflectivity or albedo of the nucleus is known (it has been taken to be various values from about 0.7, similar to somewhat dirty snow, to 0.03, darker than a lump of coal), then the observed brightness of the comet can be used to determine how large a reflecting area it presents to the Sun, and thus to measure its size. Since there may be some coma present, such deduced sizes are probably still upper limits to the actual nuclear diameters. The diameters deduced in this way are generally less than 10 km; typical values are 2 km for periodic comets ("old" comets) and 5 km for comets with nearly parabolic orbits coming into the inner solar system for the first time ("new" comets).

If we assume that comet nuclei are made of an ice with a density of roughly 1000 kg m^{-3} (such as water ice), the mass of a nucleus with a diameter of 2 km is about 4×10^{12} kg. A mass of $\sim 10^{13}$ kg is probably a reasonable estimate for a typical comet nuclear mass. This value is of the order of 10^{-12} times smaller than the mass of the Earth, so it is not surprising that even very close passes of comets by the Earth (Lexell's comet, 1770) or Jupiter (Comet Brooks, 1886) do not result in appreciable orbit changes to the planet, even though the comet orbit is completely altered. (Both the close passes mentioned above allow one to infer that the masses of the comets involved were much less than 10^{21} kg, but this value is still enormously larger than actual comet masses, so it is not a very useful result.)

The next helpful clue from observations about the nature of the nucleus comes from the fact that many comets, especially old ones, are nearly inactive until they come within about 3 AU of the Sun, at which point the coma starts developing quite rapidly. We suspect right away that this is a temperature effect, triggered by the rising surface temperature of the comet as it approaches closer and closer to the Sun.

That the comet nucleus should become warmer (at least on the surface) as it approaches the Sun is intuitively obvious, but the actual way in which this surface temperature is set requires a little explanation. The comet nucleus is of course warmed by sunlight that falls on it. It is cooled by radiating away heat, and also because heat is required to sublime gas from the surface. The heat energy that each square meter of the comet absorbs each second depends only on the distance of the comet from the Sun. The energy lost by cooling each second from a square meter depends essentially on the temperature (recall from Chapter 3 that heat radiated by a warm body increases very rapidly with temperature). Sublimation of comet ices also increases extremely rapidly with temperature; once sublimation starts, it has a powerful cooling effect. Now at any point in its orbit, the surface of the comet nucleus settles to the temperature that is determined by **equilibrium** between the heat gain from sunlight and heat losses from heat radiation and sublimation. The comet surface temperature is just the temperature at which the losses of heat balance the gains each second.

It is easy to see that this must be so. Imagine that the comet temperature is very low at some moment when a lot of heat falls on the surface. Because the surface is cold, little heat is lost, but lots comes in. Thus the temperature of the surface of the nucleus rises. As the temperature of the surface increases, the heat losses by radiation and sublimation increase too, coming closer to the value of heat received each second. As long as there is an imbalance, however, the temperature continues to rise, until finally the temperature is just high enough that the heat lost each second just balances the heat gain from sunlight. At this temperature, no net heat is gained each second, so the temperature of the comet nucleus stabilizes.

Exercise: Explain how the temperature in your house is set in winter by an equilibrium between energy gained (from heating) and energy lost (to the cold outdoors).

As the comet moves closer to the Sun, of course, the amount of heat from the Sun striking every square meter increases. This leads to an imbalance between the energy input to the nucleus and the energy lost, so the temperature of the nucleus rises again, until a new balance between gains and losses is struck. Thus the nucleus gets steadily warmer as the comet approaches the Sun, and cools again as the nucleus recedes back into deep space. In deep space, at hundreds of AU from the Sun, the surface temperature may drop as low as 10 or 20 K. At the orbit of Neptune, the temperature will be about 50 K. Near Jupiter, the temperature will have risen to over 100 K; and as the nucleus approaches closer to the Sun, its temperature will continue to rise.

It is very reasonable to suspect that the sudden onset of coma and tail production near 3 AU, where the surface temperature of the comet is expected to be about 170 K, is the result of the rapidly increased sublimation of the principal ice of the nucleus. After all, the coma appears to be made of gases released from the nucleus, and this is certainly a temperature-sensitive process. So the question we need to consider is what kind of ice begins to sublimate strongly at about –100 C. Of the ices made of the abundant light elements found in comet spectra, H, C, N, and O, only water ice begins to sublime strongly at about the right temperature. The others—dry ice (CO_2), methane (CH_4), nitrogen (N_2), ammonia (NH_3), etc.—all are much more volatile than water ice, so that a nucleus made mainly of any of these other ices should start to sublime well outside 3 AU.

Exercise: Use Figure 2.5 to explain why water ice begins to sublime near – 100 C rather than only near 0 C.

This inference has led to the view that the bulk of

a comet nucleus is composed mainly of frozen water, and that the other gases evaporated by the comet nucleus are trapped in the water ice matrix. The trapped molecules may be incorporated directly into the ice crystal structure, in which case the resulting solid is called a clathrate hydrate. Alternatively, the volatile ices might be trapped in small pockets throughout the volume of the nucleus. As long as water ice is the dominant volatile constituent, large amounts of all gases will only be released once the water ice starts to sublime, leading to the observed characteristic commencement of strong sublimation near 3 AU from the Sun.

The view that water ice is a major, and perhaps the dominant, constituent of most cometary nuclei has received support from spectroscopic observations at many wavelengths. The molecule H_2O itself was detected in Comet Bradfield in 1974 by means of a microwave emission line that can be studied with a radio telescope. Ionized H_2O^+ is sometimes seen in the emission line spectra of ion tails. And the pieces into which H_2O breaks up when bombarded by ultraviolet photons from the Sun, namely H, OH, and O, are all found to be very abundant in cometary comas. In fact, the neutral H coma (observed with spectrographs in space by means of an emission line at 1216 Å (see Figure 7.4) which is excited by resonance fluorescence) is roughly ten times larger in diameter than the visible coma due to C_2, CN, etc.

Thus, it seems well established that H_2O ice is a major component of most comet nuclei. It is still possible, however, that it is not always the dominant component; a nucleus of ices more volatile than water (NH_3, CO_2, or CH_4 for example) might not start to sublime strongly as it came into the inner solar system until near 3 AU if it were covered with a sufficiently reflective or insulating surface layer (e.g. of rocky debris) so that rather little heat from the Sun could penetrate to the ices. In fact, some comets, especially new ones, do begin to sublime gases much farther from the Sun than 3 AU, although weakly, and presumably these comets have nuclei in which ices other than water ice are important constituents. If such a comet later became a periodic comet (because of orbit changes caused by the planets), gradually subliming the ices from its nucleus but not losing all the stony matter frozen into the ice, a surface crust of dirt might build up (as it does on subliming or melting snow in the spring) that could function as an insulator and retard sublimation when the comet is in the outer solar system. If the crust is hard and rigid, it could also inhibit sublimation by mechanically preventing gas from escaping. Sublimation might only turn on near 3 AU in such a comet, even though its nucleus might be mainly made of ices more volatile than water ice.

Once the sublimation of ices really gets underway, this process has a strong effect on the temperature of the comet's surface. Sublimation of ice uses a lot of energy, and so acts as a strong cooling mechanism, adding its effect to the cooling by radiation that occurs even far from the Sun. Sublimation is such a powerful cooling agent that the temperature of the comet nucleus is not able to rise very far above 200 K even in the inner solar system. (This is very similar to the cooling effect of perspiration on a hot day....)

We now have a fairly clear picture of the nucleus of a comet, and how it behaves as the comet passes through the inner solar system. Let us summarize this view. As the comet makes its first trip to the inner solar system, the icy nucleus, probably composed mainly of water ice, begins to sublime and release gases rapidly, usually between 5 and 3 AU from the Sun. These gases expand outward to form the visible coma. Small dust particles and tiny grains of ice that come to the surface of the nucleus (as layers of ice above are lost) are swept away from the nucleus by the breeze set up by the subliming gas, so the coma contains both gas atoms and dust grains drifting away from the nucleus as it orbits the Sun. Large pieces of refractory debris (pieces of chondritic rock, perhaps?) are left on the surface of the comet, and gradually form a crust. If the comet's orbit is changed by the gravitational effects of the planets into an elliptical orbit of short period (a few years or decades), it may make further passes into the inner solar system. On later apparitions, the debris crust will reduce heating of the ice, so that vapour is lost more slowly than on the first pass near the Sun. Gas must now escape through cracks and crevices in the crust in the form of geysers or leaks. From time to time, a pocket of particularly volatile ice may reach the surface and blow out a piece of the crust, leading to occasional bursts of activity, which will also scatter larger bits of crust into the coma. After hundreds or thousands of passes through the inner solar system, the ice will be exhausted, leaving perhaps a small stony nucleus that is accompanied on its orbit through space by a swarm of tiny pieces of debris that were ejected from or lost by the nucleus earlier in its life. The stony remnant of the nucleus may become an asteroid in a fairly eccentric orbit.

The larger pieces of debris (pieces the size of a grain of sand or a peppercorn) form a swarm around the comet nucleus and gradually spreads away from the nucleus because of the small velocity given to each bit as it escaped from the nucleus. Now as each piece of debris moves slowly away from the nucleus, it feels a slightly different attraction from the Sun, and (more importantly) a slightly different attraction from the planets (particularly Jupiter and Saturn). As a result, each bit of debris follows a slightly different orbit than the comet nucleus does, usually also with a slightly different period of revolution about the Sun. Thus, the larger bits of debris gradually get ahead of the nucleus, or lag behind it. They gradually spread around the entire orbit of the comet, although this process may take many thousands of years. The bits of debris also travel along orbits slightly displaced from the orbit of the nucleus. The result is finally a kind of tube of orbiting debris spread around the whole orbit of the comet nucleus. Eventually, if the Earth passes close to this debris tube, or through it, the Earth will be showered with bits of escaped comet grains – even though the comet may be nowhere nearby in its orbit. This is the reason that *annual* meteor showers are associated with some periodically returning comets or past comets.

Each time a comet passes through the inner solar system, it loses millions of tonnes of gas and dust. Each passage will produce a new cloud of dust that for a while orbits near the comet nucleus, but eventually spreads out over the entire orbit along with debris from earlier passes through the inner solar system. If the Earth encounters one of these clouds of recently ejected debris before the cloud can disperse around the orbit, a spectacular meteor storm may be seen on Earth. The great meteor storms produced several times in the past couple of centuries by the Leonids were due to the passage of the Earth through exactly such clouds of relatively undispersed debris.

Exercise: You observe a comet night after night as it recedes from the inner solar system. As the coma shrinks to an almost invisible halo, you discover that the brightness of the nucleus appears to vary regularly, rising and falling by about 20% every 4.5 hours. What is the probable cause of these variations?

Comas

In our efforts to learn about the nucleus of a comet, we have already looked at how the coma is produced by sublimation of gases from the nucleus. Now we want to look more closely at the actual structure of the coma itself. Let us examine the distribution in space of the gas around the comet nucleus. A surprising result is that we will find that different chemical constituents (H, C_2, etc.,) form comas of different sizes.

Gas sublimes from the nucleus of a comet and flows outward with a typical velocity of roughly 0.5 $\mathrm{km\,s^{-1}}$. This speed is determined observationally, for example from measurements of the expansion rates of rings or halos sometimes observed when a burst of nuclear activity (the blowout of a gas pocket, for example) occurs. This typical speed is also expected from the theory of subliming gases: 0.5 $\mathrm{km\,s^{-1}}$ is the typical speed of a molecule in a gas with a temperature of, say, 300 K, due to the heat energy of motion (kinetic energy) that it possesses. Since the comet's gravity is quite weak, the subliming gas expands essentially freely into the space around the nucleus with roughly the mean thermal speed of the individual gas molecules.

If the expanding gas stayed constant in chemical composition and expanded at a uniform speed, the number of molecules of any particular type (say CN) passing per second through any sphere centred on the nucleus would be the same, so as one looked farther and farther from the nucleus at larger and larger spheres, the same number of molecules would be spread over a larger area and the volume density of molecules would drop (as $1/d^2$, where d is the distance from the nucleus). However, the chemical composition does not stay constant throughout the outflowing gas. It is believed that active molecules (also called radicals) such as CN are *not* actually present in large amounts in the nucleus, but are fragments of larger molecules (possibly HCN or CH_3CN?) that *are* found in the nucleus and that are broken apart not far out from the nucleus by absorption of ultraviolet photons from the Sun ("photo-dissociation") or perhaps sometimes by collision with high speed protons or electrons of the solar wind ("collisional dissociation"). Thus within about 10^4 km of the nucleus, a molecule like CN is actively being created (as a breakup fragment) in the flow near the nucleus, so its density falls off with distance from the nucleus more slowly than $1/d^2$. On the other hand, radicals such as CN can in turn be broken up by photo-dissociation (or collisional dissociation), although more slowly than their parent molecules; by the time a CN molecule has gotten roughly 5×10^5 km from the nucleus, it is quite likely to have been broken apart. Thus the CN coma (seen by an observer who is taking pictures through a filter that lets through the bright CN emission lines near 3883 Å, for example) has a fairly sharp outer edge set by the dissociation of CN. Since the lifetime before dissociation of C_2 is only a little shorter than that of CN, the C_2 coma (observed through a filter that passes one of the strong emission lines of C_2) is only a little smaller than the CN coma.

The hydrogen coma (which is not visible by eye) is much larger than the C_2 or CN comas; it sometimes extends out to $\sim 10^7$ km. This is due to two facts: first, the hydrogen atoms are ionized (again by ultraviolet photons from the Sun, or by collisions with solar wind particles) rather more slowly than CH or C_2 are dissociated, since much more energy is needed to ionize an atom of H than to disrupt most diatomic molecules. Secondly, the outflow velocity of the H gas is several times faster than the flow of CN or C_2, apparently because much of the H originates from the breakup of OH molecules, a breakup in which a lot of kinetic energy is given to the ejected H atom. Thus, the structure of the H coma is controlled by the same physics as the molecular coma, but rates of the essential processes are different, and the result is a coma more than ten times larger than the C_2 or CN comas.

Note that it is possible to observe the C_2 and CN comas in images taken in visible light through appropriate filters, and in fact the coma seen by eye during the passage of a bright comet is primarily due to sunlight absorbed and then re-radiated (by resonance fluorescence) in all directions by these molecules. In contrast, the H coma does not lead to any significant effect visible by eye. A neutral H atom ejected from the comet nucleus almost always has its single electron in the lowest energy level, from which it can easily absorb (and then re-emit) only photons far in the ultraviolet part of the spectrum. The result is that the H coma is only detectable using an ultraviolet-sensitive imager, which of course must be outside the Earth's atmosphere (which is opaque to ultraviolet radiation).

Tails

The most spectacular feature of a comet is often its tail. This part of the visible comet may be millions of km long, and if the comet passes close to the Earth, it may stretch across a considerable part of the sky. The remarkable aspect of the tail is that, unlike the coma, which is roughly spherical, the tail is extremely elongated. Furthermore, when the orientation in space of the tail relative to the comet's position is worked out, it is found that the tail always points out into space approximately on the opposite side of the comet from the Sun. Thus, as the comet enters the inner solar system, the tail lags behind the nucleus and coma; while the comet is passing closest to the Sun the tail extends outward from the coma on the side of the comet away from the Sun, and as the comet leaves again it is preceded by its tail. We thus deduce that tails are produced somehow by a repulsive effect coming from the Sun.

As mentioned above, we observe two quite different kinds of tails, one that seems to be mainly composed of dust grains, and another that is made up of *ionized* gas molecules. A comet may have mainly one kind of tail or the other, or even both kinds at once. We thus expect that we may have to find two different repulsive forces that act on these very different particles. An additional clue to the forces acting is provided by the fact that knots and clouds in a dust tail drift away from the coma only rather slowly, so that the dust grains must be only weakly accelerated away from the Sun, while blobs in the ion tail leave the coma at a far greater speed.

Figure 7.6: An image of Comet Hale-Bopp taken in 1995 when the comet was close to the Earth. Unlike Comet Hyakutake (Figure 7.1), this comet had a prominent double tail. The faint tail on the left is a gas tail, like that of Comet Hyakutake, while the brighter unstructured tail on the right is the comet's dust tail. This image appears in colour on the back cover of the book. (Courtesy of Dominique Dierick)

In fact we do find that two different mechanisms are at work, each operating effectively only on certain kinds of particles. First, the outward flow of *photons* from the Sun exerts an outward force on the gas and dust of the coma. This force is quite insignificant on molecules, atoms, and ions, which can only absorb or scatter photons of a few specific colours while all photons of the wrong colours pass by without interacting (see Chapter 2). In contrast, dust grains absorb or scatter photons of all colours, and the pressure of sunlight on them can be significant. Secondly, the comet is immersed in the very low-density hot gas that flows away from the Sun, the *solar wind* (see Chapter 3). This gas flow carries with it a (very weak) magnetic field that is pulled out of the solar atmosphere. Because of this entrained magnetic field, the solar wind is able to affect atoms and molecules in the coma that are ionized; these ionized atoms and molecules can be swept out of the coma into long tenuous tail structures pointing almost directly away from the Sun. There is thus a good reason that two major kinds of comet tail occur: they contain different kinds of particles and are accelerated by rather different physical mechanisms.

The nature of dust tails is fairly well understood. Really small dust particles (with sizes ranging up to the limit set by the rate of gas loss from the nucleus, and sometimes larger if a blow-out occurs) are swept out of the comet nucleus into the coma. At first these dust grains simply move away from the nucleus with the outflowing gas of the coma. The flow of photons of (mostly visible) light from the Sun exerts a steady pressure on the particles of the coma in a direction away from the Sun. The pressure of sunlight on atoms and molecules is quite small because most photons do not have the specific colours that can be absorbed by any particular atom or ion. Thus, little momentum is transferred to the molecules and atoms. There is also rather little pressure on really small dust grains, ones that have diameters less than about 1/3 or 1/4 of the wavelength of visible light (i.e. grains with diameters less than about 0.1 μm, which however may still contain some 10^8 or 10^9 atoms). This is because it is a general property of waves (such as light) that they do not readily interact with obstacles that are much smaller than a wavelength in size. (This behaviour is readily observed on a larger scale at the seashore. Incoming waves, with wavelengths of some meters, are completely unaffected by wooden pilings, such as those that support piers, because these pilings have much smaller diameters — perhaps 0.2m—than a wavelength. At the other extreme, the incoming waves are completely blocked by breakwaters or moles with lengths of many tens of meters, even if these are isolated structures well offshore.) Dust particles larger than about 0.1 μm in diameter are large enough to effectively block outflowing sunlight, and so a force acts on them that is proportional to the surface area presented by the grain to sunlight. However, even though the *force* outward due to sunlight is larger for larger grains, its *importance* decreases as the grain size increases because the larger grains have considerably bigger masses than smaller grains and hence are more difficult to accelerate. An example will make this clearer: a 10 μm grain has 10^2 more light collecting area than a similar 1 μm grain, and hence the pressure of sunlight on it is roughly 100 times larger than on the smaller grain. However, it has 10^3 times more mass, so the acceleration due to the pressure of sunlight is $10^2/10^3 = 1/10$ as large for the larger grain as it is for the smaller. For this reason only a rather limited range of sizes of dust grains (about 0.1 to a few μm diameters) from the coma are strongly affected by sunlight. The much larger particles that contribute to visible meteor showers are only slightly affected by solar radiation.

Even those dust grains that do feel strongly the pressure of sunlight are not necessarily accelerated enough to be actively driven out of the solar system. That is, the acceleration of solar gravity may be larger than that caused by the pressure of sunlight. But even if the radiation pressure on a grain exerts a force that is only a fraction of the force of solar gravity, this can still substantially change the orbit followed by the grain around the Sun compared to the orbit followed by the comet nucleus, once the grain is far enough from the nucleus to be largely unaffected by the gas flow. As the comet nucleus falls towards the Sun, the grains fall towards the Sun as well, but with different, smaller accelerations. They thus drift away from the nucleus, not back along the orbit followed by the nucleus (as they would if the comet were plowing through a resisting medium or facing a head wind) but *outside* it, as shown in Figure 7.7. Different parts of the tail are made up of particles released from the nucleus at different times. In general, all these dust particles lie nearly in the plane of the orbit of the nucleus.

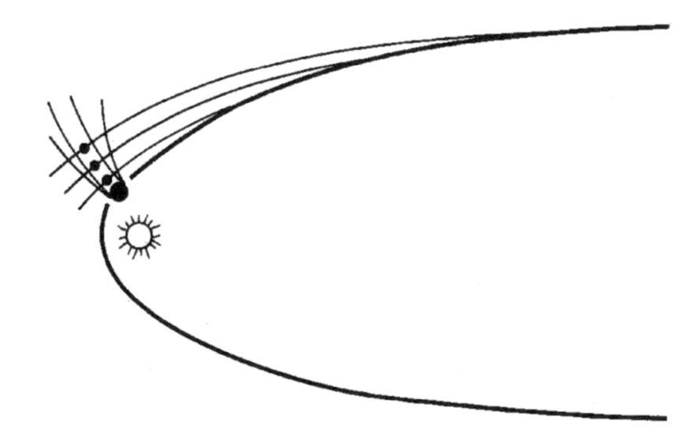

Figure 7.7: The orbit of the nucleus of a comet is shown as a heavy curved line. Light lines indicate the (less curved) orbits followed by dust grains of a particular size released from the nucleus at different times; they move along their orbits at nearly the same speed as the nucleus moves along its orbit and so at a particular instant they may be found spread out away from the nucleus as indicated.

The situation is actually somewhat more complicated than suggested above, because even among the dust grains ejected at one time, grains of different sizes feel different repulsive forces and hence follow different orbits. In spite of this complication, it is possible, from the observations of the appearance of the tail at a series of times, to deduce how rapidly dust is being ejected from the nucleus at various places in its orbit. It is (not surprisingly) found that the dust emission rate from the nucleus normally increases strongly as the comet approaches and passes perihelion, after which the dust ejection rate subsides. From the amount of dust ejected into the tail we can also estimate the total rate of outflow of gas from the nucleus that sweeps the dust particles into the coma; for an active comet near 1 AU this gas loss rate is typically about 10^{30} molecules per second, or several tonnes of material each second. It is possible from this number to estimate the total loss of mass during an entire cometary apparition; for a bright comet such as Comet Bennett (C/1969 Y1), the total mass loss during one passage is roughly 10^{11} kg = 100 million tonnes, or about 0.1 km^3 of ice!

In contrast to dust tails, the physical mechanisms leading to the observed ion tails are not yet very well understood. It is clear that such tails are produced by interactions between the solar wind and the coma, since the gas in an ion tail is observed to be blown almost directly away from the Sun at a much higher acceleration than would be caused by the force of radiation pressure on the ions; the solar wind, travelling at a few hundred km s^{-1} is able to enforce high speed. The fact that the observed constituents of an ion tail (CO^+, $N_2{}^+$, etc.) are all ionized is also consistent with acceleration caused by the solar wind: the electric charge of these ions makes them able to interact with the solar wind's magnetic field, unlike the neutral molecules which are almost unaffected by this wind.

Recall from Chapter 3 that the solar wind is a gas of protons and electrons (ionised H atoms) moving outward from the Sun at about 500 km s^{-1}. The density of this gas is roughly 10^6 m^{-3}, or one particle per cm^3. The gas carries with it a weak magnetic field of about 10γ ($1\gamma = 10^{-5}\text{G} = 10^{-9}\text{T}$) that is pulled out of the solar atmosphere and wound into a spiral shape by the rotation of the Sun. The comet nucleus and coma plow into this wind as the comet falls towards the Sun. Except for rare direct collisions with electrons or protons of the solar wind, the neutral molecules and atoms of the coma are in the main completely unaffected by the solar wind. But as cometary molecules expand away from the nucleus, they gradually become ionised, partly by photoionisation due to ultraviolet photons from the Sun, partly by collisions with solar wind protons and electrons, and probably also by chemical reactions near the nucleus. As molecules are ionised, they suddenly find themselves strongly affected by the magnetic field carried in the solar wind; in fact, they are forced to spiral around single magnetic field lines, and thus are swept along by the wind away from the nucleus in the direction away from the Sun. This in turn loads down the magnetic field lines near the nucleus, and produces a disturbance some 10^6 km across in the solar wind flow, somewhat like the expanding bow wave from a speeding motor boat. The bow wave in usually called the **bow shock** or **shock front**. Inside the shock front, the solar wind is quite distorted; its magnetic field lines are draped around the inner part of the coma, and solar wind particles are forced to avoid passing close to the comet's nucleus. The solar wind particles are completely excluded from a region near the nucleus about 10^4 km across, a volume which is controlled by outflowing coma ions. The flow of the solar wind around this obstacle leaves a void downwind from the nucleus (like a wind sock). The boundary between the region of pure cometary atoms and ions and the region containing both solar wind particles and coma particles is called the **ionopause**. The ion tail forms along the magnetic field lines that are looped around the coma. The situation is sketched in Figure 7.8.

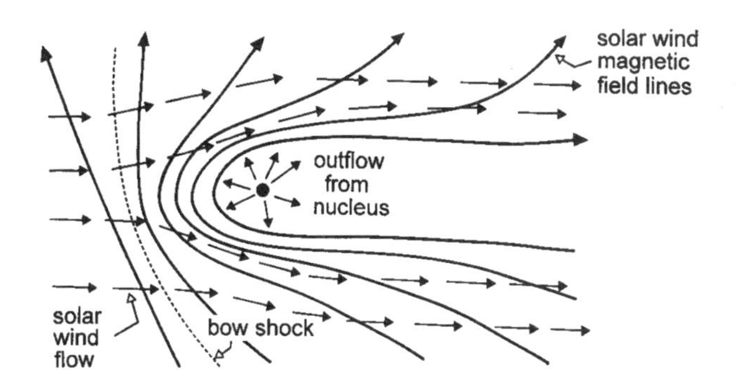

Figure 7.8: A schematic diagram showing the interaction of the outflowing solar wind with a comet (which by comparison to the solar wind is almost standing still). The bow shock is the region in the solar wind, upstream from the comet nucleus, where the impact of the comet on the solar wind sharply changes the temperature of solar wind gas particles and the direction of the solar wind magnetic field; this occurs roughly 10^6 km in front of the comet. The ionopause, where the outflow from the comet forces the solar wind to flow around the comet, is at a typical distance of 10^4 km from the nucleus. At this boundary the cometary outflow creates a sort of wind sock from which both the solar wind particles and magnetic field embedded in the solar wind are excluded. Note that the relative size of the region dominated by comet outflow is greatly exaggerated in this diagram.

The general nature of this comet—solar wind interaction is now fairly well understood. What is not well understood are the details by which the observed ion tail is formed. We do not clearly understand how molecules are ionised as rapidly and copiously as they are. We do not know how molecular ions collect into visibly patchy blobs as they sweep out into the tail. Nor do we really understand why the ion tails are so narrow compared to the overall size of the disturbed region of the solar wind. Even with the limitations of our theories, however, comets can serve as very useful probes of the solar wind, especially close to the Sun or far from it, or well out of the ecliptic plane, where it is difficult to send space probes.

7.4 Space probes to Comet Halley

The model described above of the structure of a comet was developed before it was possible to actually visit one. In 1986, at the time that Halley's comet passed through the inner solar system, many of these ideas were put to a direct test by several spacecraft that were sent to observe the comet directly.

Actually visiting a comet is not as easy as it may seem. Two major problems arise. First, a lot of advance notice of the arrival of the comet is needed, so that there is time to design, construct, and launch the space probe and its experiments to encounter the comet. Building even a fairly modest space vehicle is a large (and expensive) undertaking, and the decision to go ahead with a project is normally taken several years before the spacecraft is actually launched. Furthermore, if the probe is intended to pass close to the nucleus of the comet, then the position of this nucleus must be accurately known, to within a few tens or hundreds of km at any given moment. This requires a very well-known orbit. But bright new comets, such as Hale-Bopp and Hyakutake, are rarely discovered more than about six months before they pass the Sun, and their orbits are only know with precision after they have been observed through one full passage into the inner solar system. Since we do not know in advance that such a comet will appear, or what its orbit will be, we cannot plan to visit it. Only encounters with well-known periodic comets are practical at present.

A second problem arises from the fact that the Earth and the comet nucleus are moving rather rapidly relative to one another. Typically, as a comet passes the Earth's orbit, it has a velocity (relative to the Sun) of the order of about 42 km s^{-1} (the Earth's orbital velocity is 30 km s^{-1}). If the comet's orbit is direct (the comet moves around the Sun in the same sense that the Earth does) and approximately in the plane of the ecliptic, when it passes Earth it will have a speed relative to Earth of at least 10 km s^{-1}. If its closest approach to the Sun is at much less than one AU, or the orbit is retrograde, the relative speed of Earth and the comet can be as large as 70 km s^{-1}. Now a space probe sent to encounter a comet will have a velocity different from that of Earth, but the difference between its speed and that of the comet will still generally be some tens of km s^{-1}. This relative speed creates a problem because of the steady loss of small bits of dust and rock as the ices binding these fragments to the comet nucleus sublimate. The fragments move away from the comet at a relatively small speed; that is, they keep nearly the same speed relative to the Sun that the comet has. Thus, if the space probe collides with one of these bits of debris, the piece of debris will strike the probe at typically 10 km s^{-1} (or more!), at least 10 times the speed of a bullet fired from a gun. It does not take a very large piece of debris (a few grams would suffice) striking the probe to do a lot of damage. Thus it is quite dangerous to a spacecraft to get too close to the comet nucleus, especially if the comet orbit is retrograde.

As we have seen, Comet 1P/Halley is the brightest and most active periodic comet currently passing through the inner solar system. It returns every 76 years on average, and by now its orbit is extremely well known. The expected return of this bright comet to the inner solar system early in 1986 presented an exciting possibility for a rendezvous, and one with plenty of advance notice. Europe, the Soviet Union, and Japan decided to send missions to the comet as it passed the Sun. (U. S. participation in this venture was minimal because almost all NASA's funding in the early 1980's was tied up in other projects.) Because the orbit of Halley's comet is retrograde, the space probes encountered the comet at relative speeds of about 70 km s^{-1}, so the danger of impact of even very small dust particles was severe. Collision with a particle only one cm across would have been enough to completely destroy a probe. Careful planning of probe trajectories and equipment was important; several of the probes were fitted with armoured shields, and the smaller probes were designed to pass the comet at rather great distances.

Exercise: Explain why a space probe is in more danger from collisions with debris from a comet when it is close to the nucleus than when it is far away.

The probes involved in the comet encounter carried a variety of instruments designed to examine various aspects of the cometary environment and the nucleus. Conditions in the undisturbed solar wind on the sunward side of the comet were measured by the Japanese probe Sakigake and the U. S. probe ICE. Both Sakigake and ICE passed the comet at a relatively safe distance of closest approach of about 10^7 km. A second Japanese probe, Suisei, passed through the bow shock on the sunward side of the comet at a closest approach of about 10^5 km, and sent back measurements of conditions behind the shock front. Two Soviet probes, Vega-1 and Vega-2, passed through the interior of the bow shock and came within about 9000 km of the nucleus. These probes sent back measurements of conditions behind the shock front and also some images of the distant nucleus. But the most ambitious mission was the Giotto probe, launched by the European Space Agency and named after the famous 14th century Italian painter who had included Halley's comet in a fresco created shortly after its apparition in 1301. The Giotto probe actually entered the comet's ionosphere and passed within 600 km of the nucleus. This probe not only provided many kinds of measurements of conditions in the pure cometary gas around the nucleus, but also obtained the first clear direct images of a comet nucleus. Together, these probes provided many measurements that enabled us to test and confirm our previous ideas about the properties of the nucleus and coma of a comet.

Measurements by instruments on several of the probes detected newly ionized H ions from the comet as much as 8 million km away from the nucleus. This represented the approximate outer limit of the hydrogen coma of the comet, about where this limit was expected. At about 1 million km from the nucleus, the outer limit of the 40,000 km thick shock front, where the plasma of the comet plows into the solar wind (see Figure 7.8), was detected. Inside this shock front, the flow speed of the solar wind slowed down, the temperature of solar wind ions increased dramatically, and the solar wind became turbulent. But the solar wind is not prevented out here from approaching closer to the comet nucleus. Instead, the bow shock marks the front edge of the region where the magnetic field lines begin to drape around the head of the comet. The real boundary between solar wind and comet gases, the ionopause – where the solar wind particles and their magnetic field are actually prevented from approaching any closer to the nucleus by the pressure of outflow from the comet – was found by Giotto at about 4,600 km from the nucleus of the comet. Inside the ionopause, Giotto's instruments showed that the solar wind's magnetic field is completely absent, and the gas is pure outflowing cometary gas at about 300 K.

One of the main tasks of Giotto was to determine the chemical composition of this gas near the nucleus, before the gas has had time to be much changed by destructive collisions with solar wind ions and solar photons. Combining Giotto's results with those from remote measurements by other probes and from Earth, it is found that that the gas near the nucleus of Halley's comet is about 80% water, 10% CO, 3% CO_2, 2% CH_4, less than 1.5% NH_3, and 0.1% hydrocyanic acid. The composition found by the probes confirms that a comet nucleus has a greatly different composition from that of a terrestrial planet or asteroid, much richer in ices relative to rocky material. Furthermore, the predominance of water ice over other ices, such as frozen methane and ammonia (which we had already deduced from the characteristic Sun-comet distance at which most cometary comas begin to develop strongly) was confirmed. However, it was a surprise to find that most of the carbon in the gas subliming from the nucleus is in oxidized molecules such as CO and CO_2 rather than bound together with H in CH_4 as one might have expected from the enormous abundance of H relative to the abundance of O in the proto-solar nebula. This finding appears to show that the carbon molecules in the comet's nucleus were mostly left in the molecules in which they were bound in interstellar clouds before the solar system formed, and were not much altered by chemical reactions as the outer part of the solar nebula shrank.

The chemistry of many tiny dust particles was also determined. Some of the dust particles were found to have a similar composition to rocks, with relative proportions of the abundant refractory elements Mg, Si, and Fe (and the O that they combine with) that are similar to the proportions in the Sun. This is clearly the dust most people were expecting. However, a large number of dust grains were also observed that had high high abundances of the elements C, H, O and N, probably in the form of a variety of organic molecules. These particles, often called CHON particles, were not anticipated. Apparently the dust in comets in not just tiny fragments of rocky material, but much of it is also in the form of condensed organic molecules. These organic dust particles are gradually destroyed by ultraviolet photons from the Sun, and so contribute some light molecules to the coma. However, much of the organic material in the nucleus remains hidden in the CHON dust grains for long enough to have escaped detection from the Earth. Including the CHON grains when the composition of the nucleus is estimated brings the relative abundances of some of the light elements, particularly C and O, to nearly the relative abundances found in the Sun. It thus appears that comet nuclear material is closer to solar compostion than even the carbonaceous chondrite meteorites, (see Chapter 5), and thus is probably the least altered remmnant of the original solar nebula. Comet nuclei contain very important clues about conditions in that nebula during the inital stages of formation of the solar system.

One of the most exciting results of the Giotto mission was the return of direct images of the nucleus, obtained from a distance of about 600 km. These show, for the first time ever, the actual shape and structure of the nucleus of a comet. Halley's nucleus is shaped somewhat like peanut or a potato, about 16 km long and 8 km in diameter across its waist. The size is considerably larger than most people had expected. The reflectivity (albedo) of the nucleus was unexpectedly found to be only 4% (darker than a lump of coal), making Halley's comet one of the darkest objects in the solar system. Still another surprise was the observation that the gas evaporating from the comet is coming from vents or jets on only about 10% of the comet's surface, and these vents are as dark as the rest of the nucleus. The remaining 90% of the comet is apparently covered with a thick dust crust through which the gas does not escape, perhaps because the gas under this crust is hardly heated by the Sun. A composite image of the nucleus of the comet obtained by Giotto is shown in Figure 7.9. This image shows the irregular shape of the nucleus and the jets of escaping gas clearly.

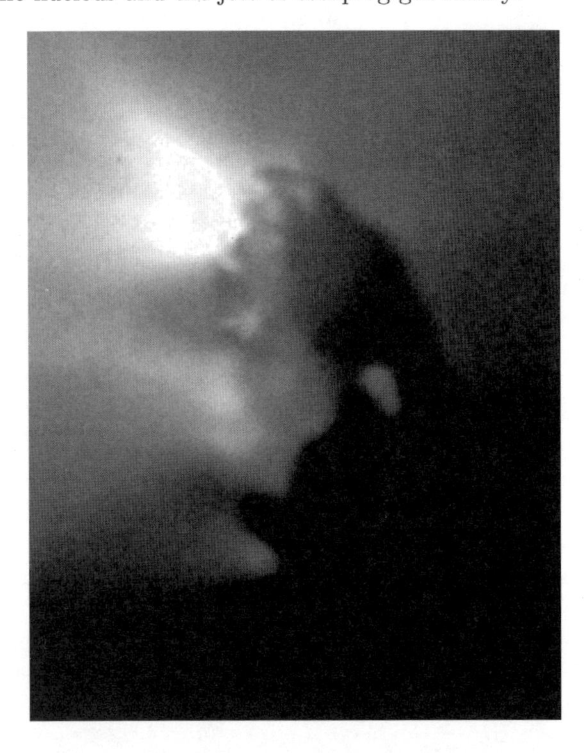

Figure 7.9: An image of the nucleus of Halley's comet obtained by the Giotto space probe from a distance of about 600 km. The dark blob on the right of the image is the unlit side of the comet (the Sun is to the left of the image). The somewhat brighter, similar blob on the left is the lit (but very poorly reflecting) side of the comet. The brilliant fan of light at upper left is light reflecting from gas escaping from the most active jet; the light area in the middle left is a less active jet. The length of the nucleus is about 16 km. Image courtesy of the European Space Agency.

Combining the surprisingly large measured dimensions of the nucleus with the mass of about 10^{11} tonnes estimated from the orbit changes due to non-gravitational (jet) forces, we deduce a mean nucleus density of the order of 300 kg m^{-3}, substantially smaller than the density of water. This strongly suggests that much of the comet's nucleus is honeycombed with voids and tunnels created by evaporation of ices from the interior of the comet during previous passes through the inner solar system, and perhaps by the imperfect fitting together of planetesimals that collided to form the comet nucleus.

The rate of flow of gas subliming from the nucleus of Halley's comet was measured. From observations of the number of gas molecules per cubic meter and of their outflow speed, a gas loss rate of about 20 tonnes per second was deduced. In addition, the nucleus was found (from measurements of impact rates of tiny dust particles on the probe) to be losing dust at a rate of between 3 and 10 tonnes per second. During the 1986 passage through the inner solar system it is estimated that the comet lost about 10^8 tonnes from the 10^{11} tonne nucleus; apparently the comet still has enough material for at least another hundred passages through the inner solar system before its gas will be exhausted.

The observations obtained by these spacecraft as they passed Halley's comet clearly confirm the general picture that astronomers have developed of comet structure and of the interaction of the coma with the solar wind. However, there were extremely important surprises in the new data: the oxidized form of carbon in the outflowing gas, the small fraction of the nucleus from which gas escapes, the large size, low density and very dark surface of the nucleus, the large fraction of the escaping dust which is in the form of organic grains, etc. Close-up observations of this famous comet as it passed the Sun were certainly worth the effort necessary to design and deploy the fleet of spacecraft.

7.5 Origin and evolution of comets

Source region for recent comets

Finally, we need to the ask where comets come from. Why do they suddenly appear in the inner solar system with no previous warning? Have the comets we now see (Halley's comet, Hyakutake, Hale-Bopp, etc) been regular (although infrequent) visitors to the inner solar system since the formation of the planets, or are these particular comets short-lived objects, which replaced earlier comets that have vanished, and which will in turn be replaced in the future by other comets? This question will bring us full circle, back to a consideration of cometary orbits again.

We can start by considering whether the comets that

we have observed entering the inner solar system in recent centuries could possibly continue to produce a coma and tail on each entry into the planetary region for a time as long as the age of the solar system. If this is possible, than perhaps the currently visible comets have been returning for billions of years. If not, then presently visible comets must be relative newcomers to the inner solar system.

We have seen above that Halley's comet loses some 10^8 tonnes of gas and dust on each passage through the inner solar system. This is probably a typical mass loss for most comets that come within one AU of the Sun, give or take a factor of ten. The nucleus of Halley's comet has a typical size of about 10 km and a mass of some 10^{11} tonnes. Both of these numbers are also fairly typical of comets. But if Halley's comet loses 0.1% of its total mass on each passage through the inner solar system, it only contains enough material to produce the comet phenomenon for about 1000 ($= 10^{11}/10^8$) passes through the inner solar system. Since it returns about once per century, we conclude that Halley's comet will continue to amaze future generations for at most about 10^5 years into the future. And since all the dimensions of Halley's comet are typical enough of other comets, we conclude that generally comets will only be able to support the creation of a coma for perhaps 10^2 to 10^4 passsages through the inner solar system. The very largest may manage 10^5 returns before exhausting their supply of volatiles.

When a comet passes through the inner solar system, one of the things astronomers study is its orbit. The orbits of all the bright comets that have entered the inner solar system in roughly the past three hundred years, since the time of Halley, have been determined. Many of these orbits are found to be closed: the comets return to the inner solar system regularly, time after time. The characteristic periods of return mostly range all the way from a few years up to millions of years. Many comets have return periods of thousands or tens of thousands of years; Halley's comet returns approximately every 75 years, while Comet Hale-Bopp visited the inner solar system 4600 years ago, more recently in 1997, and will return in about another 2600 years. Such comets, if they continue to return to the inner solar system with periods of 10^3 or 10^4 years, will use up their volatiles in a few million years or less. We are forced to conclude that the particular bright comets with periods of 10^3 years or so that we now see have *not* been coming regularly into the inner solar system since its beginning 4.5 Gyr years ago – if they had, they would have long since exhausted their volatiles and ceased to be visible as comets. Only the very longest-period comets might conceivably still be active after one Gyr. To account for the currently observed comets with periods of tens of thousands of years or less, we have to assume that new comets must be continually introduced into the inner solar system somehow, from somewhere else. Where are these potential comets stored, and how are they finally introduced into the inner solar system?

The key clue that enables us to answer these questions is found by studying the orbits of the many comets that have been carefully observed over the past three centuries. A few examples are given in Table 7.2. From these orbital studies, it seems clear that two different populations of comets are observed. One family is made up of comets that have orbital periods of about 200 years or less, and thus orbital semi-major axes of less than about 35 AU. These comets, of which more than 100 are known, are called short-period comets. They orbit essentially in among the planets. Their orbits are often direct and not very inclined to the plane of the ecliptic. The second family, with long periods (more than 200 years), includes over 300 comets. These comets mostly have very elongated orbits which can have any orientation with respect to the plane of the planetary orbits. Because these comets have long (or very long!) periods, they generally have only been seen once in historical times, and their actual orbital periods and semi-major axes are only estimated, not accurately known. Our conclusion above that many comets have entered the inner solar system only recently from somewhere else certainly applies to the short-period comets, but also applies to a significant fraction of the long-period comets. Thus we need to study the sources of comets of both families, although the two families may have different origins.

There are two obvious possibilities for the origin of comets. One is that they could wander freely through interstellar space among the other stars, and thus enter the solar system from the outside. If this is the origin of comets, we must discover ways in which such interstellar wanderers could be captured into closed orbits in the solar system. The other possibility is that comets are already members of the solar system, but normally orbit far outside the planetary region. In this case, we need to identify a means of causing a steady flow of such bodies into the inner solar system.

Following arguments presented by Laplace in 1813, it was long thought likely that long-period comets originate in interstellar space. Laplace argued that the comets of shorter periods would result from the perturbing effects of Jupiter on the orbits of interstellar comets passing by chance through the inner solar system. However, there are two important objections to this idea. First, when **original orbits** of long-period comets are computed – the orbits they follow as they come into the inner solar system, before these orbits are altered by the gravitational attraction of the giant planets – it is found that very few comets are moving fast enough at great distances from the Sun to have come into the solar system from the outside. Another way of stating this result is that as they approach the inner solar system for the first time, hardly any comets have large enough velocity to completely escape from the solar system, and these few have velocities that are only marginally large enough. Almost all observed comets appear to be bound to the Sun from the start, if only very weakly. If these comets entered the solar system from interstellar space, many would be expected (like the stars around the Sun) to have random motions of a few km s^{-1} before approaching the solar system, and thus should arrive with high enough velocity to escape easily again. The absence of *any* comets entering the planetary region with velocities large enough to easily escape from the solar system makes it seem unlikely that a significant number of comets arrive in the inner solar system from outside the sphere of influence of the Sun.

The second problem with the interstellar capture theory is a consequence of the fact that the Sun is moving through space, among the stars in its neighborhood, in the direction of the constellation Hercules at a speed of about 20 km s^{-1}. Because of this motion, we would expect that comets arriving from interstellar space would mainly enter the solar system from the hemisphere in the sky towards which the Sun is moving, just as raindrops fall more heavily on the front windshield of a rapidly moving car than on the back window. However, this effect is not observed at all; the orbits of the long-period comets are not clustered around the direction towards which the Sun is moving, but instead seem to be distributed randomly in all directions.

These arguments lead us to consider possible sources for comets in the outer solar system. In the 1940's and 1950's, work by the Dutch astronomers Adrianus Van Woerkom, Jan Oort, and Gerard Kuiper led to a new picture of where the comet nuclei are stored, and how they come to be sent into the inner solar system. This theory is now widely accepted.

We consider first where the comet nuclei are stored. A valuable clue is found by looking at the distribution of orbital semi-major axes (or periods) of the long-period comets, shown in Figure 7.10. This figure shows a histogram of the distribution of inverse semi-major axis $1/a$ of the initial orbits of some 200 comets. (This produces a more tractable figure than a plot of the distribution of a.) In this figure, $1/a$ is measured in AU^{-1}, so that a value of 0.001 on the x-axis corresponds to an orbit of semi-major axis a = 1000 AU and period of 31,600 years. As already mentioned, almost none of these comets arrived in the inner solar system with

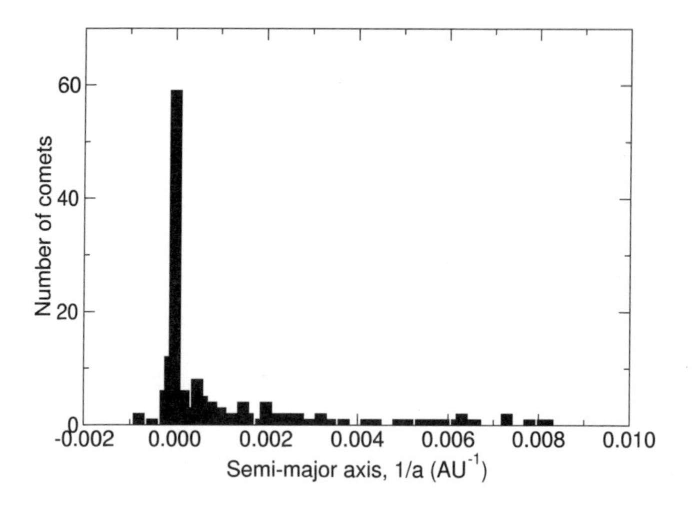

Figure 7.10: A histogram showing the number of comets whose orbits have various values of the semi-major axis a. The figure shows the distribution of orbit sizes for 175 comets, and includes almost all of the well-observed long period comets that entered the inner solar system before 1977. The value of a used for each orbit is the "original" value, the semi-major axis of the orbit as the comet entered the planetary region from the outside, before the orbit was altered by the gravitational effects of the giant planets. (Data from Marsden, Sekanina, and Everhart 1978, Astron. J. 83, 64.)

enough energy to escape into interstellar space; in this diagram, such unbound comets have $1/a < 0$. Instead, a large number of the comets (about one-third of all the comets included in the figure) are found to have semi-major axes of the order of 20,000 AU ($1/a = 0.00005$ AU^{-1}) and periods of millions of years.

In 1950, Oort recognized that this clump of long period comets probably represents the source of such comets. He proposed that a huge cloud of comet nuclei exists in 'cold storage' around the solar system. This cloud, which we now call the **Oort cloud**, probably extends out to the largest distances dominated by the gravity of the Sun, perhaps out to about 10^5 AU, halfway to the nearest stars. The comets with a values around 20,000 AU are coming into the solar system from this cloud.

But if comet nuclei normally orbit the solar system at huge distances outside the planetary region, we need to explain how a continual trickle of new comets is sent into the inner solar system. Oort showed that this is the natural result of motions of other stars near the Sun. As nearby stars drift by the Sun in various directions, they pass through the Oort cloud and gently stir the orbits of the comet nuclei that come near them. Most of the comet nuclei affected go into new orbits that still keep them at huge distances from the inner solar system, but a few of these icy bodies are deflected into orbits that carry them in among the planets as new comets. Since this stirring effect of nearby stars goes on almost continuously, new comets are regularly injected into the inner solar system.

Another effect that acts to change the orbits of comets far from the Sun is the tidal action of the disk of the Milky Way (and to a lesser extent of the bulge). Because a comet with $a \sim 10^4$ AU is usually far from the Sun, the acceleration of the comet by the galaxy is slightly different from the acceleration given to the Sun. As a result, the orbit of the comet nucleus *relative to the Sun* steadily changes. It has been found by mathematically following the orbits of many imaginary comets for hundreds of revolutions around the Sun that this effect can gradually change the orbital eccentricity of distant comet nuclei enough to send some of them into the inner solar system. Combining these two sources of cometary orbit perturbations, we estimate that to account for the observed rate of injection of new comets into the the planetary region, there must be some 10^{12} comet nuclei stored in the far reaches of the Oort cloud.

Once a long-period comet is deflected into an orbit that carries it into the region of the planets, that orbit is altered on every passage through the inner solar system by the gravitational effects of the planets, particularly Jupiter and Saturn. The orbit size and period thus change. Many new comets are ejected completely from the solar system after one passage through the planets. For others, the effect is to decrease the semi-major axis. This produces the population of comets of smaller a that is seen in Figure 7.10. Each pass through the inner solar system typically leads to a change in $1/a$ of roughly 0.001 (corresponding to a velocity change of less than 1 km s^{-1}). Eventually, some long-period comets are changed by further planetary gravitational perturbations into intermediate-period ones. They still, however, retain their random orbital inclinations, and thus both long- and intermediate-period comets enter the inner solar system from all directions.

The fact that quite a number of the comets in Figure 7.10 have $1/a \approx 0.0001$ while all the larger values of $1/a$ have smaller comet numbers is probably caused by the fact that the very first passage of a new comet through the inner solar system leads to much more rapid outgassing and thus a much brighter coma and tail than are produced on subsequent passages, when the nucleus has developed a crust of left-over rocky solids. For this reason, such comets are much less likely to be discovered on subsequent returns. Thus 'first-time ever' comets are over-represented in the figure.

The short-period comets whose orbits are not very inclined to the ecliptic plane seem to have a different origin than the long-period comets. The reason we think so is that calculations have shown that it is very unlikely that an orbit strongly inclined to the ecliptic will be converted by planetary gravitational effects into an orbit lying nearly in the plane of the ecliptic. Thus we *cannot* account for the large family of comets in only slightly inclined, small orbits as a later stage in the lives of comet nuclei that earlier belonged to the family having large, randomly inclined orbits. Because of this difficulty, astronomers have suggested the existence of a second, much more compact belt of comet nuclei orbiting roughly in the ecliptic plane, just outside the outer planets. This belt is called the Kuiper belt after Gerard Kuiper, who first clearly proposed its existence. Calculations show that objects on the inside of this belt are slowly perturbed into orbits that enter the region of the planets by the gravitational effects of the giant planets, particularly Neptune, which in turn hands the comet nuclei on to Uranus, and so on down to Jupiter. Thus a stock of comet nuclei just outside the planets, orbiting in the plane of the ecliptic, is able to continuously supply the observed short-period comets.

The reality of the Kuiper belt was confirmed in 1992 when a small object orbiting at about 40 AU from the Sun was discovered. Hundreds of other objects have since been found in this region, outside the orbit of Neptune, orbiting the Sun between 30 and 50 AU. The objects found so far are very likely among the largest bodies in the trans-Neptunian zone, and range in diameter from about 100 to about 1000 km, ten or more times the diameter of a large comet nucleus like that of Halley's comet. In size, they more nearly resemble asteroids than comets, although at this distance from the Sun they are probably composed, like the moons of the giant planets, largely of ices. As in the asteroid belt, we are virtually certain that these larger bodies are accompanied by a huge number of smaller objects, also mostly icy bodies, which are quite suitable to be nuclei of comets. (The tiny, unique planet Pluto, with a diameter of only 2300 km, and its moon Charon, 1100 km in diameter, are reasonably considered to be the largest members of the Kuiper belt, although we also continue to think of Pluto as a planet.)

Exercise: You discover a new comet. As it passes the orbit of Mars, it is observed to be moving some 15 km s^{-1} faster than any previously recorded comet at this distance from the Sun. What would you be tempted to conclude about the *origin* of your comet, and why?

Origin of the Oort cloud and the Kuiper belt

The realization that comets we observe at present originate in the Kuiper belt (the short-period comets) or

Figure 7.11: A Hubble Space Telescope image of the nearly twenty pieces of Comet Shoemaker-Levy 9 on their final, fatal approach to Jupiter. Each fragment of the comet is surrounded by its own small coma. (Courtesy of NASA.)

the Oort cloud (intermediate- and long-period comets) does not completely solve the question of origins. We have discussed in Chapter 4 how the solar system was probably formed, but this discussion did not extend beyond the region of the planets. Probably the region of planetesimal accumulation did actually extend far enough beyond Neptune to account for the material now found in the Kuiper belt. It is not too suprising that the planetesimals that accumulated beyond Neptune did not accumulate to form anything larger than Pluto and the asteroid-like objects that have been found so far in the Kuiper belt; the density of the early solar nebula would probably have been rather low out here, and so planetesimals would have been much farther apart than those formed near Jupiter, and correspondingly less likely to collide and to accumulate into large bodies. Thus the Kuiper belt probably originated by the same process that we have already discussed for the planets, although this outlying material never aggregated into any very large bodies.

However, we cannot account so directly for the Oort cloud. Models of the solar nebula suggest that the density of the nebula at thousands of AU from the forming Sun would have been much too low to enable bodies of km diameter to accumulate by collisions of condensed ice and dust grains. To explain the billions of small bodies that now populate this dark and nearly empty volume of space, we need to look more closely at processes in the planetary region of the forming solar system. In the region where the giant planets formed, there must have been enormous numbers of small icy bodies of various sizes that accumulated out of the condensed dust and ices that froze out of the primitive solar nebula. Many of these bodies ended up accreting to form the cores of the giants. Many more were swept up by these giant planets as they grew and their gravitational attraction for nearby material increased. However, a huge number of these bodies would have passed near enough to one or another of the developing giant planets to be shot out into the space beyond the planet-forming region on a comet-like orbit. Thus we expect that once the giant planets were largely formed, the sweeping-up process that ensued would have resulted in only a part of the huge population of small planetesimals being captured by the giants. Probably an equal or greater number of planetesimals would have been ejected from the planetary region of the solar system into the vast spaces beyond, some to completely leave the solar system, others to start on enormous elliptical orbits that would take millions of years to complete.

Of course, if they had been left alone, these planetesimals would all have had orbits that would have eventually brought them back into the inner solar system. (Probably during the early years of the solar system, comets were a very common sight.) However, the same forces that currently alter the orbits of comet nuclei far from the Sun (the tidal effect of the disk and bulge of the Milky Way, and the passage of nearby stars) would have changed the orbits of these small bodies. Many of these planetesimals would have been ejected from the solar system, but many others would have had their orbits altered in such a way as to leave them orbiting far outside the centre of the solar system. In fact, we now know from calculations that tides from the galaxy would have been able to quickly increase perihelion distance of comet nuclei with really large orbits so that after a few revolutions they no longer would enter the region of the planets. Thus we now believe that the

Oort cloud is populated by many of the planetesimals that originally formed in and around Jupiter, Saturn, Uranus and Neptune. These comet nuclei were ejected into the most distant parts of the solar system by the giant planets rather than being accreted, and while far outside the planet system had their orbits altered by passing stars and by tidal effects due to the galaxy to new orbits that kept them always far from the inner solar system. Finally, billions of years later, other passing stars and further tidal effects gradually nudge a few of these bodies into orbits that bring them back into the region of the planets where we see them as comets.

The final fate of comets

To conclude, we look at what becomes of old comets that have ventured once too often into the inner solar system.

As we have already noticed, a number of possible fates exist. A comet that passes fairly close to one of the giant planets can have its orbit altered enough so that the comet acquires the extra orbital energy needed to escape entirely from the solar system. In this case, it simply drifts off into deep space, never to be seen again. Less drastically, if the comet has a really long period, the continued action of galactic tides or the passage of a nearby star can alter the comet's orbit again to one with a large perihelion, so that the comet continues to orbit the Sun, but no longer enters the planetary region.

Another possible fate is exhaustion. After hundreds or thousands of returns to the inner solar system (during which the orbit may become substantially smaller than it was at the time of the first arrival), the comet may simply run out of gas to sublime. (A variant of this fate is for the comet to split apart into several fragments which then expire separately.) In this case, the remaining heap of dust and rock, perhaps porous through and through, may continue to orbit the Sun without any longer producing the characteristic coma and tail – the comet is transformed into an asteroid. In fact, we suspect that some significant fraction of the asteroids near the Earth may have originated in this way, although the idea is hard to test with observations.

Finally, more spectacularly, the comet may collide with one of the planets. Such events are rare (because the planets are tiny targets in a vast space) but potentially catastrophic (because of the tremendous energy release by such an impact). The reality of such a possibility was dramatically confirmed in July 1994 when comet Shoemaker-Levy 9 (D/1993 F2), having fragmented into more than twenty pieces, slammed into Jupiter. This previously unknown comet apparently passed within about 100,000 km of Jupiter in 1992, well within the planet's Roche limit. During this encounter, it was disrupted by tidal effects into a number of pieces that travelled away from Jupiter on an elongated elliptical orbit. This strange comet, with its many fragments strung out in a line along the orbit (Figure 7.11), was discovered in March 1993. When its orbit was calculated, it was quickly realized that the fragments would soon return to strike Jupiter on their next approach, and most of the large telescopes on Earth, and several space probes, were trained on Jupiter for the several days during which impacts occurred.

Figure 7.12: A Hubble Space Telescope image of Jupiter taken in ultraviolet light about 2.5 hrs after the impact of fragment 'R' of Comet Shoemaker-Levy 9 on Jupiter on July 21, 1994. The dust cloud produced by this impact is the dark spot near the bottom centre of the image (the third dark spot from the right). Dark dust clouds from four previous impacts are easily visible at about the same latitude. The dark spot just above the middle of the image of Jupiter is the shadow of its moon Io. (Courtesy of NASA.)

Each impact consisted of a body of mass of the order of 10^8 tonnes crashing into the upper atmosphere of Jupiter at a speed of about 60 km s^{-1}. Each giant iceberg was rapidly decelerated by the Jupiter atmosphere, depositing all its kinetic energy (each impact supplying the energy release of thousands of 10 megaton nuclear bomb explosions) in a few tens of km within the cloud layers. The result of the impact was a gargantuan explosion, producing a brilliant fireball hundreds of km across and thousands of K in temperature. Each fireball launched a huge plume of super-heated gases back out along the partly evacuated entry track of the comet. The plumes rose to altitudes thousands of km above the cloud tops, and then splashed back onto the atmosphere, generating spectacular visual fireworks. After each fireball faded, there remained a giant smoke ring formed from dust embedded in the explosion plumes, a kind of 'black eye', about the size of the Earth, which persisted for weeks after the collision. Gradually these smoke rings coalesced to become a band of dark dust slowly settling out of the high atmosphere of Jupiter. They are visible in Figure 7.12.

Such impacts occur – rarely! – on all the planets. We have already seen in Chapter 5 that such impacts undoubtedly occur, every million years or so, on Earth. It was only due to great good luck – and Jupiter's very large mass, which attracts comets from far and wide – that we were able to actually witness one of these events.

7.6 Mathematical aspects

Comet temperatures

Comets are made of ices, and thus of material that evaporates or sublimes at rather low temperatures. From the triple points listed in Table 2.5, many of the common gases in the solar system sublime at low pressure at temperatures below 100 K = –173 C. The first physical problem we look at in connection with comets is to see why comets stored in the outer solar system beyond Pluto have not completely evaporated even in the enormous length of time, 4.5 Gyr, that has elapsed since the solar system formed.

To understand this point, we look at the only significant source of heating available for a body orbiting in the outer solar system, namely radiation from the Sun. We will determine the surface temperature maintained by sunlight for an object in a circular orbit at a distance r from the Sun, and see whether this temperature is consistent with the long-term stability of ices.

The surface temperature of a comet in orbit around the Sun is determined by a balance. Each second radiation from the Sun falls onto the comet surface. If we take the comet to be spherical with radius R, the total heat input per second, the absorbed power $P_{\rm A}$, is

$$P_{\rm A} = (1 - A_{\rm v})(L_\odot/4\pi r^2)(\pi R^2), \qquad (7.1)$$

where $A_{\rm v}$ is the average albedo for visible light. In this equation, the term $(1 - A_{\rm v})$ describes the fraction of the incoming (visible light) energy which is absorbed (the reflected light fraction $A_{\rm v}$ has no heating effect); the term with the solar luminosity $L_\odot$ describes the flux of energy per second crossing each square meter of surface at the distance of the comet from the Sun; and the last term multiplies the input power per square meter by the total cross section of the comet for capture of radiation.

Exercise: Explain clearly why the last term in Equation (7.1) is πR^2 rather than $4\pi R^2$

Now if this power continued to fall on the surface of the comet year after year without any of the incoming heat being lost by the comet, the surface temperature of the comet would steadily rise until it passed the sublimation point of the gases making it up, and the comet would evaporate. However, the comet does lose energy, by radiating it back into space because of its own surface temperature. When the surface of the comet has reached a temperature T, the radiation from the comet surface per unit area is $(1 - A_{\rm ir})\sigma T^4$, from Equation (3.22). If we assume that the comet rotates and that the incoming sunlight heats all of the surface to about the same temperature, the total power radiated by the comet each second, as infrared energy, is

$$P_{\rm R} = (1 - A_{\rm ir})(\sigma T^4)(4\pi R^2). \qquad (7.2)$$

Now as long as the temperature T is low enough that the power radiated each second from the comet surface is less than that received from the Sun, the surface temperature will rise. But this will make the comet's radiation increase, although it does not affect how much sunlight is absorbed. Thus as the temperature rises, eventually a balance will be reached where the incoming energy from the Sun just balances the energy lost by radiation from the cometary surface. The surface temperature will stabilize at this value. Thus the surface temperature will be determined by the equality

$$(1 - A_{\rm v})(L_\odot/4\pi r^2)(\pi R^2) = (1 - A_{\rm ir})(\sigma T^4)(4\pi R^2)$$

or

$$T^4 = (\frac{1}{4\sigma})(\frac{1 - A_{\rm v}}{1 - A_{\rm ir}})(\frac{L_\odot}{4\pi r^2}). \qquad (7.3)$$

If we assume that $A_{\rm v}$ and $A_{\rm ir}$ are comparable so that the term with the albedos is about 1, this equation gives the numerical result that for T in Kelvins and r in astronomical units

$$T = 280/r^{1/2}. \qquad (7.4)$$

Exercise: Prove Equation 7.4.

Thus for an object circling the Sun at one AU, the equilibrium temperature is about 280 K = 7 C, not far from the actual surface temperature of the Earth. However, for for a comet beyond Pluto, where r is at least 30 AU, the equilibrium temperature will be below 50 K. At such low temperature, gaseous H_2 would sublime but the other gases of Table 2.5 would probably be in no danger. Certainly methane, ammonia, and carbon dioxide could coexist with frozen water. From this calculation we can understand how such volatile bodies as comets can continue to exist for Gyr – as long as they stay well away from the Sun.

Equation (7.3) has been derived by assuming that incoming radiation energy from the Sun reaches an equilibrium with energy loss from the warmed body by re-radiation only. This is a very good approximation for large objects such as moons and planets, and for small ones (asteroids, meteoroids) that have no other significant means of losing heat. This equation applies throughout the solar system to such bodies, and allows one to calculate reasonably accurately the temperature in the surface or atmosphere layer heated from the outside by sunlight. It does not provide useful information about the temperature in layers heated by other means, such as the interiors of the terrestrial planets which have been heated by the heat released during formation of the planet, and by radioactivity.

For comets, Equation (7.3) applies outside of perhaps 5 AU. However, closer to the Sun than this, the temperature at the surface of the comet rises to –100 C or more, and frozen gases at the surface of the comet begin to sublime (change from solid to gas). These gases are almost free to leave the comet, because of its very small gravitational attraction, and so the energy from sunlight that went into subliming gas is carried away and lost to the comet's surface. Sublimation thus provides a second means of cooling the surface of the comet, and Equation (7.3) is no longer correct. We thus need to look at the effects of sublimation on the equilibrium temperature of a comet surface.

Exercise: Use Equation (7.4) to estimate the expected "surface" temperatures of each of the nine planets.

Sublimation

As a comet nucleus comes into the inner solar system, its surface temperature begins to rise due to the increase in solar radiation heating available per m^2. This temperature rise leads both to increased infrared heat radiation by the nucleus, and to gas loss by sublimation. Because heat conductivity in a block of ice is very low, little heat is conducted into the interior of the nucleus. As before, only the surface layer is heated, but now the energy loss every second by radiation *and sublimation* approximately balances the energy input from the Sun. Equation (7.3) no longer applies. However, similar reasoning allows us to calculate both the approximate surface temperature and sublimation rate of the comet nucleus as it travels by the Sun.

We assume that the nucleus is travelling in a known orbit, and that at some particular time its distance from the Sun is r. For simplicity, we again take the nucleus to be a sphere of radius R, with appropriate average albedos A_v and A_{ir}. The solar flux of radiation (W m^{-2}) at r has the value

$$f_v = f_\oplus(r_\oplus^2/r^2) = (L_\odot/4\pi r_\oplus^2)(r_\oplus^2/r^2) \qquad (7.5)$$

where $r_\oplus$ is one astronomical unit and $f_\oplus$ is the **solar constant**, the flux of radiation per m^2 striking the outer atmosphere of Earth. The value of f_1 is 1.36x10^3 W m^{-2} (so that the heat coming through a typical house window that faces the Sun on a sunny day is roughly 1 kilowatt: no wonder solar heating is practical in sunny places). The total energy absorbed per second from the Sun (i.e the absorbed power P_A) is again given by Equation (7.1). Again making the assumption that the whole comet has a roughly uniform temperature T, the energy lost per second from the surface by radiation is given by Equation (7.2).

However, now only a part of the incoming heat energy is re-radiated as infrared thermal emission. The rest of the incoming solar radiation goes into sublimation of the material of the nucleus. This is a process similar to evaporation from a liquid, in which atoms or molecules of the nucleus detach from the solid to form a vapour around the nucleus that (because of the very weak gravity of the nucleus) expands essentially freely.

The physics governing sublimation is most easily studied experimentally by isolating a sample of the ice of interest in a vacuum chamber whose temperature T can be regulated. It is found that vapour from the ice quickly fills the chamber to a pressure which is always the same for a particular T, but which increases rapidly with increasing T. This pressure is known as the **vapour pressure** of the substance at that temperature. (Recall the discussion in Sec 2.3.) Experimentally and from thermodynamic theory, it is found that the vapour pressure varies with temperature approximately as

$$p_v = p_o \exp(\frac{L}{R_g T_o} - \frac{L}{R_g T}) \qquad (7.6)$$

where L is the latent heat of vaporization of the substance, R_g is the gas constant, and p_o is the vapour pressure at some specified temperature T_o. Values of L may be found in standard chemical tables, often in units of calories per mole. (When L is in calories per mole, as it is in Equation (7.6), the gas constant R_g must be used in compatible units, and has the value R_g = 1.9871 cal K^{-1} mole^{-1}.) Values of p_o and T_o (from tables of vapour pressure), and of the vaporization energy in both calories per mole and J per molecule are given in Table 7.3. Note that for most gases the value of L varies with temperature, especially as the temperature approaches the triple point; this is neglected in the table.

Exercise: The triple point of water is at $p = 6.0 \times 10^2$ Pa, $T = 273$ K. Evaluate the vapour pressure at 273 K using Equation (7.6) to see how closely this (approximate) equation comes to the correct value. (Use $R_g = 1.9871$ cal K^{-1} mole^{-1}, and the value of L from Table 7.3 in calories per mole.)

Table 7.3: Constants for Equation (7.6).

Gas	p_o (Pa)	T_o (K)	L (cal mole^{-1})	L (J molecule^{-1})
N_2	133	47	1600	1.1×10^{-20}
CH_4	133	67	2200	1.5×10^{-20}
CO_2	133	139	5500	3.8×10^{-20}
NH_3	133	164	7200	5.0×10^{-20}
H_2O	133	256	11000	7.6×10^{-20}

Source: Delsemme & Miller 1971, Planet. Sp. Sci. 19, 1229; Handbook Chem. Phys., 1956-57 ed., pp. 2152 – 2228.

In our chamber at a fixed T it appears that a dynamical equilibrium exists. This equilibrium involves continual evaporation of surface molecules, which are constantly being replaced by an equal number of molecules from the vapour that strike the surface and stick. As long as no energy is added or removed (the temperature is not changed), the balance between loss of molecules from the surface by sublimation and gain from the vapour of molecules that strike the surface and stick is exact. This is very convenient, because it enables us to estimate the flux of molecules subliming from the surface every second, which we shall need for our comet problem, by calculating the number that strike it from the vapour in equilibrium.

The molecules in the vapour are moving randomly with thermal kinetic energy. The average kinetic energy per molecule is $3kT/2$, and the approximate average velocity $\bar{v}$ is

$$M\bar{v}^2/2 = 3kT/2 \tag{7.7}$$

where $M = \mu m_u$ is the mass of a molecule. Actually, a distribution of velocities exists, but we may ignore this fact for a first approximation. In the same spirit, assume that at any instant 1/3 of the molecules are moving parallel to each of the x, y, and z axes, half in one direction and half in the other. Then if there are n molecules per m^3 of volume, the approximate number Z striking the surface per second per m^2 is

$$\begin{aligned} Z &= (1/2)\,(1/3)\,n\bar{v} = n\bar{v}/6 \\ &= (1/6)\,n\,(3kT/M)^{1/2} \end{aligned} \tag{7.8}$$

If we assume that these molecules all stick, we have an estimate of the flux accumulated each second by the solid, and hence of the flux leaving the solid each second. We may convert n to vapour pressure p_v by assuming that the vapour obeys the ideal gas law, $p_v = nkT$. Using Equations (2.6) and (7.6),

$$\begin{aligned} Z &= (1/6)\,p_v\,(3/kTM)^{1/2} \\ &= \left(\frac{1}{12kTM}\right)^{1/2} p_o \exp\left(\frac{L}{R_g T_o} - \frac{L}{R_g T}\right) \end{aligned} \tag{7.9}$$

Equation (7.9) shows that the flux of particles leaving the surface at temperatures below about 300 K is a very strong function of T, since the exponential function varies very rapidly with temperature.

Now at the surface of the comet, the gas vaporized is not contained, but flows away freely. This destroys the equilibrium that occurs in a closed container, but does not alter the flux of outgoing particles at a particular temperature. Since the outgoing flux is not balanced by much replenishment from the vapour, which is not able to maintain a pressure as high as the vapour pressure for that T, the surface is steadily eroded by sublimation. To sublime, gas requires an amount of energy L (in calories per mole or J per kg or some other suitable units). Thus we can finally write the energy balance equation for the comet as

$$\begin{aligned} f_v(1 - A_v)\pi R^2 &= \sigma T^4(1 - A_{ir})4\pi R^2 \\ &\quad + 4\pi R^2 Z L \end{aligned} \tag{7.10}$$

Of course, the radius of the comet can be divided out of the equation. (Note that L and Z must be in the same units, so since we are computing Z in units of molecules m^{-2} s^{-1}, as in Equation (7.8), we must take the value of L in Equation (7.10) in units of J per molecule, even though we use L in calories per mole inside the exponential when we evaluate Equation (7.9) for Z.) If there is no sublimation, so that the second term on the right vanishes, Equation (7.10) reduces to the usual equation for the equilibrium temperature of a body heated by the Sun that from the previous section, Equation (7.3).

The energy balance equation above at a particular distance from the Sun contains only one unknown, T, if one assumes a particular composition (i.e., L, T_o and p_o) and plausible values for A_v (0.1 or 0.2?) and for A_{ir} (0.5?). It cannot be solved algebraically for T as a function of r, but it can be solved in the other direction: assume a value for T, calculate $Z(T)$ from

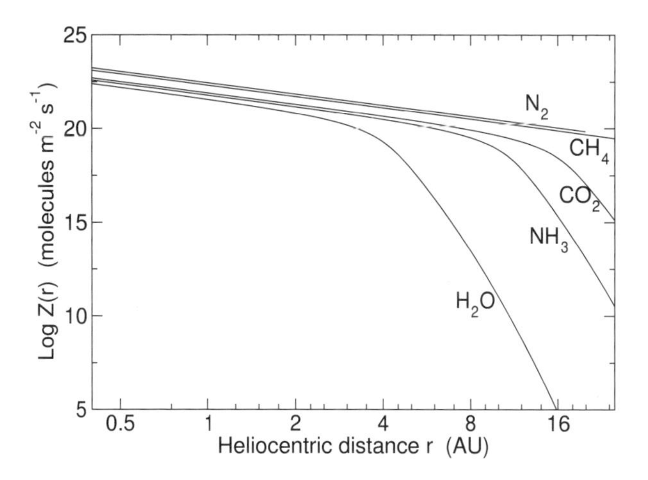

Figure 7.13: Variation of the gas outflow rate Z as a function of heliocentric distance r in AU for H_2O, NH_3, CO_2, CH_4, and N_2 (from bottom to top). The nucleus is assumed to have a visual albedo of 0.1 in these calculations. Note that water ice only begins to sublime vigorously at about 3 AU, while other ices sublime strongly at much greater distances from the Sun.

Equation (7.9), calculate the right-hand side of Equation (7.10), and finally solve for r which is on the left-hand side of Equation (7.10). In this way you can build up a table of $Z(T)$ and $r(T)$ which can be used to plot $Z(r)$ and $T(r)$. An example is shown in Figure 7.13. It is from such a calculation that it is found that water ice starts subliming rapidly at about 3 AU, while ices such as CH_4 or NH_3, which have substantially lower melting temperatures and smaller latent heats of vaporization, start subliming strongly at larger distances from the Sun. Note an important result of this equation: near the Sun the sublimation term can become much larger than the radiation term, strongly depressing the resulting temperature. When a lot of evaporation occurs, this cools the surface of the comet far below the temperature that it would reach by simply cooling by radiation.

Exercise: Evaluate Z from Equation (7.9) for water at 150 K, 175 K and 200 K, and confirm that Z varies extremely rapidly in this temperature range. Use Figure 7.13 to estimate the distance from the Sun at which a water ice comet nucleus would have these temperatures. Assume $A_v = 0.1$, $A_{ir} = 0.5$. (Hint: for $T = 175$ K, Z should be about 5.0×10^{20} molecules m^{-2} s^{-1}.)

Loss of dust grains from the nucleus

The flow of gas from the nucleus will sweep along small dust grains and loose bits of ice from the surface. Larger pieces will not be swept off the surface by the breeze of subliming molecules, but will remain in place. Equation (7.9) above for the mass flux allows us to estimate the upper limit of size for the particles swept away with the subliming gas.

The outflowing molecules are moving more-or-less vertically away from the surface of the nucleus with average velocity $\bar{v}$ (Equation (7.7)). The mass flux f crossing a unit area per second due to the flow in the breeze is

$$f = ZM \tag{7.11}$$

Now imagine a (spherical) grain of dust of radius a and density d suspended above the surface of the comet nucleus. Rising gas molecules will strike this particle from below. If it is assumed that each molecule transfers its own momentum to the grain (as the molecules would if collisions are inelastic) then the momentum p imparted to the grain per second due to collision with gas molecules is approximately

$$dp/dt = (ZM)\,\bar{v}\,(\pi a^2) \tag{7.12}$$

as the rising molecules in a column of cross section πa^2 strike the grain each second. This picture is rather simplified, of course; the molecules move with some distribution of speeds and directions, and the momentum transferred per molecule may be wrong by a factor of two or so. But we expect Equation (7.12) to have the right order of magnitude.

Now a momentum change dp/dt per second corresponds to a force $f_W = dp/dt$ by Newton's second law. Thus we have an estimate of the upward force on the grain due to the wind of rising molecules. If this force exceeds the force of gravity f_G on the grain due to the comet nucleus of radius R_c and density ρ_c, which has the value

$$\begin{aligned} f_G &= \frac{G\,(4\pi R_c^3 \rho_c/3)\,(4\pi a^3 \rho_g/3)}{R_c^2} \\ &= \frac{16\pi^2 G R_c a^3 \rho_c\,\rho_g}{9} \end{aligned} \tag{7.13}$$

(ρ_g is the density of the grain), the grain will be swept along with the wind. If $f_W < f_G$, the grain will fall, or more exactly will not be levitated in the first place. Since f_G is proportional to a^3 while f_W goes as a^2 it is clear that all grains (of given ρ_g) less than some limiting size a_m will be carried along by the sublimation while larger grains will not. This a_m is clearly given by

$$a_m = \frac{9M\bar{v}Z}{16\pi\rho_g\,\rho_c\,R_c\,G} \tag{7.14}$$

so that as the comet comes into the inner solar system and Z increases, larger and larger dust grains may be swept off.

Exercise: Use Equation (7.14) to estimate the size of a_m for dust loss from a water ice comet of 5 km radius at 1 AU from the Sun.

A few points remain to be tidied up. We have ignored the details of the outward gas flow, except to assume that it proceeds with a velocity of roughly $\bar{v}$ (Equation (7.7)); actually, the structure of this flow is an interesting but rather advanced problem in fluid dynamics. Even ignoring details of the gas flow, however, it is important to show that the gravity of the comet nucleus does not have an important effect on the gas flow.

Exercise: (a) Assume that a comet has a radius R and is made of water ice. Calculate the acceleration of gravity at the comet surface, and evaluate it for $R =$ 3 km. (b) Compute the gravitational escape velocity from the nucleus of the comet and show that it is of the order of 1 m s^{-1} per km of comet radius. Show that this is small compared to the thermal velocity of a molecule sublimed from the nucleus at $T = 200$K. (This implies that the flow of gas away from the nucleus will not be much affected by the gravitational field of the comet nucleus.)

Size of the coma

The next problem to investigate is the size of the coma developed by a particular species of molecule, such as C_2 or CN. We shall assume here that the molecules of interest originate in the flow from the nucleus, though this is probably not really true for most of the diatomic molecules (radicals) like CN and OH, which are very likely fragments produced by the destruction close to the nucleus of larger molecules. In most cases of interest the production of the radicals goes on within about 10^4 km of the nucleus and so does not greatly affect the observable coma.

Now if the flow of gas outward proceeds at a roughly constant speed $\bar{v}$, then the rate at which the number density $n(d)$ of the gas at a distance d from the nucleus depends on d is easily derived. At a particular distance d consider a shell of thickness Δd_1 and volume $4\pi d_1^2 \Delta d$,. At some later time, the gas in this shell reaches d_2. Because the flow velocity is constant, the new thickness of the shell $\Delta d_2 = \Delta d_1$. The volume of the shell is now $4\pi d_2^2 \Delta d_2$. Since the total number of molecules in the whole shell is the same at both d_1 and d_2, we have

$$n(d_1)\, 4\pi d_1^2\, \Delta d_1 \;=\; n\,(d_2)\, 4\pi d_2^2\, \Delta d_2, \qquad (7.15)$$

or

$$n\,(d_1)\,/n\,(d_2) \;=\; d_2^2/d_1^2. \qquad (7.16)$$

Thus the volume density of gas drops as d^{-2}. Note that this leads directly to the conclusion that Equation (7.14), which we derived for the neighborhood of the nucleus, is the same at all distances from the nucleus because both the comet's gravity and the gas flux drop off as d^{-2}. Thus any particles that can be swept up from the nucleus can be carried far out into the coma.

Now the fraction ε_i of the total gas number density that is made of up the molecule i of interest (i.e., $\varepsilon_i = n_i/n_{tot}$) is not constant in the flow. We assume that near the nucleus there is a constant abundance ε_i, but as gas in the coma expands, the molecules of type i are gradually ionized or dissociated by such processes as charge exchange with solar wind protons and photoionization by solar ultraviolet light. Both these processes depend on the flux of particles or light from the Sun, and one can calculate or measure approximately how quickly they occur. A C_2 molecule at 1 AU from the Sun survives on average about 6×10^4 seconds before being dissociated or ionized, while a CN molecule survives on average about 1.4×10^5 sec. (Because the destruction processes are proportional to the number of solar wind particles or photons passing close to the target molecule per second, and both these quantities decrease with increasing distance r from the Sun as $1/r^2$, the lifetimes are proportional to $(r/r_o)^2$.) Now if a particular molecule has a mean lifetime t_i sec, the probability that it will be destroyed in a particular 1-second interval is t_i^{-1}. Thus if we look at a large number N_i of molecules i that start out in some particular volume in the gas flow, the destruction rate of these molecules is

$$\frac{dN_i}{dt} \;=\; -\frac{N_i}{t_i} \qquad (7.17)$$

which has the solution

$$N_i(t) \;=\; N_o \exp(-t/t_i) \qquad (7.18)$$

Thus the abundance ε_i will decrease with time and the total volume density of the molecule of interest will vary as

$$\begin{aligned} n_i(d) &= (R_c/d)^2\, n_i(R_c)\exp(-t/t_i) \\ &\approx (R_c/d)^2\, n_i(R_c)\exp(-d/\bar{v}t_i), \end{aligned} \qquad (7.19)$$

where $n_i(R_c)$ is the volume density just above the surface of the nucleus. The density of species i falls off slowly out to a distance $d_e \sim t_i\bar{v}$ from the nucleus and then drops off quite rapidly at larger distances. We may consider d_e to define roughly the edge of the coma for molecule i. A molecule of lifetime 10^5 sec, moving out with $\bar{v} \sim 0.5$ kmsec^{-1} will thus form a coma with a typical diameter of about 10^5 km at 1 AU. The coma of this molecule at a larger distance from the Sun will be larger, but at a distance where gas production becomes very low the coma may become so thin that it is hard to detect, and will appear to shrink.

Exercise: Assume that the solar wind has a velocity of 400 $\mathrm{km\,s^{-1}}$ and a mean number density of 2×10^6 protons $\mathrm{m^{-3}}$ as a comet sweeps through it at 1 AU from the Sun. (a) If the cross section for ionizing proton-molecule collisions is about $\sigma = 1 \times 10^{-20}\ \mathrm{m^2}$, what is the mean time between collisions of a given coma molecule with a solar wind proton? (b) If the molecules are moving away from the comet nucleus at 0.4 $\mathrm{km\,s^{-1}}$, how far on average can a molecule travel from the nucleus before being ionized by a collision with a proton?

Forces on atoms and dust grains ejected from a comet

To end this section, we turn to a brief look at the forces that act on particles such as atoms and small grains of dust once they have been ejected from a comet and are off on their own in the solar system. (Of course, these same forces act on all small particles in the solar system, whatever their origin.)

Objects which are very small (but still much larger than a single atom or molecule), such as dust grains, feel a force pushing them away from the Sun, due to the pressure of sunlight. In effect, the photons streaming outward from the Sun act as a kind of rain, beating on the illuminated side of any object near the Sun. When these photons are absorbed by the illuminated object, or bounce off its illuminated side, they impart their own outward momentum to the object that they strike. This produces a steady outward force. The force due to these photons is proportional to the surface area of each particle illuminated; however, the resistance to being influenced by this force is larger, the larger the mass of the particle. Since very small particles have the largest *ratio* of surface area to mass, they are the most strongly affected. It turns out that this radiation force is stronger than the gravitational attraction of the Sun for particles of about 0.1 micron radius, so such small particles are simply blown out of the solar system. (Note that if the radiation force is larger than the gravitational attraction of the Sun at one distance from the Sun, this is true at all distances, because both the radiation force and the pull of gravity decrease with distance in the same way). Radiation pressure is not effective in driving single neutral atoms out of the solar system, in spite of their small size, because they are extremely inefficient for their size at absorbing or scattering incoming photons–they can't absorb all colours, but only those that happen to coincide with absorption lines of the atoms.

We may treat radiation pressure approximately. Consider a particle of density ρ and radius a, and the sunlight streaming outward past it, all at a distance r from the Sun. Let the local flux of sunlight energy be $\mathcal{F}_{\rm rad} = L_\odot/4\pi r^2$ (in energy per unit area per second) where $L_\odot$ is the solar luminosity, 3.85×10^{26} W. The momentum flux in the photons is $\mathcal{F}_{\rm rad}/c$, where c is the velocity of light, because a photon of energy e has momentum $p = e/c$. Now if the photons run into an obstacle, they will give up their momentum to it (if they are absorbed and later re-radiated evenly in all directions; if they are reflected back towards the Sun they actually give up twice their momentum). The transferred momentum acts as a force on the obstacle. Since the force needed to stop the photons is equal to the momentum brought in per second by them ($f = dp/dt$, Newton's second law), and this is also the force exerted by the photons on the object, it is clear that $\mathcal{F}_{\rm rad}/c$ is (approximately) the force per unit area, or pressure, available from the sunlight, and the total force f on a single particle is

$$f = Q(\pi a^2)(\mathcal{F}_{\rm rad}/c), \qquad (7.20)$$

where πa^2 is the projected area of the particle and Q is an efficiency factor, about 1 for dust grains whose sizes are comparable to or greater than the wavelength of the incoming light, but much smaller for smaller grains or single atoms. The acceleration due to radiation pressure is then

$$\begin{aligned} g_{\rm rad} &= f/m = \frac{Q(\pi a^2)(\mathcal{F}_{\rm rad}/c)}{(4\pi a^3\rho/3)} \\ &= \frac{(3/4)Q(\mathcal{F}_{\rm rad}/c)}{(\rho a)} = \frac{3Q\mathcal{F}_{\rm rad}}{(4c\rho a)}. \end{aligned} \qquad (7.21)$$

This varies as a^{-1}, and hence is larger for smaller particles. For a particle to be driven out of the solar system by radiation pressure, the radiative acceleration must be larger than the acceleration of gravity at the particle's distance r from the Sun,

$$g = GM_\odot/r^2. \qquad (7.22)$$

Exercise: (a) Estimate the radiation force on a dust grain released by a comet at 1 AU from the Sun. Assume that the dust grain is spherical with Q (the efficiency factor for radiation pressure; see Equation (7.20)) = 1.0, a diameter of 1.0 μm, and a density of 1000 $\mathrm{kg\,m^{-3}}$. (b) Compare the radiation force to the force of gravity from the Sun. Will the dust grain be driven out of the solar system by radiation pressure?

Another force that is important for electrically charged atoms (ions) is due to the solar wind. This wind is a very thin, hot plasma that is continually being boiled off the Sun's corona, and that steadily sweeps out through the solar system. It is made up mainly of hydrogen ions and free electrons, with a density of perhaps 10^6 ions per m^3, at a temperature of around 2×10^5 K, and is moving outward at about 500 $km\,s^{-1}$. Because this plasma is so thin, it exerts in general much less force than that due to radiation pressure on such objects as dust grains. However, because it carries with it a tangled magnetic field, it is able to hook onto electrically charged ions (which, as mentioned above, are almost oblivious to the radiation pressure force from the Sun) and sweep them rapidly outward from the Sun. This solar wind force is important in producing the ion tails of comets.

A third important effect, related to the pressure of sunlight, is the Poynting-Robertson effect. A dust grain revolving in orbit about the Sun will not only feel a small outward force due to the pressure of solar radiation, but will also be affected by the fact that these photons will tend to strike the particle on its forward side, much as raindrops strike the front windscreen of a car harder and in greater numbers than they strike the rear window when the car is in motion. Thus, in effect, the moving dust grain will feel a drag force that tends to slow it down in its orbit. This in turn causes it to spiral in towards the Sun. Although the effect is quite weak, it is still sufficiently effective that it has cleared out of the solar system all particles with sizes of perhaps 1 cm or less that were left over from the initial construction of the solar system about 4.6 Gyr ago. This effect has been as powerful as it has, in spite of the comparatively weak force involved, because it doesn't compete directly with gravity, but acts as a *drag* which causes small particles to eventually spiral into the Sun.

7.7 References

Balsiger, H., Fechtig, H. and Geiss, J. 1988, "A close look at Halley's Comet", *Sci. Am.*, Sep., 96. Space probe encounters with Halley's Comet during its 1986 visit to the inner solar system confirmed out general ideas of how comets function but also provided several fascinating surprises.

Brandt, J. C. and Chapman, R. D. 1981, *Comets* (Cambridge: Cambridge University Press). This semi-popular book includes interesting discussions, both qualitative and mathematical, of many aspects of comets, but is not well organized.

Brandt, J. C. and Niedner, M. B. 1986, "The structure of comet tails", *Sci. Am.*, Jan., 48. Comet tails are complex structures that are strongly affected by both sunlight and the solar wind.

Huebner, W. F. (editor) 1990, *Physics and Chemistry of Comets* (Berlin: Springer-Verlag). Several experts in the field contributed chapters to this book, which describes the state of understanding of comets in the light of the results from space probes. Much of the book is technical and mathematical, but several chapters have clear, non-mathematical introductions and final summaries, and the last chapter presents an excellent qualitative overview of comet studies.

Jewitt, D. 1999, "Kuiper belt objects", *Ann. Rev. Earth Planet. Sci.*, 27, 287. Knowledge of Kuiper belt objects is expanding explosively. This article reviews what had been learned up to 1998 about the nature and orbits of these very primitive objects.

Krishna Swamy, K.S. 1986, *Physics of Comets* (World Scientific Pub. Co.). This advanced treatise covers most aspects of comet physics.

Levy, D. H., Shoemaker, E. H. and Shoemaker, C. S. 1995, "Comet Shoemaker-Levy 9 meets Jupiter", *Sci. Am.*, Aug., 84. The chronicle of the discovery and fate of Comet Shoemaker-Levy 9 is described by its discoverers.

Luu, J. X. and Jewitt, D. C. 1996, "The Kuiper belt", *Sci. Am.*, May, 46. The discoverers of the first members of the inner storage region of comet nuclei describe their work and way in which it supports the idea of the existence of the Kuiper belt.

Luu, J. X. and Jewitt, D. C. 2002, "Kuiper belt objects: relics from the accretion disk of the sun", *Ann. Rev. Astr. Ap.*, 40, 63. This review discusses the objects in the Kuiper belt as relics of the Sun's accretion disk.

Olson, R. J. M. 1979, "Giotto's portrait of Halley's Comet, *Sci. Am.*, May, 160. Some apparitions of Halley's comet have been sufficiently spectacular to inspire artists. The comet appears in the Bayeux Tapestry (about 1070 A.D.) and was included by the great Italian artist Giotto in a fresco in the Scrovegni Chapel in Padua in about 1305.

Weissman, P. R. 1998, "The Oort cloud", *Sci. Am.*, Sep., 84. Billions of comets are stored outside the orbit of Pluto; this article explains clearly how we know they are out there, and how they sometimes arrive in the inner solar system.

Yeomans, Donald K. 1991, *Comets: a Chronological History of Observation, Science, Myth, and Folklore* (New York: Wiley). A very entertaining book about comets which emphasizes the historical aspects and public interest in comets. Definitely a good read.

7.8 Review questions

7.1 Can we ever actually see the "bare" nucleus of a comet? How can one estimate the size of the nucleus of a comet?

7.2 What observational evidence favours the model of the comet nucleus as a dirty iceberg rather than as a flying gravel bank?

7.3 How are gas and dust ejected from the nucleus to form the coma and tail of the comet?

7.4 What evidence indicates that two physically quite different kinds of comet tails exist? What is the basic difference in composition between these two kinds of tails?

7.5 How is each of the two types of comet tails visible? What mechanisms produce the light that we see when we look at these tails?

7.6 Why do some dust particles remain near the orbit of a comet nucleus and perhaps produce meteor showers, while other dust particles drift outwards in the solar system to form a cometary dust tail?

7.7 Why do comet tails always point approximately away from the Sun? Is the reason the same for both dust and ion tails?

7.8 At what distance from the Sun is a comet usually first detectable? At what distance do the coma and tail begin to be important? What physically happens to create the coma and tail at this distance from the Sun?

7.9 How do we obtain information about the chemical composition of a comet nucleus?

7.10 Are comets true solar system members, or interstellar wanderers? How do we know which is correct?

7.11 What is the association of meteor showers with comets? Why do many meteor showers occur yearly, even though their associated comets may be far outside the planet system?

7.12 What forces and effects act to change the orbital period of a comet?

7.13 What evidence leads us to believe that huge numbers of comet nuclei are stored in the Kuiper belt and the Oort cloud? How are these comets occasionally sent into the planetary region of the solar system?

7.9 Problems

7.1 (a) If a comet is moving in a parabolic orbit around the Sun with perihelion at 0.723 AU, what is the largest velocity it could have relative to Venus, ignoring the effect of Venus' own gravity on the comet velocity. With a sketch, show the orbit of the comet relative to Venus for such a maximum velocity encounter. (b) If the comet collided with Venus in this situation, what would the final velocity of the comet be relative to Venus just before reaching the surface, including the acceleration due to Venus' own gravity? Ignore the effects of Venus' atmosphere. (c) For such a maximum velocity encounter between a comet in parabolic orbit and a planet at distance r from the Sun moving at velocity v in a circular orbit, express the relative velocity at closest approach as a function of the planet's velocity around the Sun.

7.2 Suppose a comet having an orbital period of 100 years has a perihelion distance from the centre of the Sun of 2 $R_\odot$. (a) Calculate the velocity of the comet as it passes perihelion. (b) Assume that perihelion passage can be crudely described as a semi-circular trajectory past the Sun with the comet's perihelion velocity. Estimate the time spent by the comet on this semi-circle; we shall consider this the duration of perihelion passage. (c) Assuming a constant rate of heating of the comet's surface equal to that occurring when the comet is at 2.0 $R_\odot$ from the centre of the Sun, estimate the rate of loss of material from the heated side of the comet, in $\mathrm{m\,s^{-1}}$ of surface lost, if the comet has an albedo of $A = 0.1$, a density of $\rho = 1000\ \mathrm{kg\,m^{-3}}$, and a heat of sublimation of $L = 2.8 \times 10^6\ \mathrm{J\,kg^{-1}}$. You can ignore thermal radiation in making this estimate; just assume that all the heat supplied by the Sun during perihelion passage is used to sublime ices. (d) Could a cometary nucleus of radius $r = 1.0$ km survive one perihelion passage under these circumstances?

7.3 Consider the question of whether gas drag from the corona has a significant slowing effect on the comet of the previous problem. (a) If you have not done that problem, calculate the perihelion velocity and duration of perihelion passage. (b) Near perihelion, the density of the corona is about

$n \sim 10^{12}$ hydrogen ions per m^3. Estimate the total mass swept up or pushed out of the way by the comet nucleus during the perihelion passage. Express this swept mass of gas as a fraction of the mass of the comet nucleus. (b) Assume that the coronal gas particles swept out of the way by the comet are given approximately the comet's own perihelion velocity. Using conservation of momentum, estimate the order of magnitude of the total velocity change of the comet due to gas drag during perihelion passage, and express it as a fraction of the perihelion velocity. (c) Would the comet be significantly slowed by the corona during perihelion passage?

7.4 The observed location of the Moon in the sky at a particular instant is different for observers at different points on Earth due to parallax. An observer could estimate the orbital angular motion of the Moon by observing its position each day or night as it crosses the meridian (the great circle running from north to south pole directly overhead in the sky). Positions at other times could be interpolated from such observations. (a) By approximately how much will the Moon deviate from the interpolated position for an observer at a 45° north latitude if it is observed just as it rises? That is, about how much parallax will it show relative to its computed position? (Note that this question concerns the change in direction of the Moon as seen by an observer at a single latitude, not a comparison with the observation by a different observer at another latitude.) (b) Tycho Brahe's observation (from about 55° N latitude) of the positions of the comet of 1577 showed that it had less than 15 minutes of arc of parallax when observed on the meridian and at rising or setting. Estimate the lower bound to the distance to the comet.

7.5 Periodic comet Crommelin has an orbital period of 27 years and a perihelion distance of 0.73 AU. (a) Using Kepler's third law and the *vis viva* equation, calculate the aphelion distance from the Sun, the velocity at perihelion, and the velocity at aphelion for P/Crommelin. (b) Suppose a new comet enters the inner solar system on a parabolic orbit, also with a perihelion distance of 0.73 AU. How fast will this comet be moving at perihelion? What is the fractional difference in speed at perihelion between P/Crommelin and the new comet? (This is a measure of how difficult it is to establish from observations near perihelion whether P/Crommelin has a closed periodic orbit or a parabolic one.) Plot the two orbits on a graph, using polar coordinates, out to 2 AU. How far apart are the two orbits at $r = 1.0$ AU if they have the same orbital plane and major axis?

7.6 Assume that Comet Kohoutek had a visual albedo of 0.1 and an infrared albedo of 0.6, and was composed largely of water ice. Calculate the surface temperature T and sublimation rate Z as a function of distance r from the Sun, between 20 and 0.14 AU, using Equations (7.9) and (7.10). Plot your results (better use logarithmic scales for r and Z). Does your model show a rapid rise in Z that levels off as the comet enters the inner solar system? At what r does Z level off?

7.7 When comet Higgledy-Poo is at 1 AU from the Earth and also 1 AU from the Sun, the brightness of light reflected from the dust in the coma is measured by observing the brightness of the comet at wavelengths where not much molecular emission occurs. The integrated magnitude of the coma of C/Higgledy-Poo due to dust reflection at a wavelength of 5500 Å is estimated to be $m_c = 10.5$. (The magnitude m of an object is related to the observed light flux f at some wavelength, for example in $\mathrm{W\,m^{-2}\,Hz^{-1}}$, by $m = -2.5\ log\, f + C$, where C is a constant. The constant is set by the fact that the magnitude of the Sun at the same wavelength is $m_\odot = -26.73$.) Assume that the dust grains in the coma of the comet have typical radii $a \approx 1.0\ \mu$m, efficiency factors for interaction with radiation (cf. Equation (7.20)) $Q = 1.0$, albedos $A_v \approx 0.7$, and densities $\rho = 1000\ \mathrm{kg\,m^{-3}}$. The objective now is to estimate the total mass of dust in the coma of C/Higgledy-Poo at the time of observation. (a) Calculate the flux of sunlight at the position of C/Higgledy-Poo. (b) Assume an (unknown) number N of reflecting dust grains in the coma, each reflecting sunlight isotropically (uniformly in all directions) with a cross section for reflection obtained using the data given above; calculate the "luminosity" of the coma due to the sum of all these tiny reflectors each reflecting some of the solar flux. (c) Then compute the flux of reflected light arriving at the Earth, 1 AU away from C/Higgledy-Poo (which will depend on the unknown N, of course). (d) Finally, use the information about the *observed* magnitude of the comet's dust coma to determine the flux of light actually observed at Earth, then value of N, and thus the mass of dust in the coma.

Chapter 8

The Earth

8.1 Overview

The largest bodies in the solar system, apart from the Sun itself, are the planets and the larger moons (some of which are as large as the smallest planets). Judging from our own Earth, we may expect these large bodies to be complex and perhaps active objects. We now turn to surveying what is known about the internal chemical composition and structure of moons and planets, and then try to deduce possible ways in which they might have formed and developed.

We cannot, of course, directly observe the interiors of planets. Even our own has only been probed to a depth of a few km, about a tenth of one percent of the distance to the centre. We therefore have to rely fairly heavily on theoretical ideas to describe planetary interiors. However, the state of a planet's interior does affect its observable surface in many ways, and there are means of probing the interior even without obtaining physical samples of material or directly measuring the temperature. Many kinds of observations of the Earth furnish information about the state of the interior. These include measuring the length of time required for sound waves generated by an earthquake to travel through the Earth's interior from where they are produced to distant listening posts; measuring the heat that emerges from the interior at various spots on the globe; observing the structure and changes of the Earth's magnetic field, which is thought to be generated in the deep interior of the Earth; studying rocks brought to the surface from really deep volcanic eruptions; and even observing how the Earth as a whole "rings" or oscillates when set into vibration by a really large earthquake. These data may be used to provide surprisingly detailed information about what the principal chemical and mineral species are at various depths, how the pressure and density change as one goes deeper and deeper into the Earth, what the temperature is at various levels, what energy sources have supplied heat, and even what kinds of convective motions may occur in molten or plastic rock at great depth.

These measurements, and a lot of theoretical work, furnish us with a fairly detailed picture of the interior of the Earth. For other planets and moons, the available measurements are far more limited; in some cases we know little more than the mass and radius of the body. But it is possible to start from the Earth and work outwards towards bodies that are less and less like the Earth, using whatever information is available, and obtain quite a lot of insight into the basic structural features of most of the large objects in the solar system. As we shall see, we have some powerful clues about the chemical and mineral makeup of the planets and moons, and in many cases we can deduce approximately their internal structure and conditions.

Once we have learned something about the structure and chemistry of the various large bodies in the solar system, striking regularities concerning how chemical composition and structure vary with position in the solar system become apparent. It is possible to try to explain the observed nature of various planets and moons with general theories of how they might have formed. At present the available theory does not fully explain the characteristics of the planets, but we are already able to extract from what we know about planetary compositions much useful insight into the conditions that probably prevailed in the solar system at the time the planets were formed, and some ideas about how the planets evolved after formation.

Since the Earth is the planet about which we know by far the most, it is natural to begin by trying to understand its interior structure and its main surface characteristics. What we learn here will serve as a useful starting point in efforts to understand other planets.

8.2 The interior of the Earth

Chemical composition

One fundamental question concerns what the Earth is made of. We would like to know what chemical elements are the principal constituents of the Earth, and whether the Earth is (roughly?) homogeneous through-

Table 8.1: Earth's bulk chemical composition—a first guess.

Chemical Element	Abundance of element in solar atmosphere*	Common oxide		Abundance of O in oxide*	Predicted abundance of element in Earth*	Predicted percentage by mass
Mg	1070	MgO		1070	1070	14.4
Si	(1000)	SiO_2		2000	1000	15.5
Fe	890	FeO		890	890	27.5
Al	83	Al_2O_3		125	83	1.4
Ca	65	CaO		65	65	1.4
Na	60	Na_2O		30	60	0.8
Ni	50	NiO		50	50	1.6
O	19000		total:	4230	4230	37.4

*Abundances are all given in atoms per 10^3 atoms of Si.
Source: Table 2.2.

out, or layered in some way. Fortunately, we are given some very important hints about the answers to these questions by the Sun, the meteorites, and the chemical abundances of the rocks of the Earth's crust. Recall Table 2.2, which gives the abundances of the most common elements in the outer layers of the Sun and in CI carbonaceous chondrites. This table shows that in the Sun (and presumably in the original solar nebula) there is a very strong hierarchy of abundances. The commonest materials are H and He, which together account for about 99.9% of the total number of atoms and 98.1% of the total mass of material. (The less abundant elements have heavier nuclei than H and He, and therefore account for more mass than you might expect.) Next come the light elements C, N, and O, which make up almost all the remaining 0.1% of the total number of atoms, and account for about 1.4% of the remaining mass. A third group includes Ne, Mg, Si, S, and Fe, which together make up 0.02% of the total number of atoms in the solar atmosphere, and almost all of the last 0.5% of the total mass. However, when we look at meteorites and at the Earth's surface rocks, we find that both are drastically depleted relative to the Sun in the volatile elements H, He, C, N, Ne, and to a lesser extent in S. The remaining abundant elements, all of which form refractory compounds and minerals, are O, Mg, Si, and Fe. These are in fact the commonest elements found in meteorites, and together with the cosmically still rarer elements Na, Al, K, Ca, and Ni, they are also the main elements found in terrestrial surface rocks.

So let's make the obvious guess for the bulk composition of the Earth, namely that the bulk composition is dominated by these few elements. We may even go a bit further and guess that the overall composition of the Earth contains the refractory elements Si, Mg, Fe, Na, Al, K, Ca, and Ni in about the same ratio as they occur in the Sun, and that about as much O will be included as each of the metal atoms takes up when it oxidizes (combines with oxygen). This gives us the approximate composition listed in the last column of Table 8.1 as our starting guess for the Earth's overall chemical composition. This simple calculation suggests that about 20% of the O in the original nebula probably condensed with the refractory elements that make up the inner planets. From Table 8.1 we see that the main constituents of the Earth are expected to be the same ones found in meteorites, namely Mg, Fe, Si, and O with a mild sprinkling of Na, Al, K, Ca, and Ni. Considering the relative abundances of the main constituents, we see that, very roughly, the overall composition of the Earth may be similar to that of an olivine containing about the same amounts of Fe and Mg, approximately $MgFeSiO_4$, with a host of minor impurities making up a few percent of the atoms in total. We will refine this guess below.

Seismology

Next, we ask how these elements are distributed in the Earth. Is there some internal structure or layering that can be detected from outside? The answer to this question was discovered early in the twentieth century using information provided by earthquake waves, or **seismology**.

When an earthquake occurs (normally somewhere at or near the Earth's surface) because accumulated pressure or tension causes rock somewhere in the brittle crust to break or slip suddenly, strong vibrations ("sound waves") are generated. These waves travel outward away from the earthquake in all directions. A reasonably powerful earthquake can be detected all over the world at listening posts equipped with a special kind of listening apparatus called a seismograph. A wave that leaves an earthquake and is picked up in the opposite hemisphere has travelled through the deep interior of the Earth to get to its destination. Its travel has been affected by the physical state of the matter through which it travels. If we understand how sound waves travel through solid or molten rock we can decode the information in the earthquake wave and learn about the matter through which it has travelled. So we must take a detour to study briefly how sound waves travel through solids and liquids.

A sound wave of a particular pitch (or frequency) is a regular back-and-forth disturbance of the position of various parts of the material (the medium) through which the wave travels. Such a wave may travel in two ways through a solid. It may move the material back and forth in the same direction as the wave is travelling locally, in which case the wave is called a **pressure**, **primary**, or **P-wave**. It travels with a push-pull motion. Alternatively, the wave may move material from side to side perpendicular to the direction the wave is travelling, in which case the wave is called a **shear**, **secondary**, or **S-wave**. Its motion is a kind of shaking.

The sound wave consists of a series of motions (push-pull or shaking movements) that are repeated over and over at one point in the material while the wave is present. Meanwhile, the *pattern* of motion moves through the medium the way the ring of ripples expands around a stone dropped into water. We use four numbers to describe such a sound wave. If we observe one point, and watch the material oscillate to and fro, we can determine the number of oscillations each second, the **frequency**, or the time interval between successive oscillations, the **period**. A particular frequency corresponds to a pitch as heard by the ear; higher frequencies have higher pitch. Strong earthquake waves normally have such low frequencies that they are too deep to hear by ear. Another quantity of interest is the **wavelength** of the disturbance, the distance at a particular instant over which the pattern of disturbance occurs only once. And finally, as the wave moves through the material, we can measure its speed (the **sound speed**). An illustration of how P and S waves travel, and of the meaning of such terms as speed and wavelength is given in Figure 8.1.

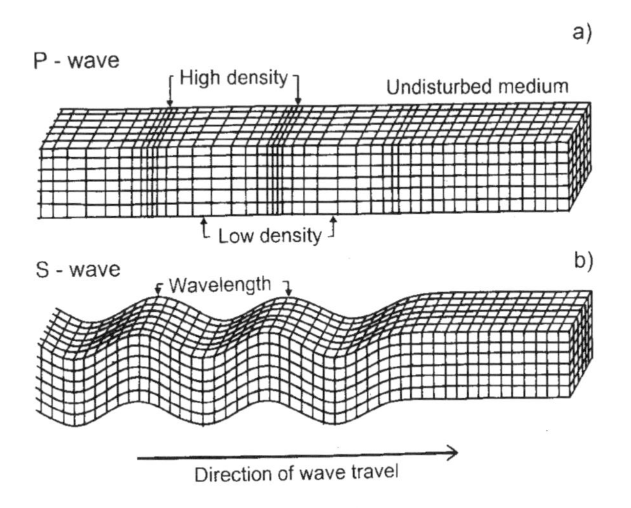

Figure 8.1: This figure shows two ways in which sound waves can move through a solid (P-waves and S-waves) or liquid (P-waves only). In the upper part of the figure, a pressure wave is arriving from the left and moving towards the right through a substance. It has moved about half-way into the column we observe; the right end is still unaffected by the wave. In the left half, the material is bunched up in some places (compressions) and stretched out in others (rarefactions). The movements that produce these compressions and rarefactions are in the same direction as the motion of the wave. In the lower part of the figure, a shear wave is moving into the column. In such a wave, the column is displaced perpendicular to the direction in which the wave is travelling. The distance from one compression to the next, or from one peak to the next, is the wavelength of the wave. The speed with which one of the high density regions, or one of the wave crests, moves to the right is the wave speed.

An extremely important difference between P- and S-waves is that P-waves, which depend only on the ability of the matter to resist compression, can travel through solids like rock, liquids such as water, and gases such as air. In contrast, S-waves, which depend on the rigidity or stiffness of the medium, can *only travel through solids*. The ordinary sound waves that we hear by ear are P-waves (with frequencies between about 20 and 20,000 oscillations each second – 20 to 20,000 Hz) travelling through the gas of the the Earth's atmosphere at a speed of about 331 meters per second. Very similar sound waves also travel through liquid water, although at considerably higher speed (about 1530 $\mathrm{m\,s^{-1}}$). In contrast, if you put your ear to the railing of a metal or concrete bridge and hear the rumble of passing cars and trucks, you are listening to both P- and S-waves travelling through the solid iron. (Light waves are S-waves, but electromagnetic waves are allowed to travel with no medium at all, so the situation is somewhat different.)

Next we look briefly at how sound waves travel over large distances, especially through materials of differing sound speed. To display how a wave moves, we can show its location and form in space at a particular instant by sketching lines along the successive "wave

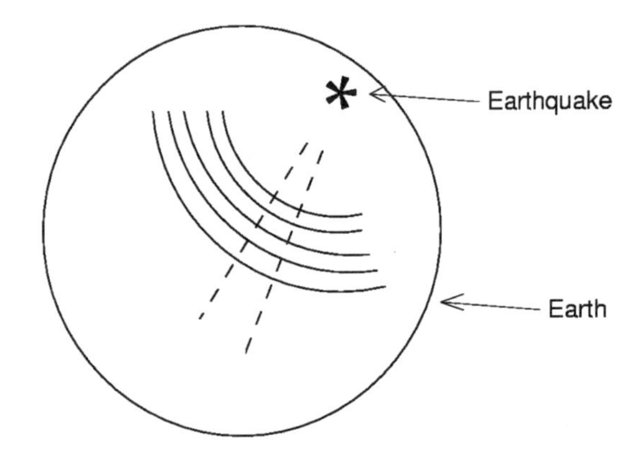

Figure 8.2: An earthquake sends out sound waves in all directions. We represent these in a drawing by sketching in the location at some instant of a number of wave crests of the sound waves emitted by the earthquake. Sometimes we shall be interested in waves sent off in a particular direction, and then we may show only the wave crests in a small beam, for example the crests lying within the pair of dashed lines.

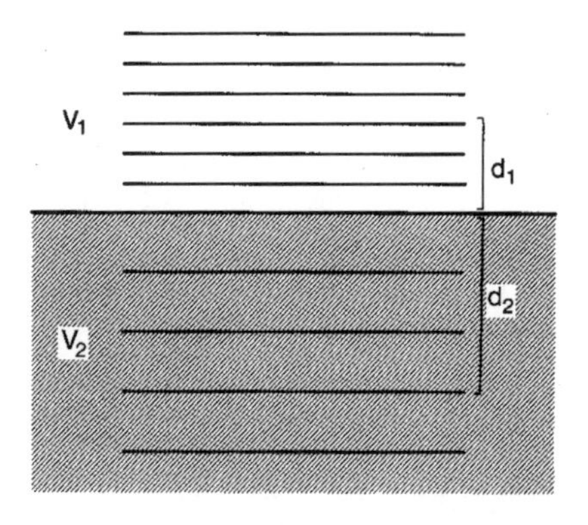

Figure 8.3: This picture shows a series of wave crests moving downward from the upper material, where the crests move slowly, into the lower medium, where they go faster. An instrument counting the crests that pass in a second finds the same number of crests (say f) each second in either the upper or lower material. But in the lower material each crest covers more distance in a second and so the wavelength (separation of crests) is larger than it is in the upper material.

crests" (imagine the crests of a wave spreading out in a pond around a pebble) such as those in Figure 8.1. The sound waves emitted by an earthquake in the Earth's crust are shown this way in Figure 8.2.

What happens when a sound wave goes from a material with a particular sound speed into another in which the sound speed is, say, higher? A simple situation is shown in Figure 8.3, where sound waves come from above to a boundary oriented parallel to the wave crests. In the upper medium, the wave travels with a particular speed and the waves have a definite wavelength. Someone stationed at the boundary will observe a certain number f of wave crests arrive from above every second (f is the frequency of the wave). The *same* number f of wave crests that arrive from above each second move across the boundary into the new medium. Now the waves move at a certain speed in the upper medium, and so a wave crest traverses a certain number v_1 of meters in one second, and all the waves within this distance from the boundary arrive at the boundary within the space of one second. (The distance v_1 travelled by a wave crest in one second is simply its speed.) Moving into the new medium, the waves travel faster, so in one second a particular wave crest will go a larger distance v_2 into the new medium, and all the f waves arriving within one second at the boundary will be within v_2 meters of the boundary at the end of the second. Since v_2 is bigger than v_1, the wave crests in the lower material will be spread out more than those in the upper medium. This is shown in Figure 8.3.

The situation of Figure 8.3 is particularly simple, because the waves move perpendicular to the boundary. If the wave crests arrive obliquely at the boundary, as each bit of a wave crest moves into the lower material it moves off at a faster speed than before. If we look at a certain wave crest at some instant and then again a short time later, the wave crest moves as shown in Figure 8.4 (a). Parts of the crest still in the upper material move slowly, but parts of the wave that have reached the lower medium go off faster and get farther away. At the later time, the originally straight wave crest has a bend in it as it crosses the boundary. Because the wave crest changes direction, the sound wave actually moves off in a new direction, as shown in Figure 8.4 (b), where a whole series of wave crests is shown. Of course, this kind of reasoning works exactly the same way for waves moving (upward) from the faster into the slower medium; a snapshot of wave crests looks just the same as in Figure 8.4, but now as the waves move from the faster material into the slower, the direction of motion changes to be more nearly normal to the boundary. This phenomenon of direction change as a wave goes through a boundary is known as **refraction**. Refraction affects a light wave in the same way as sound waves; when a light beam goes obliquely from a medium in which it travels with one speed into a medium with a different speed, for example from air into glass or water, the direction of the beam is changed.

One final aspect of refraction that is important inside a planet is what happens if a sound wave moves obliquely in a material whose sound speed increases

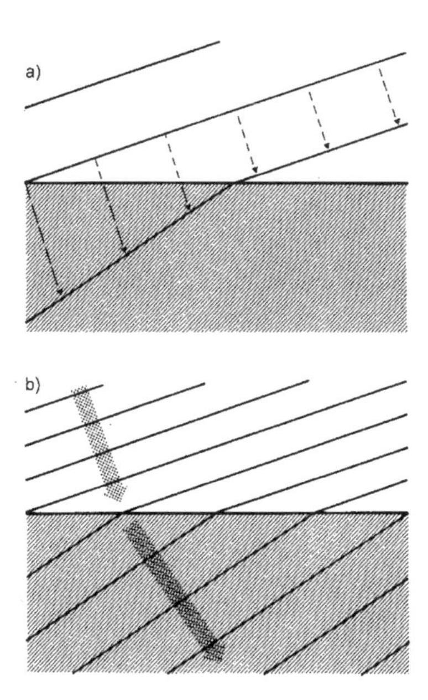

Figure 8.4: Panel (a) shows how a single wave crest moves obliquely from a material with a low speed of sound into a material with a larger wave speed. A wave crest is shown at two successive times, with the earlier and later positions connected by arrows. The parts of the crest that stay in the upper material all move a certain distance in the time interval. The parts of the wave crest that have arrived in the lower material move faster there and travel farther than those still in the upper material (the arrows on the left are longer because the crest goes farther each second). The result is that the wave crest is *bent* at the boundary. In panel (b) the effect of this bending of individual crests on the whole series of waves is shown; after entering the new medium the wave is not only moving faster but has a new direction of travel making a greater angle with the normal to the boundary.

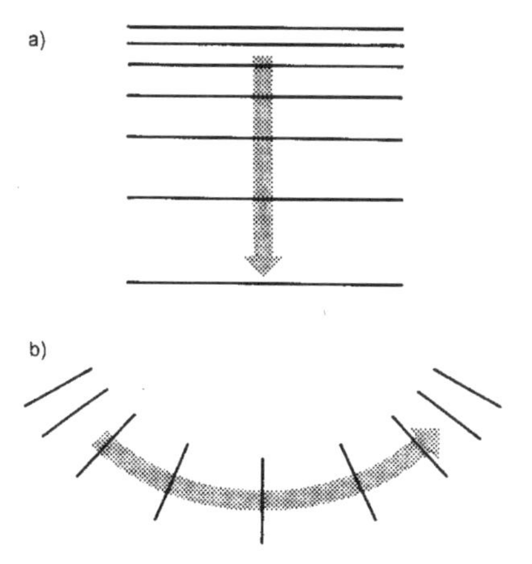

Figure 8.5: A sound wave that moves downward into a material in which the sound speed increases smoothly with depth shows still another kind of behaviour than we have seen so far. If it moves vertically, as in (a), it simply goes faster and faster and the wavelength increases with depth. In (b) it is moving obliquely. As the lower end of each wave crest travels farther in each second than the upper end, the crest gradually rotates as the wave moves along, and the beam of sound follows a curved path.

steadily and smoothly with depth, rather than increasing abruptly at a boundary. In this case as each wave crest moves downward it steadily speeds up, and if it is moving obliquely, the lower part of a particular crest moves faster than the upper part. This situation is shown in Figure 8.5. The oblique wave has its direction of motion steadily changed as one end of each crest goes faster than the other. The result is that a beam of sound waves moving obliquely follows a curved path.

Earth's internal structure

With this background about how sound waves travel through matter, we are in a position to understand how the interior of the Earth can be studied using earthquake waves.

We can imagine various possible internal structures for the Earth. It might be chemically homogeneous throughout, or it might have two or even several layers of quite different chemical compositions. The simplest possible guess (model) is that the Earth is homogeneous and solid throughout, and that the same minerals are found at all depths. With these assumptions, we can predict how earthquake waves should travel through the Earth. Because the pressure at any deep level is due to the weight of overlying rock, we expect that the pressure will increase steadily towards the centre. Substantial compression of a material normally has the effect of making sound waves travel faster through that material, and so we would expect for our model that the speed of sound waves would *increase* steadily as one goes deeper into the Earth. Because of this, individual beams of sound waves should travel through the deep Earth on curved paths. However, both P and S waves should be able to travel from an earthquake to any other point on the surface of the Earth. A few possible earthquake sound wave paths for a solid homogeneous Earth are shown in Figure 8.6.

Now in fact, when a large earthquake occurs and seismographs all over the world listen to it, it is found, contrary to the prediction of the homogeneous model, that *not* all stations can pick up sound waves sent directly from the earthquake through the Earth's interior. For any particular earthquake, direct S-waves are only detected over a little more than one half of the Earth

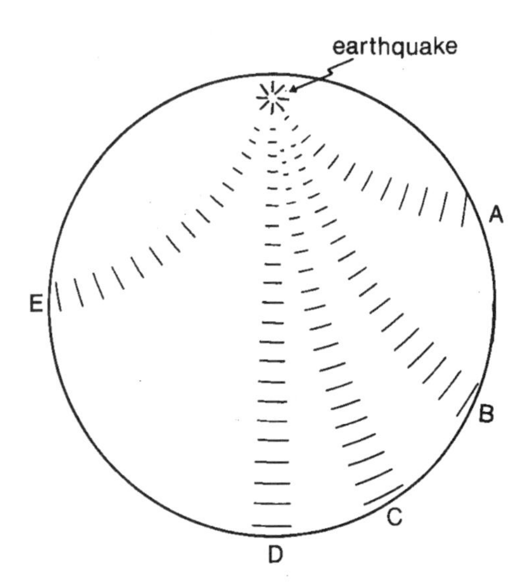

Figure 8.6: An earthquake sends out P and S waves in all directions into the Earth. These waves travel through the Earth and are detected by seismographs located in various places on the Earth. If the Earth is homogeneous, the sound waves travel along curved paths as shown. The wave reaching seismographs A through D are shown travelling directly through the Earth's interior; an example of a wave reflected from the surface is the one going to seismograph E.

(roughly in the hemisphere centred on the earthquake). Direct P-waves are detected in this same hemisphere, and also in a region centred on the opposite side of the Earth from the earthquake. The large region in the opposite hemisphere from the earthquake where no direct P- or S-waves are heard is often called the **shadow zone**. The existence of this shadow zone shows clearly that the Earth is not as simple as our initial model. We may guess that there are at least two different layers within the Earth; the interior is *not* homogeneous.

So as a next possible model of the interior of the Earth, let's try a two-layer model to see whether it is consistent with known facts. Because the Earth is very closely spherical in shape, we still assume spherical symmetry; that is, in our model all boundaries between layers will be spheres centred on the centre of the Earth. For any quantity that varies within the Earth (temperature, chemical composition etc.), we assume that it has the same value at a particular distance from the centre regardless of direction. Thus our two layer model will consist of an inner sphere of one mineral composition, called the **core**, surrounded by a larger sphere, called the **mantle**, of some different composition. We expect that the core will somehow act as an obstacle to the passage of sound from an earthquake to certain regions on the opposite side of the Earth. After some experimentation, we find that the existence of the shadow zone can be easily understood if the speed of sound in the core of the Earth is *slower* than the speed of sound in the mantle. This situation is sketched in Figure 8.7, where we show the paths followed by a number of beams of sound waves. The existence of a chemically distinct core in the Earth was discovered from just this reasoning by Englishman R. D. Oldham in 1906.

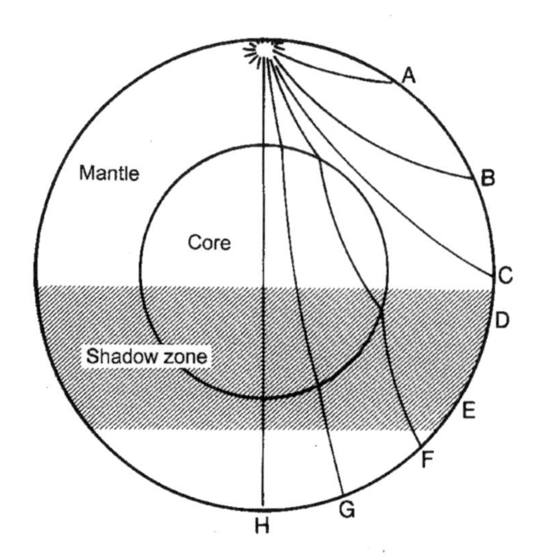

Figure 8.7: The paths followed by beams of sound waves emitted by an earthquake are shown for a two-layer Earth in which the speed of sound is lower in the core than in the mantle. The waves are observed by seismographs at locations A through H. The ring around the Earth on the opposite side of the planet from the earthquake labelled "shadow zone" is the region in which direct P-waves from the earthquake are not detected. The shadow zone for S-waves includes both that for P-waves and the cap on the opposite side of the Earth where P-waves are received.

In the figure, S- and P-waves from an earthquake travel directly through the Earth's interior and reach seismographs located at A, B, and C. The beam which starts out towards the seismograph at D is refracted at the boundary between the mantle and the core. If sound waves slow down going into the core, this beam is deflected towards the local vertical. When the beam comes to the core-mantle boundary on the other side of the core, it is refracted away from the local vertical because it speeds up. (A fraction of the wave is also reflected upwards at the boundary, complicating somewhat the observations. We will ignore such complications and focus on the essentials.) The refracted wave is therefore detected not at D but at F. Other beams that start out more directly toward the centre of the Earth all end up surfacing in a region on the opposite side of the Earth from the earthquake. Seismographs between D and E do not receive any sound waves that travel directly through the interior of the Earth. This two-layer model leads to an explanation for the shadow zone.

Exercise: Predict qualitatively where on the Earth waves would arrive directly from an earthquake if the speed of sound were *faster* in the core than in the mantle.

Exercise: Suppose that the speed of sound in the Earth's core were the same as the speed in the lower mantle, and that the core were completely molten. Would one observe a shadow zone for either P-waves or S-waves? Explain.

The fact that no direct S-waves are detected any farther from the quake than the edge of the shadow zone, even though P-waves *are* detected on the far side of the globe from the wave source, furnishes further information about the Earth's interior. The P-waves that reach the far side of the Earth from an earthquake do so after passing through the core. The fact that S-waves cannot make this same trip clearly suggests that the Earth's core offers some obstacle to S-wave that it does not present to P-waves. Recall that S-waves cannot travel through a liquid, but P-waves can. A reasonable guess as to how the core filters out the S-waves is that it is a liquid. Since the only way to turn a refractory material into a liquid is to melt it, we conclude that the Earth's core must be very hot, with a temperature of the order of 4000 K or more. This idea is supported, of course, by the widespread occurrence over the surface of the Earth of volcanos and hot springs, where strongly heated material is emerging from the crust of the Earth.

Thus the study of how earthquake waves travel through the Earth allows us to draw several very important conclusions about the Earth's interior. From the existence of the shadow zone, we find that the Earth has a distinct core surrounded by a mantle of different sound speed, and, presumably, composition. From the size of the shadow zone, we can actually measure the radius of that core; its surface is about 2890 km from the centre of the Earth. And from the fact that S-waves cannot pass through the core, we also deduce that the core is liquid, and therefore very hot, with a characteristic temperature of some thousands of K.

Compositions of the core and mantle

Now, what are the likely chemical and mineral compositions of the core and mantle? To help us to guess these, we use one other very important piece of information that we have about the Earth, namely that its average density (the total mass divided by the total volume $4\pi R^3/3$) is 5520 kilograms per cubic meter (5520 kg m^{-3}), or 5.52 times the density of water. This is actually a rather large value. An average density for rocks of the Earth's surface is about 2.7 times the density of water. This is not representative of the mantle; the surface layer of the Earth, called the crust, seems to be a thin veneer of relatively low-density rock, varying from a few km thick (under the oceans) to a few tens of km thick (under the continents), which has been separated out of the mantle. A more direct estimate of the mantle's density (and composition) may be obtained by studying magmas that come to the surface from the upper mantle; from these magmas we infer the primitive mantle composition (before the Earth's crust separated out) given in Table 8.2. This material is often called **pyrolite**. Its uncompressed density is about 3300 kg m^{-3}. Notice that the composition of pyrolite, relative to our guess of the bulk composition of the Earth as a whole (Table 8.1), has fairly similar abundances of various atoms relative to Si, except for iron, of which only about 15% as much as we predicted is present. If we consider only the most abundant elements in pyrolite, this substance has about 1.3 Mg or Fe atoms per Si atom, and thus may be thought of as having an approximate chemical formula intermediate between Mg-rich pyroxene ($MgSiO_3$) and Mg-rich olivine (Mg_2SiO_4), with a small fraction of the Mg atoms replaced by Fe.

Table 8.2: Composition of the Earth's (primitive) mantle

Element	Percentage by mass	Abundance per 10^3 Si atoms
O	45.2	3600
Mg	22.8	1220
Si	21.5	(1000)
Fe	5.9	135
Al	2.2	105
Ca	2.3	75
Na	0.2	10

Source: K. C. Condie 1997, *Plate Tectonics and Crustal Evolution* (Oxford: Butterworth & Heinemann), Table 4.1.

If we assume that the mantle is pyrolite throughout, even making reasonable allowance for an increase in density of the mantle due to the high pressures deep in the Earth's interior, the average density in the mantle is still only about 4400 kg m^{-3}. To have the mean density of the whole Earth be 25% larger than the average mantle density, the core (which occupies only about 1/6th of the total volume of the Earth) must have a very large density, about 11,000 kg m^{-3}. Allowing for the effects of pressure, we guess that the core material would have to have a density of nearly 8,000 kg m^{-3} when not compressed. The only abundant refractory element or mineral with such a high density is more or less pure iron, and so we infer that the Earth's core is composed mainly of iron. This conclusion is consistent with the existence of iron meteorites, which show that nature can fairly readily separate out nearly pure iron from a mix of the four abundant refractory elements. It also gives us a possible explanation for the low abundance of Fe in the mantle.

Our deductions about the probable compositions of the mantle (pyrolite) and the core (nearly pure iron) are consistent with the seismic data as well. The speed of P-waves in the mantle increases from about 8 to 13 km s^{-1} with depth, which is about what is expected for compressed pyrolite; in the core the speed of P-waves increases from the outer boundary to the centre from about 8 to 11 km s^{-1}, nearly correct for (highly compressed!) iron. (In fact, the density of the core inferred from seismic data requires that iron be alloyed with about 10% of a lighter material. The nature of this lighter substance is debated; water, sulphur, oxygen, and silicon are popular choices.)

We may now make a somewhat better estimate of the chemical composition of the Earth as a whole. We ignore the crust, which has less than 0.5% of the Earth's mass. We assume from detailed seismic models of the Earth's interior that the mantle comprises 67% of the Earth's mass, and that it has throughout the chemical composition of Table 8.2. The core is assumed to make up 33% of the total Earth mass, and to be composed 90% of iron and 10% of other elements (certainly some Ni, as is found in iron meteorites; probably some O, S, or Si, as discussed above) which we cannot identify with any certainty. Adding up the masses of these parts, we find the composition shown in Table 8.3. In this table, we have taken the abundances assumed for the core and mantle and re-expressed them as fractions of the whole Earth, then added them to get the final column.

Two interesting features emerge from comparing this table to Table 8.1, which contains in the last column our original guess for the Earth's bulk composition. The first is the fact that our original guess for the Earth's overall composition, based on the relative abundances of easily condensed elements in the solar nebula (as represented by the present Sun), is really pretty good. The most abundant elements in the Earth are simply the most abundant refractory elements in the Sun, in about the same relative proportions. However, a second point is that O is substantially less abundant in the Earth as a whole than it would be if the matter of the Earth were fully oxidized. This situation arises essentially because the iron core of the Earth is

Table 8.3: Estimated bulk composition of the whole Earth (percentage by mass).

Element	Mantle	Core	Whole Earth
O	30.3%		30.3%
Mg	15.3		15.3
Si	14.4		14.4
Fe	4.0	29.7%	33.7
Al	1.5		1.5
Ca	1.5		1.5
Other & uncertain		3.3	3.3
Total	67.0%	33.0%	100.0%

Source: Table 8.2.

(nearly?) unoxidized. The other elements have nearly the relative abundance expected from Table 8.1, except for iron which is somewhat more abundant in the Earth than we would expect from the solar abundances of non-volatile elements. This depletion of oxygen and the excess of iron, and the general retention otherwise of solar proportions of refractory elements, are valuable clues bearing on how the formation of the Earth occurred.

A more complex model of the Earth

Naturally, the Earth's structure is somewhat more complicated than we have so far indicated. We have already mentioned that the surface of the Earth is covered with a thin crust of rock that has become separated from the mantle by partial melting and has risen as lava to or near the surface. This crust is different under the continents from that found under the deep ocean floors. Under the oceans it is fairly thin, typically 5–10 km in thickness, and is composed primarily of basalt (recall Figure 2.12). The oceanic crust is therefore rich in silicates of Mg and Fe, and in calcic feldspar (anorthite). In contrast, the continental crust is several times thicker, typically 30–40 km, and is composed mainly of granitic rocks, rich in quartz and in calcic and sodic feldspars, and having a relatively small fraction of ferromagnesian silicates. (The continental crust contains a lot of Na, K, Ca, and Al, which may give a misleading impression of how important these four elements are in the bulk composition of the Earth.) The composition boundary between the crust and the mantle is another surface where seismic waves are refracted (and reflected); this is known as the Mohorovičić (or Moho) discontinuity.

There is also seismic evidence that the core is actually composed of an outer core that is liquid and an inner core that is solid. Both are primarily iron. Now, if the outer core is liquid because it is hot, it may seem surprising that the inner core is solid, since it should probably be still hotter than the outer core. The explanation comes from the fact that as a given substance (iron) is subjected to higher and higher pressures, the atoms are pressed closer together and it is harder to get them to move freely around one another, as they do in a liquid. This means that a higher temperature is required for melting, so that as the pressure on a material increases, the melting point rises. This idea gives us several constraints on the actual internal temperature of the Earth: in the inner core, the temperature must be *below* the melting point of iron (at that pressure); in the outer core, the temperature must be *above* the melting point; and in the rocky mantle the temperature is again *below* the melting point.

We have further information bearing on the internal temperature of the Earth in the outer layers. The observed temperature below the surface increases at an astonishing 20 degrees K (or C) or so per kilometer of depth (20 $\mathrm{K\,km^{-1}}$). If the temperature went on rising at this rate throughout the Earth, the Earth's central temperature would be about 130,000 K, and virtually the entire Earth would be gaseous! In fact, the temperature rises rapidly down to a depth of about 100 km, where the local temperature is fairly close to the melting point of the rock. The rock in this outer layer of rapid temperature rise is far enough below its melting point to be almost rigid, and is called the **lithosphere**. Below the lithosphere, everywhere in the mantle, the rock temperature is not too far below its melting temperature, and in fact the rock is soft enough to be able to deform slowly. In the mantle, the temperature rises much more slowly with depth, at a rate of less than 1 K per km (we will see why later). The approximate temperature profile of the interior of the Earth, as it has been deduced from arguments like those above, is shown in Figure 8.8.

The softness of the upper mantle rock below the crust means that if we made a particularly high pile of rock (a mountain, for example) in one spot, it would gradually sink into the mantle until its weight could be supported by the mantle. In fact, the Earth's crust is not supported by the rigidity of the mantle, but rather by *buoyancy*. Both the continental and the oceanic crust (with densities of about 2800 and 3000 kg $\mathrm{m^{-3}}$) are less dense than the mantle (which has a density of about 3300 kg $\mathrm{m^{-3}}$). They therefore effectively float on the surface of the mantle. The oceanic crust, which has a relatively constant thickness, floats rather like a board or an ice sheet on water. The continental situation is a little more complicated. The continents rise higher than the ocean floor (more like a log than a board), but to provide enough buoyancy to support this extra height they must also extend deeper below sea level. Where mountains are elevated on the continents, the continental crust extends even farther below sea level, as shown in Figure 8.9.

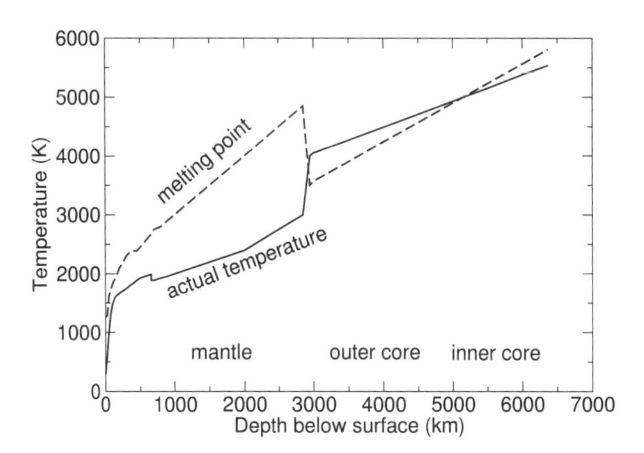

Figure 8.8: The approximate variation of temperature in the interior of the Earth as a function of distance from the surface of the Earth (solid curve). The estimated melting temperature at various levels is also shown (dashed curve). Since the actual temperature is below the melting temperature in the inner core (where pressure is high) and in the mantle (which has a high melting temperature because it is rock), both are solid, although the mantle is somewhat soft. In the outer core, the actual temperature is above the melting temperature and this region is liquid. All temperatures are uncertain by several hundred K.

8.3 The dynamic Earth and drifting continents

So far, we have looked at the Earth as an essentially static body. However, our home planet, beneath the skin, is constantly in motion. This is not obvious to the casual observer because of the very slow pace at which this motion occurs, but over millions of year the surface of the Earth changes dramatically in response to the dynamic behaviour of the Earth's interior. Geologists and geophysicists now understand this internal activity, and the surface responses to it, well enough to see the Earth as a coherent whole. But this vision was not easy to achieve.

The first hints that the Earth has a dynamic, changing nature come from examination of its surface structure. As the deep seas were explored, particularly in the years following World War II, it gradually became apparent that the Earth has two quite different types of crust. The continents, which (including their shallow offshore continental shelves) cover about 35% of the globe, mostly lie at approximately sea level. They

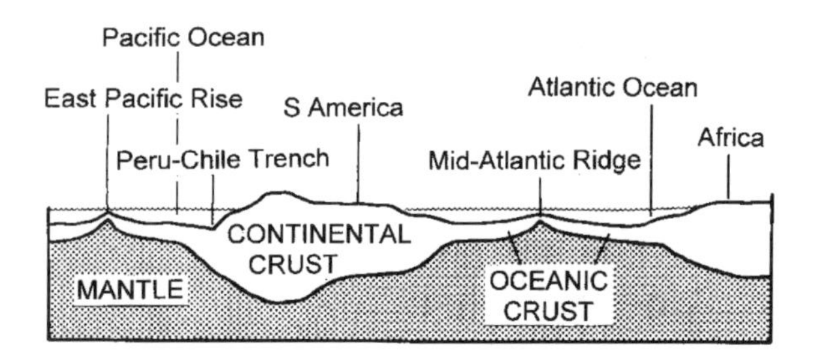

Figure 8.9: Thickness of the oceanic and continental crust in a cross section of the Earth between the Pacific Ocean and Africa. Notice how much thinner the oceanic crust is than the continental crust, and how the continental crust is especially thick under the Andes mountains. The sketch is exaggerated vertically about 1000 times.

are largely made up of granitic rock, rich in feldspars and quartz (recall Figure 2.12). The continents extend downward from 20 to 90 km, to the level at which true mantle rock, mainly composed of magnesium silicates, begins. In contrast, the sea floors, which cover the remaining 65% of the Earth's surface, are mostly at a level of about 5 km below sea level. They are composed essentially of basalt, a mixture of plagioclase feldspar and ferromagnesians. This crust is about 5% denser than the continental crust. The sea floor crust is only a few km thick above the level at which it changes to the mantle. This bimodal structure is at first glance quite puzzling: why do the continents and sea floors have such different chemistry, altitude, and thickness, and why have the continents not simply eroded down to below sea level and disappeared?

Further examination reveals another mystery. A very prominent aspect of continents is the presence on some 5% of the Earth's surface of **mountain chains**, which are also the principal continental regions of earthquake and volcanic activity. Remarkably, a close look at a globe reveals that almost all the highest mountains on Earth belong to one of two enormous, essentially continuous, chains. One chain almost encircles the Pacific Ocean. This mountain chain starts as the Andes in South America, which run the full north-south length of the continent. The chain continues through Central America, along the west coast of Mexico as the Sierra Madres, through the western U. S. A. and Canada as the Rockies, and from there circles the northern Pacific as the Alaska Range and the Aleutian islands (which are simply submerged mountains poking up through the sea). Japan forms the next link in the chain. The mountains continue as an irregular string of islands in the western Pacific, through the Philippines and New Guinea, and end south of New Zealand. Because of the intense volcanic and earthquake activity all along this string of mountains (recall the spectacular explosion of Mount Saint Helens in the northwestern U. S. A.in 1980), this chain is often called the *Ring of Fire.*

The second chain starts in Europe in the Pyrenees between France and Spain, continues across southern Europe as the Alps and Carpathians, becomes the mountains of Turkey, the Caucasus chain in southern Russia, then the Zagros mountains in Iran, and passes north of India as the Hindu Kush and Himalayan mountains. This chain then turns south into the Indian Ocean in a great arc that includes Malaysia and Indonesia, and ends by joining the Pacific chain in New Guinea. How did these two great mountain chains come into existence, what gives them structure on a global scale, and why are they the sites of most of the volcanic eruptions and earthquakes that occur on the continents?

In the past half-century, with the development of sonar and deep-diving submarine devices, the seas have also unexpectedly been found to conceal enormous mountain chains. The Atlantic Ocean, for example, is bisected by a 2 km high ridge that runs from Iceland to the southern end of the ocean. This **mid-ocean ridge** joins onto other long ridge chains that rise from the abyssal plains of other seas and oceans. Remarkably, these undersea mountain chains are also the sites of frequent earthquakes, like their visible continental cousins. In fact, both the ocean ridge system and the high continental mountain chains can virtually be mapped using the positions of shallow earthquakes. On the continents, these earthquakes clearly occur in a band along the mountain chains. Almost all oceanic earthquakes occur in the oceanic ridges, particularly down the middle of the Atlantic.

A third, apparently unrelated, mystery concerns the western coast of Africa and the eastern coast of South America. The bulge in the South American coast in Brazil is almost the same shape as the dent in the west coast of Africa (look at Figure 8.10). In fact, if one continent is moved over next to the other on a globe, they can be fitted together quite closely, especially if the fit is made at the edge of the continental shelves. This could be dismissed as a bizarre coincidence if it were not for a number of other striking features that are found when the two continents are matched up in this way. First, each continent is made up of smaller geologic provinces of various ages and rock type. When the two continents are fitted together, a number of the boundaries between provinces appear to line up across the shorelines, from one continent to the other. Furthermore, when the succession of rock layers and fossils in western Africa and eastern South America are compared, similar layers are found on the two sides of the Atlantic in regions that join when the two continents are matched up – for layers between about 500 and 100 million years old. More recent layers do not match. A particularly bizarre aspect of this correspondence is that around 270 million years ago, regions in both continents – that today are near the equator – were covered by glacial ice. Although it is not obvious how this could have happened, all this evidence – and much more like it – points in the same direction. At one time, hundreds of millions of years ago, it seems that the coasts of Africa and South America were in contact.

The realization that South America and Africa seem to fit together, and that the fit joins up similar geological structures on the two continents, led German meteorologist Alfred Wegener (1880–1930) to propose in 1915 that the continents actually move about, very slowly, on the surface of the Earth. This idea, called **continental drift**, quickly ran up against the very reasonable objection that a huge slab of solid rock (a continent) could hardly plow through another slab (the solid ocean floor), and so for many years Wegener's theory was not accepted by most Earth scientists.

However, in the early 1960's, American geophysicist Harry Hess proposed a new theory of how continental drift might operate. His idea is known as **sea-floor spreading**. Hess based his idea on the then recent discovery of the mid-ocean ridge system, and on measurements showing that the oceanic crust is much thinner than the continental crust. He suggested that, rather than the continents plowing through the ocean floor, new oceanic crust is continuously created at the mid-ocean ridges, moves away from these ridges, and eventually returns into the mantle at deep ocean trenches and continental margins. Hess suggested that the ocean floor is continuously moving slowly over the planet's surface, along with the continents, like a giant conveyor belt.

In Hess' theory, these crust motions are in response to heat carried by slowly moving flow of solid rock in the Earth's mantle. The temperature throughout the mantle is not far below the melting point of the rocks there, so that mantle rock is able to deform very slowly, like silly putty. The temperature difference between the bottom and top of the mantle is large enough to drive mantle rock to very slowly turn over and over in giant convective motions, moving at a rate of only a few cm per year. As we have already seen (Figure 8.9), the continents and the ocean crust both float on the denser mantle, like thin sheets of ice on water. Hess' idea was that because of convection in the mantle, *both* the continents and the sea floor drift together over the soft mantle rock. Sea floor (only marginally less dense than the upper mantle) is created at the ocean ridges, floats a few thousand km in a time of the order of 100 million years, and then sinks back into the mantle. In contrast, the continents, which have lower density than oceanic crust, resist being swept back into the mantle. They move about in a rather disorderly manner, sometimes separating from one another and sometimes colliding, but never sinking. An important piece of evidence consistent with this basic idea is the fact that *nowhere* on the ocean floor are sediments known to be more than about 160 million years old, although rocks more than 3000 million years old are found in small parts of most of the continents.

Crucial new data supporting the idea of sea-floor spreading came to light at about the same time as Hess' proposal, with the discovery of **magnetic sea-floor anomalies**. To follow the argument here, we need to understand several points. First, the Earth's general magnetic field leaves a permanent imprint in rock that forms by solidification of molten lava. As the lava cools below a temperature of about 800 to 900 K (500 to 600 C), it takes on a weak permanent magnetism aligned with the local direction of the Earth's magnetic field. This "remnant magnetism" actually enables us to study the strength and direction of the Earth's magnetic field in the past, by examining regions where a long series of (radioactively datable) lava flows have occurred, one on top of another. Studying such series of lava flows, we find that the Earth's magnetic field has not been constant in the past, but instead the direction of the field has *reversed* at irregular intervals, roughly once or twice per million years. Now if Hess' theory of sea-floor spreading is correct, and new sea floor is rising as lava and solidifying at the mid-ocean ridges, the ocean floors should acquire the magnetic imprint of the current magnetic field as a weak magnetization in the rocks.

Just such magnetization was discovered in magnetic measurements made from oceanographic vessels during the 1950's. The magnetization of the sea-floor revealed a remarkable pattern: the weak magnetic field left in the rocks is in the form of bands parallel to the axis of the mid-ocean ridge, symmetric about the ridge axis, and with rock magnetization alternately parallel to and opposite to the current direction of the Earth's magnetic field. These stripes of rock magnetization were interpreted by Vine and Matthews as a natural consequence of Hess' theory of sea-floor spreading. At the time the lava injected into the ridge cools enough to retain magnetization, it takes on the direction of the Earth's current field. As old lava moves away from the ridges and new lava is injected, the magnetic record of the Earth's magnetism is carried away from the ridge. When the Earth's field reverses, new lava takes on the new field direction, and is subsequently carried away

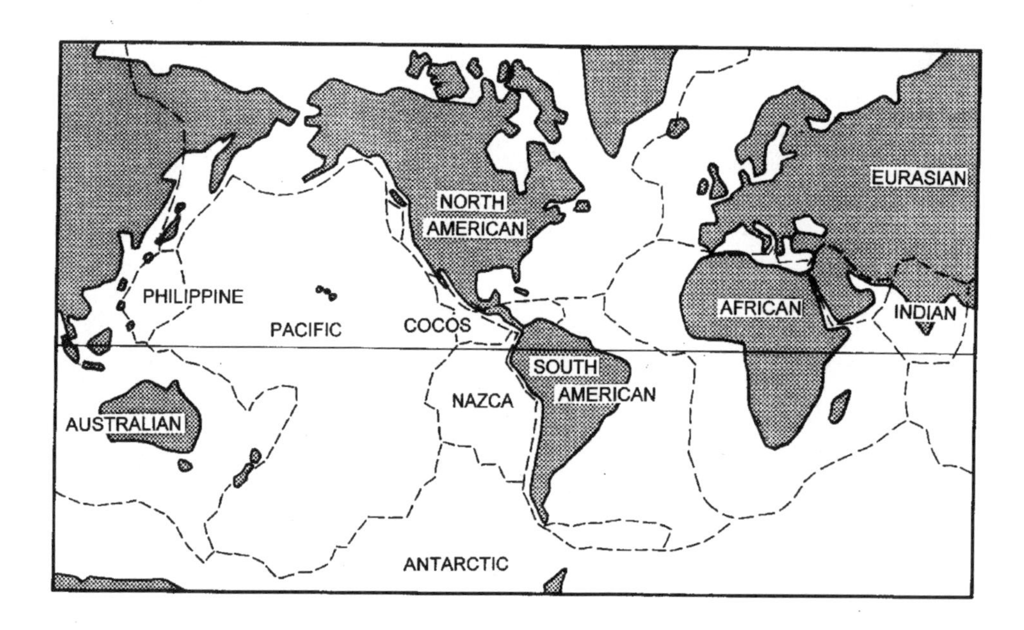

Figure 8.10: A world map showing the major tectonic plates currently moving about on the surface of the Earth. The names given to the larger plates are labelled. The plate boundary running down the middle of the Atlantic, the Mid-Atlantic Ridge, is a region of new crust formation; the boundary on the west side of North and South America is mostly a converging boundary.

from the ridge axis, and so on. In effect, the sea floor is a slowly moving magnetic tape, carrying a recording of the alternating magnetic field of the Earth away from both sides of the ridge axis. This argument explained the magnetic anomalies so naturally by using the ideas of sea-floor spreading, and the magnetic stripes were so difficult to understand in any other way, that within a few years in the 1960's almost everyone had come to accept sea-floor spreading – and continental drift – as correct.

Plate tectonics and the Earth's crust

Continental drift and sea-floor spreading have developed into a more general framework of ideas, now called **plate tectonics**, that enable us to understand in a coherent way a myriad of previously puzzling and apparently unrelated aspects of the Earth's surface. It appears that the Earth's crust is divided into a number of irregular plates, of which about twelve are relatively large. Each of these plates moves about independently on the Earth's surface as a result of the slow movements of rock in the mantle. Where two plates are separating, as in the middle of the Atlantic Ocean and around Antarctica, new oceanic crust forms on an oceanic ridge from lava rising out of the mantle, and spreads away from the ridge axis. Where an oceanic plate collides with a continent on another plate, as is currently occurring along the east coast of the Pacific Ocean, the denser oceanic plate sinks down into the mantle under the less dense continent: the ocean plate is **subducted**. In such a region, mountains are uplifted on the continent that is riding over the ocean plate as fresh lava is released into the continental plate from the subducting ocean plate. Similarly, where two oceanic plates collide, as in the northern and the western Pacific, one is subducted under the other, usually with the creation of an arc of islands. Where two continental plates collide, as the Indian subcontinent is currently colliding with Asia, the plate motion is gradually stopped and a particularly high mountain chain (in this case the Himalayas) is produced. The processes of emplacement of new crust on the oceanic ridges, and of collision and subduction, are the underlying cause of volcanic and earthquake activity. This geological activity allows us to identify the boundaries of the plates and map them. The current plates are shown in Figure 8.10. The cycle of ocean floor creation and subduction are shown in Figure 8.11, which illustrates the creation of new crust along an oceanic ridge, and in Figure 8.12, which show the subduction of ocean floor offshore from an island arc such as the islands of Japan.

Exercise: Find a good map of North and South America and trace the mountain chain along the west coast of the two continents, following it as far as possible into Alaska and the Pacific Ocean.

Plate tectonics quite naturally explains the world-

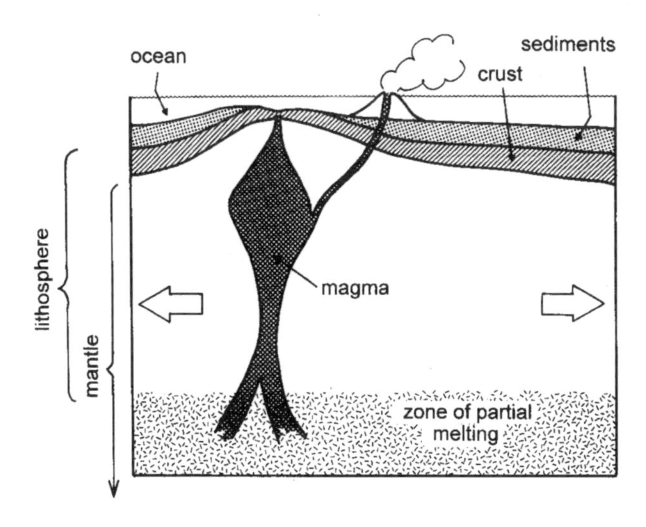

Figure 8.11: A sketch showing the creation of new sea floor in the middle of an ocean. Magma rises from a deep chamber fed by the zone of partial melting, and forms the volcanic mountain chain of the mid-ocean ridge system. Some of the lava forms an oceanic island. Newly created ocean floor slowly moves away from the ridge as indicated by the large arrows in the lithosphere, gradually acquiring an ever-increasing cover of sediments as time goes on.

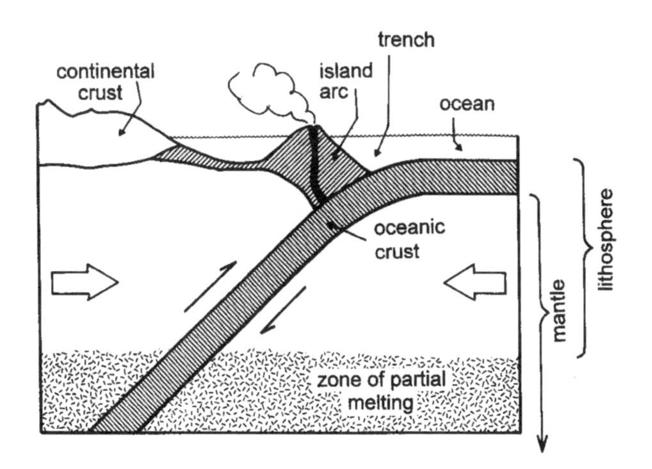

Figure 8.12: Ocean floor collides with the outer edge of a continental plate, and sinks down into the mantle beneath the oncoming plate. It penetrates several hundred km into the zone of partial melting before being absorbed into the mantle. Where the plate dives beneath the surface, volatiles (such as sea water and CO_2) sweated out of the descending rock rise to the surface with some molten rock and form volcanos, often in the form of an elongated island arc.

wide nature of mountain chains by the geography of the plates. The Ring of Fire in the Pacific is a consequence of the convergence of several plates towards the Pacific Ocean, which is shrinking in size at a rate of a few cm per year. The ongoing uplifting of new continental mountain chains, replacing older ones worn down by erosion, is driven by the continuing slow turnover of mantle rock due to the temperature difference between the bottom and top of the mantle. The continents are carried around by this process, sometimes colliding to form larger units often called supercontinents, sometimes breaking apart to form smaller units. The continents of today coalesced to form a supercontinent known as "Pangaea" between 450 and 320 million years ago (see Figure 8.13). This continent broke apart about 160 million years ago, and we live in the era following the breakup, when the continents are once again adrift. Earlier eras of supercontinent formation are recognized; a supercontinent we call "Rodinia" formed between 1.3 and 1 Gyr ago and fragmented about 750 million years ago.

Another interesting aspect of plate tectonics is the creation of islands or island chains by lava production in a **hot spot**. Apparently there are several tens of regions throughout the mantle in which plumes of relatively hot rock are moving slowly upwards, like smoke rising from a chimney on a windless day. Such a plume produces magma when it approaches the surface, and the molten rock flows out onto the crust, often as an active volcano. If the tectonic plate above the hot spot has little motion relative to the plume, a large island may gradually be built up. This is how Iceland, which sits nearly astride the mid-Atlantic ridge, is growing. Where the crustal plate is moving over the hot spot, as is the case in the Pacific, a chain of islands will develop. The more or less continuous string of islands and undersea mountains (called seamounts) that extends north-west from the Hawaiian island chain, through Midway and into the Emperor chain, is an example of such activity. The plate is moving towards the north-west over the hot spot, so the site of volcanic activity is shifting steadily towards the south-east. It is currently offshore from the "Big Island" of Hawaii, the largest and most recent of the Hawaiian islands, and volcanic mountain building is going on undersea as well as on the Big Island, where eruptions from the volcanos of Mauna Loa and Kilauea are common.

Mantle convection and plate motion

The unifying idea of plate tectonics allows us to understand a large variety of geological and geophysical phenomena. However, so far we have only discussed how plate motions produce the observed features on the Earth's surface. We still need to examine the mechanism by which plate motion occurs.

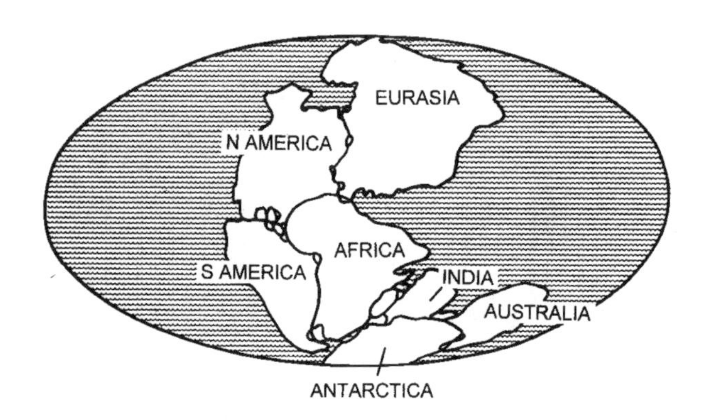

Figure 8.13: A world map showing the distribution of the continents over the globe about 200 million years ago when they were assembled in the supercontinent Pangaea.

Probably the most puzzling aspect of plate tectonic for most people is the idea that flow of material can occur in solid rock. This phenomenon is related to the convective motions that occur in a pot on a stove when a thick liquid such as a cream soup has almost reached the boiling point. As the temperature rises, the liquid starts to turn over gently in "cells", visibly separated circulation patterns, in which liquid rises near the centre of the pot, flows out towards the outer edge, and descends again towards the bottom of the pot. (These smooth motions should be distinguished from the ones that happen when vigorous boiling is established; then, bubbles of water vapour rise rapidly from the bottom of the pot, producing a chaotic motion of the fluid.)

Just such motions, intermixed columns of rising and descending material, can occur in the Earth's mantle. The driving force is the temperature difference between the inner and outer boundaries of the mantle, and the existence of small temperature variations within the mantle. If a volume of rock near the bottom of the mantle becomes somewhat hotter than nearby material, it expands a little, becomes a little less dense than its surroundings, and feels a buoyant force upwards from its surroundings. Similarly, an unusually cool volume of rock near the surface tends to not be supported enough by its surrounding, and so it sinks. These motions are possible *even in solid rock* because the rock in the mantle is near enough its melting point that it can be deformed slowly. (Roughly, the temperature must be more than about 2/3rds of the melting temperature for yielding or "plastic" behaviour to occur in a solid.) For quick motions, such as the passage of an earthquake wave, the rock acts as a solid, but under a force applied for long enough it gradually yields. The mantle behaves very much like silly putty, which will bounce when dropped, but which gradually settles from a ball into a puddle when left on a table. Because rock only yields very slowly, mantle motions occur at a glacial pace; a single cycle of convective overturn in the mantle may take a billion years! (Glaciers offers another example of flowing solid material, a flow also made possible by the fact that the ice is not far below its melting point.)

In spite of the extreme slowness of mantle motions, heat is carried outward from the relatively hot region near the core boundary to the cooler boundary with the crust with such high efficiency that the mantle maintains the very low temperature drop rate of less than 1 K per km of depth change.

In contrast to the bulk of the mantle, the rocks close to the surface, which lose heat to the ocean and atmosphere and ultimately to space, are at low enough temperatures relative to their melting temperatures that they are *not* plastic and deformable. Instead, they are more brittle and elastic, in the sense that they can bend or break, like a sheet of plywood, but not flow. This region, you recall, is the lithosphere. In this layer, heat is not carried by (efficient) convection of solids, but by (inefficient) conduction. The drop in temperature across one km of lithosphere is between 10 and 30 K compared to a drop of order 1 K across one km in the convecting mantle. Thus the region of plastic flow in the mantle is capped by a rigid surface layer in which a significant part of the total temperature drop from centre to surface of the Earth occurs. This rigid surface layer, as we have already seen, essentially floats on the softer mantle.

Note that the boundary between the rigid lithosphere and the softer rock of the underlying mantle is a *thermal* boundary that occurs, under the oceans, well down into the mantle. The bottom of the lithosphere is *not* a composition boundary. The main composition change in this region is the change from crustal basalt to mantle pyrolite, which occurs at a depth of only a few km in the oceanic crust. Even the bottom of a slab of thicker continental crust is usually shallower than the bottom of the lithosphere.

The next question to take up is to try to understand how plate motion occurs. That is, we need to identify the force or forces that move the tectonic plates over the Earth's surface. Several plausible solutions are available:

- The plates may be simply swept along by the circulation of mantle rock, like logs floating on a river. In this model **basal drive** is applied directly by the mantle circulation to the underside of each plate, and the plates just try to keep up with the mantle circulation.

- The oceanic ridges represent regions of hot upwelling mantle rock, and the intrusion of magma from such upwelling regions may force the plates apart. This is called the **ridge-push** model.

- The subduction of an ocean plate may be the result of sufficient negative buoyancy (tendency to sink) that the sinking region pulls the plate along towards the subduction zone. This is called the **slab-pull** model.

Whatever combination of these forces is important, the drive force acts against various resistance forces. These resistive forces include the resistance produced by plates colliding against or sliding past one another, and the resistance of mantle rock as a plate descends into a subduction zone. There could also be resistance if a plate is moving faster than the mantle rock beneath it. In any case, we expect that the resistance forces will increase with increasing plate speed, and so whatever the driving forces, a speed will be found for each plate at which the driving force just overcomes (balances) the resistive, frictional forces and keeps the plate moving at an approximately constant speed. This is just the situation that occurs when driving an automobile or a boat; the drive furnished by the engine increases the speed of the vehicle until the forward force provided just balances the friction due to wind, motion through the water, etc. If the engine power is increased, the vehicle accelerates until a new balance is reached, and then moves forward at a new constant speed. A similar balance is presumably struck between the plate driving force(s) and resistance, so that plates subjected to a larger force move more quickly than plates propelled by less force.

Thus, one way to test the importance of the various forces above is to compare their speeds to the amount of the various drive forces as estimated simply by the size of surface area available for basal drive, or the length of edges available for ridge-push and slab-pull forces. To do this, we first need a frame of reference relative to which we can measure plate speed. Since the whole surface of the Earth is in (very slow) motion, it isn't obvious how to find such a reference frame. However, it appears that the hot spots define approximately what we need. They are observed to be in motion relative to one another, but their relative speeds are only about 1/10th as large as the relative speeds of the tectonic plates. They can therefore be used to define a suitable frame of reference for us, relative to which we measure the speeds of the plates.

The first model of plate driving force, with the plate simply riding passively on convective circulation motions of mantle rock, seems to be worth considering for some plates. The Pacific plate, the South American plate, the North American plate, and the Nazca plate (along the west coast of South America) all originate on ocean ridges and move (relative to the host spot frame of reference) towards subduction zones. However, for other plates, this model makes less sense. The Antarctic plate and the African plate both are practically completely surrounded by ocean ridges, and hardly move at all. If mantle rock is rising along all their edges and moving under them, where is it descending? We can go one step further, and compare the speeds of the various plates to their surface areas. If we consider two plate, one twice as large in all horizontal dimensions as the other, on the basal drive model the larger plate should feel four times the drive force of the smaller plate, but have only twice as much friction since the length of the subducting edge (where most of the friction would probably arise) is only doubled. Thus the larger the plate, the larger (on average) we would expect the drift speed to be. However, when we compare speeds with sizes, no relationship (correlation) is apparent. Some large area plates (Pacific, South American, Indian) are moving at several cm yr^{-1} while others (African, Antarctic, Eurasian) move at less than 1 cm yr^{-1}. The tiny Philippine plate has one of the largest speeds. The basal pull model does not seem to provide a coherent explanation of plate motion.

Similarly, we can test the ridge-push model by comparing plate speed to the percentage of its edge which is ocean ridge (introducing a correction to account for the fact that in some plates ocean ridges occur on opposite sides of the plate, thus presumably pushing in opposite directions). When we make this comparison, only a weak relationship between the length of ocean ridge edge surrounding a plate and the plate speed is found. The North American and South American plates both have long ridges mostly on only one side, but are moving several time slower than the Pacific plate which has a similar (net) amount of ocean ridge. The ridge-push force also does not seem to be the dominant force, although it may be significant.

However, when the speed is compared to the length of the (uncanceled) subducting edges, a very strong relation emerges clearly. Plates with a small fraction of their edges on subduction zones *all* move slowly, while *all* plates with a substantial fraction of their boundaries on subduction zones move quickly. Subduction seems to be the prime suspect for the main driving force moving the Earth's tectonic plates. But now how can subduction provide a force that can pull on a large, rigid lithospheric plate and make it move over the soft mantle rock beneath it? To understand this point we need to look at why and how subduction occurs.

New oceanic crust is formed by partial melting of the top layers of the mantle. The rock there is near its melting point, and a certain fraction of the rock actually becomes liquid, although most remains solid. (Recall the discussion of partial melting in Chapter 2.) The fraction of mantle rock with the lowest melting point is basalt, and it is this basalt which melts, rises to the surface, and cools to form the new oceanic crust at ocean ridges. The density of the new oceanic crust (about 3000 kg m^{-3}) is somewhat lower than that of mantle rock (about 3300 kg m^{-3}). Below this layer of new crust is a rather thin layer of rigid mantle, so that the newly formed lithosphere is a two-layer cake perhaps 10 km thick. Because about a third of this new lithosphere is low density basalt, the average density of the lithosphere is less than that of the mantle rock below, and the new plate floats on the softer rock.

As the new ocean crust moves away from the ocean ridge, it continues to thicken as further low melting-point basalt from the top of the mantle leaks upwards and collects beneath the crust. As heat leaks upwards to the surface, this basalt gradually cools and freezes onto the underside of the crust. At the same time, the layer of rigid mantle rock beneath the crust is thickening at a more rapid pace. As the new lithosphere moves away from the ocean ridge, the crust increases in thickness from one or two km to about six or eight km in 1000 km of lateral movement. At the same time, the *total* thickness of the rigid lithospheric plate increases from about ten km to about 100 km. This process is similar to the gradual thickening of ice on a lake in winter, which also occurs as heat leaks out through the ice, allowing more and more water to freeze onto the underside of the surface ice sheet. However, as the layer of solid crustal rock (or the ice sheet on a lake) thickens, the insulating ability of the sheet increases, and so the heat leakage rate falls, and the rate of freezing and accumulation of new material slows down.

This gradual thickening and cooling of the lithosphere as it moves away from its source at the oceanic ridge has very important consequences for its eventual fate. This rigid outer layer is cooler than the hot mantle rock beneath, but it is partly composed of crustal basalt of lower average density compared to mantle rock. The lower temperature tends to make the mantle layer of the lithosphere denser than the soft mantle rock beneath, but the low density crustal rocks tend to make the average lithosphere density somewhat less than the uppermost mantle rock. However, as the crust and lithosphere thicken, the increasing fraction of relatively cool mantle rock in the plate gradually increases the local average density. Roughly 20 million years after its formation at the oceanic ridge, at a distance of several hundred km from its origin, the average density of the plate has risen to about the same value as in the underlying soft mantle, and the plate ceases to have positive buoyancy. From this point on, it is able to spontaneously descend into the mantle, although subduction usually does not happen until the slab is of order 80 or 100 million years old. This loss of buoyancy is the fundamental cause of subduction.

When the plate eventually has a large enough overdensity to begin to sink into the mantle, it bends and starts to descend at an angle of roughly 45°. As it sinks, the hotter surrounding mantle rock begins to heat the descending slab. However, the slab is typically about 100 km thick, and heat leaks in rather slowly. As a result, the slab remains cooler – and hence denser – than its surroundings for some hundreds of km down into the mantle. Its excess density insures that the slab continues to experience a net downward force for many hundred of km. This is the origin of the slab-pull force. As the slab descends, it pulls behind it the plate of which it is a part, thus driving plate motion on the Earth's surface.

The ocean ridge where new crust is forming is a relatively passive region. It is basically a tension fault (a graben) that is being pulled open by the slab-pull force of the subducting edge of the plate. As the fault opens, the pressure on the underlying mantle is reduced, and mantle rock rises into the opening. As it rises, the decreasing pressure lowers the melting point of the rock, and much partial melting – and some complete melting – takes place. A magma chamber forms under the ridge, where the basalt of the new oceanic crust is produced as the low melting point component of the upper mantle.

Thus it appears that the plate motion of continental drift and sea-floor spreading is produced by the continuous formation of a rigid surface skin on top of the soft mantle rock, followed by the movement of the plate away from the production region and eventually by the development of negative buoyancy leading to sinking. As the skin sinks, it pulls the plate behind it along, driving the plate motions that we observe on the surface. The ultimate energy source for the motion is the transport of heat from the Earth's core and mantle to the surface, where it is partly dissipated in tectonic activity (earthquakes, volcanism) and eventually radiated out into space.

The continents

Now, how do the continents fit into this picture? We have already seen how they are rafted about, floating on the mantle and pulled and pushed by motions of the ocean floor, and how this motion leads to the repeated creation of mountain chains in regions where plates collide. But we have not yet understood how the continents came to exist, or what mechanism has given them an average chemical composition substantially different from that of the oceanic crust.

To find answers to both of these questions, we try to find regions where new continental crust may be forming today. There is no obvious evidence of continent formation over most of the continental surface of the Earth; for example, in North America east of the Rocky Mountains the land is generally quiet. If anything, that part of the continent is *losing* mass by erosion, which every year carries millions of tons of soil and rock out to sea, where it becomes part of the sediment layer on top of the basaltic ocean crust. However, the mountain arcs of the western part of continent, with volcanic lava eruptions and high mountain terrain that was clearly (from the fossil record) once below sea level, are prime suspects as regions of new continent formation.

When we look more closely at such regions – *destructive* plate margins from the point of view of the subducting ocean crust – our suspicions are confirmed. A good example is the western side of South America, where the Nazca (oceanic) plate is descending beneath the edge of the continent. On the continent, the ridge of the Andes mountains, rising in places to 5 km above sea level, reveals new continental crust recently created from underground and surface lava flows. This vast mass of rock can rise to such heights because it is supported below ground by the buoyancy of a particularly deep low density crust, which under the mountain chain can extend to more than 60 km below sea level, as seen in Figure 8.9. The regions of current mountain building, and the deep crust beneath, is where new continental crust is being created, at a rate (adding up all such regions in the world) of nearly one km^3 per year.

However, we want to go beyond simply identifying the site of new continental crust production, and try to understand how volcanism occurs in such regions, and why it adds low density rock to the continents.

The lava which eventually heats and adds mass to the continental ridge at a subduction zone is the result of a series of processes which begin with the descending slab of oceanic crust. As the slab descends, it is resisted by friction, and this friction generates quite a lot of heat. Furthermore, as the slab sinks, it moves into mantle of higher and higher temperature. The heat flowing into the descending slab of basalt raises its temperature. Since the top few km of the descending slab solidified originally under water, the minerals of this layer contain much water built into their crystal structure. As the temperature of the slab gets higher, this water is cooked out of the rock and rises into the overlying wedge of mantle (see Figure 8.12), where it both heats the mantle rock and (by adding water) lowers the melting point of the lowest temperature melt fraction (recall the discussion of partial melting in Chapter 2). The low melting point minerals in the mantle wedge are, roughly, the same basalt that separates to form the oceanic crust, and any "incompatible" atoms that simply don't fit easily into the structure of the dominant residual solid minerals. Some fraction of the mantle wedge melts, and this melt rises towards the bottom of the continental crust. As this basalt reaches the bottom of the crustal layer, it heats the crust and passes some of the water on to higher layers. The added heat and water, in turn, lead to partial melting within the crust, producing magma, some of which erupts on the surface, but much of which accumulates in great underground pools (batholiths) at higher levels within the crust. This process of underplating the continental crust with partly molten material gradually results in the transfer into the crustal layer of the lower density magma, together with incompatible elements. The partial melting at the mantle-crust boundary leaves behind a residue of increasingly dense rock, which eventually becomes too dense to be buoyant, and which sinks back into the mantle, having been stripped of its lowest density component. Thus the continental crust gradually accumulates granitic rock separated out of the underlying mantle at the subduction zone.

This is the principal process of continent growth. It is continuing today, so that the fraction of the Earth's surface covered by continental rock is slowly increasing. However, the current rate of increase is too small to have built the continents in the 4.5 Gyr available; the rate of growth of continents must have been at least two to three times faster in the distant past. This is reasonable, considering that the younger Earth was almost certainly hotter than it is today, so that mantle convection would have occurred more rapidly than at present.

Of course, the continents are also losing mass, mainly by erosion, but the rate of mass loss by erosion is lower than the rate of creation of new continental crust. Furthermore, as a slab of sea floor dives beneath a continent, a substantial fraction of the eroded material, which has accumulated as sediment on the sea floor, is scraped off the descending oceanic plate and forms a wedge of sediment at the continental margin. Thus much of the eroded material is in fact recycled back into continental crust.

8.4 Origin and early evolution of the Earth

Although the interior of the Earth is remote from direct experiment, we have managed to learn quite a lot about its gross chemical, physical, and thermal structure. We now try to use the available information about the present state of the Earth to obtain at least a plausible idea of how the interior structure could have formed and developed early in the Earth's history.

We have already looked at some aspects of the situation in the solar system at the time that the planets formed. The state of affairs has been examined in connection with the formation of the Sun, the origin of chondritic meteorites, and the development of asteroids. We suppose that the planets, like meteorites and asteroids, formed almost entirely out of material in the inner solar nebula that had condensed into solid form, first as dust grains orbiting the proto-Sun with various speeds due to the effect of gas drag, then as planetesimals formed by collisions of the grains, and finally as planets produced by coagulation of colliding planetesimals. Within two or three AU of the proto-Sun, the condensed matter was almost exclusively rocky (mainly oxides of Fe, Mg and Si, and perhaps some free iron). The most abundant substances in the nebula, H and He, as well as the main compounds of C, N, and O that can become ices (CH_4, NH_3, H_2O, etc.) were almost entirely still in the form of gases, and were not incorporated to any important extent into the forming planets.

Three basic questions that we would like to answer are the following.

- How did the Earth come to have its specific bulk chemical composition, which (as we shall shortly see) is somewhat different from that of each of the other terrestrial planets?
- How did the Earth develop its layered structure? In particular, how did it obtain a metallic core?
- Finally, how was the high temperature of the Earth's interior produced, how has this temperature changed over time, and how has it influenced the Earth's internal structure and subsequent history?

We currently have at best rather tentative and uncertain answers to these questions. This is because we do not yet know much about two key aspects of the formation of the Earth. First, we have rather little information about the state of the solar nebula as the Earth formed. We do not know the exact composition of the material that had condensed as solids when the Earth started to form. We also are unsure whether the composition of the solids in the Earth's accretion region changed as the Earth formed, either because the nebula was cooling or because of mixing between different regions of the nebula. Did the nebula condense first (with a specific composition at each distance from the Sun) and then the planets form from what was available at each distance, or was the condensing matter swept up into proto-planets as fast at it froze out, so that cooling of the nebula during formation of the planets produced a layered planet?

Secondly, we don't know enough about how the planetary accretion process occurred to deduce how much of the heat released during accretion was retained by forming planets. We also do not know just how important for planetary heating the various short-lived radioactive heat sources (see Chapter 5 were. As a result, we are somewhat uncertain about how early in the accretion process the forming Earth would have melted significantly, thus allowing differentiation to occur, if it had not already occurred as a result of sweeping up various substances as they condensed.

A good place to start is with the question of how the Earth came to have about 30% of its mass in the form of free (unoxidized or metallic) iron. Two obvious possibilities arise, depending on the (uncertain) state of the condensed refractory material in the solar nebula at the Earth's distance from the Sun when the planets accreted. One possibility is that the nebula was able to cool to a fairly low temperature, below 1000 K, before the tiny solid dust grains began to coalesce into larger bodies and were protected from further chemical reactions with nebular gas. In this case (recall the discussion of the condensation of solids in a cooling nebula in our discussion of meteorites) the iron in the dust grains would have reacted with the excess oxygen in the nebula and with the magnesium silicates in the grains to form olivines and pyroxenes. The iron available for accretion by a planet would then be fully oxidized. In this case the forming planet would have to find a method of separating the iron from the minerals in which it would be combined. It has been suggested that this might be possible if the matter from which the Earth accreted also contained a significant mass of free carbon, as is found in CI carbonaceous chondrites. If enough C were present, the Fe could be separated from O by the same reaction used in blast furnaces on Earth:

$$Fe_3O_4 + 2C \rightarrow 3Fe + 2CO_2.$$

In this reaction, free C removes the O from oxidized Fe (*reduces* the iron) to give metallic iron and carbon dioxide. This theory is sometimes known as the **reduction during accretion model**. The reaction only functions to de-oxidize iron if the temperature is high, and so we would expect that reduction of iron in a CI-like proto-planet would go on most strongly in the layers most strongly heated by accretion, near the surface. The planet would have to be hot enough for the metallic iron produced near the surface to flow towards the planetary centre, displacing the more oxidized matter which would end up in the planetary mantle. A fairly specific prediction of this theory is that since accretion heating and hence the extent of reduction of the iron to metallic form increases with planetary mass, the most massive planets would be expected to have the largest mass fractions in the metallic cores.

This means of supplying reduced iron to a planet has several major weaknesses. First, judging from the meteorites that now strike the Earth, only a small fraction of the planetesimals that accreted to form planets in the inner solar system were as carbon-rich as CI chondrites. It is not at all clear how the Earth could have formed almost entirely from CI-like planetesimals, when they are so rare in the inner solar system now. Furthermore, even most CI chondrites don't have a high enough carbon mass fraction to reduce the amount of iron found in the Earth's core. A typical CI has about 3.5% C by mass, which is enough to reduce Fe amounting to about 25% of the mass of a planet if fully used; the iron in Earth's core, however, makes up about 30% of the planetary mass. The situation is even worse for Mercury, where the core makes up about 60% of the planet's mass. Furthermore, Mercury is the smallest of the terrestrial planets, but has the largest fraction of its mass in an iron core, clearly violating the prediction of this theory that the fractional size of the core should increase with planetary mass. Another problem is that the reduced iron has to trade places with highly oxidized iron from the planetary centre; as the metallic iron dribbles through the iron oxide-bearing rock, some of the metallic Fe would take up O from the highly oxidized Fe_3O_4, converting most of the Fe_3O_4 into less oxidized FeO, and reducing the amount of metallic Fe available for the core. It is very hard to understand how the Fe_3O_4 found in the present mantle could have survived close contact with metallic Fe; it would have to have been accreted after the formation of the core. But this reduces the total mass of the Earth at the time of core formation and makes the problem of producing such a massive iron core even more severe. A final difficulty with this theory is that it leaves about 10% of the planet's mass in the form of CO_2, which must then be almost entirely removed to leave only 0.02% of the Earth's mass composed of CO_2, as is now observed. It does not seem likely that a strong solar wind, which might be able to remove so much CO_2 would still be occurring at the time the full Earth finished accreting. All in all, the possibility of forming the Earth from oxidized matter which is subsequently reduced does not seem a very attractive way of accounting for the metallic iron in the core of the Earth.

The alternative is that the matter which accreted to form the Earth contained a lot of metallic iron in at least some of the individual planetesimals. This is a very attractive possibility. As we recall from the discussion of freezing out of minerals from the solar nebula, metallic iron condenses around 1475 K, followed by Mg-rich olivine and pyroxenes between about 1450 and 1350 K. Metallic iron does not become incorporated into silicates until the temperature has dropped to about 1000 K, and even at that temperature the free Fe only is incorporated into silicates if the two substances are still in intimate contact with each other and with nebular oxygen, and are held at a temperature of around 800–1000 K long enough for the conversion to occur. If the free iron has been separated from the oxygen before the temperature drops this low (e.g. by incorporation in a planet), or the cooling is fairly quick, much free iron will remain in the refractory solids. In fact, most ordinary chondritic meteorites (but not the rarer carbonaceous ones) are *observed* to contain 10–20% metallic iron, mostly in the form of small crystals. Since present meteorites seem mainly to represent the planetesimals produced between Mars and Jupiter, where the solar nebula was cooler, it is not hard to imagine that the solid planetesimals produced closer to the Sun in the hotter parts of the nebula might have formed under conditions of less complete condensation of silicates, so that a still larger fraction of condensed solid matter could have been composed of free iron. Furthermore, this possibility offers a natural explanation for the large iron core of Mercury; if the free Fe fraction increased inward into the inner solar system, the *innermost* planet should have the fractionally largest metal core. (The theory that each planet formed from all the substances condensed from the solar nebula down to some temperature associated with that planet's distance from the Sun is known as the **equilibrium condensation model**.)

Now if free iron was available in the fragments and planetesimals from which the Earth formed, we must next explain how it came to be localized in the core. Here again we have two major possible alternatives: either the core-mantle structure was a direct consequence of the accretion process itself, or the core developed as a result of processes operating within the forming (or formed) Earth.

The first of these possibilities arises because free iron is one of the first substances to condense as a solid in a cooling nebula of solar composition. If the nebula cooled slowly enough that each major condensing substance (Ca-Al rich refractories, metallic iron, magnesium silicates, sulfur compounds, and hydrated and carbonaceous minerals) had time to freeze out as dust, settle to the nebular mid-plane, coalesce into fragments and be accreted into forming proto-planets, the Earth might have formed with first a small core of Ca-Al rich material, then a large core of iron (combined with trace elements such as Ni), then a mantle of Mg-rich silicates, and finally a veneer of sulfur compounds and highly oxidized and hydrated minerals. This theory is sometimes called the **heterogeneous accretion model**, or the **accretion during condensation model**.

However, the possibility of producing a chemically zoned Earth by this kind of heterogeneous accretion does not seem very attractive for several reasons. First, the difference between the temperature at which metallic iron condenses (about 1475 K) and the condensation temperatures for the main Mg silicates (1450–1350 K) is very small. It is hard to think that the nebular temperature could be held uniform enough to induce a really large scale separation of these two components. Even small temperature fluctuations in the nebula, or modest radial mixing, would be enough to destroy the separation of the two components. Furthermore, theoretical estimates of the cooling time of the solar nebula suggest that it should have cooled more quickly than the time required for solids to condense and aggregate into planets. If the various solids all condensed before they could be swept into planets, even if they were in different mineral grains, we assume that they would have ended up mixed together as they are in ordinary chondritic meteorites.

Thus we should consider the possibility that the Earth accreted from small objects that contained some free iron, but mixed in with other minerals as we find in ordinary chondrites, or even already separated into the core-mantle structure that we infer for many asteroids from the common occurrence of igneous meteorites. This possibility is sometimes referred to as the **non-equilibrium components model**. Now if the Earth formed out of planetesimals that contained the free iron that now forms the core, mixed in with silicates, we must next explain how the Earth's core separated from the mantle. Presumably this occurred when the Earth's internal temperature rose high enough to melt free Fe and allowed it to seep towards the centre of the planet. This could have occurred either as a result of accretion heating, or from subsequent heating by radioactive decay of U, Th, etc. Now the problem with radioactive heating is that it does not work very fast. If we assume that the Earth accreted so slowly that its initial internal temperature remained at about 1000 K, the approximate nebular temperature near the Earth, so that accretion heating was negligible, it would have taken of the order of one Gyr for the temperature to rise high enough in the outer layers for iron to melt. Since the temperature required to melt iron rises quickly with pressure (the melting temperature is in the neighbourhood of 4–6000 K near the Earth's centre), an even longer time would have been needed before the central regions were hot enough to allow iron to drain right to the core. But the oldest known rocks, formed at the Earth's surface less than one Gyr after the formation of the Earth, are magnetized, just as they would be if they had formed today from cooling lava in the present Earth's magnetic field. This is strong circumstantial evidence that the Earth had a magnetic field less than one Gyr after it formed. Since generation of a strong planetary magnetic field probably requires a molten metallic core, it appears that the Earth already had this within about 0.5–1 Gyr after it formed. Thus we are led to the conclusion that most of the heating must have been from accretion energy (with perhaps some contribution from short-lived radioactive nuclei), since radioactivity due to currently active sources acts too slowly.

While the proto-Earth was small, less than a few hundred km in radius, the heating possible from impact is at most a couple hundreds of degrees. However, by the time the radius of the Earth had reached about 1500 km (40% of the radius of the Earth's present core), the potential temperature rise from impact was of the order of 2000 K, and melting of infalling material became possible. But melting would only have occurred if enough of the energy released by infall was retained by the proto-planet. If the accretion of new material occurred very slowly, in the form of a rain of tiny objects striking the surface of the proto-Earth, the heat released by impact would have been released right at the planetary surface, and much or most of it would be radiated back into space rather than retained to heat the forming planet. There are at least three ways in which the proto-planet could have retain much of the impact energy:

- accretion could have occur so rapidly (in less than about 10^5 years in the case of the Earth) that there simply was not enough time to radiate away much of the heat released by accretion;
- the accretion could have taken the form of impacts of fairly large objects (like those that produced the maria of the Moon), small enough not to disrupt the Earth totally, but large enough to bury themselves, and their energy, deep inside the proto-planet, from where the heat could not easily escape;
- or the growing atmosphere could have provided a sufficiently powerful insulating blanket that it could have trapped much of the heat released by accretion by making its loss by radiation rather inefficient.

Since we have concluded already that much accretion energy must have gone into melting the proto-Earth, one or more of these conditions was probably met.

When the proto-Earth first formed, it would have been small enough that energy released by accretion of further material did not heat it much. Until the radius reached $\sim 10^3$ km, the temperature was not a lot hotter than the nebular temperature, which might still have been $\sim$ 1000 K. (The fact that sulfur, an abundant element which condenses from the nebula at about 700 K, is not observed to be abundant in the Earth's mantle or crust strongly suggests that the temperature of the solar nebula in the Earth's vicinity never dropped much below 800 K before the nebular gases were cleaned away, presumably by a strong solar wind.) As the proto-Earth continued to grow beyond 10^3 km, surface heating by accretion of small fragments, and heating to a depth of the order of 100 km by impacts of large planetesimals, gradually heated the outer layers to temperatures in excess of 2000 K. Metallic iron near the surface, much denser than the surrounding silicate rocks, began to melt and seep towards the centre. As the Earth grew still larger, even the rocks near the surface (which have a considerably higher melting temperature than metallic iron) melted at least partially. However, as the Earth grew larger, the zone of melted rock probably did not become much thicker, but stayed near the surface, even though deep interior temperatures continued to rise from heat released both by sinking iron, carried inward by slow convective motions in the plastic (but solid) rock, and also released by radioactivity. The reason that the hot rock in the deep interior of the proto-Earth was solid is that as rock is compressed, the temperature required to melt it increases rapidly (see Figure 8.8). The actual temperature deep in the interior of the forming planet was not high enough to reach the melting point of the compressed rock, even though lower temperatures were high enough to partially melt a region 1–200 km deep close to the surface.

Partial melting in the outer mantle allowed magmas formed largely by the melting of incompatible and low density minerals to seep towards the surface. Because the melt zone swept through most of the mantle as the planet grew, this allowed rather efficient separation of some elements into the expanding surface layer that was becoming the Earth's crust. If we estimate the total amounts of the elements potassium (K), barium (Ba), rubidium (Rb), cesium (Cs), thorium (Th), and uranium (U) that the Earth should have, assuming roughly the same proportions relative to Si that are found in the Sun, it is found that more than 30% of the total mass of each of these elements expected in the entire Earth has been segregated into the present continental crust! This shows clearly how efficient the "zone-refining" carried out by the moving zone of partial melting in the Earth actually was. The segregation of Ca, Al and Na-rich matter into the crust, where these elements constitute a fraction of the rocks far out of proportion to their total abundance in the Earth, was also achieved in this way. However, only about 10% of the total mass of Ca, Al, and Na in the whole Earth is found in the continental crust. Most of the rest is in the mantle. The reason that the Earth does not have a much deeper crust of these elements is apparently because the density of feldspars is more sensitive to pressure than the mantle silicates. Once a fairly deep feldspar-rich crust had formed, its lower layers became *denser* than the underlying mantle, and parts of the deep crust then sank back into the mantle.

Finally, we need to account for the presence of some highly oxidized iron in the outer mantle, for the occurrence of such elements as Ni and Cr in the mantle (these elements should have been stripped out by the sinking metallic iron), and for the large amounts of water and carbon dioxide in the crust and upper mantle. These substances were probably accreted very late in the formation of the Earth, from planetesimals formed much farther out in the solar nebula than the Earth's distance from the Sun, that were shot into the inner solar system by close encounters with outer planets, especially Jupiter. These planetesimals would have been much more volatile-rich than the Earth as a whole, and their trace elements and highly oxidized matter would not have come into contact with the Earth's core iron, which had long since sunk to the centre. Some of the volatiles were also furnished by collisions with comets.

8.5 Mathematical aspects

Hydrostatic equilibrium again

The smaller asteroids are essentially large rocks or rubble piles. They are certainly held together by gravity in the sense that gravity prevents loose pieces from escaping freely, but gravity has little other effect. Individual boulders are not distorted or forced to merge with other boulders by gravity. However, when the size of an asteroid, moon or planet exceeds $R \sim 300$ km, gravity becomes powerful enough to force the body into a spherical shape, by imposing such high internal pressures that rock deforms like silly putty, especially if the body is hot inside. For bodies larger than this size, gravity is the dominant force in defining the shape of the body and its internal conditions.

When an object is large enough that the internal pressure can deform the material it is made of, the internal structure is described by the equation of hydrostatic equilibrium, Equation (3.4). This equation states that in a fluid (e.g. an ocean, an atmosphere, or rock under high pressure) in a gravitational field, the pressure increases with depth in such a way that the increase in pressure from the top of a particular thin layer to the bottom is just enough to support the weight of that layer. This led to the equation

$$\frac{dp}{dr} = -\rho(r)g(r) \tag{8.1}$$

where $p(r)$ is the pressure at depth r in the object, where the local acceleration of gravity is $g(r)$ and the density is $\rho(r)$. We have already looked at how this equation may be solved in a gas held in a gravitational field. Here we need to see how the equation is to be solved in a (deformable) solid (that is, in a solid which is soft enough to settle – slowly! – into a round form as a liquid would). In the case of large asteroids, moons, and the smallest planets, we are helped greatly by the fact that the internal pressure is not large enough even at the centre to compress the material of such bodies very much, and so if the body is not differentiated, its material will have nearly uniform density, independent of location or pressure.

As a first example of the use of the equation of hydrostatic equilibrium in a solid body, look at the situation in the first few km below the surface of a body with a radius of a few hundred km or more. In this situation, it is a good approximation to take the local gravitational acceleration $g(r)$ to be constant and equal to the surface value, $g = GM/R^2$, where the body has mass M and radius R. In this case, Equation (8.1) is trivial to integrate:

$$\begin{aligned}\int_{p(r_1)}^{p(r_2)} dp &= p(r_2) - p(r_1) = -\rho g \int_{r_1}^{r_2} dr \\ &= -\rho g(r_2 - r_1).\end{aligned} \tag{8.2}$$

If we measure the depth d from the surface at r_2, using $d = (r_2 - r_1)$ as the independent variable, and notice that the surface pressure $p(r_2)$ is 0 (nothing is squeezing the body from the outside, and it has no atmosphere or ocean resting on its surface), then the pressure at depth d is just $p(r_1)$ and is given by

$$p(d) = \rho g d. \tag{8.3}$$

Exercise: Sea water has a density of approximately 1027 kg m^{-3}. (a) Neglecting the pressure of the atmosphere, what is the pressure at a depth of 10 m and at a depth of 1 km? (b) How much do these pressures change when you include the pressure of the atmosphere?

The variation of pressure farther inside a body of uniform composition and density may be found with only a little more work. The only change from the treatment above is that we must deal with a gravity that varies with depth. To calculate the gravity at a particular depth, recall Newton's result, discussed in all elementary physics texts, that the gravitational acceleration of an object inside a spherical body at a distance r from the centre due to the matter interior to r is the same as if that matter were concentrated at the centre, while the matter exterior to r exerts *no net gravitational effect* on the object. For a sphere of uniform density ρ, the mass interior to r is

$$M_r = 4\pi r^3 \rho/3, \tag{8.4}$$

and so the acceleration of gravity at a distance r from the centre is

$$g(r) = GM_r/r^2 = 4\pi r \rho G/3. \tag{8.5}$$

Notice that the gravitational acceleration *increases* with r. With this expression for $g(r)$, the equation of hydrostatic equilibrium becomes

$$\frac{dp}{dr} = -\rho g(r) = -4\pi r \rho^2 G/3, \tag{8.6}$$

which is easily integrated to find

$$\begin{aligned}p(r_2) - p(r_1) &= -\frac{4\pi\rho^2 G}{3}\int_{r_1}^{r_2} r dr \\ &= -\frac{2\pi\rho^2 G}{3}(r_2^2 - r_1^2).\end{aligned} \tag{8.7}$$

Now take $r_2 = R$, the radius of the body; recall that the pressure vanishes at the surface, so that $p(r_2) = 0$; and take r_1 to be any other point r inside the body. Then

$$p(r) = (2\pi/3)\rho^2 G(R^2 - r^2), \tag{8.8}$$

and in particular the central pressure is

$$p_c = p(0) = 2\pi\rho^2 GR^2/3 = 1.26 \times 10^{-3} R^2, \tag{8.9}$$

where the last equality assumes $\rho = 3000$ kg m^{-3} and that R is measured in meters.

We can also estimate the central pressure for this situation by treating Equation (8.1) as an order-of-magnitude difference equation, as we did in Chapter 3:

$$p_c - p_s = p_c \sim \overline{\rho}\,\overline{g}R = (4\pi/3)\overline{\rho}^2 GR^2, \tag{8.10}$$

where we have estimated that $\overline{g}$ will everywhere be of the order of the surface gravity GM/R^2, used the definition of mean density $\overline{\rho}$ to eliminate M through

$$M = (4\pi/3)R^3\overline{\rho}, \tag{8.11}$$

and replaced dp by $p_c - p_s = p_c$ and dr by R. Equation (8.10) differs from the exact result of Equation (8.9) only by a factor of 2, due to our over-estimate of gravity.

Exercise: Verify that this is the same result as Equation (3.14) except for a numerical factor of order 1.

Inside a large planet, the density of a particular mineral depends on the pressure (this information is of

Table 8.4: Density, sound speeds, pressure, and gravity at various levels in the interior of the Earth.

Radius (km)	Depth (km)	Density ($kg\,m^{-3}$)	V_p ($km\,s^{-1}$)	V_s ($km\,s^{-1}$)	Pressure (10^{11} Pa)	Gravity ($m\,s^{-2}$)
		* * * * centre of Earth * * * *				
0	6371	13090	11.26	3.67	3.64	0
200	6171	13080	11.26	3.66	3.63	0.73
400	5971	13050	11.24	3.65	3.60	1.46
600	5771	13010	11.21	3.63	3.55	2.18
800	5571	12950	11.16	3.60	3.49	2.90
1000	5371	12870	11.11	3.56	3.40	3.62
1200	5171	12770	11.04	3.51	3.30	4.32
1221.5	5149.5	12760	11.03	3.50	3.29	4.40
		* * * * boundary of inner core * * * *				
1221.5	5149.5	12170	10.36	0	3.29	4.40
1400	4971	12070	10.24	0	3.19	4.94
1600	4771	11950	10.12	0	3.06	5.55
1800	4571	11810	9.99	0	2.92	6.17
2000	4371	11650	9.83	0	2.77	6.77
2200	4171	11480	9.67	0	2.61	7.36
2400	3971	11290	9.48	0	2.43	7.94
2600	3771	11080	9.27	0	2.25	8.50
2800	3571	10850	9.05	0	2.06	9.04
3000	3371	10600	8.80	0	1.86	9.56
3200	3171	10330	8.51	0	1.65	10.05
3400	2971	10030	8.20	0	1.44	10.51
3480	2891	9900	8.06	0	1.36	10.68
		* * * * boundary of outer core * * * *				
3480	2891	5570	13.72	7.26	1.36	10.68
3600	2771	5510	13.69	7.27	1.29	10.52
3800	2571	5410	13.48	7.19	1.17	10.31
4000	2371	5310	13.25	7.10	1.06	10.16
4200	2171	5210	13.02	7.01	0.958	10.05
4400	1971	5110	12.78	6.92	0.854	9.99
4600	1771	5000	12.54	6.83	0.754	9.95
4800	1571	4900	12.29	6.73	0.655	9.93
5000	1371	4790	12.02	6.62	0.559	9.93
5200	1171	4680	11.73	6.50	0.465	9.95
5400	971	4560	11.42	6.38	0.373	9.97
5600	771	4440	11.07	6.24	0.283	10.00
5800	571	3940	10.01	5.43	0.199	10.00
6000	371	3530	8.85	4.75	0.140	9.97
6200	171	3360	8.03	4.44	0.055	9.89
6371	0				0	9.82
		* * * * surface of Earth * * * *				

Source: Adapted from A. M. Dziewonski and D. L. Anderson 1981, *Phys. Earth and Planet. Int.*, **25**, 297.

course just the equation of state of the substance). To determine the variation of pressure and density with depth, we combine knowledge of the equation of state with Equation (8.1) and solve both equations numerically. A model of the Earth's interior deduced in this way (the Preliminary Reference Earth Model, or PREM) is given in Table 8.4, which lists the density, sound speeds V_p (pressure waves) and V_s (shear waves), pressure, and local acceleration of gravity at a number of depths in the Earth.

Exercise: Assume that the Earth has uniform density $\rho = 5520$ kg m^{-3} throughout. Use the analytical solution to the equation of hydrostatic equilibrium to determine the variation of pressure $p(r)$ and local gravity $g(r)$ as functions of depth. Graph the resulting functions and compare them to the run of pressure and gravity given in Table 8.4.

For a body of asteroidal dimensions, we may use Equation (8.9) to find the minimum size R_s at which the internal pressure is high enough, roughly $p \sim 1\times10^8$ Pa, to deform rock, at least very slowly, and force the asteroid to be spherical. Assuming $\rho = 3000$ kg m^{-3}, we find $R_s \sim 280$ km.

At the other extreme, rock is significantly compressed for pressures greater than about $p \sim 1 \times 10^{10}$ Pa = 1×10^5 atm (look at the way in which density inside the Earth varies with pressure as given in Table 8.4). A planet large enough to achieve this pressure at least at the centre with a density of 3000 kg m^{-3} has a radius of about 2800 km. Thus all asteroids and moons, and the terrestrial planets Mercury and Mars, are small enough that compression of their material may be ignored in the first approximation.

Internal heating from core separation

A potentially significant source of planetary internal energy arises if a newly formed homogeneous planet differentiates into a planet with a core and mantle structure. This will occur if the accreting material becomes hot enough that metallic iron can sink to the centre of the body. The energy released is the difference between the gravitational energy of the body while it is homogeneous (Equation (4.3)) and the gravitational energy of the body after differentiation. This latter energy may be calculated using the reasoning used to obtain that equation, but now with a core density ρ_c between $r = 0$ and $r = r_c$, and a mantle density ρ_m between r_c and R. This discontinuity makes the expression for the mass M_r inside r a bit more complex than before. In the inner part, for $r < r_c$, M_r is given by

$$M_{r,i} = 4\pi\rho_c r^3/3, \qquad (8.12)$$

while for the outer region, $r > r_c$, the expression is

$$\begin{aligned} M_{r,o} &= 4\pi\rho_c r_c^3/3 + 4\pi\rho_m (r^3 - r_c^3)/3 \\ &= \frac{4\pi}{3}[(\rho_c - \rho_m) r_c^3 + \rho_m r^3]. \qquad (8.13) \end{aligned}$$

Then

$$\begin{aligned} E_g &= -G\int_0^{r_c} \frac{M_{r,i}\, 4\pi\rho_c r^2\, dr}{r} \\ &\quad + G\int_{r_c}^{R} \frac{M_{r,o}\, 4\pi\rho_m r^2\, dr}{r} \qquad (8.14) \\ &= -\frac{16\pi^2 G R^5}{15}\{\rho_c^2 a^5 + \rho_m^2[(1-a^5) \\ &\quad + (5/2)(\rho_c - \rho_m)a^3(1-a^2)/\rho_m]\}, \end{aligned}$$

where $a = r_c/R$.

Exercise: Show that Equation (8.14) reduces to Equation (4.3) when ρ_c and ρ_m are equal.

In the case of the Earth, comparison of Equation (8.14) from Equation (4.3) reveals that differentiation releases about one-tenth as much energy as was originally released by the formation of the planet if it formed homogeneously. Energy released by differentiation is of course essentially retained by the planet as internal (heat) energy when it is first released, although eventually it slowly leaks out.

8.6 References

Brown, G. C. and Mussett, A. E. 1993, *The Inaccessible Earth*, 2nd Ed. (London: Chapman & Hall). The internal structure of the Earth, its dynamic nature, its tectonic plates, and the origin and evolution the planet as a whole are discussed in this clear introductory text.

Condie, K. C. 1997, *Plate Tectonics and Crustal Evolution*, 4th Ed. (Oxford: Butterworth Heinemann). The evidence allowing us to deduce the internal workings of the Earth and the history of plate tectonics, particularly from chemical analysis and study of tectonic activity, are discussed in this advanced text.

Grieve, R. A. F. 1990, "Impact cratering on the Earth", *Sci. Am.*, Apr., 66. Grieve explains what occurs during the impact on Earth of a comet nucleus or small asteroid, how old craters are recognized, and how major impacts may have affected early life on Earth.

Jeanloz, R. and Romanowicz, B. 1997, "Geophysical dynamics at the center of the Earth", *Phys. Today*, Aug. 22. In addition to a discussion of how the deep interior of the Earth is being studied, this article has a nice summary in sidebars of how we study the interior of the Earth.

Murphy, J. B. and Nance, R. D. 1992, "Mountain belts and the supercontinent cycle", *Sci. Am.*, Apr., 84. It seems that every few hundred million years the Earth's continents form a single supercontinent, with much associated mountain building.

Wetherill, G. W. 1981, "The formation of the Earth from planetesimals", *Sci. Am.*, Jun., 162. The formation of the planets of the solar system from the solar nebula is studied with the aid of computer simulations.

8.7 Review questions

8.1 How do we find a reasonable initial guess for the Earth's bulk chemical composition?

8.2 How do we know that the Earth has an inhomogeneous (core – mantle) internal structure? How can we find the depth of the core – mantle boundary?

8.3 What evidence leads us to conclude that the Earth's core is nearly pure iron, and is partly molten?

8.4 Why is the core partly molten, while the (cooler) mantle is solid throughout?

8.5 Why is the inner core solid even though the (somewhat cooler) outer core is liquid?

8.6 How does the theory of plate tectonics account for the occurrence of large-scale mountain chains, and for bands of oppositely magnetized sediments on the ocean floors parallel to mid-ocean trenches?

8.7 What is the mechanism that probably drives plate motion over the Earth's surface?

8.8 How did the layered structure of the Earth probably originate?

8.9 How did the Earth's crust probably obtain such a large fraction of the total amount available of such elements as potassium and uranium?

8.8 Problems

8.1 Consider the possibility of modelling the Earth assuming that the density varies as $\rho(r) = \rho_o(1 - kr/R)$ where ρ_o is the assumed central density, r is radial distance from the centre in a body of radius R, and k is a number less than 1. (a) Consider first some radius r, where the mass interior to r is $M(r)$. Write down the expression for the small increase dM produced by the addition of a shell of mass of thickness dr of the local density $\rho(r)$. (b) Now integrate this expression from 0 to r to find an analytical equation for the total mass $M(r)$ interior to radius r as a function of the two parameters ρ_o and k. (c) Assuming $\rho_o = 12500\ \mathrm{kg\,m^{-3}}$ (appropriate for compressed iron), find the value of k that leads to the correct $M = 6.0 \times 10^{24}$ kg if the Earth's radius is 6371 km. (d) What is the resulting surface density of the model? Do you expect this number to have any physical relationship to the density of the Earth's crustal rocks? (e) Integrate the equation of hydrostatic equilibrium analytically to derive expressions for the variation of pressure $p(r)$ and local gravity $g(r)$ with depth. Graph the resulting functions and the density $\rho(r)$ and compare them to the run of pressure, gravity and density given in Table 8.4 in the text.

8.2 From seismic data, it is clear that a strong composition discontinuity occurs within the Earth at a radial distance from the centre of $r/R = 0.55$, where R is the Earth's radius. Consider modelling the Earth under the assumption that for $r/R < 0.55$ the density has one constant value ρ_i, and for $r/R > 0.55$ it has a second value ρ_o. (a) Write down an equation relating the total mass M of the Earth to these two densities. Using the known values of $M = 6.0 \times 10^{24}$ kg and $R = 6371$ km, and assuming that ρ_o has a (suitably compressed) value appropriate for crustal rocks of $\rho_o = 4.4 \times 10^3\ \mathrm{kg\,m^{-3}}$, derive a value for ρ_i. (b) Calculate the total gravitational potential energy of the Earth on this model, and the potential energy of a body of the same mass and radius but of uniform density. How large is the difference, numerically and as a fraction of the gravitational energy of the constant-density model? (c) Assume that the Earth originally formed with uniform density and its present size, and that the core subsequently sank to the centre. Using the results from part (b), estimate the total energy released by this event. (d) Now find an expression for, and evaluate, the total number of atoms N in the whole Earth, using the composition of Table 8.3. (e) Assuming that the energy required to raise the temperature of the Earth from T_1 to T_2 is given by $E = 3Nk(T_2 - T_1)$, how much could core separation have raised the average temperature of the whole Earth? Is this enough to melt the whole Earth?

8.3 Consider the thermal state of the interior of the Earth. (a) Using the fact that the central temperature of the Earth is about 4000 K, and assuming that the thermal conductivity of the mantle is similar to that of normal dielectrics (such as rocks), roughly $\kappa \sim 2.5\ \mathrm{W\,m^{-2}\,(K/m)^{-1}}$, estimate the order of magnitude of the heat flux q emerging from the interior of the Earth as a result of thermal conduction. Compare your estimate to the Earth's observed value, $q \sim 6 \times 10^{-2}\ \mathrm{W\,m^{-2}}$. Can you draw any conclusion about how heat is probably transported in the deep interior of the Earth? (b) The total thermal energy content of the Earth may be estimated assuming that the thermal energy per atom is $3kT$. Estimate the total number N of atoms in the whole Earth from the composition of Table 8.3. Assuming an average interior temperature of 3000 K for the Earth, estimate the total internal thermal energy in the Earth. (c) Estimate the length of time (in years) that the Earth could lose heat from the present internal thermal energy, at the present observed energy loss rate, to the point that internal energy of the Earth is exhausted. (This is a rough estimate of the actual time required for the Earth to cool from its present state assuming that it has no important internal heat sources.) (d) Heat is certainly carried through the lithosphere by conduction. Use the observed heat flow and the conductivity given above to estimate the vertical temperature gradient in K km^{-1} near the surface. Should the estimated gradient be measurable? How?

8.4 Write a small computer programme to use the values of density as a function of distance from the centre of the Earth listed in Table 8.4 to determine the total mass inside each radius listed in the table, and the local acceleration of gravity at that radius. Compare your values for the gravity to the last column of Table 8.4. (The table will be available via the Web.)

Chapter 9

Other Terrestrial Planets

9.1 The Earth's Moon

Having surveyed what we know about the interior and surface of the earth – and how we know it – we can now turn our attention to the other Earth-like planets in the inner solar system. All have internal structures that are similar to that of the Earth. Many of the surface features we find are related to structures that are familiar from our own planet. We can make a lot of progress in understanding other terrestrial planets by assuming as a starting point that each is fairly similar to the earth, and then trying to understand the differences that we find when we study their surface features and chemistry. This will be our task in this chapter.

The terrestrial body about which we have the most information is the Earth's Moon. We know a lot about this nearly planet-sized body both as a result of intense observation from the Earth by telescope, and particularly as a result of the U. S. Apollo and the Soviet Luna lander programmes, which led to the return of hundreds of kilograms of surface rocks for later study. We start our study of the other terrestrial planets with an examination of this nearly planet-sized object to see what we can learn about its internal structure and history.

Surface of the Moon

When we look at the Moon from Earth with a telescope, we see a lot of detail (but only on the side of the Moon that always faces the Earth). In fact, from Earth we can discern single objects or structures on the Moon only a few km in size, so we can see things the size of single mountains or large craters, but we can not discern lunar landers, astronauts, etc. From the Earth, we observe several kinds of surface features. Most of the Moon's surface, about 80%, is light grey in colour, and is absolutely saturated with craters that range in size from as small as we can see up to diameters of more than 200 km. The craters are normally circular in shape, fairly shallow, and surrounded by raised crater rims. Sometimes, in the larger ones, a rather lumpy central mountain is found. This landscape of jumbled, intensely cratered terrain is usually called the **lunar highlands**. This region is visible as the light grey surface in the image of the full Moon seen in Figure 9.1, and a large crater of the highlands is seen in more detail in Figure 9.2.

Figure 9.1: This image of the fully illuminated Moon was taken by the Galileo spacecraft on its way to the Jupiter system in 1992. The dark, roughly circular regions are mare basins (huge, lava-filled impact craters), from left to right Oceanus Procellarum, Mare Imbrium, Mare Serenetatis and Mare Tranquilitatis (just to the right of centre) and Mare Crisium near the right edge. The bright crater at the bottom is Tycho. Because Galileo was fairly near the Moon, less than one full hemisphere is visible. (Courtesy of NASA.)

Several smaller regions on the Moon are dark, almost black in colour, and far less heavily covered with craters. These dark areas, called **maria** ("seas" in

Figure 9.2: A fairly large lunar crater simply named IAU Crater 308, on the far side of the Moon, is seen obliquely from the Apollo 11 space craft. This crater (near the top of the image) is about 80 km in diameter, and has a raised rim, slumped interior walls, and a central mountain peak raised during the impact. This crater is surrounded by other craters of all sizes; the fact that this crater is relatively intact shows that it was one of the last large craters created on the Moon during the period of sweeping up small bodies. (Courtesy of NASA.)

Figure 9.3: Mare Imbrium, one of the major mare basins on the near-side of the Moon, is in the foreground in this oblique view towards the south. This huge basin is about 1300 km in diameter, and its rim is formed by huge mountain chains such as the Montes Carpates seen in the distance. These mountains can rise to 5 km above the plains. Near the horizon, 400 km away at the top of the picture, is the Copernicus crater, a relatively young crater with a diameter of 107 km. (Courtesy of NASA.)

Latin; the singular is **mare**), are usually full or partial circular basins hundreds of km or more in diameter. They are often rimmed by what look like circular mountain chains, which resemble the rims of craters. Several mare basins are visible in Figure 9.1, and a closer view of one of the large near-side mare basins is shown in Figure 9.3. One of the largest such features is the 900 km diameter Orientale Basin, seen in Figure 9.4, which has three clearly visible concentric circular mountain rings. A few large craters and some smaller ones are visible on each mare, but generally the maria appear relatively flat. Some mare surfaces have systems of low irregular ridges, and a few are traversed by sinuous rilles which look a lot like dry river beds, such as the Hadley Rille seen in Figure 9.5.

The craters of the lunar highlands look like impact features, rather like artillery shell holes, and even from Earth we can see enough to suspect that we might be looking at the scars produced by the final stages of accretion of the planetesimals from which the Moon presumably formed. If this is correct, the Moon is remarkably different from Earth in preserving in the highlands much of the landscape created during its process of formation. In contrast, the less textured surfaces of the maria appear to be circular basins flooded with lava. Some ridge systems seem to mark the ends of individual flows. These single flows are quite large, sometimes hundreds of km across; apparently lava on the Moon was quite runny.

Interior

Looking at the Moon, it is not obvious how evolved a body it is. It would be natural to imagine that it is a homogeneous, undifferentiated body simply made up of the planetesimals that combined to form it (although the presence of the dark maria basins shows that some substantial, but perhaps superficial and local, differentiation has occurred). In this case, our model of the Moon's interior would be of uniform chemical composition throughout, with abundances of individual elements reflecting the abundances in the small bodies from which it was made; perhaps the bulk composition should resemble ordinary or carbonaceous chondritic meteorites. On the other hand, one should also consider the possibility that the Moon is differentiated as the Earth is; an alternative possible model of the lunar

Figure 9.4: On the western limb of the Moon is the huge impact basin Mare Orientale. This basin contains three concentric rings of mountains formed at the time of the impact; the largest ring has a diameter of about 900 km. Unlike the majority of large basins on the near-side of the Moon, this basin has not filled with dark basalt. (Courtesy of NASA.)

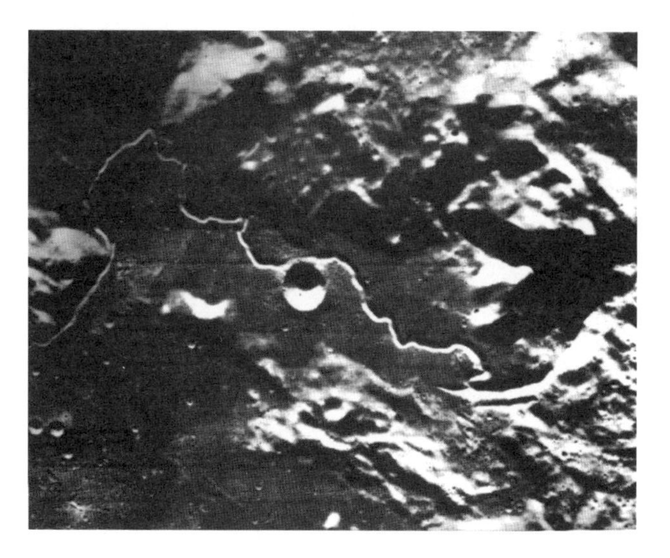

Figure 9.5: The 120-km long Hadley Rille is a typical sinuous channel near the edge of the Imbrium basin. It was probably a lava flow tube at the time when Mare Imbrium was being flooded with lava. At that time it would have been covered with a roof (like the covering of ice on a river in winter), which later collapsed after the tube had emptied. (Courtesy of NASA.)

interior could resemble that of the Earth, perhaps with a core, mantle, and crust, or possibly even more layers. If this is the correct model, we would like to find ways of establishing the sizes and chemical compositions of the various layers.

An important constraint on possible interior models is provided by the fact that we have been able to measure quite accurately the Moon's mass and radius, by timing the motions of spacecraft as they circle the Moon. The mass is found to be 1/81.3006 times that of the Earth, or about 7.35×10^{22} kg. The mean radius is 1737.53 km. From these numbers we can calculate the mean density, 3344 kg m^{-3}, or 3.34 times the density of water. Because the Moon is a small body, this value is hardly affected by compression. Whatever the Moon is made of, it must have this average density.

The observed value for the mean density of the Moon certainly suggests that the Moon is mainly rocky in composition. If the Moon is mainly rocky, it seems quite plausible that it may be undifferentiated. An undifferentiated Moon could probably not have the same bulk chemical composition as C1 or C2 carbonaceous chondrites, because such material would have too low a density, somewhere between 2200 and 2900 kg m^{-3} (see Table 5.3). However, if the Moon were formed from a mixture of different chondritic meteoroid types, carbonaceous and ordinary, it could easily have the observed mean density. Before the Moon was explored by space probe landing, the mean density was considered a powerful argument in favour of the idea that the Moon is chondritic in composition, and undifferentiated.

What constraints are imposed on a differentiated model? Clearly, this will depend on what kind of a model we try. Suppose we look at an Earth-like model, with an iron core, a pyrolite mantle, and a low-density crust. If we consider a model with a crust as thick as the Earth's continental crust, about 50 km, with a density of 2850 kg m^{-3}, and a pyrolite mantle (density 3350 kg m^{-3}), we find that an iron core with a density of 8000 kg m^{-3} would have a radius of only 350 km, which would make it a *much* smaller fraction (about 2%) of the mass of the Moon than the Earth's core is of the Earth (recall that the Earth's core makes up about 33% of the mass of the Earth). Although this particular model is not by any means the only possible one, the conclusion about the smallness of an iron lunar core remains valid unless the mantle can be made somehow of rather low density rock; only if we take the whole mantle to have a density of 2700 kg m^{-3} or less (like volatile-rich carbonaceous chondrites) it is possible for the Moon to have an iron core that makes up

30% or more of the total mass of the Moon.

A huge step forward in our knowledge of the Moon resulted from space probe visits to it during the period 1969–1976 by six manned U. S. Apollo missions and three unmanned Soviet Luna probes. One very important result of these missions was to bring back to Earth many rock samples from several spots on the lunar surfaces for detailed chemical and mineral analysis. (Note that the Soviet probes showed that this very important result can be achieved without the fantastic expense and great risk of actually sending people to the Moon; this result can also be achieved by identifying lunar rocks in the world meteorite collection.)

Broadly, the returned rock samples fall generally into three groups. The rocks from the lunar highlands are mainly **anorthositic**. They are similar to terrestrial feldspars, but unlike their terrestrial counterparts contain mainly anorthosite, with only small fractions of albite and orthoclase (cf. Table 2.7). They are thus relatively rich in Ca and Al, and poor in K and Na. The light gray colour of such rocks is responsible for the light colour of the highlands. In the highlands we also find a second, less common kind of rock, a **norite** composed mainly of olivine (or pyroxene) and plagioclase. Many norite samples have relatively large amounts of such trace elements as potassium, rare earths, and phosphorus, and are accordingly called KREEP norites (KREEP is an acronym for potassium [atomic symbol *K*], *R*are *E*arth *E*lements and *P*hosphorus). This norite is similar to terrestrial basaltic lavas produced by partial melting of feldspar.

The mare rocks are predominantly **basalts**, composed chiefly of calcium-rich pyroxenes (clinopyroxene), ilmenite ($FeTiO_3$), and plagioclase. They are similar to terrestrial basaltic lavas, which on Earth are produced by partial melting of the mantle. However, some have more titanium (mostly as ilmenite) than terrestrial basalts do, and in the lunar basalts the plagioclase is richer in Ca and poorer in Na than in terrestrial lavas. The lunar basalts are completely free of included water (they are **anhydrous**), again unlike terrestrial lavas. The dark colour of these basalts gives the maria their colour.

None of these principal surface rock types has a chemical composition at all similar to the composition of chondritic meteorites or of pyrolite. On Earth, rocks such as basalt and anorthosite are produced by melting and chemical separation (fractionation), and we must suppose that such processes have occurred on the Moon as well. Further strong evidence that the interior of the Moon has been extensively melted is found from the measured abundances of trace elements. Siderophile elements (ones which tend to dissolve in molten iron and hence would concentrate into a metallic core if one had formed), such as Ge, Co, Ag, Cd, Au and Pt, are found to be deficient compared to their abundances in CI meteorites relative to Si by factors of 10 to 1000. In contrast, refractory lithophiles (which tend to concentrate into the crust if one is separated by partial melting), such as U, Th, Ti and Ba, are more abundant than in CI meteorites by factors of the order of 100. These deficiencies and excesses are very strong evidence that extensive melting and separation has occurred in the lunar material. Study of lunar surface rock chemistry thus leads us to the extremely important deduction that the Moon is *not* homogeneous. Instead, it must be a chemically differentiated body, probably layered as the Earth is. This is the most important discovery about the Moon to have come from the lunar landings.

The lunar highlands cover most of the surface of the Moon, and so we must try to understand their chemical composition if we are to guess what the layering of the Moon is. As we have seen, the anorthosites of the highlands are similar to terrestrial anorthosites, a type of feldspar. On Earth, feldspars are the product of crystal fractionation from a melt. This means that if one takes a rock mass of roughly pyrolitic composition and melts it completely, the feldspar component (which has relatively low density) rises to the surface. When such a melt cools, the feldspar is left as the uppermost layer. It seems likely that the anorthositic rock of the lunar highlands was separated in the same way.

Now the layer of anorthositic rock in the highlands cannot be a thin veneer only tens or hundreds of meters thick, on top of some other kind of rock. This is because the obvious impact cratering of the highlands has completely mixed the highland surface down to the depth excavated by the impacts that produced the large craters. The largest craters have diameters of more than 200 km, and they must have been some tens of km deep at the moment of impact. (Because the crater floors rebounded after the impact, and material slumped in from the surrounding crater walls and rim as it does when you try to dig a deep hole in dry sand, the present crater floors are less than 10 km deep at most.) Thus the surface of the Moon must be roughly homogeneous to a depth of perhaps 50 km or more; if the surface rocks are primarily anorthositic, the entire crust of the Moon must be anorthositic.

It seems probable that the average chemical composition of the Moon as a whole must be something like pyrolite; that is, it is probably mainly made of Mg, Fe, Si, and O. Elements like Ca and Al are expected to make up only a few percent of the bulk chemistry. But the anorthositic rock of the highlands contains about 13% Al, which makes up only 2% of pyrolite (see Table 8.2). To obtain the mass of aluminum needed for a layer of anorthositic rock roughly 50 km thick, one must melt a layer at least six times deeper to allow all its aluminum to rise to the surface. We thus come to the astonishing conclusion that the Moon must at one time have been melted to a depth of at least 300 km. (In fact, if the separation of anorthositic rock from the rest was not complete, or if the crust is thicker than we have estimated, the Moon might have been melted to an even greater depth.) Now 300 km is almost 20% of the radius of the Moon, and more than 40% of the total lunar volume is within this distance of the surface. At one time nearly half the volume of the Moon was melted, either all at once or in a wave of melting that allowed the low-density anorthosites to rise to the surface. This must have required a very powerful heat source.

Ages have been measured for many lunar rock samples using radioactive decay techniques like those used to date meteorites. These ages allow one to deduce when the rock sample was last intensely heated, so that radioactive atoms could separate from their decay products. The rocks of the highlands mostly have ages of about 4.4 or about 3.9 Gyr, between 0.1 – 0.6 Gyr younger than the age of the Earth and the oldest meteorites. The oldest rocks are usually assumed to record the time when the magma ocean first solidified. It is not clear what events set the radioactive clocks of the rocks with the younger ages. Some scientists believe that the radioactive clocks in the highlands were reset by the last part of the intense bombardment of the lunar surface by planetesimals, but this view is disputed. We tentatively conclude that the period of intense bombardment probably ended about 4 Gyr ago, after the crust had formed (and thus after the Moon had differentiated). Thus it appears that the Moon retains a record on its surface of events that occurred within the first half billion years of its history. On Earth, geological activity (mountain-building, erosion, etc.) has been so intense that the record of this era has been completely erased as far as we now know, except for a very few sedimentary rocks with ages slightly over 4 Gyr.

The rocks from the maria mostly have ages between 3.2 and 3.9 Gyr. (They are thus comparable to the ages of the oldest known Earth crustal rocks.) The circular shapes of the mare basins suggest that they were formed by impacts, like the craters of the highlands. The maria appear to record impacts on the Moon of several really large planetesimals, objects with diameters of tens of kilometers or more. The basalt filling them is apparently lava which escaped from the Moon's interior to cover over these huge craters, and the variety of ages found for basaltic rocks in the maria suggests that lava continued to escape from the lunar interior intermittently for almost a Gyr. The fact that the oldest lavas are at most 4 Gyr old suggests that the impacts that formed the maria occurred near the end of the accretion process for the Moon; the relative scarcity of craters on the mare surfaces also suggests this.

The Apollo programme not only brought back rock samples from the Moon, it also set up a small network of six seismographs that were monitored from Earth until they were turned off in 1977. These seismographs detected some 12,000 small moonquakes, which appear to occur both near the surface of the Moon and deep in its interior. They are produced by impact of large meteorites, by stress release in the lunar crust, and by varying tidal stressing of the Moon's deep interior as it moves closer to and then farther away from the Earth in its orbit. From study of the moonquakes detected by these seismographs, several significant characteristics of the lunar interior have been deduced. (a) S-waves seem not to travel well below depths of about 1100 km; the innermost 600 km of the Moon is probably at least partly molten (and hence quite hot). The temperature in the deep interior is thought to be around 1200 – 1500 K. (b) The Moon does indeed have a chemically distinct crust (the anorthosite layer), with a depth of about 50 km. (The prominent basalt plains of the mare basins are quite shallow and comprise only about 1% of the volume of the crust.) (c) The speeds of P-waves (about 7.5–8.5 km s^{-1}) and of S-waves (about 4.1–4.4 km s^{-1}) in the lunar mantle are consistent with the idea that the mantle of the Moon is composed of something rather like pyrolite, though this does not prove that the lunar mantle is pyrolite. (d) There may be a small core of low-velocity material (i.e. iron) no more than about 400 km in radius. Its existence is not clearly established.

Seismology has again showed its power as a probe of planetary interiors, and reveals a core(?)-mantle-crust structure qualitatively somewhat like that of Earth. There are a couple of quite important differences, however. First, the lunar iron core, if it exists at all, makes up a far smaller fraction of the total mass of the Moon than the Earth's core does of the Earth. Secondly, the inner part of the lunar *mantle* seems to be at least partly molten, unlike the Earth's mantle, which is solid throughout. Finally, the lunar crust seems to have been separated out from almost half the planet's volume. The Earth's much thinner crust reflects a rather less extreme differentiation.

If we try to estimate the bulk lunar chemical composition as we did for the Earth, our results are naturally less secure. Our estimate depends mainly on what we think the lunar mantle is made of, since the mantle contains about 90% of the lunar mass. The most important information about the lunar mantle comes from studies of mare basalts. These basalts, like most of those found on Earth, seem to be produced by partial melting of mantle rock. Now when a rock that is composed primarily of two or three minerals (for example, forsterite [Mg_2SiO_4], an olivine, and diopside [$CaMgSi_2O_6$], a Ca-rich pyroxene) is heated enough to just melt it a little, the resulting lava has a specific composition that depends on *which* minerals are present in the original mix, but very little on their proportions. It is this specific composition of the lava which allows us to recognize it as the product of partial melting. However, the composition of the lavas does allow us to deduce what minerals are the main constituents of the parent rock from which the lava is melted out.

When this kind of reasoning is applied to the mare basalts, it is deduced that the composition of the mantle is probably in bulk much like the Earth's mantle pyrolite (a result consistent with measured seismic speeds, as mentioned earlier), except that the lunar pyrolite seems to be a little *richer* in iron than the terrestrial material, with about 8–12% Fe (compared to about 6.5% in the Earth). However, there is only a little iron in the tiny core, and if we do the same calculation for total iron abundance in the Moon (say 90% Fe in the core, 10% in the mantle, and none in the crust) as we did for the Earth (Table 8.3), we find that iron only makes up about 11% of the mass of the Moon as a whole. This is a very surprising result. It means that the Moon is extremely depleted in a common, refractory element compared both to the Earth (Table 8.3), and to the value expected from the fractions of various refractory materials in the primitive solar nebula (Table 8.1).

This peculiarity of lunar chemistry, however, is only one aspect of the much more general peculiarity which was discovered when Moon rocks were analyzed to determine the fractions of various rare trace atoms that they contain. It is found that virtually *all* the chemical elements more volatile than iron (elements such as sodium, potassium, lead, zinc, and silver; see Table 2.2) are less abundant in Moon rocks than in corresponding Earth rocks. In contrast, more refractory elements (Mg, Al, Si, Ca, Ti, Cr, etc.) have about the same relative proportions in lunar and terrestrial rocks. The peculiar composition of the highland feldspars, which are rich in Ca (anorthosite) but have only small amounts of Na and K (albite and orthoclase; see Table 2.2) is a specific example of this depletion of volatiles. In contrast, Ca-rich feldspars are not common on Earth, while Na- and K-rich rocks are far more common. Another example of volatile depletion is the fact that Moon rocks are completely free of water, again unlike terrestrial rocks, many of which (such as clays and micas) have water bound in their mineral structure. The depletion of volatiles in the Moon seems to be a general feature of its bulk chemistry, as is the low abundance of iron. Both of these features are important clues about the processes that operated when the Moon formed, if only we can interpret them correctly.

Thus, we find that the most probable model of the Moon is reminiscent of the structure of the Earth, with a (possible) core, mantle, and crust, but with very important differences. The lunar core is – at most – relatively much smaller than the terrestrial one, reflecting the very much smaller iron content of the Moon compared to Earth. The mantle of the Moon makes up 90% or more of the total mass compared to 67% for Earth, and is strongly depleted in volatile elements. The lunar crust makes up about 8% of the planet's mass, a much larger fraction than on Earth, and reveals the products of extensive internal melting and separation of low-density rock. No similar relic of massive melting is found on Earth. The Moon, like the Earth, is hot inside, as is confirmed by the fact that the maria were filled with successive lava flows over a billion year interval, by the damping of seismic S-waves below a depth of 1100 km, and by heat flow from the interior measured during two Apollo landings.

Origin and history

The fact that the Earth has an almost planet-sized companion is puzzling. Neither Mercury nor Venus has any moon; Mars has only two tiny bodies, all that is left of the disk of gas and dust which surrounded Mars as it formed. Among the inner planets, the Earth-Moon system is unique. The situation is made still more confusing by the dramatic chemical composition differences between the Earth and the Moon, discussed in the previous section. How does the Earth come to have a large companion that is so different from itself?

Several theories have been put forward to explain the Moon's existence. One possibility is that the Moon was once a part of the Earth that was somehow ejected. On this theory the Moon might be seen as the child of Earth. A common version of this idea is that the original Earth was spinning so rapidly that a piece split away to become a separate body. If the split-off piece came from the mantle or crust of an Earth already separated into a core-mantle structure, the two bodies might be expected to have quite different compositions. However, there are several major problems with this theory. First, it is not clear how to explain the deficiency of volatile elements, and particularly water, incorporated into minerals of the Moon. Secondly, if the Earth-Moon system was once spinning rapidly enough to fission, it ought now to still have the same total amount of spin in the rotation of the Earth and of the Moon about their axes, and in their revolution about each other, since "spin" (actually what is called "angular momentum") is very hard to lose from a system. But the present Earth-Moon system has only about half the expected total spin. Finally, if the Moon split off the Earth because of rotation, its orbit should be quite close to the plane of the Earth's equator. Instead, the lunar orbit is close to the plane of the ecliptic, and is inclined to the equator by an amount that varies between 18° and 29°.

Another reasonable possibility is that the Moon accreted out of the same small rotating disk of material that formed the proto-Earth. (This is how the larger moons of Jupiter, Saturn, Uranus and Neptune, which revolve around their respective planets in a single plane, formed.) This theory suggests that the Moon could be the sibling of Earth. The biggest difficulty with this theory is that it is then very hard to understand why Moon and Earth are so different chemically. It is particularly hard to understand how the Moon could have come to be so depleted in metallic iron relative to the Earth (which suggests that the Moon formed of material that condensed farther out in the solar system than that which went into making up the Earth), and also be so depleted in volatiles such as Na, K, and water (which suggests exactly the opposite).

Finally, the Moon might have formed somewhere else, only to be captured later, more or less undamaged, by the Earth. On this theory the Moon might be thought of as the spouse of Earth. Such an origin might explain the Moon's chemical differences from Earth in some way, although it is hard to see why the Moon should be so depleted in both iron and in volatiles, and have little or no core. The main problem with this idea is that if the Moon passed near the Earth, but well outside the Roche limit, at some time in the distant past, it would almost certainly not be captured. It would simply have its orbit changed drastically by the near miss, and go on its way about the Sun. It could only be captured if something acted to slow it down while it was near the Earth.

A version of the capture theory is now widely accepted. As proposed by A. G. W. Cameron, the idea is that a body with about a tenth of the Earth's mass (i.e., about as big as Mars), with an already separated iron core, actually grazed the Earth, passing well within the Roche limit. Numerical calculations of what would happen in such a collision imply that the impacting body would be completely fragmented by the collision, as well as intensely heated. Much of the shattered material from the impactor's mantle would be ejected from the Earth-Moon system, and most volatile elements would be evaporated away as well. About a fifth of the original mantle mass would re-coalesce (with some debris from the Earth as well) into a single body orbiting the Earth as the Moon actually does. The iron core of the impactor would apparently sink into the Earth's core. This theory appears to explain with one process the depletion of volatiles from the Moon, the lack of a core, and the heat source for melting the lunar mantle (the Moon would re-assemble so fast that almost all gravitation energy released by accretion would be retained as internal heat). The impact would also have made a substantial contribution to the internal heat of the Earth.

The Moon's history since its formation is now, we think, roughly understood. The first recorded event after final accretion was the separation of the thick anorthositic crust by crystal fractionation due to melting of the outer mantle. It is not really clear yet whether the energy needed for this melting was provided primarily by the rapid re-accretion of small bodies in orbit around the Earth to form the present Moon. Significant energy could also have been furnished by continual tidal distortion of the newly formed and rotating Moon by the Earth (see Chapter 1); continually changing distortion as the Moon rotated could have deposited energy into the interior of the Moon, as is currently happening in Jupiter's moon Io (see Chapter 11). These same tidal effects would lead to a very gradual slowing of the rotation of the Earth about its axis, and an increase in the size of the Moon's orbit, as has already been described in Chapter 1. Tidal interaction between the Earth and Moon has evidently moved the Moon out from just outside the Earth's Roche limit to its present position about $60\,R_\oplus$ from the Earth.

After the lunar crust cooled and solidified, considerable further proto-planetary material was accreted, leaving the highlands saturated with craters of all sizes. About 4 Gyr ago, several very large projectiles struck the Moon, creating the huge basins that later became the maria. After these giant impacts, the rate of cratering declined greatly. During the next billion years, basaltic lava flowed up from the mantle through fractures to cover some of the largest basins with successive flows of dark rock, creating the mare basins. As time went on and the Moon cooled, lava would have had to have come from deeper and deeper sources. Eventually, about 3 Gyr ago, the solid upper mantle became so thick that lava could no longer escape to the surface, and all further reshaping of the surface from internal activity ceased. Since that time the Moon's surface has changed only because of continued occasional impacts with Apollo asteroids, comets, and meteoroids.

The Moon's orbital history since its formation has been

9.2 Impacts and craters, again

The physics of impacts

Our examination of the Moon has revealed that the most prominent kind of surface feature is one that is only found with difficulty on the Earth (Chapter 5). Almost all the major surface features on the Moon are connected with its cratering history. This applies to features ranging from the giant Mare Orientale basin and the near side maria basins such as Oceanus Procellarum and Mare Tranquilitatis, to isolated craters such as Copernicus, to the jumbled, crater-saturated regions of the lunar highlands. We need to pause in our study of the terrestrial planets and find out a little more about what happens during a really large meteoroid impact, and how craters are formed and decay.

Almost all the craters produced on an airless body like the Moon, and the large ones created on a planet such as the Earth which has an atmosphere, are the result of small bodies from space impacting the larger moon or planet, just as must have happened over and over during the original accretion of these major bodies from the protoplanetary nebula. On an airless body, the speed with which a meteoroid impacts the surface is at least as large as the escape velocity from the body (2.4 km s^{-1} for the Moon, 4.2 km s^{-1} for Mercury, 11.2 km s^{-1} for the Earth). Generally the impact speed will be significantly larger than this, since the impactor is usually moving in an orbit which is significantly different from that of the moon or planet, and the difference in orbital velocities at the time of impact contributes to the final impact speed. If the Moon is struck by a meteoroid originating in the asteroid belt, the difference in orbital velocities can be several km s^{-1}; a comet in a large retrograde orbit could have an orbital velocity difference of more than 70 km s^{-1}. Thus on the Moon we expect impact speeds ranging from about 2.5 km s^{-1} to about 70 km s^{-1}. A typical impact might have a speed of 10 or 20 km s^{-1}.

The maximum difference in orbital speeds between a meteoroid and a larger body with which it collides depends on two factors. The closer to the Sun the event occurs, the faster both bodies are moving, because of the accelerating effect of the Sun's gravity as bodies get closer to it. Orbital speeds of the planets vary from nearly 50 km s^{-1} at the distance of Mercury, to about 30 km s^{-1} for the Earth, to only 5 km s^{-1} for Neptune (Table A.1). Speeds of asteroids and comets at these various distances from the Sun may be as much as 1.4 times these values, in any direction, but it is still clear that velocity differences due to orbital motion can be much larger in the inner solar system than farther out.

The second factor is one that affects moons. A moon that is orbiting near a major planet (such as a moon of Jupiter) will be struck by bodies whose speeds relative to the moon have been increased by the gravitational attraction of the *planet* to a larger value than they would otherwise reach. Comets impacting one of the outermost moons of Jupiter can strike with velocities of up to about 30 km s^{-1}; the effect of attraction by Jupiter itself raises this maximum velocity of impact on the innermost large moon, Io, to about 50 km s^{-1}.

On the other hand, planets like the Earth and Venus that have massive atmospheres will suffer high speed impacts only with meteoroids that have such a large mass that they push out of their way only much less than their own mass as they fall towards the planet. We have already seen in Chapter 5 that only bodies with sizes of tens of m (and masses in excess of some hundreds of tonnes) will arrive at the surface of Earth with nearly their full arrival velocity. On Venus, the massive atmosphere drastically slows any bodies much less than one km in diameter. However, a number of asteroids (and occasional comet nuclei) in the inner solar system are large enough to produce occasional full velocity impacts on both planets.

Thus we are interested in looking at what happens when a meteoroid slams into a moon or planet at a speed of 10 or 20 km s^{-1} or even more. These are the impacts in which the arriving body hits the ground with a speed comparable to or even well in excess of the speed of sound in the surface rock. Recall that such collisions are called hypervelocity impacts. We have already looked at some examples of hypervelocity impacts on the Earth in Chapter 5. Now we examine the underlying physics a little more closely.

The amount of kinetic energy that a hypervelocity impactor carries is enormous. It typically carries enough energy to crush both itself and hundreds of times its own mass of target rock, to melt a mass several times its own mass, to vaporize more than its own mass (thus there is usually little left of the impactor after a hypervelocity impact), and to eject roughly 100 times its own mass from the impact crater. All of these consequences occur during a hypervelocity impact.

The impact event may usefully be divided into three stages: contact and compression, ejection and excavation, and collapse and modification. In the first stage, contact and compression, the incoming meteoroid contacts the surface and compresses both itself and the ground at the point of impact. The impactor will not be substantially slowed down until it has penetrated into the ground far enough to have encountered roughly its own mass. Thus it will be slowed down and stop after driving into the surface of the planet to a depth of the order of its own diameter. This happens *very* quickly: the in incoming meteoroid comes to a stop in roughly the time it takes to travel its own diameter. The im-

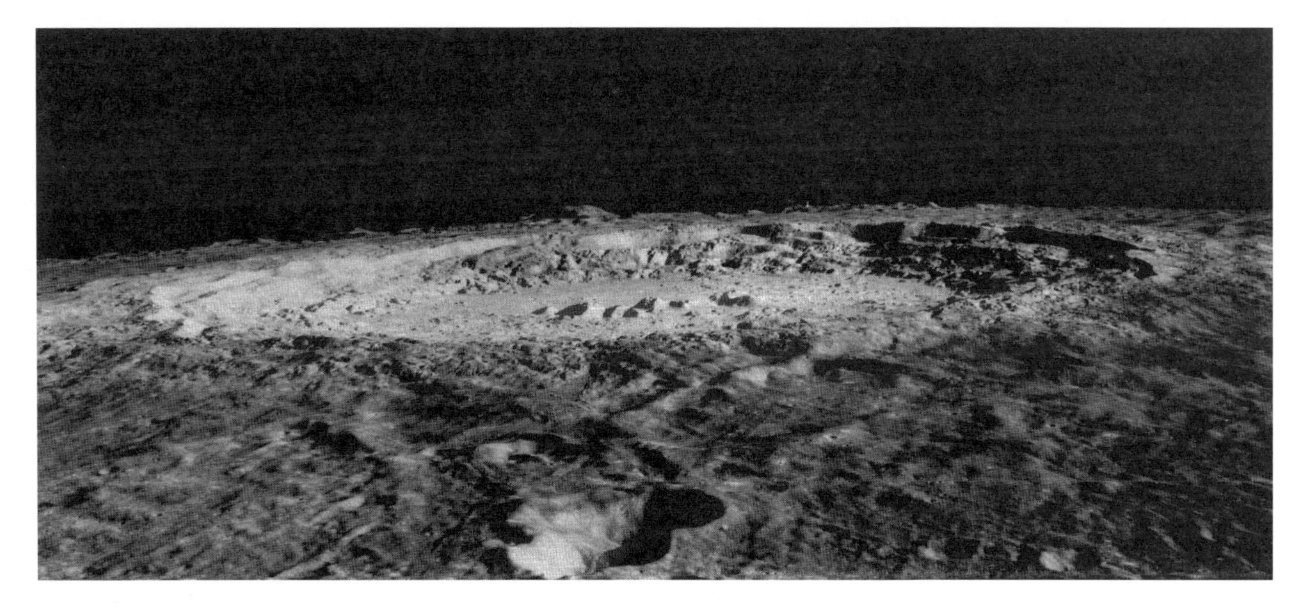

Figure 9.6: This oblique view of the "young" 107-km diameter crater Copernicus clearly shows both the central mountain ring and the terraced crater walls produced as material slumps back into the crater. (Courtesy of NASA.)

pact of a meteoroid with a diameter of 100 m, striking the ground at 20 km s^{-1}, lasts only about 0.005 s.

During this short period the meteoroid suffers an acceleration thousands of times larger than the normal acceleration of gravity at the planetary surface. The pressure that this abrupt stop generates in the interior of the meteoroid, and in the ground at the impact site, can easily reach Mbar (10^{11} Pa) levels. During this stage, both the meteoroid and the impacted rock are intensely compressed and flattened. A little of the planetary surface material is ejected around the edges of the impacting body at speeds comparable to the initial speed of the incoming body; this is probably how the SNC meteorites (Chapter 5) were ejected into space from the surface of Mars.

As the meteoroid comes to a halt, and the pressure inside the meteoroid and the surrounding rock decreases, we enter the second stage, ejection and excavation, of the impact. During this stage the meteoroid is disposed of, and the crater is excavated. The rapid fall in pressure in the impacting body and its immediate environment leads to the abrupt vaporization of most of the meteoroid and a substantial amount of surface rock. This vapor explodes out of the hole dug by the impact at a temperature of thousands of K, producing a brilliant fireball lasting a few seconds. In the case of a major impact by a meteoroid having a diameter of the order of 1 km, the fireball may expand to a diameter of hundreds of km before it cools off substantially. This is certainly one of the most destructive aspects of a large impact on Earth. The fireball explosion will carry with it a very large amount of pulverized rock from the target region; on a planet with an atmosphere, this dust may remain high in the atmosphere for months or years before it finally all settles back to the ground, causing an extended period of near darkness and cold on the ground.

At the same time, a mass of rock tens or hundreds of times larger than that of the incoming body is being ejected from the crater. It is loosely confined by the hole from which it emerges, so the mass comes out at about a 45° angle to the ground (for a roughly vertical impact). During a minute or more after the impact, fragmented and crushed rock falls onto the ground surrounding the impact point, out to a distance 10 or 20 times the diameter of the crater, which itself grows to roughly ten times the diameter of the impactor. The hole that forms is nearly hemispherical until the depth reaches two or three times the diameter of the impactor; after that, the crater grows mainly in the horizontal direction. At the end of this period, a crater roughly ten times larger in diameter and perhaps three or four times deeper than the diameter of the original meteoroid has been created. This new crater is surrounded by a lip of ejected rock; the newly created crater rim would usually extend out to one or two crater diameters beyond the edge of the crater (look at Figures 5.2, 9.2, and 9.3). Some of the ejected rock is in pieces so large that their impact on the surface generates smaller secondary craters on the newly formed crater rim.

At the end of the second phase, we have what is called a transient crater. It is quickly modified by what could be called geological effects during the third stage of collapse and modification. As matter gradually stops raining down on the new crater rim, the compressed rock beneath the impact point rebounds. In small craters (up to roughly 10 or 15 km in diameter), this simply makes the crater a little shallower. In larger craters, the rebound produces a small central mountain peak, like the one clearly visible in Figure 9.2. If the crater diameter is more than roughly 100 km in diameter, this central peak becomes a central mountain ring, as in Figures 9.6.

At the same time, the walls of the crater collapse and slump in towards the centre of the crater until they become shallow enough not to collapse further. This often leads to crater walls that have a distinct terraced appearance, a feature also seen in Figures 9.2 and 9.6. Simultaneously, debris left in the crater, together with the material sliding back in from the transient crater walls, flows back towards the crater centre, so that the floor of the crater is left covered with a thick lens-shaped mass of rubble.

The largest craters of all, those with diameters of many hundreds of km, take on a somewhat different form, that of a **multiring basin**. This is the form of the giant Orientale Basin in Figure 9.4. It is not clear which of the several rings in such a huge crater was the edge of the transient crater, but it appears that at least one of the visible rings formed outside the transient crater. The physics underlying the formation of such rings is not yet well understood, but they are observed in several places in the solar system, such as the Caloris Basin on Mercury (Figure 9.9) and the Valhalla structure on Jupiter's moon Callisto (Figure 11.9).

We shall soon see that impact craters are found on the surface of almost every moon and planet that has an accessible surface. The few exceptions will also be of considerable interest.

Crater counts and dating of surfaces

Craters are not only created, they are also gradually destroyed. The lunar highlands (Figure 9.2) offer one example of how this can occur; there the number of impacts since the surface solidified has been so great that the surface is completely saturated with craters. As new craters formed, they were created on top of previous ones, and eventually a point was reached at which every new crater on average obliterated one old one. Terrain that has reached the point of saturation can be recognized by counting the numbers of craters of various diameters that are visible; at saturation, roughly one crater of any particular diameter will occur in every area ten times larger than the surface of the crater. (For example, one 1-km diameter crater will be found – on average, of course – for roughly every 10 km^2 of surface.)

Exercise: Explain why a region of crater saturation would *not* be expected to have one 1-km diameter crater for every 1 km^2 of surface area.

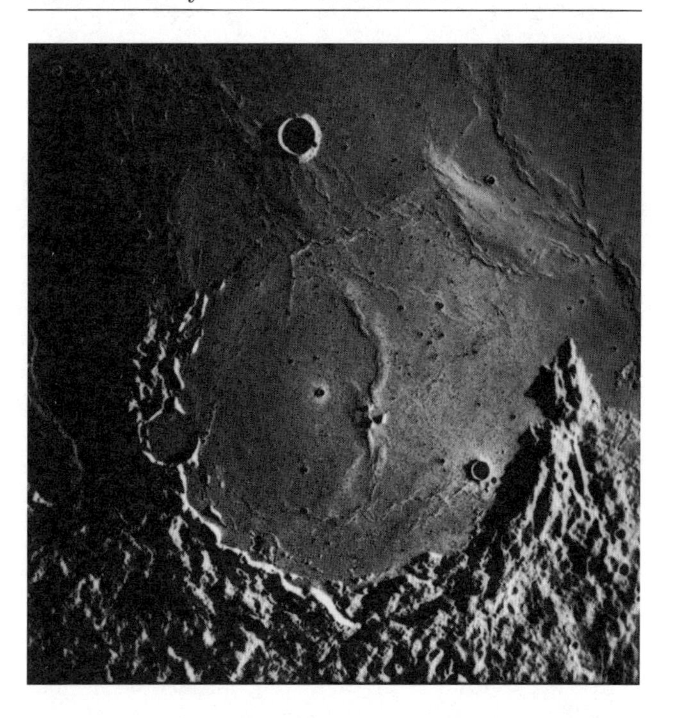

Figure 9.7: This image of the 116-km diameter lunar crater Letronne, the large nearly circular object filling much of the image, was taken from Apollo 16. The crater has largely been filled in by the mare lavas that flowed over the surface of Oceanus Procellarum. The southern half of the original crater wall is still visible in the lower part of the picture, and three central peaks still protrude above the lava. A smaller crater in the lower left crater rim of Letronne has also been largely flooded and must have been created before the mare lavas flowed; several sharp and complete small craters were excavated in the mare floor after it solidified. (Courtesy of NASA.)

Craters can also be removed by other processes. On the Moon, the huge craters that today form the maria basins gradually filled with lava over a period of roughly 0.5 Gyr. This event certainly obliterated smaller craters formed within the huge maria craters; we find a number of mostly submerged (drowned) craters inside the rim of several maria basins (Figure 9.7). We shall see that craters have been obliterated by lava flows or some similar process on the surface of Venus. On the icy moons of the outer planets, craters gradually flatten into ghostly outlines of their former selves as the ice slowly flows to take on a flatter shape. On Earth, craters are rather rapidly disguised and removed by erosion through the action of ice, water, and wind. A crater with a diameter of one km (Figure 5.3) has a typical lifetime on Earth of roughly one Myr before it disappears, unless it is in a region which is very flat and therefore has relatively slow erosion. Larger craters last longer, especially in the shield regions of the continents, but very old craters, even huge ones (Figure 5.4), have been modified so greatly that they are rather hard to recognize.

A fundamental aspect of crater creation, one that strongly influences how many craters there are on any particular surface, is the fact that the rate of crater creation appears to have been *much* higher during the first 0.5 Gyr of the solar system's existence than it has been since. The rate of creation of new craters was about 10 times smaller 3.8 Gyr ago than at 4.2 Gyr, and the current rate is at least ten times lower again. This steep decline in the rate of creation of new craters is certainly what one would expect; as the planetesimals of the primitive solar system were swept up by the planets and moons, less and less debris would be left to form craters.

The decline is also recorded in the surface of the Moon, and the samples that the Apollo and Luna missions brought back allow us to put dates onto the decline in cratering. On the Moon, we observe that the highlands are saturated in craters, and the rocks from that kind of terrain have ages of up to 4.45 Gyr. In contrast, the maria basins, which were flooded with lava between about 4 and 3 Gyr ago, are far from saturated with craters. It is by studying the numbers of craters per km^2 in various terrains, for which we have datable rocks, that we can work out how the cratering rate declined with time.

Knowing something about how the cratering rate tapered off after the formation of the solar system, we can obtain rough estimates of the ages of terrains on other bodies. This is rather imprecise, because we do not have any very clear evidence about how the rate of cratering would have varied with distance from the Sun, but useful estimates can still be obtained. For example, Mars has large regions in the southern highlands which are nearly saturated with craters, while other areas, for example around the giant volcanos of the Tharsis bulge, have far fewer craters. It is estimated that the heavily cratered regions have ages of the order of 4 Gyr, while the Tharsis bulge is probably only 1 Gyr or so in age.

9.3 Mercury

We now turn to the other large, Earth-like bodies of the inner solar system, which we examine roughly in order of increasingly complex structure and history. We start with Mercury, a small planet where most of the important events, like those that led to the present appearance of the Earth's Moon, seem to have occurred during the first billion years of our solar system. We then turn to Mars, a somewhat larger body which has definitely had a geologically active past but which may now be largely quiescent. Finally, we will examine our near twin, Venus, whose level of volcanic activity continues to be similar to that of our own Earth.

Far less information is available about these objects than for either the Earth or the Moon. The terrestrial planets have all been observed from Earth for hundreds of years, but that reveals little about even their largest surface features. All have also been visited by orbiting space probes which have photographed (or mapped, using radar or laser beams) their surfaces. Some surface exploration of Mars and Venus has also been carried out by landing probes. We now have enough information to understand quite a lot about the internal structures and histories of these bodies, but many important questions remain.

The least studied of the terrestrial planets is Mercury, which is very difficult to observe from Earth, and which has been visited only by a single space probe. We have detailed images of less than half of the surface of this planet, with about the resolution (objects a few km or more across are visible) that can be achieved by Earth-based observations of our Moon. Nevertheless, even for Mercury we can deduce quite a lot about the planet's internal structure and its past.

Observational data about Mercury

The small innermost planet of the solar system is never seen from Earth at a separation on the sky of more than 28° from the Sun. As a result, it can be observed visually at night for only about an hour after sunset or an hour before sunrise, when the sky is still fairly bright, and the planet is seen obliquely through a long path of (often turbulent) air. (Infrared radiation from Mercury, at wavelengths at which the sky is a lot darker than it is in visible light, may be observed during the day.) Furthermore, it is a rather small body, whose disk is only 13″ in diameter at its nearest approach to Earth, and is about 8″ in diameter when the planet is at its largest separation from the Sun. As a result, very little is known about surface features from terrestrial observations.

Some characteristics of the planet can be measured from Earth, however. Its orbit around the Sun, which is fairly eccentric, was already described accurately by Kepler in 1618 on the basis of Brahe's visual position measurements. In 1835, Encke's comet passed close to Mercury (the perihelion point of the comet's orbit is inside Mercury's orbit), and observations by Encke of the changes to the comet's orbit allowed him to obtain

Figure 9.8: A mosaic of images of Mercury obtained as the Mariner spacecraft departed from the planet shows the overall similarity of the planetary surface to that of the Moon. Note however that the craters are not quite as densely overlapping as in the lunar highlands. (Courtesy of NASA.)

a value of the planet's mass which is very close to the value accepted today. The planetary diameter is known only approximately from visual measurements; an accurate value was determined only when radar echoes from the planet were obtained in 1962. Radar measurements also made possible the first correct determination of the planet's intrinsic rotation period, which (relative to the stars around the solar system) is about 59 days, exactly 2/3rds of the orbital period of revolution of the planet around the Sun.

Exercise: Mercury rotates about its own axis and revolves about the Sun in the same direction, and its rotation axis is perpendicular to its orbital plane. By sketching the orbital position of the planet at several times (say every 15 or 30 Earth days) and following its axial rotation, show that the length of a "day" on Mercury, from one midnight to the next, is 176 Earth days.

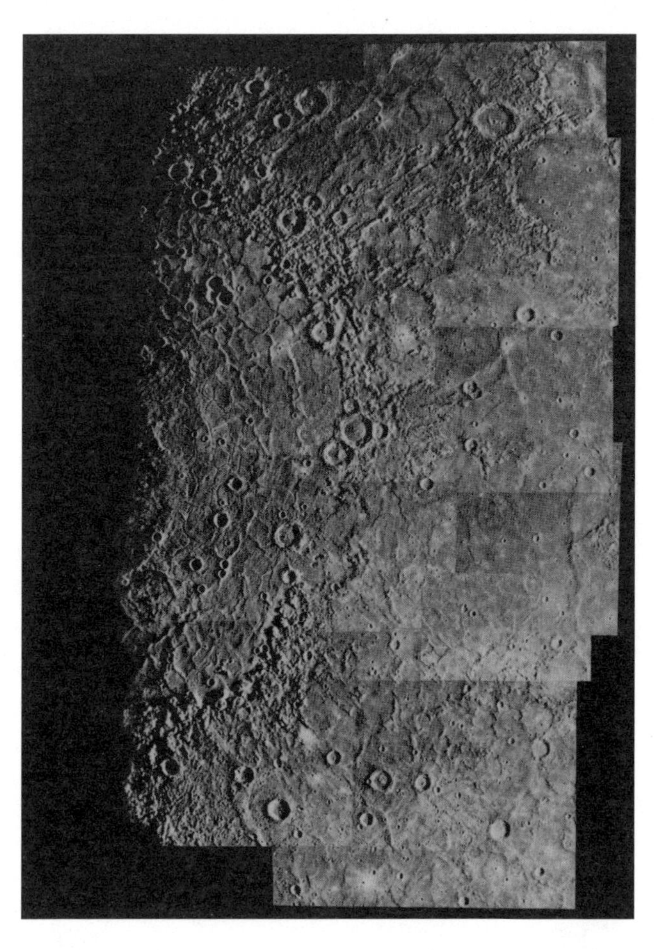

Figure 9.9: Mercury's largest known impact crater, the Caloris Basin, is visible at the left centre of this mosaic of images. Wave-like undulations are seen in the 1300 km diameter circular scar. From the number of smaller crater superimposed on the large basin, it is deduced that the Caloris impact occurred about 3.6 Gyr ago. (Courtesy of NASA.)

Mercury has been observed by only one space probe. In 1974, Mariner 10 was placed into an eccentric orbit about the Sun with exactly twice Mercury's orbital period, and in 1974 and 1975 the probe and the planet made three close approaches to one another. Mariner 10 provided a view of some 40% of Mercury's surface, which is about as detailed as our knowledge of the surface of our own Moon prior to the first space probes. The many images of the surface that were radioed back to Earth reveal a body strikingly similar in appearance to the Moon. This similarity is apparent in Figure 9.8, an image showing the planet lit from the side, like the first quarter Moon.

Mercury's surface is composed of very dark rock and

heavily pitted with craters of many sizes. This is a world whose surface layers, like those of the Moon, retain a detailed record of the later stages of accretion of the planet from planetesimals. There is even a giant impact basin on the surface of Mercury, rather similar to the Moon's Orientale Basin (Figure 9.4): the Caloris Basin is a huge impact feature some 1300 kilometers in diameter, with several clear concentric rings. This basin (Figure 9.9) was produced by the impact of a planetesimal with a diameter of more than 100 km which instantaneously melted the surface over more than 1000 km.

Exercise: Examine Figure 9.8 carefully. Try to identify near the terminator of this figure the region of the Caloris Basin seen in greater detail in Figure 9.9.

Another similarity of the surfaces of the Moon and Mercury is that the spectrum of light reflected from their surfaces is relatively featureless, rather like curve (d) in Figure 6.9. This suggests that the surface of Mercury, like the lunar highlands, may be mainly plagioclase feldspar, but this is still quite uncertain. In any case, Mercury's reflection spectrum shows little if any trace of iron.

There are important differences in appearance between the surfaces of Mercury and the Moon. The larger craters on Mercury do not saturate the surface as they do in the lunar highlands, but appear to pepper a surface which was somehow smoothed out shortly before the end of the bombardment epoch. Furthermore, Mercury has no known features similar to the lava-filled mare basins of the Moon's near side. The single giant impact basin observed is the same colour as the surrounding cratered terrain, and has clear concentric rings not submerged in a lava floor. (A number of large lunar basins also show traces of such concentric rings, often just emerging here and there from the lava flows that cover the interior of the crater.) Elsewhere, fairly smooth plains occur which may also be lava flow regions. Another distinctive feature of Mercury's surface is the presence of a planet-wide system of km-high ridges or scarps, which appear to be what geologists call "thrust faults", wrinkle lines where one part of the planetary crust has ridden up over the adjacent ground. These scarps suggest that Mercury has undergone a planet-wide contraction of the order of one or two kilometers in radius, probably as a result of global cooling.

One unexpected discovery was the detection by the spacecraft of a global magnetic field about 0.1% as strong as Earth's. Although this is a very small magnetic field, it is a great deal larger than the magnetic fields of Mars, Venus or the Moon. No global magnetic field is observed on any of these bodies, although strong magnetism imprinted in ancient Martian rocks was detected by the Mars Global Surveyor mission, suggesting that the planet had a substantial field early in its history.

Composition and internal structure of Mercury

Mercury's mass is only 5.5% of that of Earth, but its mean density, at 5440 kg m^{-3}, is almost identical to Earth's 5510 kg m^{-3}. This is really extremely surprising. The matter in the Earth's interior is quite strongly compressed by the very high pressure in the deep interior, which is produced by the great weight of overlying layers. Mercury has a sufficiently smaller mass that its central pressure is only about 10% of that in the Earth, and so compression of material inside Mercury does not increase its density by more than 10 or 20% over laboratory values. The very high average density of Mercury must mean that it has a considerably larger fraction of some dense chemical element than the Earth does. The obvious candidate is iron, which is both dense and cosmically abundant.

When we try to deduce the bulk chemical composition of Mercury, we can start as we did for the Earth by looking again at the chemical composition of the solar nebula and the most primitive meteorites (Table 2.2). Since we have very little information with which to directly constrain the composition of Mercury, it is reasonable to aim for only a rough first approximation, and so we consider only the three most abundant refractory elements, Mg, Si, and Fe, and their accompanying O. (Because Mercury formed close to the Sun, it is probably safe to ignore the fifth abundant condensible – but more volatile – element, sulphur.) From our observations elsewhere in the solar system, we can probably assume that the Mg and Si will be present in roughly the solar ratio, and that both will be fully oxidized. However, the ratio of iron to silicon is observed to vary in nature, and that iron may be more or less oxidized, as is clear from Figure 5.7. Thus as a first approximation we may consider the ratio of Mg to Si to be known, but both Fe/Si and O/Si are very uncertain. With only one observational fact (the mean density) with which to determine the composition, even this very schematic model has too many unknowns for a definite solution.

One possible model is that Mercury has a core-mantle structure like the Earth, and that its mantle composition is similar to pyrolite. If we assume that Mercury's mantle has a density of about 3300 kg m^{-3}, and that its iron core has a (somewhat compressed) average density of perhaps 8950 kg m^{-3}, we find that to arrive at the observed average density, almost 40% of the planet's volume must be filled with iron, making up about 60% of the planet's total mass, compared to about 35% for Earth and perhaps 10% for the Moon. On this model, the radius of Mercury's core is about 75% of the total planetary radius, compared to a core radius in the Earth which is about 55% of the planet's radius. Somewhat different assumptions are plausible, but because any useful assumptions must account for the planet's very large mean density, all models agree that a large fraction of the planet's mass is metallic iron.

The origin of this very large iron fraction is still not understood with certainty. The high iron abundance might have resulted from a particularly high nebular temperature at the time or in the region where the planetesimals that formed Mercury first accreted, favouring metallic iron over silicates. However, it seems clear that because of the gas drag on m-sized bodies (see Chapter 4), a lot of mixing inwards and outwards of planetesimals occurred, so this seems somewhat unlikely. It now seems most likely that the high iron fraction was the result of an early catastrophic collision – after the separation of Mercury's core, mantle and crust – that vaporized and blasted away a substantial part of the planet's primitive mantle. In any case, although the details of the interior of Mercury are still very uncertain, it is certain that the small innermost planet has a much higher fraction of iron than any other terrestrial planet.

There is no very strong direct evidence to tell us whether the planet is homogeneous throughout or whether it has developed a differentiated internal structure, since no space probes have landed on the planet and we have no seismic data at all. However, two lines of argument strongly suggest that the planet is differentiated. First, the surface is not saturated with large craters. The crust seems to have been smoothed off (probably by global melting of the outer layers of the planet, or by extensive lava flows) before the end of the bombardment phase. There are even some regions seen in the images of the planetary surface that seem to be lava flow plains. These facts strongly suggest that the crust of Mercury is differentiated, which in turn implies high enough internal temperature to have differentiated the core as well.

A second reason for thinking the planet is differentiated results from trying to deduce its internal temperature history. Mercury formed in the innermost part of the proto-solar nebula, where the temperature of the condensed solids was probably rather high; this may in fact be the reason the planet has such a high iron fraction. It is quite plausible that the internal temperature as the planet formed was at least about 1000 K. If we then make a reasonable estimate of the radioactive heating sources available (mainly uranium and thorium; volatile potassium may be quite underabundant in Mercury), it seems that enough heat could have been released within about the first two Gyr to raise the internal temperature of the planet to the melting point of iron and to supply the necessary energy to melt the metal. Core separation would then have occurred if it had not already happened earlier.

But if core separation occurred one or two Gyr after the planet formed, enough heat would have been released as the iron sank to the planet's centre to melt the crust. This would have erased the record on the surface of the last stages of accretion, which (from dating highland rocks on the Moon) we think ended about 4×10^9 years ago, about 0.5 Gyr after the planet formed. Thus the heavily cratered surface of Mercury suggests either that the planet formed with a core–mantle structure initially (from a process like the hypothesized heterogeneous accretion model for the Earth's formation), or that core separation took place soon enough after the planet formed to allow the crust to have solidified by four Gyr ago. Perhaps it was core separation that erased the surface record of the early stages of the accretion. Certainly enough gravitational energy was available from the accretion to raise the interior temperature to the melting point; but we don't know how much of this energy was trapped inside the forming planet.

Thus we conclude that Mercury very probably does have a core-mantle structure because if it *didn't* achieve one early in its history, radioactive heating would have insured that this structure developed eventually, and we deduce from the heavily cratered surface that the core-mantle structure must have developed early in Mercury's history rather than later on.

Another fact suggesting that Mercury does have an iron core is the presence of the global magnetic field, which has a structure rather like that of Earth, with a north and a south pole. The presence of a field in the Earth is thought to require several co-operating conditions: the presence of a liquid metallic (and electrically conducting) core, the relatively rapid rotation of the Earth, and probably convective motions of the core liquid. The field of Mercury probably requires much the same conditions, which suggests that there is a metallic core, and that it is still molten.

In fact, the evidence pointing to a *molten* core in Mercury is somewhat puzzling, because it is not obvious that the core should still be sufficiently hot. Mercury is a fairly small planet, and even if it once was hot enough to separate a metallic core early in its history, it should have lost much of its initial heat by leakage to the surface and subsequent radiation into space, and thus to have cooled the core to below the freezing point of iron. (The presence of scarps all over the surface also suggests that the planet has shrunk since the crust formed, which in turn certainly suggests global cooling.) The cooling problem is particularly severe because the mantle of the planet was both hot and fairly thin, which should have led to slow (solid state) convection in the rock. We know that this process carries heat to the surface (as in the Earth's mantle) much more efficiently than conduction would do. On the other hand, some heating from radioactive species is expected to continue, but after core separation these species are expected to be mainly in the mantle, so that much of the heat generated is rapidly lost to the surface. Thus it is hard to understand why the core of Mercury should have rapid (liquid) convection occurring, as we deduce from the presence of a contemporary magnetic field; possibly the core contains an impurity – perhaps sulphur – that lowers its melting point so that part of it is still molten. All in all, deductions from the presence of a magnetic field are still rather uncertain, but the detection of a magnetic field in Mercury is an important clue to the planet's interior.

To conclude, we note the rather paradoxical situation. On one hand, Mercury superficially resembles our own Moon more closely than any other known body does, and both (in spite of their heavily cratered surfaces) are internally differentiated bodies. On the other hand, the two objects have very different internal structure. Mercury has a massive iron core which makes up more than half its mass, while the Moon is very deficient in iron compared to other inner solar system bodies, and might actually not have a separate metallic core at all.

The history we deduce for Mercury, however, is rather similar to that of the Moon. The planet formed by accretion, with formation of a separate core very probably within the first half billion years. Late in the accretion process, the surface was partly or fully melted (which presumably led to a differentiated crust for the planet as well), or at least resurfaced by extensive lava flows. This may have been precipitated by a giant impact that stripped off much of the mantle (if such an impact did remove much of the mantle, it had to occur after core separation). After the surface solidified, the final stages of the accretion bombardment left a record of intense (but not saturated) cratering. Towards the end of the final accretion stage, a huge impact formed the Caloris basin feature. Since the end of the bombardment, the history of Mercury has been one of cooling with a modest global shrinkage. Neither the surface nor the interior have changed much in structure since that time, and thus Mercury, like the Moon – and unlike the Earth – preserves a partial record of the era of planetary accretion.

9.4 Mars

Observations

The orbit of Mars is fairly eccentric, and so when the Earth passes Mars (**opposition**), the closest separation depends on where in its orbit Mars is. When Mars is near its perihelion, the separation of the two planets can be as small (!) as 56 million km, about 0.37 AU, as the two planets pass. When Mars is near aphelion in its orbit, the smallest separation of the two planets may be as large as 100 million km, almost twice as large as at the most favourable encounters. (The first three oppositions of the 21st century, in June 2001, August 2003, and November 2005) are relatively close ones, with the 2003 opposition being about as favourable as possible.) During the closest encounters, Mars has an apparent diameter of 25 seconds of arc, and some large-scale features may be discerned through a telescope.

Mars is seen to be generally reddish in colour with several large, irregular regions, about the size of terrestrial continents, near the equator; they are somewhat darker than the rest of the planet, and grey or blue-green in hue (Figure 1.2). These features reveal that Mars rotates on its axis once every 24 hours, 37.6 minutes. The planet's rotation axis is inclined to its orbital plane by about 25°, very similar to the 23.5° inclination of Earth's axis, and so Mars too has seasons. In fact, the most obvious features visible on the planetary surface from Earth are the two large polar ice caps, which wax and wane with the seasons, as the snow cover of the Earth's northern polar regions does. This characteristic reveals that Mars must have an atmosphere (a conclusion verified by spectroscopy from Earth), since the polar caps are presumably due to condensation on the surface of some constituent of the atmosphere during the cold winter months, just as terrestrial water vapour condenses (as snow and ice) in the Earth's polar caps. Unlike the atmosphere of Venus, the Martian atmosphere is largely transparent, and we can usually see the planetary surface.

The nature of the dark regions was never obvious from Earth observations. As their colour changes with the Martian seasons, it was long thought that they might be large regions of vegetation. In 1877, the Italian astronomer Schiaparelli (who discovered the association of meteor streams with comets) reported finding long linear markings on Mars. This report led the wealthy American Percival Lowell (1855–1916) to build a planetary observatory in Flagstaff, Arizona, and to begin an intensive study of Mars. Lowell eventually claimed to see an elaborate tracery of criss-crossing lines on Mars, which he interpreted as a network of canals built by an advanced civilization, perhaps to bring water from the polar caps to the equator.

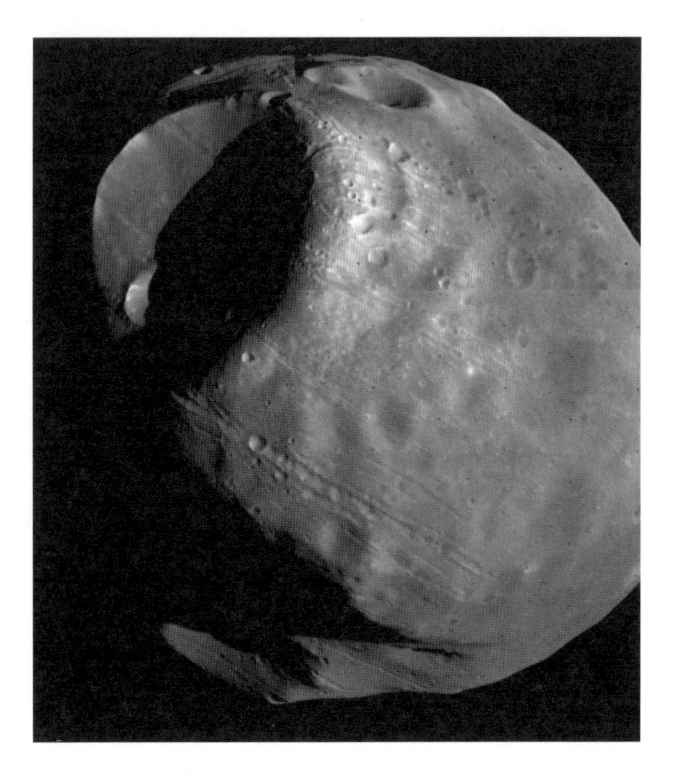

Figure 9.10: This image of Mars' larger moon Phobos was created out of three images obtained by the Viking 1 orbiter in 1978 from a distance of about 600 km. The crater on the upper left of the image has a diameter which is almost half the smallest dimension of the moon. Notice the great similarity to asteroids. (Courtesy of NASA.)

Figure 9.11: The planet Mars as viewed from one of the Viking spacecraft as it approached Mars. The dark region in the middle of the disk, which looks like a crack in the Martian crust, is the Valles Marineris, a huge rift valley. The ovals on the left near the edge of the planet are volcanos. (Courtesy of NASA.)

In 1877, Asaph Hall used the 26 inch refractor of the U.S. Naval Observatory to discover two tiny satellites circling Mars. We now know that these tiny bodies, named Phobos and Deimos, are not spherical, but are shaped roughly like potatoes. Phobos has a largest dimension of 27 km, while Deimos is only 15 km at its longest. Their discovery immediately allowed an accurate measurement of the mass of Mars, which is only about one-tenth that of Earth, and thus also led to a determination of the planet's mean density. A close-up view of Phobos from the Viking space probe is shown in Figure 9.10. Phobos and Deimos are often thought to be small captured asteroids, but the difficulties of capturing two small bodies into circular, equatorial orbits are very severe, and the moons may instead be the remnants of a proto-Martian nebula.

Study of Mars was greatly advanced when the planet was visited by a series of U. S. space probes, starting with simple fly-bys by Mariner 4 in 1965 and then by Mariners 6 and 7 in 1969. These probes sent back photographs taken of the planet as they passed. The first photos came as something of a shock after the years of speculation about civilizations on Mars; the images (such as Figure 9.12) revealed a cratered world nearly as barren and pitted as Mercury or the lunar highlands. It was tempting to conclude that Mars is a planet with a cool interior which has experienced little or no geological activity or differentiation. However, when Mariner 9 was placed in orbit around Mars in 1971 and over the course of a Martian year returned photos of every part of the planetary surface, it was quickly realized that the Martian surface is far more varied and complex than was revealed by the first flybys, all of which observed only small parts of the southern hemisphere in detail.

When Mariner 9 went into orbit around Mars, a giant planet-wide dust storm (an event that occurs once each Martian year) was raging, making the whole atmosphere opaque, so that it was at first impossible to make out any features on the surface at all. As the dust gradually cleared, the first visible objects provided positive proof that the Martian interior is hot and that the planet is internally differentiated: the peaks of four giant shield volcanos began to be visible above the dust. The largest of these (Figure 9.13) is almost 600 km in diameter and about 26 km high, two to three times larger in every dimension compared to the largest similar terrestrial structures, such as the (volcanic) Big Island of Hawaii. Further examination of photos re-

Figure 9.12: A barren and cratered plain in the southern hemisphere of Mars as recorded by the Mariner 6 probe. The only obvious surface features are craters, although the terrain is clearly not as saturated with craters as the lunar landscape shown in Figure 9.2. (Courtesy of NASA.)

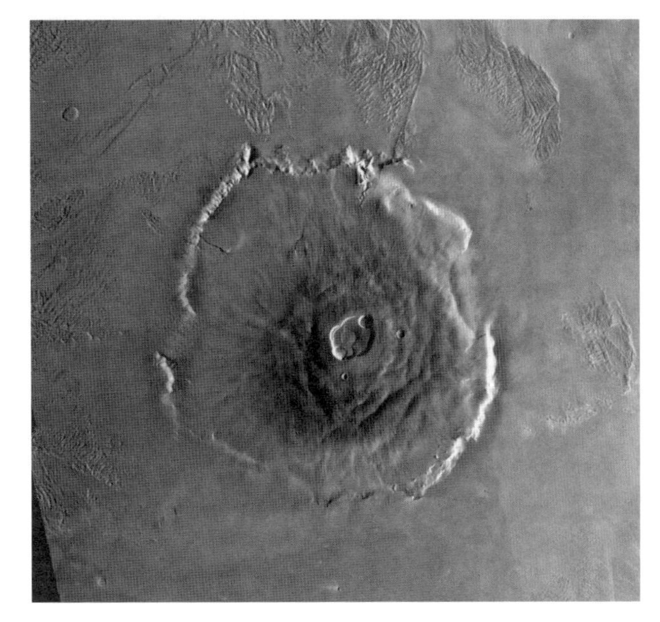

Figure 9.13: The largest volcano on Mars is Olympus Mons. It towers about 26 km above the surrounding plain, and the clearly visible steep scarp that surrounds the volcano is some 500 km in diameter. The oval crater at the summit of the volcano is the caldera, the vent from which molten lava has at times emerged. Similar (but smaller) calderas are found in terrestrial shield volcanos. (Courtesy of NASA.)

vealed many other clearly volcanic features, ranging from large distinct shield volcanos with clear central calderas to enormous lava flow plains hundreds of km across.

As photographing of the surface proceeded, other spectacular discoveries were made. A huge canyon system is present that runs roughly parallel to the planetary equator. This system of parallel cracks in the Martian crust is some 4000 km long, about the same as the width of the North American continent. Individual fissures are sometimes 75 km wide and several km deep. This system resembles the Grand Canyon of the Colorado River, but on a scale more than ten times larger. This enormous canyon system has been named Valles Marineris (Valleys of the Mariner) in honour of the little spacecraft that first revealed details of the Martian surface. The entire canyon is visible in Figure 9.11, and a closer view is seen in Figure 9.14

On a still larger scale, the observations showed that Mars has two quite dissimilar hemispheres. Half of the planetary surface (roughly, the southern hemisphere, imaged by the early Mariner missions) is heavily cratered (although not as heavily as the Earth's Moon or Mercury), while the opposite hemisphere is quite flat and only lightly scarred with craters. Some 16 craters larger than 250 km in diameter are found on the Martian surface, all in the heavily cratered hemisphere. The largest of these ancient impact scars are the 900-km diameter Argyre Planitia and the 2000-km diameter Hellas Planitia. Hellas is an enormous feature; its floor lies more than six km below the mean level of the cratered plains, and it is surrounded by a rim of ejecta extending out to 3000 km from the centre of the impact, and almost two km thick. These large basins generally have relatively smooth interiors, rather like the lunar mare basins. Figure 9.15 is an oblique view over the Argyre basin.

Probably the most exciting of all the startling discoveries about the Martian surface was the observation of dry stream beds flowing down hillsides, gullies on the walls of canyons that bear striking similarity to the gullies produced in terrestrial canyons by erosion due to rainwater, and rounded islands such as the ones seen in Figure 9.16. All of these features seem to have been produced by a fluid considerably less viscous (gooey) than lava. Almost everyone agrees that they were produced by flowing water (although it has also been argued that the fluid that created the channels was a mix of CO_2 and soil) . At present, the atmospheric temperature is too low over almost all of the planet for water to occur in liquid form; water exists essentially as vapour in the atmosphere, and as frost or snow near the poles. The islands and dry stream beds appear to record an era when the Martian atmosphere and climate were far different from today. Here at last is some evidence for the temperate, wet climate that Lowell believed to

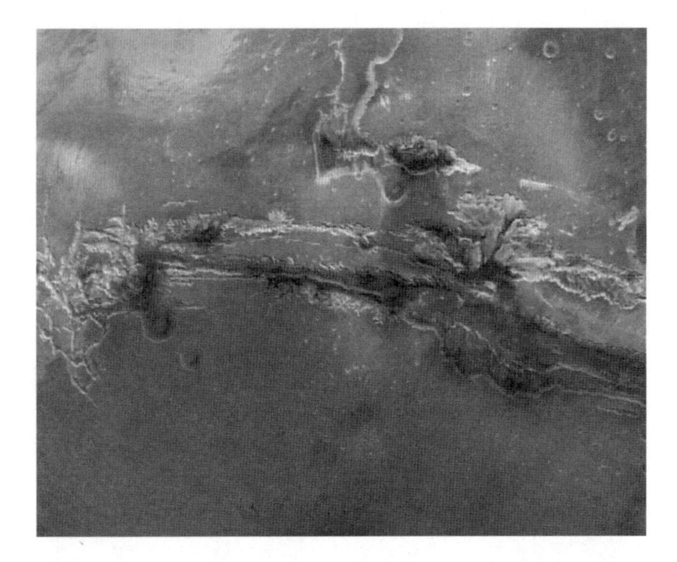

Figure 9.14: This view from overhead of the 4000-km long Valles Marineris rift canyon reveals a surface feature with no close parallel on Earth. If this feature were present on Earth, it would reach across most of the United States. The jumbled terrain at the west (left) end of the canyon contrasts with the more organized central part, with a dominant main canyon and smaller parallel faults. (Courtesy of NASA.)

characterize Mars. However, the river beds found by the space probes are far smaller and more irregular than the features described by Lowell; they are natural, not built; and they are very, very old. No real features on the planet correspond to the network of canals that Lowell reported seeing, and we now suppose that he was fooled by optical illusions when observing the brilliant, shimmering image of the red planet through a telescope. We shall return to the significance of this evidence of a time when water flowed on Mars in the next chapter, when we discuss Mars' atmosphere.

The brilliant imaging of Mars by the Mariner missions was quickly followed up by the U. S. Viking space probes. Two orbiters from this programme produced an enormous quantity of superb views from orbit of every kind of Martian feature.

The planet has not only been observed from space, but also from the Martian surface. After three failed Soviet attempts, two Viking landing vehicles successfully reached the surface of Mars in 1976. These probes returned spectacular views of the rocky desert surface of Mars. They also carried out extremely valuable but rather rough chemical analyses of the soil at the landing sites. However, the Viking landers were primarily designed to search for evidence of life on Mars, so they did not obtain as much information about the chemical and physical structure of the planet as one would like.

Figure 9.15: The second largest impact basin visible on the surface of Mars is the Argyre Planitia, seen here in the middle left of this oblique view towards the east. The far wall of Argyre has been obliterated by a more recent impact, and many smaller impact craters are visible in the image, along with an irregular mountain chain around the crater, the remnant of the crater wall. (Courtesy of NASA.)

Following the great wave of exploration of Mars in the 1970's, a long period of inactivity followed during which only one short-lived Soviet orbiter (Phobos 2) returned any data. The launch of the Hubble Space Telescope in 1990 made possible substantially sharper imaging of Mars than was possible from the ground. The ambitious and expensive Mars Observer probe, the first major attempt to resume study of the Red Planet, was launched in 1992 but lost radio contact en route to Mars. Finally, in 1997 the Mars Pathfinder landed successfully on the surface, deploying a small rover, and the Mars Global Surveyor was inserted into orbit around the planet. These two missions have provided a fresh burst of very important observations, including close-up chemical analysis of a number of rocks and accurate topographic and gravity mapping of the surface. Further missions are underway, including the successful Mars 2001 Odyssey orbiter and several more landers like the Pathfinder.

One final very important source of information about Mars is a small group of extraordinary meteorites,

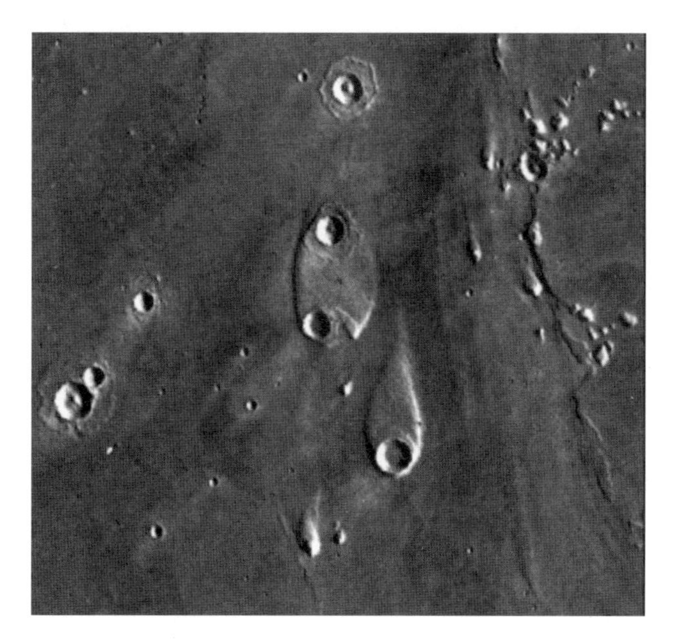

Figure 9.16: Small teardrop-shaped "islands" are seen near the southern border of Chryse Planitia. Water apparently flowed from the south (from bottom to top in this image), and as it flowed around obstacles such as craters it left islands with rounded upstream ends and long tails. (Courtesy of NASA.)

known as the SNC meteorites (for shergottite-nakhlite-chassignite, after the first three identified). These are a small family of more than a dozen igneous meteorites with much younger ages (mostly between 150 million and 1.3 Gyr, although one has an age of about 4 Gyr) than other meteorites, and with chemical composition quite different from those of other igneous meteorites. When the relative amounts of various elements (particularly the isotopes of the noble gases) in these rare meteorites were compared to Viking lander observations of Martian rocks and atmospheric gases, it became clear that the SNC meteorites almost certainly originated on Mars. They are apparently surface rocks ejected from Mars during major meteoroid impacts, later swept up by Earth either because they were really numerous or by sheer good luck. We thus already have in hand for detailed analysis a number of actual samples of the Martian surface, even without the enormous expense of a round-trip mission – although unfortunately we don't know where on Mars they originated.

Interior of Mars

Observations of the planet give us a number of useful clues about the composition and state of its interior. From the measured mass (6.45×10^{23} kg) and mean radius (3394 km) we find an average density of 3960 kg m^{-3}. This is less than 75% of the value for the Earth. Some of this difference in density is due to the lower degree of self-compression of Mars compared to the more massive Earth, but we shall see that Mars also must differ substantially in interior structure from the Earth.

A first question to ask about the interior of Mars is whether it has a differentiated core – mantle – crust structure like that of the Earth, or is a homogeneous body. There are a number of arguments that combined, make it quite clear that Mars must be differentiated. First, Mars is large enough that more than enough heat was released during accretion (from conversion of gravitational energy into heat) to melt the iron inside and start separation of a core; in fact, Mars would have had to retain in its interior less than one-quarter of the gravitational energy released by accretion to guarantee this result. Secondly, the Mars Global Surveyor probe has discovered that large areas of remnant magnetism exist in rocks in the old, cratered terrain of the southern hemisphere, indicating that Mars once possessed a magnetic field and presumably thus a molten metallic core. (No global field is found at present; Mars is no longer able to generate a magnetic field.) A third kind of evidence comes from study of the surface. Mars has many (apparently extinct) volcanos, including Olympus Mons (Figure 9.13), showing clearly that the interior has been hot enough to melt lava. Furthermore, chemical analyses of surface rocks and soil by the Viking and Pathfinder landers, from space using an infrared spectrometer on Mars Global Surveyor (recall the discussion of remote sensing of mineral composition in Chapter 6), and from the SNC meteorites, have shown that the surface is largely basaltic. This composition is produced by partial melting of subsurface rocks, again testifying to high internal temperatures. Finally, the internal distribution of material (the "moment of inertia") in a planet affects how rapidly its axis of rotation changes direction in response to tidal effects from the Sun; this effect has been measured using the accurate positions of the Viking and Pathfinder landers, and shows that Mars cannot have uniform density inside; the centre must have substantially higher density than the outer layers. We conclude that Mars certainly has undergone differentiation.

A next question might be to ask whether the internal structure of Mars could be a smaller copy of that of Earth. Could the planet have an iron-nickel core (uncompressed density about 8000 kg m^{-3}) and a pyrolite mantle containing about one Fe atom for every nine Mg atoms (uncompressed density about 3340 kg m^{-3})? If we try such a model, setting the core size by requiring the model to agree with the uncompressed mean density of Mars (estimated to be about 3730 kg

m^{-3}, not much less than the actual mean density of 3930 kg m^{-3}), it is found that the core must contain less than 10% of the mass of the planet, compared to the Earth's core which makes up more than 30% of the total planetary mass. Furthermore, this model does not agree with the overall internal distribution of mass deduced from tidal effects; it has too much mass concentration towards the centre. Mars is definitely not a smaller twin of Earth.

The failure of the Earth-like model leaves us with two questions. Can we find any other hints about the internal composition of Mars? And how shall we modify our model to bring it into agreement with the few available data?

The chemical analyses carried out by the landers, and studies of the SNC meteorites, give us some valuable clues. These analyses reveal surface rock compositions similar to terrestrial basalts, but substantially richer in iron. This suggests that, if Mars has the familiar core-mantle structure, the mantle is enriched in iron compared to the Earth. This is also consistent with the enormous sizes and shallow slopes of observed Martian lava flood plains, which suggest a very runny kind of lava. Iron-rich lava is runny in just this way. If we assume that the mantle is made up of pyrolite with a roughly doubled Fe content, the (uncompressed) mantle density of Mars should be about 3550 kg m^{-3}, compared to 3340 for Earth. This is a step in the right direction, as it reduces the difference in density between core and mantle. Furthermore, the landers have found that the Martian soil is far richer in sulphur than terrestrial soil is, while the SNC meteorites reveal a deficiency of chalcophile elements (elements that tend to associate with sulphur in a melt). This suggests, first, that Mars has a much larger total mass of S than Earth, and secondly, that much of this may have settled into the core. That is, we guess that the large observed S abundance in surface rocks is nevertheless only a small fraction of the S abundance in the planet as a whole. Thus we have a hint that the core could be more nearly FeS (uncompressed density around 6000 kg m^{-3}) than FeNi. Again, this reduces the difference in density between core and mantle and diminishes the degree of concentration towards the centre.

These two changes at least allow us to find models that are consistent both with the overall mean density of the planet, and with its degree of central mass concentration. However, there are still far too many unknown quantities (amount of S in the core, and thus core density; total mass of the core; actual chemical composition and density of the mantle; thickness and composition of a crust, etc) that it is simply not possible at present to identify a unique model for the interior of Mars. One set of recent models (Bertka & Fei 1998, *Science* 281, 1838) have considered cores composed of Fe, FeS, Fe_7C_3 and even FeH, with mantle composition enhanced in Fe compared to the Earth (Fe/(Fe + Mg) ≈ 0.25); acceptable models are found with radii of between about 1300 (for a small core of high density) and 1700 km (a larger core of lower density), and core masses making up between 12 and 21% of the total mass. There is still considerable uncertainty about the correct internal model for Mars.

In the face of the uncertainty about the internal structure of Mars, you might think that little would be known about whether the planet has a crust like (or unlike) that of Earth. However, two quite different kinds of data provide information about the Martian crust. First, the numerous obviously volcanic constructs on the surface suggests that the planetary surface has been plated with lava, a process that intrinsically involves the separation of a low melting point rock fraction, and thus strongly suggests that a low-density crust may be present. This idea is supported by the observation (discussed above) that the surface rocks are apparently largely basaltic (mainly basalt and andesite: see Figure 2.12). Recall that on Earth the oceanic crust is basaltic rock produced by partial melting of the upper mantle rocks, so the widespread occurrence of basaltic rocks on Mars is a strong indication that Mars too has a crust of some kind.

A second very different kind of information about the Martian crust comes from the study of the planet's gravity and shape by the Mars Global Surveyor. The orbit of the spacecraft around the planet is determined, of course, both by the global gravity of the planet as a whole and by the local regions of higher and lower altitude and density. Careful monitoring of the spacecraft motion has made it possible to map the variations over the surface of the gravitational attraction from the planet. At the same time, the laser altimeter on board obtained accurate measurement of the distance of the spacecraft from the surface, so that the shape of the planet is now known with high precision.

The shape of Mars is only approximately spherical. The relatively rapid rotation of the planet (once every 24.6 hours) leads to planet-wide flattening; the equatorial radius is about 20 km larger than the polar radius. This effect was expected. However, the precise measurements from the Mars Global Surveyor also revealed the very surprising fact that that the centre of the mass of the planet is displaced about three km to the north from the centre of the planet's shape. That is, the typical altitude of the heavily cratered southern highlands, measured from the centre of the planet's mass, is about 6 km higher than the average altitude of the terrain in the smooth northern plains! This situation is not possible in a planet that has the same distribution of material along all radial lines from the centre of mass. Clearly, Mars has some important internal difference between the northern and southern hemispheres. The simplest interpretation of the decentering of the shape (usually called the "figure" of the planet) is to assume that the planet is approximately symmetric inside, but that it has a low-density crust which is much thicker in the southern hemisphere than in the northern. This situation would make it possible for the planet to "stick out" farther in the south than in the north. There would be the same mass in the southern hemisphere as in the northern, but having a thicker crust of low density material in the south than in the north would make the southern half of the planet somewhat larger in radial extent than the northern half. The altitude difference would be the result.

To qualitatively account for the offset between the centre of the planet's mass and its figure seems to require two distinct crustal units: a region of crust perhaps 20 km in thickness under the smooth northern hemisphere, and a second region with crust 60 km or more thick under most of the cratered southern hemisphere. From detailed gravity maps, it is deduced that the extremes of thickness may range from only a few km (in the Hellas basin and under most of the smooth northern hemisphere) to more than 90 km (under the Tharsis volcanic bulge). The absolute thickness of the crust is not very well constrained by available data; the whole crust may be considerably thicker than the numbers above suggest. The crust on Mars thus appears to be similar to Earth's oceanic crust in chemical composition, but to the continental crust in thickness; however, the Martian crust appears to constitute a considerably larger fraction of the total planetary volume than on Earth. Interestingly, although the region of thick crust largely coincides with the cratered terrain (and the crustal bulge under the volcanic region in Tharsis), the change from thick to thin crust follows the edge of the cratered southern terrain over only about 40% of the boundary; the two boundaries do not coincide northwest of Hellas or in the Tharsis region. The reason for these planet-scale hemispheric differences is still not certain.

Surface of Mars

The surface of Mars offers many clues to the state of the interior and to the history of the planet, but we are only able to interpret some of them with confidence at present. A spectacular view of one tiny part of the surface is seen in Figure 9.17, taken by the Viking 2 lander.

Mars is similar to the Earth's Moon in showing both large areas of heavily cratered surface and also areas with only light cratering, analogous to the lunar highlands and mare basins, though in quite different proportions. Clearly, the heavily cratered areas must be older than those with less cratering, but we are hindered in putting definite ages to various terrain by lack of knowledge of the rate at which small bodies were swept up in distant parts of the solar system. We provisionally *assume* that the impact cratering rate was similar to that which we deduce from dating rocks from the Earth's Moon, with a high rate of impact up to about 3.9 Gyr ago, after which the cratering rate fell off rapidly to a level similar to that found at present. When we compare the heavily cratered terrain of the lunar highlands and of Mercury to that of Mars (look at Figures 9.2, 9.9 and 9.12), it is evident that in the lunar highlands and on Mercury, the cratering is nearly saturated – craters are formed on top of other older ones – while on Mars the older craters in many parts of the cratered terrain have been effaced and the visible ones are often separated from one another. This difference indicates that the cratered regions of Mars were largely resurfaced, probably by lava flows, about 4 – 3.9 Gyr ago, just at the time when the rate of impacts was dropping off rapidly. The much lighter cratering of the northern lowlands suggests that this hemisphere was resurfaced about 1 – 2 Gyr ago, and in places perhaps still more recently.

The Martian craters are rather varied in structure. Small craters, up to 10 or 15 km in diameter, are simple bowls. Larger ones are more complex, usually with central peaks, slumped inner walls, and with floors often showing ridges and flow fronts. Some craters seem to be surrounded by ejecta which has *flowed* like mud; these are sometimes called splash craters. It appears that these may have resulted from impacts into terrain with subsurface water or permafrost which melted from the heat of impact and lubricated the flow, leading to crater rims that resemble mud slides rather than piles of ejected rock.

Volcano-like constructs form another important category of Martian surface features. In studying volcanic activity on Mars, it is useful to start by recalling the forms of volcanism observed on Earth. The main sites here are (1) at mid-ocean ridges where new crust is being created, as in Iceland and all along the mid-Atlantic Ridge; (2) at subduction zones where one crustal slab is descending beneath another, as in Japan, where the volcanos are steep-sided and the eruptions often explosive; (3) over mantle hot spots, where the volcanos are usually wide and shallow shields and the eruptions are less violent, as on the Big Island of Hawaii; and (4) in lava flood plains such as the Columbia River plateau in the U.S., where a vast plain was covered at one time by very low-viscosity (runny) lava that emerged from

Figure 9.17: This image shows the surface of Mars as viewed from the Viking 2 lander at Utopia Planitia in 1979. (The tilt of the horizon is due to the fact that the lander is not quite vertical.) The ground is strewn with large boulders having sizes up to several tens of cm, probably the debris from nearby impacts. The sky is bright rather than black (as it is on planets without atmospheres) because of scattering of sunlight by CO_2 molecules and suspended dust particles. A very thin layer of water ice blankets the ground; it will stay until the end of the Martian winter. (Courtesy of NASA.)

surface vents rather than from obvious volcanos.

On Mars, we find no evidence of long sinuous ridge systems like the terrestrial oceanic ridge systems, nor do we find any mountain chains like those that occur on Earth in regions of plate convergence. We conclude that plate tectonics is not operating on Mars, and may well not have ever done so. We do not expect, nor do we find, the kinds of volcanic activity associated with continental drift. However, numerous volcanic structures *are* found that strongly resemble the terrestrial shield volcanos that develop over mantle hot spots. Except for the fact that it is two or three times higher and wider than the Big Island of Hawaii, the current site of active volcanism in the Hawaiian Islands, Olympus Mons (Figure 9.13) on Mars strongly resembles the large shields of Hawaii. Near Olympus Mons, on the Tharsis ridge, astride the boundary between the southern highlands and the northern plains, several relatively young shield volcanos are found. These are visible on the left side of Figure 9.11; they are all larger than any terrestrial volcanos. Another small group of three volcanos is found in the Elysium region of the northern plains. Both these groups of volcanos occur on large bulges in the Martian crust; the bulge under Tharsis rises two or three km above the surrounding terrain. Judging from the relatively small number of impact craters per square km, the surface of the Tharsis volcanic region is fairly young, probably of the order of 300 million years old, and this region may still be occasionally active. The region around Elysium is more heavily cratered, and may have an age of 1 – 2 Gyr since it was last active.

Mars possesses the analogue of terrestrial flood plains in abundance. The northern plains are vast, quite flat regions which probably are covered with flood plain lava. The modest number of craters observed per square km in this hemisphere suggests that this region has been flooded with lava within the past 1 – 2 Gyr, although proponents of past surface water on Mars sometimes suggest that the smoothness is dues to ancient sediments. The older terrain in the southern hemisphere also shows ample evidence of lava flooding. The surface terrain seen in Figure 9.12 contains well-separated craters produced by impacts onto a surface somewhat reminiscent of the lunar mare basins, although this terrain is more heavily cratered, and thus probably older, than the maria (compare with Figure 9.3). The nature of the southern plains as lava flow plains is confirmed by the presence of lava flow fronts and wrinkle ridges. The fact that lava flows in the southern hemisphere have not obliterated the craters there shows clearly that the rate of production of lava on Mars is far lower than on the Earth, in spite of the spectacular nature of some Martian volcanic features.

One type of volcanic feature on Mars does not closely resemble anything we find on Earth. On Mars we observe what seem to be enormous, very flat and ancient volcanos, often largely buried in the surrounding lava plains, with huge calderas. These structures are called **pateras**. The largest, Alba Patera, is located northeast of Olympus Mons on the edge of the Tharsis bulge; it is the largest volcanic structure known on Mars. Because the pateras do not rise much above the surrounding terrain they are not easy to recognize. Most of the known ones are located in the ancient southern terrain, and thus probably have ages of 2 – 4 Gyr.

It appears that Mars has had volcanic activity throughout its history, although at a considerably lower general level of activity than on Earth. Since the most recent volcanic constructs are less than a tenth of the age of the planet, it is very likely that volcanic activity continues at the present, although it seems to be infrequent enough that we may not observe any activity directly for many centuries. This volcanic activity has occurred both in a form that hints at the presence of mantle plumes and hot spots, and in a form that left little evidence of the sources of lava.

The huge canyon system Valles Marineris (Figures 9.11 and 9.14) has no close terrestrial analogue. This vast system of parallel valleys starts on the edge of the volcanic Tharsis bulge in the west and runs some 4000 km eastward to Chryse Planitia on the boundary between the two unlike hemispheres. In places it is 8 km deeper than the surrounding terrain; the main canyon is tens of km wide and the whole system is up to 600 km across. Valles Marineris has three main sections. The western end shows quite complex faulting; the central 2400 km contains the long central troughs (which appear to have layered walls punctuated in places by enormous landslides); and the eastern end is quite chaotic and is one of the locations where strong evidence for water flow in the past is found (Figure 9.16). Valles Marineris is somewhat reminiscent of the Grand Canyon of the Colorado River in the southwestern U. S., though on a vastly larger scale. However, unlike the Grand Canyon, Valles Marineris is not an erosion feature, and closer terrestrial analogues are probably the Red Sea (a region where two continental plates are pulling away from each other) and the East African rift valleys. The Valles Marineris appears to be a huge tension fault system, apparently opened by forces pulling towards the north and south, creating parallel cracks in the Martian crust along the long east-west axis. Perhaps this tension reflects a period during which the crust shrank in area as it cooled. Alternatively, the existence of Valles Marineris may be related to the volcanic activity that created the bulge of Tharsis at the west end of the canyons.

Formation and early evolution

We now have enough information to begin to understand the history and evolution of Mars. The planet certainly formed by accretion of solid planetesimals, as did the other terrestrial planets. A major mystery is the question of why Mars is so much smaller than either Earth or Venus. Perhaps this is due to the effect of Jupiter on the accretion process near it; we presumably see this same effect much more strongly in the fact that the asteroid belt contains still less mass than Mars, and was indeed never able to accrete into a single planet at all. However, we can plausibly guess that the composition of Mars in bulk is not very different from that of the carbonaceous meteorites, and that it probably accreted (like Earth) as an originally homogeneous mass.

A first important question is to try to understand when Mars may have differentiated (recall that the basaltic composition of the SNC meteorites shows clearly that Mars *did* differentiate). A number of kinds of evidence now show that differentiation almost certainly occurred shortly after the planet accreted. These include the following points.

- The SNC meteorites have differentiation ages from Rb/Sr and U/Th dating of about 4.5 Gyr, very likely the time when the core and mantle of the planet separated.
- The heavy cratering of the southern hemisphere suggests that no major heat release that could remelt the crust (such as would happen upon core formation) occurred after about 4 Gyr ago.
- Early flood and valley features, probably due to surface water which in turn required a much more massive atmosphere than exists at present, suggest that both atmospheric gases and water were released from the interior rather early in the planet's history.

Thus we deduce that the core separated probably less than 100 million years after the planet formed. The energy for this separation could not have come from radioactivity, because this energy is released too slowly; instead, the planet must have retained more than about 1/3 of the accretion energy released by impacts of planetesimals on the surface. This would have been possible if much mass arrived in the form of fairly large bodies that buried themselves, and their kinetic energy, deep below the planet's surface.

Assuming that the planet differentiated soon after its formation out of the swarm of planetesimals, it is possible to compute how the planetary interior would have evolved. Of course such models are somewhat uncertain because of the important gaps in our knowledge of the interior of Mars (for example, how much sulphur is found in the core and even how large it is, what fraction of the total material is made up of important radioactive heating sources such as ^{40}K, U and Th, etc), but we can still gain useful insight into the internal state of the planet from such computations.

Model computations reveal a number of interesting points about the interior of Mars. First, they show that the present state of the core depends quite strongly on whether it has more or less than about 15% by mass of S. If Mars has a small core mainly made of FeNi, it appears that the core probably started out as a liquid in which convection is occurring. As the core cooled, the central region began to freeze out, releasing latent heat and causing impurities to separate into the liquid outer core, so that some gravitational energy would be released. As a result of the heat release from the inner core, convection would still be going on in the outer core today. In contrast, if the core is rich in S, the melting point would be depressed enough that the core would still be entirely liquid. Furthermore, since the liquid core transports heat quite efficiently, it would have settled into a state of nearly constant temperature, and would no longer be convecting. This difference is of interest because we think that core convection is required to generate a planetary magnetic field. Thus the fact that the Mars Global Surveyor detected no present global field, but *did* find remnant magnetism in rocks in the southern hemisphere, suggests that Mars has had core convection in the past but no longer does. This in turn suggests that the core of the planet is relatively rich in S.

Another result of computations of the history of the Martian interior is that it is found that convective motions occur in the solid rock of the Martian mantle, as they do in the Earth's mantle. The convection is expected to be in the form of a few plumes of heated rock rising slowly from the core-mantle boundary, like the plumes that underly hot spots on the Earth. A consequence of both the core convection and the mixing motions in the mantle is that many trace chemical elements (those that associate with silicates) are concentrated into the mantle or even the crust; this includes most of the important radioactive elements. Another consequence of mantle convection is that we naturally expect the planet to have developed a differentiated crust; if almost all the low density elements that could float to form a crust have done so (aluminum, potassium, sodium, calcium, etc), the crust could have an average thickness of about 150 km. Since we find no evidence of continental drift on Mars, we conclude that processes that recycle the crust back into the mantle (as plate tectonics does on Earth) are much weaker, and we would not be surprised to find a thick crust on the Red Planet.

The plume-like convective motions in the mantle are expected to lead to volcanic activity on the surface, as we observe in the Tharsis and Elysium regions, but there are expected to be at least about six plumes, and so we do *not* have an obvious explanation for the fact that there is only one currently active volcanic region. Perhaps a plume can only lead to active surface volcanism if the lithosphere above it is particularly weak, or is fractured by a major impact. The computations do not provide any obvious answer to the puzzle presented by the hemispheric dichotomy between the cratered southern plains and the smooth northern ones.

The planetary interior history suggested by the model computations is roughly as follows. During the first Gyr of the planet's history, the heat released by accretion and core formation (which occurred very soon after the planet was assembled) led to a very hot interior, active mantle convection, outgassing of volatiles such as CO_2 and H_2O from the interior and much volcanic activity both in volcanos and in release of flood lavas. The volcanic activity may have triggered release of subsurface water and cause the floods whose traces are still visible. However, within a few hundred million years after the planet's formation, much of the heat was lost to the surface, radioactive sources were concentrated near the surface, and the planet developed a thick lithosphere. The planet probably shrank slightly (attested to by a planet-wide system of wrinkle ridges). During the last 3.5 Gyr Martian history has been one of ever slower cooling, with volcanic activity concentrated into smaller and smaller regions.

Mars still presents us with some major unsolved mysteries. We do not really understand the planet's accretion history, particularly why it Mars so low in mass compared to the Earth or Venus. Its internal history depends strongly on the sulphur fraction in the planet, a poorly known quantity (although the magnetic field evidence appears to point to a high S fraction in the core). The reason for the planet-wide asymmetry (the hemispheric dichotomy) is still unknown. In fact, the factors controlling surface volcanism and crust formation are far from clear; we don't understand why almost all recent volcanic activity has been confined to the Tharsis region around Olympus Mons. The huge Valles Marineris appears to be a "local" feature, one produced somehow during the development of the Tharsis volcanism, but again we have no clear picture of how this occurred. Finally, we may wonder why Mars is so unlike Mercury, which differs from it only by a factor of about two in mass, but clearly similar to Venus and the Earth, both of which are nearly ten times more massive. Mars will continue to fascinate planetary scientists for years to come.

Exercise: List the main differences between Mercury and Mars. Try to identify those which are probably due to the fact that Mars has been able to retain an atmosphere while Mercury cannot, and those which arise from differences in internal structure.

9.5 Venus

Observed features

Venus is the planet that approaches nearest to Earth. At closest approach it is only about 40 million km (0.3 AU) away. Nevertheless, it is not easy to study from Earth, because it has a dense atmosphere, in which a layer of thick white clouds completely obscures the surface. From Earth-based visual observations, one can determine approximately the size (the size observed includes the cloud layer, whose top turns out to lie some 65 km above the solid surface) and the mass (through the effect of the planet on its neighbour's orbital motions and on passing comets), and hence derive a mean density. Venus is only a little smaller and less massive than Earth, and has a very similar mean density.

Venus' atmosphere is composed primarily of CO_2, and contains a small amount of N_2 and a tiny amount of water vapour (about 0.1% of the gas). This atmosphere is nearly opaque to both visible and infrared waves, and so measurements of heat radiation from the planet in the infrared simply measure how hot it is at the top of the atmosphere, where the temperature is about 240 K. When much longer wavelength heat radiation from Venus (which penetrates the whole atmosphere freely) was detected in the 1960's, it was found that the solid surface is far hotter, with a temperature in excess of 700 K, due to an intense greenhouse effect in the atmosphere. (This will be discussed in Chapter 10.) There is therefore no liquid water on the surface of the planet.

The planet has also been studied from Earth by radar. Radar echoes were first detected in 1961. In this method of observing, a very short pulse of radio waves is sent out from Earth, which strikes the target planet and is reflected back to Earth. The time interval between sending the pulse and receiving the echo allows one to calculate how far away the reflector is, and so to obtain an accurate distance to Venus. Furthermore, reflections from the point nearest to Earth at the centre of the visible disk of the planet return sooner (about 0.02 second sooner!) than waves reflected near the edge of the planet, which made possible the first accurate measurement of the planet's radius. The reflected waves also have their frequencies changed by the Doppler effect because the planet is rotating, so that one part of the edge of the planet (the limb) is rotating towards the Earth while the opposite edge is receding. From Doppler shift measurements, the rotation of the planet has been found to be **retrograde** (in the opposite sense to the revolution about the Sun), and very, very slow; it takes 243 days (as viewed from a distant star) for Venus to complete one rotation.

Venus has been visited by many space probes, both Soviet and U. S. Some of these probes have been orbiters, but quite a number have entered the dense atmosphere, and several have successfully landed on the surface. Soviet Venera and Vega landers have carried out some chemical analysis of the rock and soil material at their landing sites, and have sent back photographs of the landscape around them (the atmospheric clouds exist at high altitude; at ground level the air is clear). U. S. and Soviet probes have carried out surface mapping from orbit using radar altimeters, devices which determine the height of the satellite above the surface directly below by measuring the time interval between the instant of transmission of a short radio pulse and the instant when an echo returns to the spacecraft. Knowing the height of the spacecraft from the centre of the planet from its orbit, and its height above ground from the altimeter, the local altitude of the ground relative to the planetary centre or the average surface can easily be found. When a radar altimeter is operated continuously while the spacecraft circles the planet in an orbit that carries it over the poles, and the planet revolves slowly beneath the probe, the local heights measured may be used to build up a relief map of the whole planet. The U. S. spacecraft Pioneer Venus I obtained the necessary observations in 1979 to derive the first (almost) complete relief map of the cloud-shrouded planet. Two Soviet Venera probes also carried out substantial radar mapping. The most detailed radar mapping has been done by the U. S. Magellan probe, which orbited Venus between 1989 and 1994, obtaining maps having an altitude precision of better than 50 m. The Magellan topographic maps show detail on the ground down to about 10 km in size. The probe also produced spectacular radar images of surface reflectivity that can reveal features smaller than 100 m across.

The mapping reveals a planetary surface somewhat reminiscent of Earth. Most of Venus is covered with low-lying, rolling plains which are similar to how the deep ocean floors on Earth would look if the oceans were removed. Long belts of hills or low mountains (a few hundred meters high) cross these plains; these are reminiscent of folded mountain chains on Earth, and may reflect planetary shrinkage or more local crustal compression, as the scarps of Mercury and the wrinkle ridges of Mars do. Continent-like regions are also found, rising four or five km above the plains. The largest of these continents, named Aphrodite Terra, is about as large as Africa; the next largest, Ishtar Terra, is roughly the size of Australia. Altogether, the continental highlands cover less than 10% of the surface of Venus, in contrast to Earth, where continents (including continental shelves now below sea level) occupy almost 40% of the total planetary surface.

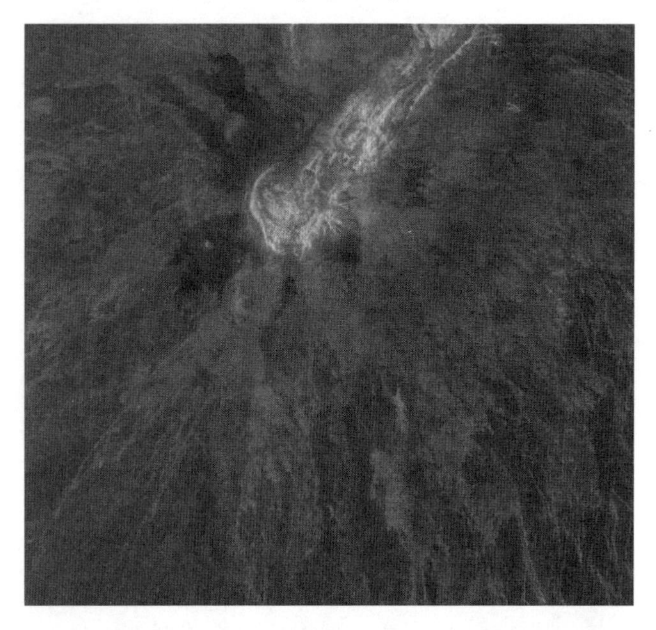

Figure 9.18: The large shield volcano Gula Mons has a bright central caldera which is roughly circular, with a prominent lava flow running away from it towards the upper right of the image. (Courtesy of NASA.)

The high resolution of the Magellan radar maps has made it possible to identify thousands of volcanic and tectonic structures, ranging from small vents one km or so across to shield volcanos with diameters of hundreds of km. These structures come in a variety of forms, some familiar from the Earth and some quite strange. The highland (continental) regions such as Ishtar Terra may be regarded as the largest of the tectonic structures on Venus. All of the continent-like regions are more or less mountainous. The highest mountain belt on the surface of Venus is located in Ishtar Terra. This belt includes the giant Maxwell Montes, which rise to an altitude of 12 km (higher than Mt Everest on Earth) above the low-lying plains.

One familiar volcanic form found on Venus is the shield volcano. About 150 are recognized having diameters of over 100 km. Flows from the central calderas of these huge volcanos may extend for hundreds of km. One such shield is the volcano Gula Mons, seen in Figure 9.18. In addition to the shield volcanos, nearly one hundred calderas and numerous pateras (recall the pateras – old, shallow volcanic shields – of Mars) are found

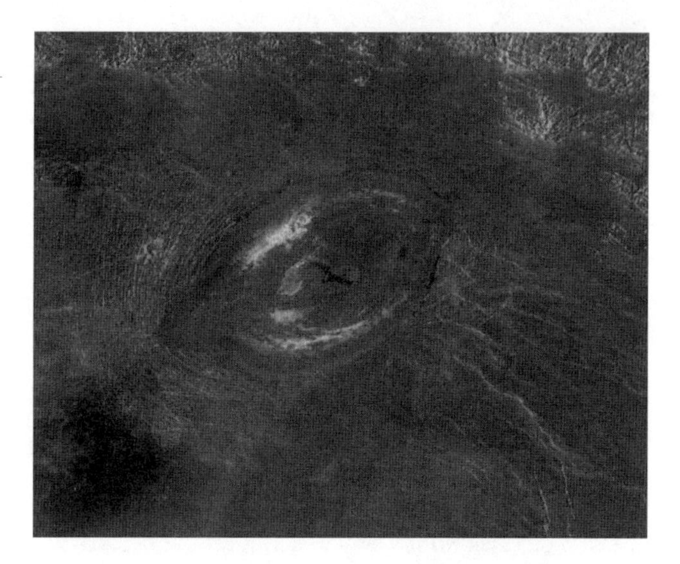

Figure 9.19: The oval feature Sacajawea, a structure about 160 km across that is one of the largest features in Ishtar Terra, is clearly volcanic in origin. It resembles the caldera of a volcano. (Courtesy of NASA.)

(see Figure 9.19).

Other tectonic features have overall circular or oval forms reminiscent of calderas, but have different topography. Large circular or oval structures which are bounded by elevated ring-like mounds, somewhat like the rims of impact craters but smoother, are known as coronae (singular: corona); one may be seen in Figure 9.20. Other similar forms are known as arachnoids; these differ from coronae mainly in lacking the surrounding elevated ring (Figure 9.21). A number of other kinds of tectonic features with unfamiliar names such as tesserae (regions of criss-crossing ridges and troughs) and ticks (flat or depressed circular domes surrounded by radial ridges and troughs) have also been identified. The surface of Venus is simply littered with volcanic structures of various kinds.

Early Soviet Venera landers sampled the chemical composition of several spots on the surface by detecting the natural radioactivity of the rocks, which made it possible to measure the relative amounts of the naturally radioactive elements K, U, and Th. Two later Veneras, and the Vega 2 lander, were equipped with X-ray fluorescence experiments, which irradiated the soil with X-rays and looked at the wavelengths and relative strength of the returned X-rays to determine the abundance ratios of the principal elements Si, Al, Mg, Ca, Fe and a few others. Both kinds of chemical analysis indicate that the surface material of Venus has a composition similar to terrestrial basalt, which on Earth originates as magma produced by partial melting deep in the crust or in the mantle; this magma subsequently

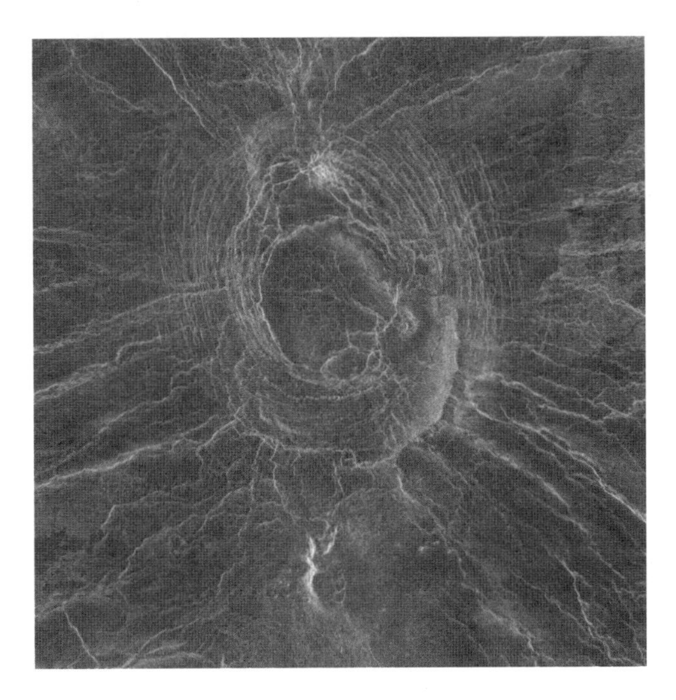

Figure 9.20: The oval form of a corona is seen in this Magellan image, which shows a region roughly 100 km square. (Courtesy of NASA.)

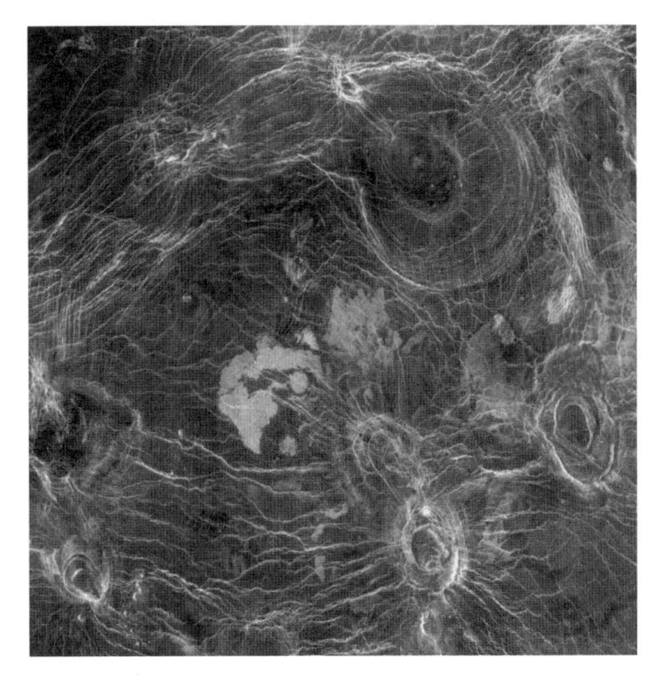

Figure 9.21: Several arachnoids, ranging in diameter up to about 200 km, are seen here embedded in a field of radiating cracks that resemble a spider's web. (Courtesy of NASA.)

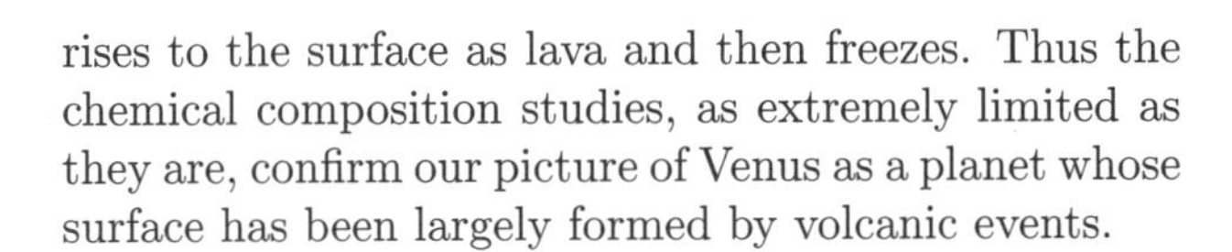

rises to the surface as lava and then freezes. Thus the chemical composition studies, as extremely limited as they are, confirm our picture of Venus as a planet whose surface has been largely formed by volcanic events.

The Magellan radar maps have revealed the surface in fine enough detail to clearly identify craters made by impacting asteroids and comets. The maps show that the surface of Venus is *not* heavily marked with impact craters. On the whole planet only about 1000 are found, ranging from 1.5 to 270 km in diameter (see Figure 9.22). This is a far smaller number than is found on the Moon or on Mars. The surface of Venus has certainly been resurfaced or reworked, possibly several times during the life of the planet. Note that the observed lower limit to crater size is not set by the fineness of the maps; the space debris that would make craters with diameters of less than 1.5 km on Earth is slowed down so much in the massive atmosphere of Venus that no visible craters result. Most of the observed craters are remarkably well preserved; few are partly flooded by subsequent lava flows, and none are degraded by erosion, since Venus has no surface water and only very slow breezes.

Chemical composition and basic internal structure

From the highly accurate mass (4.869×10^{24} kg, 81% of the value for Earth) and radius (6051.5 km, 95% of the Earth's radius) measured by space probes, a mean density of 5245 $\mathrm{kg\,m^{-3}}$ (95% of the terrestrial value) is found. Since Venus is near the Earth in the solar system, only a little smaller, and has about the same density as Earth, a roughly Earth-like structure would not be surprising. Unfortunately, we have little data with which to test this idea. One possible model for Venus is that it is *exactly* a scaled-down Earth, with the same fraction of the interior given over to core, mantle, and crust, and the same chemical composition. When we try to construct a mathematical model of Venus along these lines, it is found that the model has a radius which is between 20 and 40 km less that of the actual planet, for the same mass. That is, a scaled-down Earth with Venus' mass would have a slightly (about 1–2%) larger mean density than Venus actually does. Since the error in calculated mean density is so small, we are probably correct in regarding the scaled-down Earth as a good first approximation. However, the error makes it clear that the interior of Venus does differ in some measurable way from that of the scaled-down Earth model.

It is not clear at present what the difference between

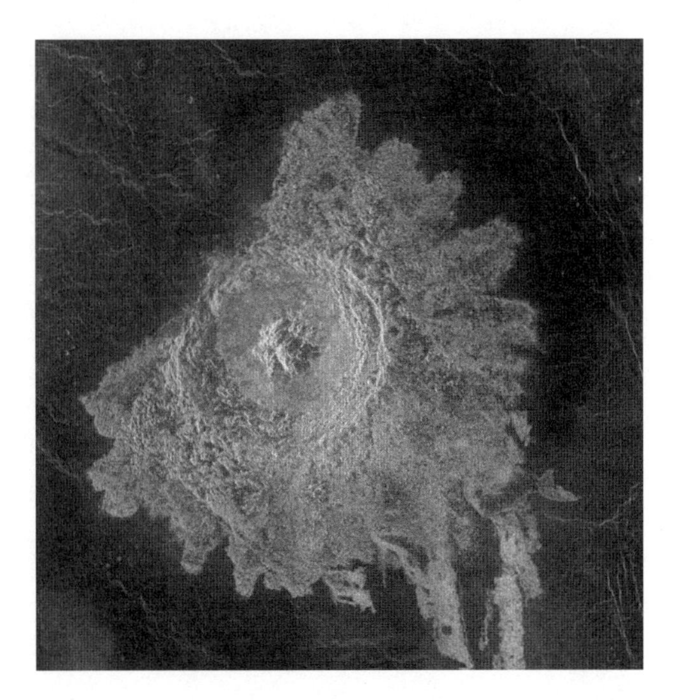

Figure 9.22: An impact crater on the surface of Venus, imaged by radar from the Magellan probe. The crater itself is the circular feature (about 30 km in diameter) at the centre of the image; it has a rather prominent central peak. The bright regions outside the crater itself are areas of high radar reflectivity, due to the fact that the ejected material is quite rough; this region forms the rim of the crater, and looks somewhat like splash craters on Mars. (Courtesy of NASA.)

the Earth and Venus is due to. One possibility is that Venus has no sulfur in its core, while the Earth has quite a lot (recall the unknown 10% of the Earth's core mass). This is plausible because sulfur is fairly volatile; more might have condensed in the solar nebula at 1 AU than at 0.7 AU. In this case, since S combines with Fe to form FeS, the core of the Earth would be proportionally more massive than that of Venus, and compression in the Earth would be more severe. This difference could account for the slightly lower density of Venus compared to the scaled-down Earth model. A quite different possibility is that less of the Fe inside Venus is concentrated in the core than in the Earth. If the lower mass of Venus compared to Earth led to lower surface temperature on the proto-planet, perhaps more of the Fe combined with O before being incorporated into the planet. The result would be a planet with a proportionally smaller iron core than Earth and a higher iron abundance in the mantle. It seems doubtful that we will know which of these possibilities, if either, is the correct explanation for the low density of Venus until a network of seismographs can be set up on the oven-like surface of the planet and successfully monitored for some years. In the meantime, we can only estimate that the iron content in Venus is probably no higher than in Earth, and perhaps somewhat smaller, and that abundances of other elements are very similar in the two planets.

The existence of mountains, continents, volcanos and other clearly volcanic structures, and lava flow fields, the presence of basalts on the surface, and the rarity of large craters, provide conclusive evidence that Venus has a hot core and that the planet has undergone extensive differentiation, probably comparable to that of the Earth. This is not surprising considering the similarity of Venus to Earth in size and distance from the Sun. Since the size of the planet is similar to that of Earth, it is reasonable to guess that the amount of heat retained during accretion was probably similar; the chemical similarity of the surfaces of Venus and the Earth suggests also that the internal radioactive heating rate may be similar. Thus we would expect the internal temperature of Venus to be similar to that inside the Earth.

In particular, the core is probably at least partly molten. However, we have almost no data bearing directly on the state of the core with which to compare this idea, except for the observation that (unlike the Earth, with its partly molten, rapidly rotating core) Venus has no detectable global magnetic field. This difference from the Earth might be due to the very slow rotation of our sister planet; rapid rotation may well be a necessary requirement for generation of a global magnetic field. Alternatively, it is possible that a partly solid, partly molten core is needed for generating a magnetic field, and this could be lacking on Venus if the core is, for example, still fully molten. The nature of the core of Venus will probably not be known until we can establish a network of (high-temperature resistant) seismographs on Venus.

With a hot, differentiated interior, the mantle of Venus is probably much like that of Earth. The mantle chemistry is expected to be dominated by the four common refractory elements O, Si, Mg and Fe. In fact, from our earlier argument about the close similarity of the Earth and Venus, we expect the mantle of Venus to have a mafic composition probably rather like that given in Table 8.2. This mantle probably undergoes (very!) slow convection. Numerical models of the mantle suggest that this convection, like that of the Earth, involves a small number of rising plumes of relatively hot, buoyant mantle rock, balanced by larger areas of descending cooler rock. Such plumes probably underly some of the larger volcanic structures on the planetary surface.

The lander observations of the basaltic nature of the

Figure 9.23: The Soviet Union successfully landed several probes on the surface of Venus. Each was able to make observations and measurements for an hour or so before succumbing to the intense heat. These images of the ground around the lander were sent back by Venera 14. The fact that photography of the barren and rocky landscape was possible shows that some light penetrates even to the bottom of the massive atmosphere. (Courtesy of Russian Academy of Sciences)

Venusian surface indicate that Venus has a crust – that is, a thin surface layer of chemical composition substantially different from the pyrolite of the mantle, which because of its relatively low density floats on the surface of the planet. The present crust of Venus does not have the chemical composition of the anorthositic composition of the lunar crust, and thus is probably *not* the result of a planet-wide magma ocean. The Venusian crust is much more like the oceanic crust of the Earth, or the basalt of the Martian crust or the lunar mare basins, which are the result of partial melting of the mantle followed by expulsion of the magma to the surface. On Earth (at present), new basaltic crust is mainly formed at plate tectonic spreading centres such as mid-ocean ridges, but the examples of the Moon and Mars show that basalt plains do not need plate tectonics to form; partial melting in the mantle under a variety of conditions can produce a differentiated crust. (An image of the surface as seen from the Venera 14 lander is shown in Figure 9.23.)

We do not have any evidence clearly showing just how thick the crust of Venus is. Unlike Mars, there is no planet-wide dichotomy with a thick crust in one hemisphere and a much thinner one in the other hemisphere. The crust is almost certainly not more than a few tens of km thick; below this depth, the high pressure converts basalt to eclogite, a mineral which is denser than the mantle rock. Because of its high density, the eclogite layer would eventually peel off the underside of the crust and sink back into the mantle. A reasonable guess for the thickness of the crust of Venus might be about 30 km. One very important difference between the crust of Venus and the oceanic crust of the Earth is that the basalt of Venus is completely dry – virtually no water is incorporated into the minerals, unlike the basalt of Earth, which is full of water. As a result, basalt on Venus is probably much stronger, and more resistant to flow, than that of Earth (the water acts as a kind of lubricant during rock deformation). A similar difference in water content, and rock properties, exists between the mantles of the two planets.

Internal thermal structure and the present surface

The surface of Venus provides us with several extremely valuable clues about the thermal state of the planetary interior, and about the history of the planetary surface. One of the most important of these clues comes from a study of impact craters on the planet. As mentioned previously, there are not nearly as many craters as would be expected if the surface of Venus were, say, 4 Gyr old. If we make a reasonable estimate of the cratering rate at the orbit of Venus (based on the observed cratering rate on the Earth and Moon), we find that the present surface of Venus is between 300 and 600 million years old. Furthermore, the *distribution* of craters over the surface is astonishingly uniform. It appears that between 80 and 90% of the surface has an age which is the same within about 100 million years. Thus, the cratering record reveals that virtually all of Venus was resurfaced in one relatively short episode about half a Gyr ago. The fact that only a very few craters are partly flooded with lava (unlike the situation in the lunar mare basins or the heavily cratered hemisphere of Mars) shows that the resurfacing was an event which did not simply deposit a thin veneer of new lava on the surface, but added km thick layers of crust, completely destroying older craters.

A further very significant fact about the cratering record is that the continent-sized elevated areas are not, in general, older than the lowlands. This situation is very different from the Earth, where the typical age of continental areas – and the retention of ancient craters – is several times larger than the sea floors. The continents on Venus do *not* appear to be an older kind of crust, floating high above the denser mantle and preserved by buoyancy from recycling. Their present surfaces are not much older than the era of resurfacing.

The nature of this resurfacing event is still unknown. At least three possible modes of resurfacing present themselves. One possibility is that resurfacing has taken place mainly by volcanic surface flows, from obvious calderas or as flood lavas from vents, covering the previous surface but perhaps not recycling it. A second possibility is that the resurfacing has occurred through an analogue of terrestrial plate tectonics, with new crust created at spreading centres and old crust recycled back into the mantle, as occurs with terrestrial oceanic crust. A third is that the mantle was unable to leak its radioactively generated heat away through a rigid mantle, leading to gradual heating and a catastrophic era of crustal breakup, melting, and turnover. Let us look at the surface of Venus and see what evidence it offers about the resurfacing mechanism.

Consider first volcanic flows, both the obvious volcanic constructs such as shield volcanos and also possible lava plains. It is clear that the surface of Venus is dotted with volcanic constructs, but the rate of ejection of lava onto the surface at present (deduced from the regions that are relatively free of craters) is far lower than would be needed to explain the global resurfacing event. If the resurfacing was the result of volcanic flows covering the previous crust, we must explain why the rate of lava flow onto the surface was everywhere 20 or more times larger half a Gyr ago than it appears to be at present, and then dropped abruptly to roughly the present rate. Although the surface record shows the abrupt fall-off of resurfacing a few hundred million years ago, it does not provide any clue as to why this might have occurred, if the resurfacing was mainly due to lava flows.

What about resurfacing by plate tectonics? This might well operate fast enough; on Earth the oceans are completely recycled roughly every 200 million years. Plate tectonic recycling would also explain the general absence of old, degraded craters. However, studying the surface, we do not see on the surface any clear signs of planet-wide plate tectonics. No global network of ridges marks out spreading centres like those of the Earth's ocean ridges, although some local regions have surface forms like small tectonic plates. No long subduction zones are visible. It is of course possible that plate tectonics operated vigorously 500 million years ago, and then for some reason stopped; in this case, many of the surface symptoms might have become difficult to see through crustal relaxation and possibly from lava flows filling some low areas. But if this is the case, we have the same problem as before – if plate tectonics operated vigorously a few hundred million years ago, why did it suddenly stop?

A third possibility is some kind of catastrophic turnover of the crust, caused perhaps by a larger rate of heat generation in the mantle than was balanced by heat loss from the surface. This actually may be the case at present; the loss of mantle heat to the surface through volcanic flows and through heat conduction through the lithosphere seems to be less than the estimated heat production by radioactive decay of K, U, and Th. In the Earth, a similar amount of radioactive heat is transported to the surface through plate tectonics, but the surface of Venus is apparently not subducting at present, and in fact seems to be rather rigid, so heat can be carried out to the surface only via the two less effective mechanisms of volcanism and conduction through the lithosphere. An imbalance between the heat generated internally and that transported to the surface would lead to gradual heating of the mantle and perhaps eventually to weakening of the lithosphere as heats up from below, followed by breakup and replacement of the crust, perhaps more than once, or even at regular intervals. If this was the cause of the resurfacing event, then another resurfacing event may occur in the future.

Thus at present we can suggest a number of possible ways in which the planet could have been quickly resurfaced half a Gyr ago, but we do not have enough information to decide clearly among them.

Early history and evolution

To conclude our study of Venus, we examine what we can deduce – or guess – about the early history of our sister planet. This is a rather hazardous enterprise, since Venus has been even more thorough than Earth in eradicating all surface traces of its early history. As we have seen, essentially the entire crust was replaced less than one Gyr ago. (Even the Earth has not been this thorough in erasing traces of its past; tiny regions of continental crust about four Gyr old have been found in Canada and Greenland.) However, by thinking about what we have learned about the other terrestrial planets we have studied, we can make a little progress on this problem.

From its similarity in size, chemical composition, distance from the Sun, and continued geological activity, we can guess without much uncertainty that Venus formed much the same way that the Earth did. It probably retained enough of the gravitational energy released by the planetesimals that it accreted to quickly become hot enough to separate out a metallic iron core from the rocky mantle above. This process may have released enough low-density melted rock to form an anorthosite crust like that of the Moon, although such a primitive crust might have been fairly thin (at high pressures, this melt fraction would not be less dense than the general mantle rock). However, we are unsure whether there was such a primitive crust or not.

Early in its history, Venus would almost certainly have been hotter inside than it is now, both from the retained gravitational energy and from the more rapid rate of release of heat from radioactivity. This would probably have led to more rapid convection in the mantle than at present, and very likely to much more surface tectonic activity. This vigorous surface activity would have mirrored important convective motions in the mantle, with up- and down-flows and very likely plumes like those we now infer inside both Venus and the Earth. One consequence of this high level of internal activity would have been the rapid replacement of the primitive crust (if there ever was one) with a secondary crust of basalt much like the present crust, produced by partial melting of upper mantle rocks and subsequent magma escape onto the planetary surface.

However, because of the total absence of ancient surface features, we have not been able to learn much about the early history of Venus. We do not know how the high level of internal heat production affected the surface – perhaps something like terrestrial continental drift occurred, or possibly the planet suffered repeated episodes of massive sinking and replacement of the crust, with intervening periods of calm. Thus, not only do we not know what kind of event resurfaced the planet half a Gyr ago, but we also do not know whether this process was one event in a series, or a unique event in the history of Venus. We still have a lot to learn about the history of our near neighbor – as we do about our own planet.

9.6 The terrestrial planets: a final comparison

Now that we have examined each of the terrestrial planets individually, it is worthwhile to look back and observe a number of general features of their histories and internal structures that are worth noticing. Here are a few of the points that should be considered.

The terrestrial planets all have fairly similar bulk chemical composition, dominated by the abundant refractory elements in the solar nebula: O, Mg, Si, Fe. However, there are significant, and systematic, differences in overall composition as well. The fraction of total mass made up of metallic iron decreases steadily as one goes outward from Mercury to Mars, from about 60% in Mercury to around 25% in Mars. (The Earth's Moon had special formation circumstances leading to its overall very low iron content.)

All the terrestrial planets (even the Earth's small Moon) appear to have formed a chemically distinct crust of melted rock which obliterated some of the impact craters from the period of accretion. This fact indicates that the terrestrial planets heated up quickly as they formed, and most probably means that they all were able to retain as internal heat an important fraction of the energy released by gravity, to supplement the heat released more slowly from radioactive decay of K, U and Th. We are fairly sure that because of the combination of gravitational and radioactive internal heating, the terrestrial planets all developed structures consisting of metallic iron cores surrounded by rocky mantles rather early in the history of the solar system.

Only Venus and Earth, the two largest terrestrial planets, still retain enough internal heat to have important ongoing geological and volcanic activity at present. The smaller bodies appear to have become inactive, although of Mars may have had important activity in the past billion years. Correspondingly, the smaller and inactive bodies all show large areas saturated by impact craters, and a few huge impact sites (the Caloris Basin on Mercury, Imbrium and Orientalis on the Moon, and Hellas and Argyre on Mars). These heavily cratered areas have been preserved from the period of final accretion more than four Gyr ago. In contrast, both Venus and the Earth have completely remade their earliest crusts, and have no surface record at all of the final accretion period.

The great variety of surface features we observe on the terrestrial planets, and the range of internal structures and past histories that we deduce for these bodies, remind us what a huge challenge it is even to understand fully our own planet. We are still far from piecing together the whole story that is the subject of this chapter, but an impressive start has been made.

9.7 Mathematical aspects

Hypervelocity impacts

Let's look quantitatively at some of the effects of a hypervelocity impact. As in Chapter 5, it is convenient to express energies in electron volts (1 eV $= 1.6 \times 10^{-19}$ J) because this is a natural unit for seeing what happens on an atomic scale.

The energy available in a hypervelocity impact is very large. A stony meteoroid travelling at 20 km s^{-1} has roughly 40 eV per atom; at 30 km s^{-1} this rises to 90 eV per atom. The energy needed to crush rock, which means to break a very small fraction of the chemical bonds so that the rock ends up in tiny fragments, is of the order of 10^4 J kg^{-1}, or 2×10^{-3} eV per atom. Thus a hypervelocity meteoroid has enough energy to crush of order 10^4 times its own mass. To heat rock to the melting point (about 1500 K) requires of order $3kT \approx 0.3$ eV, so a hypervelocity impact can melt something like 100 times its own mass. To vaporize a substance, we need to break essentially all the chemical bonds, so roughly 3 or 4 eV per atom must be supplied; the impactor carries enough energy to vaporize about 10 times its own mass. (This would be expected to raise the temperature of the vaporized atoms to some thousands of K.) Still another effect is to accelerate the material struck by the meteoroid to some modest fraction of the impact speed (this is what excavates the crater): the impactor energy could supply the energy, for example, to give roughly 1000 times its own mass a speed of roughly 0.03 times the initial impact speed, a speed of some hundreds of m s^{-1}.

Exercise: Verify these numbers, making rough but reasonable assumptions about the composition of the meteorite.

In reality the impactor does all of these things. It is not simple to describe the impact accurately enough to predict how the energy will be divided among the various possible outcomes, but we can get a rough idea of the magnitude of various effects by guessing that in an impact something like 10 or 20% of the available energy will go into each effect (we assume a simple kind of energy equipartition). So we might estimate that a hypervelocity impactor would crush of the order of 10^3 times its own mass, melt 10 or 20 times its mass, eject hundreds of times its own mass from the crater at speeds of hundreds of m s^{-1} (and thus create a crater with a volume hundreds of times that of the meteoroid, and a lip extending out to several crater diameters), and vaporize a couple of times its own mass. This still leaves a significant fraction of the kinetic energy to power a fireball and a blast wave, and produce powerful seismic waves.

We can easily estimate the time required for the initial impact to transfer the kinetic energy of the impactor into other forms. This will occur in roughly the time required for the impactor to encounter its own mass in surface material, or in other words to drive roughly its own diameter into the ground. Thus for a meteoroid of diameter D moving at v, the duration of the initial impact will be $\tau \approx D/v$. This will be a time of the order of some milliseconds for impactors with diameters of tens or hundreds of m.

The peak pressure generated may be estimated from the force required to bring the meteoroid of radius R mass $M \approx 4R^3\rho$ to a halt in time τ. The force F required to do this is about

$$F = \frac{dp}{dt} \approx \frac{Mv}{\tau} \approx \frac{4R^3\rho v}{2R/v} \approx 2R^2\rho v^2, \qquad (9.1)$$

and the pressure is then of order

$$P \approx \frac{F}{\pi R^2} \approx \frac{2\rho v^2}{3}, \qquad (9.2)$$

which is of the order of 10^{12} Pa.

Planetary crust

We can use reasoning that we have met before to estimate the order of magnitude of the thickness of the crust that a planet can form out of elements less abundant than Mg and Si.

Exercise: Assume that all the Al, Na, Ca and K, together with an appropriate amount of O, and approximately one atom of Si per atom of Al, etc, has separated to form the crust of Mars. If the mass fraction of these elements is the same as in the Earth, and the resulting crust has a density of 3000 kg m^{-3}, estimate the thickness of the crust.

9.8 References

Albee, A. L. 2000, "Mars 2000", *Ann. Rev. Earth Planet. Sci.*, 28, 281. The successful Mars Global Surveyor and Mars Pathfinder missions have returned a wealth of valuable new information summarized in this readable review article.

Bougher, S. W., Hunten, D. M. and Phillips, R. J. 1997, *Venus II: Geology, Geophysics, Atmosphere and Solar Wind Environment* (Tucson, AZ: University of Arizona Press). From one hundred contributing authors, everything you ever wanted to know about Venus but were afraid to ask.

Carr, M. H. 1976, "The volcanos of Mars", *Sci. Am.*, Jan., 32. Mars has a number of huge volcanos, some dating from its earliest history and some relatively recent.

Cattermole, P. 1992, *Mars: the Story of the Red Planet*, (London: Chapman & Hall). The surface features of Mars are described in detail in this nicely illustrated, readable book.

Goldreich, P. 1972, "Tides and the Earth-Moon system", *Sci. Am.*, Apr., 42.

Golombek, M. P. 1998, "The Mars Pathfinder mission", *Sci. Am.*, Jul., 40. The highly successful Pathfinder mission to Mars studied the surface chemistry and weather on the Red Planet.

Golombek, M. P. and 13 others 1997, "Overview of the Mars Pathfinder missions and assessment of landing site predictions", *Science*, 278, 1743. This is the first of several articles in this issue of Science describing the early results from the Pathfinder mission.

Grinspoon, D. H. 1997, *Venus Revealed* (Reading, MA: Addison-Wesley Publ. Co.). The flood of new data from Venus, with emphasis on the atmosphere and surface, is discussed in this detailed and very readable popular-level book by an active participant in the Magellan mission.

Guest, J., Butterworth, P., Murray, J. and O'Donnell, W. 1979, *Planetary Geology* (Newton Abbot: David & Charles). This delightful small book contains a compilation of some of the best early (black and white) space probe images of the inner planets. Each page of photos is matched with a page of detailed description and discussion of possible origins of the features visible.

Hartmann, W. K. 1977, "Cratering in the solar system", *Sci. Am.*, Jan., 84. Hartmann explains how crater counts on the surfaces of planets and moons make it possible to roughly date these surfaces.

Hubbard, William. B. 1984, *Planetary Interiors* (New York: Van Nostrand Reinhold Co.) Hubbard's book is a comprehensive survey of the mathematical theory of planetary interiors at an advanced undergraduate or graduate level, with many useful references.

Kieffer, H. H. et al 1992, *Mars* (Tucson, AZ: Univ. of Arizona Press). If you want one big source reviewing technical studies of Mars (with some quite readable general parts as well), this is the book to get.

Murray, B., Malin, M. C., and Greeley, R. 1981, *Earthlike Planets* (San Francisco, CA: W. H. Freeman and Co.). This book made a first effort at qualitatively understanding the structure and history of the inner planets in the light of the data from the first wave of space probe exploration of the solar system. It has some great illustrations.

Nelson, R. M. 1997, "Mercury: the forgotten planet", *Sci. Am.*, Nov., 56. Mercury has not been visited by a space probe for more than a quarter of a century. Nelson reviews what we know about this small body and explains why it is important to visit it again.

Nimmo, F. and McKenzie, D. 1998, "Volcanism and tectonics on Venus", *Ann. Rev. Earth Planet. Sci.* 26, 23. A somewhat technical review of how we deduce conditions inside Venus from surface observations, lab measurements, and theory.

Saunders, R. S., "The surface of Venus", *Sci. Am.*, Dec 1990, 60. Some of the first images of Venus from radar mapping by the Magellan spacecraft provide an intriguing glimpse of this strange volcanic world.

Schultz, P. H. 1985, "Polar wandering on Mars", *Sci. Am.*, Dec., 94. Surface features of Mars hint that the position of the planet's poles may have shifted a lot during the planet's history.

Smith, D. E. et al. 1999, *Science*, 284, 1495. The elevation maps of Mars obtained by the laser altimeter on the Mars Global Surveyor mission have revealed much about the surface features of the Red Planet.

Taylor, G. J. 1994, "The scientific legacy of Apollo", *Sci. Am.*, Jul., 40. The Apollo Moon landings provided raw material from which to understand the origin and early history of the Moon.

Wood, J. A. 1975, "The Moon", *Sci. Am.*, Sep., 92. Wood's classic article explains the reasoning that led to the decipherment of the early lunar history from the rocks returned by the Apollo landers.

Zuber, M. T. et al. 2000, "Internal structure and early thermal evolution of Mars from Mars Global Surveyor topography and gravity", *Science*, 287, 1788. This article draws interesting conclusions about the crust and mantle of Mars from altimeter and gravity measurements of the Red Planet.

9.9 Review questions

9.1 What are the most prominent surface features on the Earth's Moon? How did they probably originate?

9.2 What are the main rock types found in (a) the lunar highlands and (b) the lunar maria, and how did the surface come to be dominated by these two rock types (that is, what does the surface chemistry of the Moon tell us about its history)?

9.3 How did the Earth's Moon probably originate? What are the arguments that lead us to prefer one theory for the origin of the Moon over other possible ones?

9.4 What are the main surface features on Mercury, and how did they probably originate?

9.5 What information do we have about the bulk chemical composition of Mercury? How does the internal structure of Mercury probably differ from that of the Earth?

9.6 What is the main difficulty in studying the surface features of Venus? What technique has allowed us to map this surface? What principal surface features occur, and how did they probably originate?

9.7 What is the bulk internal structure of Venus like compared to that of the Earth? What information allows us to compare the internal structure of the two planets?

9.8 Are the bulk chemical composition and internal structure of Mars closely similar to those of the Earth? Is (or was) Mars hot inside? What observations allow us to answer these question?

9.9 Why is the overall chemical composition of the four inner planets and the Earth's Moon not the same? What is the main difference in composition from one inner planet to another?

9.10 How can we tell from observations of the surface of a terrestrial planet how recently (or how frequently) the crust is renewed?

9.11 On which planets is there evidence for continental drift?

9.10 Problems

9.1 Assume that the Earth-Moon system formed by fission of a rapidly rotating Earth, and that no mass was lost from the Earth-Moon system in the process. (a) Calculate the total angular momentum that the original mass ($M_{\odot} + m$) would have had if it were spherical and of the Earth's present mean density, but rotating so rapidly that gravity was just barely sufficient to hold material on the surface at the equator. This is at least a rough estimate of the angular momentum of the presumed original system. (Take the moment of inertia of the Earth to be given by kMR^2, where the moment of inertia factor $k = 0.33$ is smaller than for a sphere of uniform density.) (b) Calculate the angular momentum of the present Earth-Moon system, including the terrestrial spin angular momentum (again with $k = 0.33$) and the lunar orbital angular momentum about the centre of the Earth. Use an accurate value for the mean lunar distance (Table A.3), and the *sidereal* period (that's the period measured by an observer watching from a nearby star) of the Moon's motion. Compare this angular momentum to the result you found in (a). What does this comparison suggest about the plausibility of this particular theory? (c) Tidal forces will ultimately slow the Earth's rotation, and increase the Moon's orbital radius, so that one face of the Earth always points towards the Moon. Assuming that this final state has the same angular momentum as the present state, write down an expression relating the final angular momentum (when both Earth's rotation and the Moon orbital motion occur with a single angular velocity) to the present values. Recall that at the new radius, the Moon will have a *new* sidereal period. (d) Calculate the final radius of the Moon's orbit and its final sidereal period. The equation you need to solve may either be solved by a suitable simple numerical method, or by neglecting the final angular momentum of the Earth.

9.2 Assume that the Moon is made of three concentric layers: a core of radius $r_{\rm co}$ and density 8000 kg m^{-3}, a mantle lying between $r_{\rm co}$ and the bottom of the crust at $r_{\rm cr} = (R - 50)$ km with density $\rho_{\rm m}$, and a 50 km thick crust of density 2850 kg m^{-3}. Write down an equation expressing the total mass of the Moon as a sum of these three layers. (b) Solve the expression from (a) for $r_{\rm co}$. Verify that for a reasonable mantle rock density of $\rho_{\rm m} =$ 3350 kg m^{-3} the core radius is less than 500 km; calculate the value from your expression. (c) Now reorganize the equation from (a) to solve for the mantle density as a function of the other variables. Find the required value of $\rho_{\rm m}$ on the assumption that an iron core of density 8000 kg m^{-3} makes up the same fraction of the total mass of the Moon, 33%, as it does of of the total mass of the Earth.

(You will need to calculate the radius r_{co} of this core; assume that the mantle is confined between r_{co} and the same r_{cr} as before.) Is the mantle density derived in this way plausible? Is this a plausible model?

9.3 Consider a simple model of the Moon that assumes that it is homogeneous, and that the speed of travel v_p of moonquake P-waves is the same everywhere in the interior. Suppose a moonquake occurs at the location (x_e, y_e, z_e) in a suitable Cartesian coordinate system; of course

$$x_e^2 + y_e^2 + z_e^2 \leq R^2$$

where R is the radius of the Moon, since the moonquake must occur on the surface or inside the Moon. Now, imagine that we have several seismographs i located (on the surface) at known locations (x_i, y_i, z_i). (a) Write down the general expression for the time delay $\Delta t_i = t_i - t_e$ between the time t_e when a moonquake occurs at (x_e, y_e, z_e) and the time t_i when it is detected at seismograph i. (b) Take $v_p = 8$ km s^{-1}; suppose there is a seismograph at a point 75° away from a large meteorite impact on the surface; what is the time delay Δt_i between impact and detection in this case? (c) Now suppose that a moonquake occurs at a location (x_e, y_e, z_e) which is not known, at an unknown time t_e. It is detected at measured times t_i by the seismographs at (x_i, y_i, z_i). What is the minimum number i of seismographs needed to determine (x_e, y_e, z_e) and t_e if v is known? Explain clearly how you could determine the unknowns (x_e, y_e, z_e) and t_e.

9.4 Consider the accretion process that formed the planet Mercury. Suppose that the accreting material was homogeneous, with the same mean density as the present mean density of the planet, and had an initial temperature of 800 K. Suppose further that 20% of the energy released by the accretion of a particular shell of matter was retained as internal thermal energy in the planet, and 80% was radiated into space. (This is a simple but probably not very accurate assumption.) (a) Write down the expression for the gravitational energy dE_g released by the accretion onto the planet of a shell of mass of thickness dr. Assume that a fraction f of this energy is used to raise the temperature of the shell by an amount ΔT by increasing the internal energy by $dE_i = 3(dn)k\Delta T$, where dn is the number of atoms in the accreted shell. Find an expression relating dn to the mass of the shell of thickness dr, assuming the mean molecular weight μ is that of a substance made up of 60% iron and 40% pyrolite. By equating $f dE_g$ to the dE_i it produces, find an expression for the initial temperature profile of the planet, $T_i(r)$. (b) Use the value of $f = 0.2$, assume that the melting point of the iron to be 1800 K, and find the radius in the planet outside of which the temperature is hot enough to melt iron. (c) Now assume that virtually none of the accretion energy goes into raising the temperature of the accreted rock. Instead, assume that the radioactive heat release inside the planet initially is about 2.5×10^{-11} W kg^{-1} throughout. Ignoring the effects of heat flow and heat loss to the surface, estimate how long it would take this radioactive heating to raise the temperature from the initial temperature of 800 K up to 1800 K. (This is a rough estimate of how long after accretion it might have taken to melt the iron in the interior and form a metallic core in Mercury, if accretion energy had not been available to heat the planet's interior.)

Chapter 10

Terrestrial Planetary Atmospheres

10.1 Overview

The solid and liquid surface of the Earth is covered by a layer of gas called the **atmosphere**. Although we cannot usually see this atmosphere, it surrounds us, and we feel it as we breathe, or when the wind blows. It supports floating clouds, which we can see, and when conditions are foggy we are keenly aware of being immersed in the atmosphere. From climbing mountains, watching birds fly, and traveling in airplanes, we know that this atmosphere extends to some considerable height above sea level and above the ground, at least up to several kilometers. In fact, we find that although the Earth's atmosphere becomes "thinner" (less dense) and cooler with height above the ground, it is still present (and full of unfamiliar phenomena) at a height of well over 100 km.

The Earth's atmosphere has a fairly definite and constant chemical composition, given (together with the compositions of the atmospheres of Venus and Mars for comparison) in Table 10.1. The Earth's atmosphere is composed mainly of gaseous nitrogen (N_2, 77%) and oxygen (O_2, 21%). However, the atmosphere is really not a fixed body of gas. It participates in important exchanges with living organisms and with the reservoir of liquid water (lakes, rivers, seas). For example, water from lakes and seas evaporates to become (gaseous) water vapour mixed in with other atoms and molecules of the atmosphere. Conversely, when too many water molecules are present in each cubic meter of air, they tend to condense to form small liquid droplets or solid flakes that can fall to the ground, thereby reducing the water content in the air. Another example of exchange is the production and liberation into the atmosphere of oxygen (O_2) by photosynthesizing organisms such as green plants; in fact, virtually all the free oxygen in the Earth's atmosphere has been produced as a waste product by such organisms. And when organic matter (wood, leaves, buried petroleum) is burned, atmospheric oxygen is combined by combustion with atoms of H, C, N, etc. in the fuel to produce such atmospheric gases as H_2O (water vapour), CO_2 (carbon dioxide), NO and NO_2 (nitrous and nitric oxide), etc. Natural decay of dead vegetation produces a similar result.

Important exchanges with the rocky crust and mantle of the Earth also occur, although they are slower and not so obvious. Gases trapped in the crust and upper mantle (ranging from water trapped in sediments that are carried into the mantle by continental drift, to argon atoms created by radioactive decay of potassium atoms) are released during volcanic eruptions. Conversely, N_2 is removed from the atmosphere by nitrogen-fixing plants (legumes), and deposited in the soil as nitrates. CO_2 is absorbed in seas and ends up in the shells of sea creatures which eventually become part of the sea floor, or else combines with dissolved salts in the seas to precipitate as limestone or dolomite rock ($CaCO_3$ or $MgCO_3$) like that which underlies much of southern Ontario, and which forms the white cliffs of Dover in the UK.

Similarly, the Earth's atmosphere is not really closed at the top, but participates in (presently rather modest) exchanges with outer space. For example, most incoming meteoroids are completely vaporized by frictional heating at an altitude of about 100 km. Their atoms then become part of the atmosphere, for a while at least. On the other hand, a molecule of water which is mixed up to an altitude of a couple of hundred km is likely to be broken apart into H and O atoms by energetic ultraviolet photons from the Sun. This disruption often leaves the light H atoms with enough kinetic energy – high enough speed – to escape completely from the Earth's gravity, into space.

Thus the Earth's atmosphere, although it is a clearly defined layer of the Earth, has important interactions and exchanges with the solid Earth, with the seas, with living organisms, and with outer space. The interaction with the crust and seas is sufficiently important, in fact, that the mass and composition of the atmosphere has changed considerably since the Earth first formed, as we will see later.

Most of the other planets, and three large moons in

Table 10.1: Global properties of terrestrial planetary atmospheres

planet	global features					principal gases					surface characteristics		
	m_{atm}/M_{pl}	μ	$h_{1/2}$ (km)	T_{eff} (K)	g (m s^{-2})	CO_2	N_2	O_2	H_2O	Ar	T_{surf} (K)	p_{surf} (kPa)	ρ_{surf} (kg m^{-3})
						(number per unit volume, %)							
Venus	9.6×10^{-5}	43.4	10.8	245	8.88	96.5	3.5				730	9000	65
Earth	8.7×10^{-7}	28.8	5.9	245	9.78	0.03	78.1	21.0	< 3	0.9	288	100	1.2
Mars	4.2×10^{-8}	43.1	7.8	220	3.73	95.3	2.7			1.6	210	0.56	0.017

the outer solar system, also have atmospheres. Not surprisingly, however, these atmospheres occur in a variety of forms sometimes very different from that of the Earth. Among the terrestrial planets, Venus and Mars have atmospheres that resemble the atmosphere of the Earth. Both of these planets have solid surfaces above which a veneer of gas is found, with clouds, winds, and other phenomena familiar from the Earth. However, these atmospheres also differ strikingly from one another in mass, chemical composition, and surface temperature. The present atmosphere of Venus constitutes about 10^{-4} of the total planetary mass; that of Earth is about 10^{-6} of the Earth's mass; and that of Mars makes up about 4×10^{-8} of the total mass. (On Earth, another potential volatile – of which only a tiny fraction is actually in the atmosphere – is water, H_2O; The mass in the oceans is about 1.4×10^{21} kg, or 2×10^{-4} of the total planetary mass.) The atmospheres of Venus and Mars are both predominantly composed of CO_2 mixed with roughly 3% of N_2, while that of the Earth is mostly N_2 mixed with about 20% O_2 (and a tiny amount of CO_2). Finally, the thin atmosphere of Mars has almost no effect on the surface temperature of the planet, while on Earth the presence of the atmosphere raises the average surface temperature from about −4 C to about +15 C (269 K to 288 K). The Venus atmosphere is so massive that it raises the surface temperature from the value of about +40 C (313 K) that would occur without an atmosphere, to the astonishing value of about 460 C (730 K). Later in this chapter we will look at how these differences occur.

A number of physical properties of the atmospheres of the terrestrial planets are summarized in Table 10.1. In this table m_{atm}/M_{pl} is the mass fraction of the planet in the atmosphere, μ is the mean molecular weight of the atmospheric gas mixture, $h_{1/2}$ is the altitude change which reduces the atmospheric pressure and density by 1/2, T_{eff} is the "effective" temperature at which the planet radiates sunlight back into space, g is the surface acceleration of gravity, and T_{surf}, p_{surf} and ρ_{surf} are mean values at the planetary surface of atmospheric temperature, pressure, and density. The significance of most of these quantities should become clear as you read the chapter.

The four giant planets all possess atmospheres too, but on these planets the atmospheres make up a far more important fraction of the planet than is the case for the terrestrial planets, and have very different chemistry. For Uranus and Neptune, the deep atmospheres of H and He make up $\sim$ 10% of the total planetary mass, and rest on cores of strongly compressed rock and ices. The atmospheres of Saturn and Jupiter are also composed of H with some He, but these atmospheres constitute respectively 80 and 95% of the total planetary mass! In effect, all four giant planets have cores of rock and ices of about 10 − 20 $M_\oplus$, surrounded by atmospheres which in Uranus and Neptune do not greatly affect the total size or mean density of the planet, but which in Jupiter and Saturn make up the bulk of the planet's total mass. These atmospheres will be discussed in the next chapter.

One moon of a giant planet, Saturn's largest moon Titan, also has a surprisingly Earth-like atmosphere. Like our atmosphere, Titan's gas veneer is primarily composed of N_2, and makes up about 10^{-4} of the total mass of the moon. Saturn's moon Io and Neptune's largest moon Triton are also found to have very thin atmospheres, as does the outermost planet Pluto. The planet Mercury and the remaining moons, including our own, have essentially no atmospheres.

From our experience with the Earth's atmosphere, we know that the gaseous outer layer of our planet is able to flow from place to place (winds), to change temperature from month to month (seasons) and from day to day, and to form clouds and produce rain, ice and snow (weather). We may confidently expect that other atmospheres will exhibit similarly complicated behaviour. However, if we step back from this complex detail, we find a number of relatively simple and intelligible aspects. This chapter will discuss mainly these basic structural features of planetary atmospheres. We will look first at the Earth, our best-understood example. We begin by discussing how the pressure varies with height in an atmosphere. Next we turn to heating and cooling processes, and consider how the global atmospheric temperature is set; then we examine processes that carry heat from one level to another, and that determine the vertical temperature structure (i. e. how the temperature varies with height), and discuss the greenhouse effect. We shall look briefly at motions of gas in the atmosphere which create weather. We then turn to an examination of the atmospheres of Venus and Mars. Finally, we consider the formation and evolution of the atmospheres of the terrestrial planets, to try to understand how they came to be so different. We defer discussion of the atmospheres of bodies in the outer solar system until Chapter 11.

10.2 Variation of pressure and density with height

The first characteristics of an atmosphere that we want to look at are the pressure and density, and how these vary with height. Although we are subjected to the pressure of the atmosphere all the time, we are usually aware of it only when it changes (think of your ears popping in the elevator of a tall building, or in an airplane as it climbs or descends). This pressure is essentially the weight of the atmospheric gas above each unit of surface area. For the Earth at ground level, the mass of atmospheric N_2 and O_2 above each square cm is about 1 kg, so that the pressure at the surface is the weight of 1 kg per cm^2, or about 10 tons m^{-2}! The surface pressure is approximately the same as the pressure produced by a column of water 10 m high. (The pressure at the base of the Earth's atmosphere is about 10^5 Pascals, or 100 kPa. This pressure – recall Chapter 2 – is also often called one atmosphere, or one bar.) At this pressure and a typical terrestrial surface temperature of +15 C, the density of air is about 1.2 kg m^{-3}, about 10^{-3} times the density of water (Table 10.1).

Now as you go up in the Earth's atmosphere, the pressure decreases. This occurs because as you climb, less and less of the mass of the atmosphere lies above you, and so its weight on you decreases. If you climb to a height of about 6 km above sea level, roughly the height of the tallest mountains in the Americas and Europe (Mount McKinley in the Canadian Rockies, Aconcagua in the Andes of Argentina, Elbrus in the Russian Caucasus range), you will have risen above about half of the Earth's atmosphere, and the pressure is decreased to half of its sea level value. However, if you climb another 6 km (to roughly the altitude at which long distance airplane flights operate), you do *not* reach the top of the atmosphere. Gases are compressible – springy – and reduction of the pressure by half means that the atmospheric gas is able to expand to fill twice the volume with each kilogram at 6 km altitude that it does at sea level. Its density has dropped to about 0.6 kg m^{-3}. (This is why it is really hard to breathe at this altitude – when you take a breath, only half as much gas flows in as would flow in at sea level, and you get only half the oxygen your body expects with each breath.) Thus, the second climb of 6 km brings us above only half of the remaining gas of the atmosphere. At 12 km, the pressure and density are both about 1/4 of their values at sea level. Another 6 km rise brings you above about half of the remaining atmosphere. And so it goes. The fall of pressure with height above the surface of the Earth is shown in Figure 10.1. The important point is that the atmosphere has no definite top surface. It just keeps getting thinner as you go up.

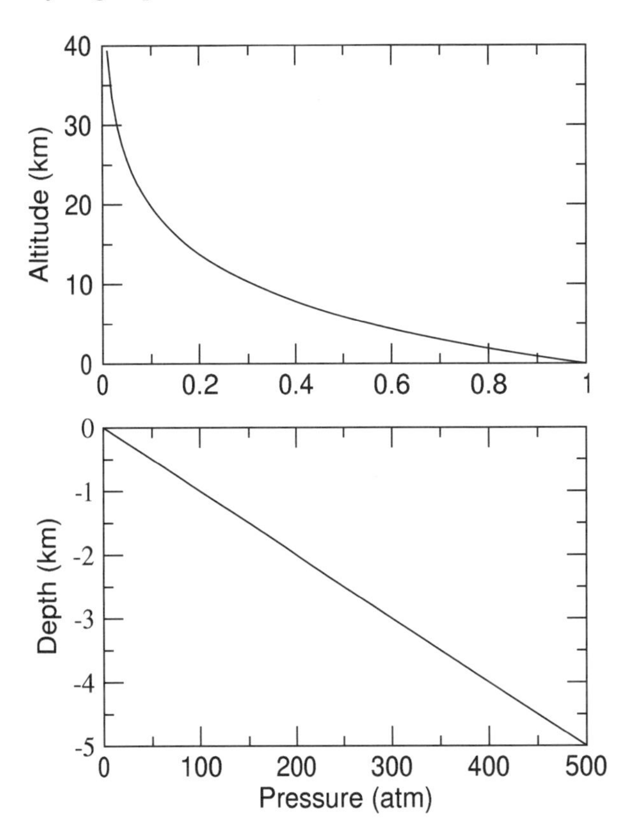

Figure 10.1: (Top) Variation of pressure with height in Earth's atmosphere. (Bottom) Variation of pressure with depth in the ocean.

This is in striking contrast to the situation in the ocean, which is made of incompressible water. If you start at a depth of 5 km (a typical deep ocean floor depth, where the pressure is equal to the weight of about 500 kg on each square cm, or about 500 atmospheres), and go up 2 1/2 km, you find the pressure reduced by half, but the density of the water is essentially the same, 1000 kg m^{-3}, as it is at the bottom –

and the top – of the sea. Another 2 1/2 km up, and you are at the surface. No more liquid water lies above you. The behaviour of pressure in the ocean is also shown in Figure 10.1.

The height which you must rise through in a planetary atmosphere in order to decrease the pressure by half, by rising above half the mass (call this height $h_{1/2}$) depends on several factors. If the temperature is high at the bottom of the atmosphere, the surface pressure (which is simply the weight of the atmosphere above a unit area, and does *not* depend on the temperature) corresponds to a relatively low density (recall the discussion of the gas law in Chapter 2), and so the height $h_{1/2}$ to which you must climb to get to half the surface pressure (where you are above half the mass) is large. If the temperature near the surface is lowered, the surface pressure stays the same but (because of the gas law) the density rises, so the height $h_{1/2}$ to which you must rise to get above half the atmosphere mass decreases. The acceleration of gravity also influences $h_{1/2}$; as gravity increases, the weight of the atmosphere above each unit area increases, and so does the density of the gas, and $h_{1/2}$ decreases. Even the molecular weight of the gas matters; the greater the molecular weight of the average atom, the smaller $h_{1/2}$ becomes. But as we have seen, $h_{1/2}$ does *not* depend on the total mass of the atmosphere over each unit surface area. As you rise in an atmosphere in which the temperature does not vary too much, so that you have less and less gas above you, $h_{1/2}$ stays essentially constant.

The variation of pressure and density with height in the atmospheres of Venus and Mars is very similar to that of the Earth. For Venus, $h_{1/2} = 11$ km (see Table 10.1), somewhat larger than that of Earth mainly because the gas of the lower atmosphere of Venus is much hotter than that of Earth, while for Mars $h_{1/2} = 8$ km, close to that of Earth, because the effect of weaker gravity on Mars is largely offset by lower temperature and higher mean molecular weight. The actual surface pressure of Venus (Table 10.1 again) is about 90 times larger than on Earth because the mass of gas in the atmosphere of Venus is roughly 100 times larger than in the Earth's atmosphere. The surface pressure on Mars is tiny because that planet has so little atmospheric mass. But starting from the surface, the relative pressure and density decrease with height in much the same way as is shown in Figure 10.1 for all three planets.

Exercise: You are climbing a mountain 3000 m tall, taking with you a barometer (an instrument that measures pressure with an accuracy of better than 1%). Would you be able to see any difference in the barometer reading between the start and end of your climb?

10.3 The temperature of the atmosphere

Basic ideas

The temperature of the Earth's atmosphere varies over the surface of the planet. The temperature is generally lower close to the poles than it is near the equator, is mostly lower in the hemisphere where it is winter than in the hemisphere where it is summer, and drops with increasing altitude, at least up to 10 or 12 km above the surface. Nevertheless, over most of the surface, the temperature usually remains confined to a limited range of values, roughly between -30 C and +40 C (243 – 313 K), and so it makes sense to talk about an average surface temperature T_{surf} (see Table 10.1). The temperature near the surface of Mars is somewhat colder than the terrestrial temperature, with a larger daily variation, and mostly lies between -120 and 0 C (153 – 273 K). At ground level on Venus, the temperature is constant to within a few degrees at any particular altitude, but decreases slowly with height from a surface value of about 460 C (733 K). Thus although there are significant variations of temperature with time, height, and geographical location within the atmospheres of each of the terrestrial planets, each may be characterized by a typical surface temperature which diminishes as one goes farther out in the solar system. We now look at the basic physical processes that determine this average temperature, and the typical vertical structure, in a planetary atmosphere. The ideas discussed here are very similar to those considered when we looked at how the surface temperature of a comet is established (Chapter 7).

This basic temperature structure is set, throughout the atmosphere of a terrestrial planet, and in the upper layers (above the cloud decks) of the giant planets, by the heat input that the atmosphere receives from the Sun's luminosity. At 1 AU from the Sun, the energy delivered by the Sun, essentially in the form of visible light (together with a smaller amount of ultraviolet and near infrared radiation) is about 1400 W through any square meter orientated face on to the incoming sunlight. The available heat from the Sun varies strongly with distance from the Sun; at the distance of Neptune, about 30 AU out in the solar system, sunlight delivers only about 1.5 W per square meter, a factor of almost *one thousand times less* than is available near the Earth.

When this sunlight strikes a planet, some fraction of it is reflected back into space from clouds, from dust particles and gas molecules in the atmosphere, and from the ground. This reflected radiation is lost to the planet, and *has no effect on the temperature of the planetary atmosphere*. The rest of the sunlight striking the planet is absorbed by the gases, cloud droplets, and dust particles of the atmosphere, and (in the terrestrial planets) by the ground. This absorbed radiation is available to warm the atmosphere.

The fraction of the sunlight which is reflected from a planet is of course the albedo (usually denoted by A; we have already discussed this idea in connection with asteroids and comets). This fraction varies substantially from one planet to another. Venus, with its solid covering of light coloured clouds, reflects back about 76% of the incoming sunlight ($A = 0.76$). The Earth reflects back about 30%, a value similar to the reflecting efficiency of the giant planets with their coloured clouds. Mars, which has few clouds and a dark surface, reflects only about 15% of the arriving sunlight.

However, the amount of sunlight absorbed per second by each square meter of planet is not all that must be considered in order to understand the temperatures of planetary atmospheres. In fact, if the radiation absorbed each second from the Sun were retained by the atmosphere, the temperature would rise steadily, as the temperature in a kitchen oven does as long as the heating element is turned on. *For the atmosphere to stay at a fairly steady temperature, the planetary surface and atmosphere must lose back into space, on average, as much heat as is deposited by incoming sunlight.*

The idea that a *steady* temperature is maintained by a situation in which heat input is balanced by heat loss is not a very obvious one. However, it does correspond to your experience of keeping your home warm during the winter. To maintain a comfortable temperature in your home, you require a fairly steady input of heat (provided by natural gas or fuel oil burned in a furnace, by electric power dissipated in electric heaters or radiators, etc.) at just the right rate to balance the heat loss to the outside through walls, windows, draughts, etc. If you stop the heat input (you don't pay your electric bill, for example), the heat loss continues until the indoor temperature reaches the average outdoor temperature, freezing you and perhaps your water pipes. To keep your leaky home at a constant comfortable temperature, you need a continuous heat input which balances your heat leakage to the outdoors.

Because heat loss increases as the temperature difference between the outdoors and the interior rises, you need a greater heat input to keep your preferred interior temperature in the coldest winter months than you do in the spring or fall, and you need a larger heat input if you prefer to keep your house hot (say around +23 or +24 C) than if you are willing to keep it cool (+18 C). Your home's thermostat adjusts the heat input rate to just balance the heat loss and maintain the temperature that you select. The larger the heat loss (the colder the weather, or the hotter you keep your home), the larger the fraction of the time the thermostat must run the furnace to maintain your chosen temperature. Thus, the *balance* between the rate of heat input (controlled by your thermostat) and the rate of heat loss (controlled by the insulation of your home, how often windows and door are opened, etc) determines the temperature of your indoor environment.

Exercise: Explain why the daily energy cost of operating a central air conditioning system increases as the outdoor temperature rises.

A similar balance is struck in planetary atmospheres. Heat input is provided by the absorbed visible sunlight. This quantity is usually fairly constant for a planet, unless the amount of cloud cover in the atmosphere is quite variable (more clouds increase the fraction of the incoming light that is reflected directly back into space without warming the planet). In principle, the balancing heat loss could be provided by any of the main means by which heat is carried from one place to another, namely conduction, convection, and radiation. However, both conduction and convection require matter to carry the heat, and the near vacuum of interplanetary space makes these means of carrying away incoming heat quite insignificant for cooling planets. Instead, the surface and atmosphere of a planet are cooled by radiation of heat into space.

The loss of heat from a planet's exterior surface by radiation into space is a natural and essentially inexorable process. Recall from Chapter 3 that any warm body (i.e. any body not at absolute zero, 0 K) radiates heat away from itself. The rate of heat radiation per square meter of surface rises rapidly with the temperature of the object, as the fourth power of the temperature (T^4). Thus, the amount of heat radiated into space by each square meter of the Sun's atmosphere, which is at about 6000 K, is about 160,000 times larger than the rate at which each square meter of your body, kitchen table, etc., at about 300 K, radiates. No wonder you can get a sunburn from the Sun but not from your friends....

As we discussed in Chapter 3, the heat radiated by warm objects comes out over a range of wavelengths centred on a typical wavelength which depends on the temperature of the warm object. This typical wavelength decreases with increasing temperature. For the Sun, at 6000 K, the typical wavelength is about 5000 Å, in the middle of the visible spectrum. For you, or a terrestrial planet, with a temperature of around 300 K, the characteristic wavelength is around 10^5 Å (10 μm), in the infrared.

The balancing of incoming and outgoing radiation occurs as follows. A certain amount of solar energy is absorbed by the planetary surface and atmosphere each second. The rate at which energy is absorbed by the whole planet is approximately constant. Suppose now that the planet radiates back into space at an average temperature at which the energy re-emitted per second is *less* than the energy arriving each second. In this case, the difference between the energy that arrives each second and that which is re-emitted each second accumulates in the low atmosphere, raising the temperature. As the temperature rises, so does the rate of energy radiation into space. Thus, the effect of the imbalance is to raise the average temperature, which increases the radiation back into space. This in turn decreases the difference between the energy input and output. Eventually, the temperature rises to the value at which the rate of input of solar energy equals the rate at which this energy is radiated back into space by the planet. At this temperature, no energy accumulation occurs to drive further temperature change, and the temperature of the planetary surface stays constant.

The temperature of the planetary atmosphere determined by this balance between energy input and loss is called the "effective" temperature of the atmosphere. It is tabulated as $T_{\rm eff}$ for the terrestrial planets with atmospheres in Table 10.1. Because the energy input from the Sun decreases strongly with distance from the Sun, the corresponding temperature at which energy loss balances input is lower in the outer solar system than in the inner solar system. The balancing temperature for the Earth is about 245 K, while that for Uranus is only about 55 K.

Exercise: You turn on the oven of your stove to bake a pie. Suppose that the oven has settled to the correct temperature. What is the relationship (approximately) between the amount of energy you supply to the oven through the heating element or gas flame, and the energy that leaks out of the oven into the room, while the pie is cooking at a constant temperature?

Energy balance and the greenhouse effect

The description so far of the basic balance between incoming energy from the Sun and re-radiated planetary energy has not been very specific about where in the atmosphere, or how, the absorption and emission of radiation take place. As you might expect, significant complexity appears when we start looking at these details. We will continue to ignore horizontal variations within the atmosphere, but look more closely at the energy exchanges between the incoming solar radiation, the Earth's surface, and the atmosphere averaged over the Earth.

Of the sunlight that strikes the illuminated side of the Earth, on average about 33% is reflected back into space without affecting the atmosphere at all (this is the albedo), largely (26%) from clouds but some (7%) from the seas and ground. Because the Earth's atmosphere is fairly transparent to visible light, which carries a large part of the energy radiated by the Sun, most of the sunlight (about 45% of the available total) passes through the atmosphere and is absorbed by the ground. About one fifth of the available radiation (22%) is absorbed by the gases of the lower atmosphere before reaching the ground. Most of the absorbed sunlight passes through the atmosphere and heats the ground directly.

However, the heated surface of the Earth has a temperature near 300 K. It cannot radiate visible light; instead, the surface radiates away energy as heat radiation, in the infrared part of the spectrum, with a typical wavelength of around 10 μm. Now the Earth's atmosphere, although it is transparent to visible light, is quite opaque to most infrared wavelengths near 10 μm. As a result, the heat radiated back towards space by the surface is not able to escape freely into space. Instead, it is absorbed in the lowest few kilometers of the atmosphere, heating it. This is the dominant means of heating the lower atmosphere; in fact, it is a good approximation to think of the atmosphere as being heated *from below*. In turn, the atmosphere radiates away the heat it has received, again as infrared radiation around 10 μm. Less than half of this radiation is able to escape directly to space; the rest is sent back towards the surface, raising its temperature.

Thus we have the situation that heat from the Sun, in the form of visible light, is able to pass fairly freely through the Earth's atmosphere and heat the surface directly. However, the warmed surface tries to return this heat to space (remember that the net energy input must be zero, so that losses must balance gains) as infrared radiation, which passes through the Earth's atmosphere only with considerable difficulty. Because the heat loss process is inefficient, the temperature at the surface of the Earth, and in the low atmosphere, must be *higher* than it would be in the absence of the atmosphere in order to return as much heat to space as is absorbed every second from the Sun.

This is the phenomenon we call the **greenhouse effect** because of its similarity to the operation of a greenhouse, in which visible sunlight passes through the transparent glass walls to heat the interior of the building, but the heat cannot freely escape again (as infrared radiation), partly because the glass is fairly opaque to infrared rays, but mostly because the glass walls inhibit heat loss by convection and evaporation. The effect is familiar to everyone from its operation in a car parked in the sun in summer. If you leave all

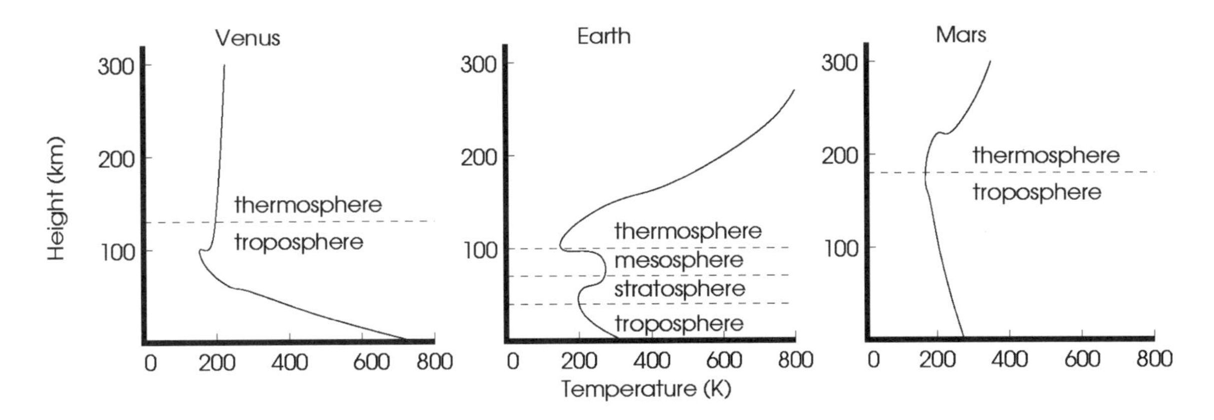

Figure 10.2: Temperature variation with height in the terrestrial planetary atmospheres.

the windows of the car closed on a sunny day, the interior temperature can rise to 10 or 20 C higher than the outside temperature. Silvered or white reflectors placed in the front and back windows can reduce the amount of solar heat entering the car (in effect, increasing the car's albedo!), and thus lower the equilibrium temperature reached.

10.4 Variations of temperature with height

It is interesting to look at the absorption and emission of radiation by the atmosphere in more detail, to understand something about the substantial variations of temperature with height that are observed in the Earth's atmosphere.

The typical vertical variation of temperature with height in the atmospheres of Venus, the middle latitudes of Earth, and the (daytime) tropics of Mars are shown in Figure 10.2. Near the ground, in the layer called the **troposphere**, temperature decreases with height in all three. However, after reaching a minimum of about 210 K (-63 C) at an altitude of roughly 20 km (the tropopause), the temperature of the Earth's atmosphere rises again with height in the **stratosphere** to reach a second maximum at the stratopause, about 50 km up, where the temperature is about 270 K (–3 C). Above this height, in the **mesosphere**, the temperature again drops, to a new low of about 190 K (–83 C) at the mesopause at about 90 km altitude. Finally, in the **thermosphere**, the temperature rises again to a value which is quite variable but which can often be more than 1000 K at a height of about 300 km. Neither Venus nor Mars has a stratosphere. Both have tropospheres in which temperature declines with altitude, an extended layer above the tropopause with roughly constant temperature which we might consider a mesosphere, and on top of that a thermosphere.

These variations of temperature with height in the Earth's atmosphere are symptoms of the details of the processes of energy input from the Sun and energy reradiation back into space by the Earth's surface and atmosphere. Because the various wavelengths of incoming sunlight are absorbed and emitted with greatly varying efficiency by the gases of the atmosphere, both absorption and emission of energy actually take place over a wide range of heights.

We now ask why the Earth shows such significant temperature variations with height. To answer this question, we must look at the details of heating and cooling the gases of the atmosphere at a particular altitude. The gas at that level receives heat directly from sunlight, and also via infrared radiation emitted by the warm planetary surface and by other warm layers in the atmosphere. The amount and wavelength distribution of radiation which is available to heat the layer we are looking at depends on the height of the layer above the ground. In the troposphere, most of the heating is due to infrared radiation emitted by the ground, but since this radiation is absorbed in the lower atmosphere, the amount of infrared radiation coming from the ground diminishes as one goes higher. This diminishing input of radiation from the ground is partly replaced by infrared radiation from lower layers of the atmosphere, but overall the input of infrared heating diminishes with increasing altitude. On the other hand, there is also an input of heat directly from absorbed sunlight. Since some sunlight is absorbed in the atmosphere, the intensity of incoming sunlight increases with height above the surface, and so this is relatively a more important heating source at high altitudes.

The heat input to a given layer of the atmosphere also depends on the particular molecules that are present in the layer that can absorb radiation, which determines what wavelengths the gas can absorb. In the troposphere, the main absorbers of radiation are the molecules of H_2O and CO_2, which have a very small abundance relative to the dominant atmospheric constituents N_2 and O_2. Close to the ground, these molecules make up a fairly constant fraction of all the molecules present, but in the high troposphere, the amount of H_2O vapour is greatly diminished by the fact that it tends to freeze out as water droplets or ice crystals and fall back towards the ground below the tropopause. Thus the efficiency with which infrared radiation is absorbed is decreased above the tropopause. However, as we shall see below, other molecules and atoms present at high altitudes very efficiently absorb ultraviolet radiation from the Sun, providing strong local heating at altitudes where these molecules are present.

The gas cools itself by radiating heat away, mostly as infrared rays emitted by molecules stimulated to radiate by collisions among themselves. The gas radiates away very little heat when it is cold, but radiates a great deal when it is hot. Thus, the gas *at a particular level* will come to an equilibrium much like the equilibrium that occurs for the atmosphere as a whole: the layer will end up at the temperature at which it is able to radiate away as much energy as it absorbs each second. This is the temperature at which heat neither accumulates (heating the gas further) nor decreases (cooling the gas).

We are now in a position to understand some of the wiggles in the curves of Figure 10.2. The temperature decrease in the troposphere with increasing height is mainly a consequence of the fact that much of the heat input to each level in the troposphere is radiation from the ground. This radiation decreases with height because it is absorbed by the lower atmosphere. Furthermore, as we go up in the atmosphere, the higher layers receive less heat from layers above them. For both these reasons, the heat input decreases with altitude, and so the equilibrium temperature reached also decreases with height.

The very high temperature reached above 150 km in the Earth's thermosphere is the result of a combination of several circumstances. First, there is a source of heat available directly from the Sun, namely ultraviolet radiation of wavelength less than about 900 Å, which is absorbed in these very high layers (and therefore penetrates no farther into the atmosphere). This ultraviolet energy, though it makes up a very small fraction of the total solar radiation, serves as an efficient heat source for the very small mass of gas present in the uppermost atmosphere. Secondly, the gas is so thin, and molecules are so far apart, that collisions between molecules are exceedingly rare. Under these conditions, the ability of the atmospheric gas to transform heat energy (in the form of high-speed motions of atoms and molecules) into heat radiation (emitted as single photons by atoms after collisions have lifted electrons into upper levels, or by molecules after collisions have led to rapid rotation or vibration) is very much inhibited. In fact, the gases of the upper atmosphere are so thin that they are hardly able to radiate away their heat at all. It turns out that the only effective way for the atmosphere above 150 km to get rid of heat is to carry it by *conduction* to lower levels, around 100 km, where the gas is able to radiate the excess heat away as infrared radiation. This combination of effective heat input and very inefficient heat loss leads to the very high temperatures (sometimes as high as 1800 K) found in the terrestrial thermosphere.

Notice that though the temperature of the gas in the Earth's thermosphere is very high (i.e., the atoms and molecules rush around with rather high speeds), the amount of gas involved is tiny (at 120 km the number of molecules per cubic meter is only about one ten-millionth of the number per cubic meter at ground level), and the high gas temperature is *not* accompanied by a large amount of heat radiation. The hot thermosphere is not a hazard to space navigation!

The relatively high temperature of the Earth's atmosphere at the boundary between the stratosphere and mesosphere may be understood in a similar way. In the gas at that level, about one oxygen molecule in 10^5 is not normal O_2 but ozone, O_3 . Ozone absorbs very strongly the solar ultraviolet radiation between 2000 and 3000 Å, which provides the atmosphere at $\sim$50 km with an efficient mode of direct heat input from sunlight. As the radiation of heat at this level is only about as efficient as elsewhere in the atmosphere, but the input of heat locally (per molecule) is much greater than to layers above or below, the temperature at which the rather high heat input balances heat losses is about 290 K (17 C) at 50 km altitude.

The absorption of radiation in the 2000 to 3000 Å wavelength region is very important to many terrestrial creatures such as human beings, since sunlight in this wavelength band is quite harmful to cells. We depend on the presence of the minute fraction of ozone that occurs at this altitude to absorb this harmful radiation and prevent it from reaching the ground. It is for this reason that we are very concerned by the recent appearance in the atmosphere of large areas depleted in ozone ("ozone holes"), as the Earth's surface below these holes receives much more of the dangerous ultraviolet radiation than is safe for humans.

10.5 Motions in the atmosphere

Convection

The variation of temperature with height is not determined in all situations simply by the local heat input and output via radiation, but in certain circumstances may be strongly influenced by physical movement of currents or blobs of air from one level of the atmosphere to another, carrying heat. This process is known as **convection**, and it is quite important in the tropospheres of the terrestrial planets.

An atmosphere will be susceptible to convection if the temperature falls very rapidly with increasing height. To understand what occurs in this situation, imagine a blob of gas at some level in the atmosphere that is at the same temperature as its surroundings. Suppose that for some reason the blob rises slightly above this level (a gust of wind, perhaps). In rising, it will move into a level where the atmospheric pressure is slightly lower than it was at the initial level, so it will expand slightly. This slight expansion occurs at the expense of internal heat energy in the blob, whose atoms and molecules give up some of their individual random (thermal) motions in pushing back the gas surrounding the blob, and so the temperature in the blob will fall slightly. Now if the blob is in a region of the atmosphere in which the temperature decreases slowly with height, or stays constant or increases with height, the blob will find itself cooler, and therefore denser, than its surroundings, and it will sink back to its original level. But if it is in a layer in which the temperature decreases rapidly with height, it will find that even though it has cooled slightly in rising, it is *warmer* than its surroundings. In this case, it will be less dense than the surrounding gas, and this will make it buoyant, so it will continue to rise spontaneously.

Exercise: Use similar reasoning to show that if the blob drops slightly below its original level in a region in which the temperature decreases rapidly with height (i.e. increases rapidly with depth), the blob will continue to sink, while in a layer in which the temperature decreases slowly with height, or stays constant or increases with height, the blob will return to its original level.

Thus we see that in a region of the atmosphere in which temperature decreases rapidly with height, gas from one level spontaneously mixes with gas from other levels. This process transports heat (and molecules) from one level to another. The fact that a rising blob finds itself warmer than its surroundings not only propels it upward, but means that when it finally mixes into the surrounding gas at some considerably higher level, it will be warmer than the gas into which it mixes, so that it will have transported heat upwards. A descending blob, which sinks because it finds itself cooler and denser than its surroundings, will still be cooler than its neighbors when it finally dissolves into them, and so will cool the layer to which it descends. Thus again we have transported heat upwards, by removing it from the lower layer. This process mixes heat throughout the convecting region of the atmosphere, carrying it from warmer layers up to cooler ones.

Convection is a very efficient process for transporting heat; so efficient, in fact, that it alters the temperature variation in the region of the atmosphere where it operates, effectively preventing the temperature from decreasing with height at a significantly faster rate than the rate at which rising blobs cool because of their expansion. Among the inner planets, convection is important in limiting the rate of decrease of temperature with height in the lower atmospheres of Venus (below about 50 km altitude) to a value of about 8 $\mathrm{K\,km^{-1}}$, and of Earth (below about 12 km) to a value of about 6.5 $\mathrm{K\,km^{-1}}$. The atmosphere of Jupiter is believed to be convectively mixed from the top of the uppermost (ammonia) cloud deck on down; the maximum rate of decrease of temperature with increasing height is near 2 $\mathrm{K\,km^{-1}}$.

Clouds and precipitation

Convection has another very important effect on planetary atmospheres besides carrying heat and limiting the rate at which the the temperature can fall with increasing height. It also physically mixes the atmosphere, transporting molecules from one altitude to another. This has the important effect of maintaining an almost constant chemical composition throughout most of the atmosphere. Furthermore, in many situations, convection leads to the formation of **clouds**. To see how this can occur, look at the situation in the Earth's atmosphere. Normally, at ground level, the water vapour in the atmosphere is not saturated. That is, the amount of water vapour in the atmosphere is less than the vapour pressure of water for that temperature (see Figure 2.5), and so water does not spontaneously condense; in fact, water droplets and puddles spontaneously evaporate. (When the humidity of the air equals the vapour pressure of water, usually as a result of night-time cooling of the lower atmosphere, spontaneous condensation of water or ice occurs as dew or frost.)

Now the result of convection is to mix parcels of surface air, carrying their water vapour, up to higher altitude. As a parcel of air rises, its temperature falls. Even a small decrease in temperature can lead to a large decrease in the equilibrium vapour pressure of water, and so at a certain height, the equilibrium vapour pressure of water in the blob of air becomes smaller than the actual vapour pressure. At this level, or not too far above it, water will start to condense. Because at a microscopic level it is much easier for the water to condense onto a solid surface that is already present than it is for the water to spontaneously form droplets where none exist, the water will generally condense onto dust particles in the atmosphere, which act as nuclei for condensation. As the parcel of air continues to rise, and its temperature drops further, more and more of the water vapour will condense out onto the water droplets.

Now water vapour in gaseous form in the atmosphere is essentially transparent to visible light, but water droplets efficiently scatter light. As a result, the air at the level where the droplets form becomes opaque: a cloud has formed. However, although water droplets scatter light, they are quite inefficient at absorbing it. The light passing into the cloud has its direction changed many times by reflections from droplets, but still mostly emerges from the cloud somewhere. Thus, you cannot see through the cloud (i.e. you cannot see things on the other side of it) but a small cloud is usually bright (white) rather than dark (black).

A simple example of the formation of clouds by the rising of convecting parcels of air is the development of isolated cumulus clouds (puffy white clouds with roughly flat bottoms) on a sunny day. These clouds form in rising currents of air driven by the local heating of the ground by sunlight. The flat cloud bottoms are at the altitude where water starts condensing into droplets, and the puffy tops show the altitude at which the air parcels cease to rise and dissolve into their surroundings. Such a cloud is white because much of the sunlight striking it, of all colours, is scattered in all directions, and a part of this light emerges from the bottom.

Now clouds are intrinsically short-lived, because once the water has condensed into droplets, these tend to fall downward in the atmosphere. As long as the droplets are really small, say a few μm in radius, they fall so slowly (at perhaps 1 cm s^{-1}) relative to the speed of the rising air parcels (which is usually of the order of some m s^{-1}) that they are carried upward with the parcel as long as it rises. However, the droplets have a strong tendency to grow, by further condensation while they are small, and then, when they become larger, by collisions between droplets that lead to coalescence. As small droplets become larger and more massive, they fall through the air more rapidly. When the parcel of air ceases to rise, these larger droplets fall downwards slowly until they reach the level where the partial pressure of water vapour is below the saturated level. At this altitude, the droplets start to evaporate, and often will evaporate completely before falling very far below the altitude where condensation starts. If they survive to the surface, we have rain.

Thus if the convection ceases (because the sun sets, for example) the water droplets formed in the rising columns of air will gradually fall downward to the level where they evaporate, and the clouds will disappear.

Clouds generally occur only where two conditions are met: there must be a substance (such as water) in the atmosphere that can condense at the available temperature, and there must be a process that mixes this material up to the level at which it can condense. In the absence of mixing, the droplets that form slowly fall downward to a level where water is no longer saturated, where they evaporate, and the cloud disappears. Thus the presence of clouds indicates either convection or sufficiently strong winds to mix water up to a level where it can condense.

Under some conditions, the rising currents of air are sufficiently powerful to drive the rising parcels of air to great heights at relatively high speed. In this situation, for example when we see the huge, towering white clouds we call cumulonimbus clouds or thunderheads, the growing water droplets may be supported by the rising column of air even when they have grown as large as one mm in radius and are falling downward relative to the rising air current at a speed of the order of 1 m s^{-1}. When such droplets grow large enough to fall out of their clouds, they can often survive the fairly quick trip to the surface without evaporating, and we have a thunderstorm (or a snow squall if the temperature is low enough).

Temperature variations over the surface

The fact that a planetary atmosphere, such as that of Earth, is heated by the Sun means that the heating is quite non-uniform over the surface of the planet. One obvious variation is between the day side of the planet and the night side; the day side is strongly heated, while the night side has no solar heating whatever. A second, somewhat less drastic, variation is between the region of the planet where the Sun is nearly overhead (near the equator on Earth) and regions where the Sun is only seen low in the sky (near the illuminated – summer – pole of the Earth). Where the Sun is overhead, the energy contained in one square meter of solar rays heats approximately one square meter of ground and its overlying atmosphere; where the Sun is never high in the sky, the sunlight strikes the ground obliquely and the solar energy available in a beam one square meter in area may be spread over two or three square meters of ground, providing a correspondingly smaller energy input to each square meter.

These horizontal variations in the rate at which the atmosphere receives heat from the Sun lead, of course, to horizontal variations in temperature. Where the heat input is high, the ground and atmospheric temperature at which the heat loss balances the heat input is high as well, and where heat input is low or absent the corresponding equilibrium temperature is low. The most visible consequence of such variations in heat input on Earth are the systematic differences between the ground temperatures near the equator, which are typically of order 20 C or 293 K throughout the year, and the temperatures at high latitudes, which are frequently below the freezing point of water.

The temperature variation with latitude on Earth is made more complicated by the 23.5° tilt (the **obliquity** of the Earth's rotation axis) to the plane of the orbit, the ecliptic plane. This obliquity is the cause of the seasons. Although the Earth's rotation axis very slowly changes direction relative to the distant stars because of tidal effects produced by the Moon and Sun (the axis twists around in a conical movement like that of a spinning top, always staying inclined to the ecliptic by about 23.5°, and taking about 26,000 years to return to its original position), during one year the rotation axis remains practically fixed in orientation as the Earth revolves about the Sun. As a result, during the northern summer, when the north pole is inclined towards the Sun and is heated for 24 hours per day (and northern latitudes such as those of Canada or northern Europe have long days and short nights), the temperature far in the north is much warmer than it is near the south pole, which is undergoing an extended period of darkness. At this time high southern latitudes have short days and long nights. Six months later, during the southern summer, it is the south pole which is inclined towards the Sun and the north pole which is inclined away from it, reversing the situation. The effect of the Earth's axial inclination on heating is shown in Figure 10.3. (Notice that seasons are *not* caused by variations in the distance between the Earth and the Sun; the Earth is actually closest to the Sun in early January.)

Two main effects combine to prevent the temperature on the night side of a planet, or at the winter pole, where there is no solar heat input at all for some months, from dropping right down to absolute zero. One way in which the temperature of the unlit region is kept from changing too much is the fact that the atmosphere of the planet may have a considerable capacity to store heat; its ability to lose heat and to cool is limited by the rate at which it can radiate away this stored internal energy. On Earth, for example, the atmosphere on the night side can only radiate away about 1% of its total heat content during one night, and so during the night the average temperature of the whole night-side atmosphere only drops by a couple of degrees before dawn arrives and the solar heat input returns. (The larger temperature variations that you actually observe at night, often amounting to a drop of the order of 10 C, affect only a rather shallow layer of the atmosphere close to the ground. The higher layers of the air change temperature very little during the night.) The capacity of the atmosphere to store heat is supplemented by that of the oceans, which have a still larger capacity to store and release heat with little temperature change.

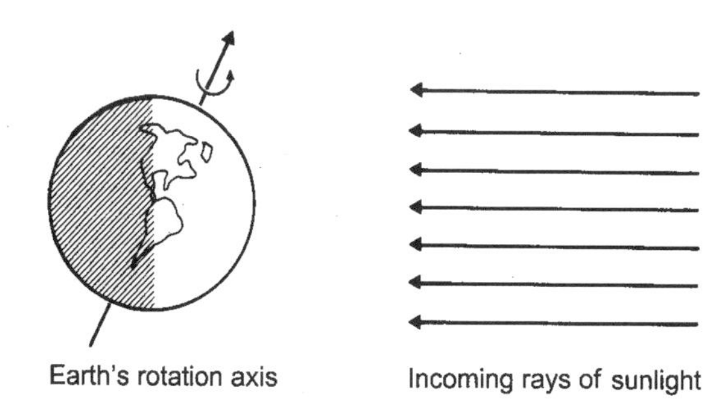

Figure 10.3: Effects of the inclination of the Earth's rotation axis on local heating. The pole inclined towards the Sun is heated for 24 hours per day, while the opposite pole is in darkness for six months. At high latitude, near the lit (summer) pole, the rotation of the Earth leads to solar heat input for most of the 24 hour period, while near the dark (winter) pole heat is received – from a Sun which appears quite low above the horizon – for only a few hours per day.

Winds

The second effect that tends to keep the temperature from varying too greatly over a planetary surface (for example between the strongly heated equatorial regions and the weakly heated polar ones) is the existence of horizontal air movements, or **winds**. These horizontal flows normally act to transport warm air from more strongly heated regions to less heated regions, and to carry cool air back to the region of greater heating. To see why winds flow, and how they act to reduce horizontal temperature differences, imagine the situation near the equator of a planet like the Earth, and that near one of the poles. Assume for the moment that the planet is not rotating. Suppose that the air pressure at the surface is approximately the same everywhere over the planet, as we would expect from the tendency of the air to redistribute itself to have the same total weight of air over each point on the surface, and as is actually observed.

Now because of the difference of heating, the air temperature at each altitude over the equator is higher than the temperature at the same altitude over the pole. As a result, the pressure and density of the air at the equator decrease with increasing altitude more slowly than they do over the pole: the half-height $h_{1/2}$ of Section 9.2 is larger over the equator than over the pole. For example, in the winter hemisphere on Earth, the altitude at which the pressure has dropped to half its surface value is near 6000 m over the equator, but below 5000 m over the pole. At 5000 m the pressure is about 20% higher over the equator than over the winter pole. This pressure difference at high altitude tends to make warm air over the equator flow towards the two poles, especially towards the colder winter one. As high-altitude air moves towards the poles, the total weight of air above each square m increases, and the ground pressure rises to a higher value than at the equator, forcing the cold low-altitude air to flow towards the equator.

Thus (in the absence of complications due to rapid planetary rotation, which will be discussed below) the planet tends to set up a kind of conveyor belt circulation between the poles and equator, with warm air rising over the equator and flowing at high altitude towards the poles, while colder air from the poles flows on the surface back towards the equator. Such a loop-like circulation is called a **Hadley cell**. Clearly, the effect of this circulation is to reduce the temperature difference between the strongly heated regions near the equator and the weakly heated regions around the poles. In a relatively dense and massive atmosphere of the Earth, the bulk circulation of air between the polar and equatorial regions (together with a corresponding circulation in the oceans) is the predominant effect that limits the drop in temperature at the winter pole during the long polar winter night.

Notice one of the observable effects of such a circulation: as gas flows from one place to another, we are aware of wind. At ground level we detect wind directly, by feeling it blowing past; higher in the atmosphere, it can be observed by its effects in moving isolated clouds (quite possibly in a different direction from the direction in which the wind blows close to the ground).

Effects of planetary rotation

If the planet is rotating rapidly, the situation is substantially more complicated than the one described above. ("Rapid" rotation means that one rotation of the planet about its axis takes a few days or less; all the planets from Earth out to Pluto rotate rapidly in this sense.)

The basic effect of planetary rotation is to cause wind currents moving over the surface of the planet to move in unexpected directions. To see why this occurs requires a small excursion into physics. Recall from Chapter 1 that Newton's first law, the law of inertia, states that an object will tend to continue in a uniform direction at a uniform speed if it is not acted on by any net external forces. An important feature of this law is that it is only true in what are called "inertial" frames of reference. It does not describe what is observed by a person in a rotating frame of reference.

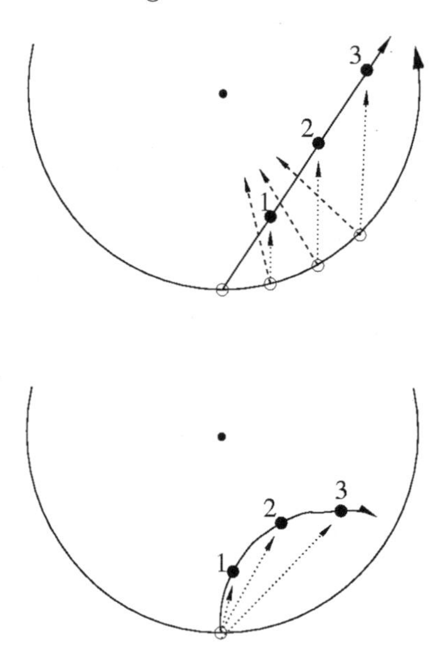

Figure 10.4: The figures above should help to understand the Coriolis force, as explained in the text. A person on a merry-go-round throws a ball towards the centre of the merry-go-round. The upper figure schematically shows the event as seen by a stationary person on the ground; the ball travels in a straight line (points 1, 2, 3), and the merry-go-round carries the thrower in a circle. The line of sight from the person on the merry-go-round towards the centre is shown as dashed arrows, and towards the ball as dotted arrows. In the lower figure, the same event is viewed by the person on the merry-go-round, whose position on the merry-go-round is stationary. This person sees the ball veer to the right, away from the direction in which it was thrown.

To see what goes wrong in a rotating frame of reference, we will carry out an imaginary experiment (see Figure 10.4). Pretend that you are on a large merry-go-round or other rotating platform which is completely enclosed by curtains. If you are seated on one of the wooden horses, a first symptom of something contrary to what Newton's laws predict is the fact that, even though you are apparently sitting still on the merry-go-round, you constantly feel a force pushing you towards the centre of the platform. Of course, seen from the inertial frame of reference of a friend outside the curtain on the ground, this force is required to make you move in a circle, just as the force of gravity from the Sun causes the Earth to orbit around the Sun rather than drifting off in a straight line away from the solar system.

Now suppose that you try to throw a ball directly towards the centre of the platform. From the vantage point of your friend on the ground, you give the ball a velocity towards the centre of the merry-go-round – but the ball also has a velocity in the direction of rotation. Hence from the inertial point of view, it is not surprising that that the ball misses the centre on the side towards which the rotation is carrying it (if the platform is rotating counter-clockwise, the ball will appear to veer to the right). However, from your point of view on the platform, the ball appears to veer off to one side of the centre of the platform, as if some unknown force were acting on it (Figure 10.4).

Exercise: Use similar reasoning to show that if you throw a ball towards the horse in front of you, in the direction in which the motion of the merry-go-round is carrying you, the ball will appear to veer towards the outside of the platform and miss the horse, an effect which your friend on the ground will understand as the result of the merry-go-round carrying both you and the horse in front around in a circle while the ball continues in a straight line.

We can deal with such effects in two different ways. One is to be sure to describe them from an inertial (non-rotating) point of view. This allows us to use Newton's laws in their usual form. However, since (at least on the Earth) we are on the platform, not outside it, and our point of view is most conveniently taken to be that of the person on the merry-go-round, we look for an alternative description of what we see. This may be achieved by ignoring the fact that Newton's laws only work in an inertial frame of reference, but introducing a fictitious force acting on moving objects which makes them veer clockwise if our platform is rotating counter-clockwise, and *vice versa*. This fictitious force is called the **Coriolis force**. This force has the properties that it increases with the rotation rate of the system (so it is very important on Earth, but quite unimportant on Venus). It also increases with the speed at which objects move relative to the rotating frame of reference.

From our vantage point on the rotating Earth, the Coriolis force appears to act on any rapid, large-scale motion such as the movement of air currents in the Hadley cell. In the northern hemisphere, the Coriolis force appears to force air flows to bend in a clockwise direction; in the southern hemisphere, the effect is to veer counterclockwise. Near the equator, where the ground is almost parallel to the rotation axis of the Earth, the effect of the Coriolis force is small, but at mid-latitudes this effect is quite powerful.

Figure 10.5: This image of the Earth as seen from space shows South America in the middle of the image, and Antarctica near the bottom. The abundance and variety of clouds seen in the image is clear evidence of the variety of convective and mixing motions operating in the Earth's atmosphere on a large scale. Curving cloud forms, particularly in the Atlantic east of South America, reveal the action of the Coriolis force. (Courtesy of NASA.)

One of the most important, and counter-intuitive, effects of the Coriolis force is to force air movements that "ought" to flow from equator to pole or *vice versa* to flow instead in a predominantly east-west direction. Suppose there is pressure difference along a north-south direction, such as would be set up by the difference in heating between pole and equator, as discussed in the previous section. Suppose that this pressure difference tends to start a flow of air towards the north. The air starts moving in a northerly direction. However, as the wind picks up speed, the Coriolis force increases, bending the motion towards the right or east (in the northern hemisphere). Eventually the pressure difference speeds the air up enough that the Coriolis force makes it actually flow towards the east.

In this situation, a balance can be achieved in which the north-directed force due to the pressure difference is just equal to the south-directed Coriolis force on the air flow. In this case, in the rotating frame of reference, there is no net force on the wind (the pressure force is equal and opposite to the Coriolis force) and so the flow can now go on without changing further. But the very strange result is that this balance is achieved with the wind flowing at 90° to the pressure force that started the movement in the first place! Thus the predominantly north-south pressure differences set up by the very non-uniform heating of the Earth lead to mainly east-west air flow, such as the winds that blow from east to west near the equator (the trade winds) and the mainly west-to-east winds of mid latitudes.

Exercise: If a large region of locally high pressure develops in the northern hemisphere, the pressure difference between this region and its surroundings will tend to make air flow away from the centre of the region. Use the reasoning above to show why this will lead to a clockwise flow of air *around* the centre of the high pressure region.

This effect is quite important in interfering with transport of heat from the warm equatorial regions towards the poles of a rapidly rotating planet. On Earth, near the equator, flow of air is in a plane that is nearly perpendicular to the line towards the Earth's rotation axis, so the Coriolis force is fairly small and a Hadley-type circulation occurs between the equator and about 30° north and south latitudes. However, closer to the poles, the Coriolis force makes this kind of circulation break down. In the winter hemisphere, the pressure difference between the pole and low latitudes is so large that it causes the atmosphere to break into a kind of horizontal convection, in which huge eddies form and flow, carrying heat between the low latitude Hadley cell and the cold polar regions. These are the mid-latitude high and low pressure regions whose clouds form distinctive swirls on images of the Earth from space (Figure 10.5).

As you can imagine, these ideas can be developed to describe many aspects of weather and climate on the Earth. However, we will not penetrate farther into this subject.

10.6 The atmosphere of Venus

The ideas from the previous sections apply fairly directly to the atmospheres of the other terrestrial planets. Nevertheless, both Venus and Mars have atmospheres which in many ways are very different from that of Earth.

The characteristics of the atmosphere of Venus that particularly strike the terrestrial observer are the very large mass and surface pressure of the Venus atmosphere (both about 10^2 times larger than on Earth), the greatly different chemical composition (predominantly CO_2 rather than the N_2 which dominates the Earth's atmosphere, no free O_2 and practically no water vapour), the solid cloud cover on Venus (compared to an average 50% coverage on Earth), and particularly the remarkably high surface temperature, about 730 K or 460 C everywhere over the surface of the planet.

The great mass of Venus' atmosphere is the basic fact that underlies most of the differences between this atmosphere and the terrestrial one. Because the total mass of the atmosphere is about 90 times greater than that of Earth, the pressure at the surface of the planet (the total weight over each square meter) is similar to that found at a depth of about 1 km in the Earth's oceans. This huge mass per unit area means that it is sometimes useful to think of the oceans when trying to imagine conditions on Venus, rather than making comparison with our atmosphere. In fact, the temperature and pressure at the surface of the Earth are similar to conditions at about 50 km altitude in the atmosphere of Venus.

The chemical composition of the atmosphere of Venus has been studied both by observing the spectrum of sunlight reflected from the clouds, by direct sampling by several Soviet Venera probes that landed on the surface, and by the U. S. Pioneer Venus atmospheric probes. The chemistry which these measurements reveal is that of an atmosphere primarily composed of CO_2, about 96.5% by numbers of molecules. Almost all the remaining 3.5% is composed of N_2. Trace amounts of SO_2 (sulphur dioxide) and H_2O (water) are present. Free oxygen (O_2) is essentially absent.

Near the surface where the temperature is high, the pressure falls off with altitude more slowly than on Earth (on Venus $h_{1/2}$ = 10.8 km, compared to 5.9 km for Earth), but the overall picture of pressure and density declining rather rapidly with height is similar to the situation on the Earth. However, the great mass of the atmosphere leads to a much more powerful greenhouse effect than on the Earth, and directly causes the remarkably high surface temperature. The light-coloured clouds reflect 77% of the incoming sunlight (which at 0.72 AU delivers about 2700 W m^{-2}). The remainder is absorbed throughout the atmosphere; only about 2% actually reaches the ground. However, the great mass of the atmosphere, and its predominantly CO_2 composition, make the atmosphere extremely opaque to the infrared radiation that the warm gases and surface radiate. Infrared heat can be radiated directly to space only from above an altitude of about 70 km, near the top of the cloud deck (Figure 10.6). Below this height, heat must make its way slowly upward from layer to layer. As on the Earth, this has the consequence that

Figure 10.6: This image of Venus, taken from the Pioneer Venus orbiter, shows a completely cloud-covered planet. No surface features are visible. The top of the clouds seen here are about 70 km above the surface. In visible light the clouds are virtually featureless, but when an image is obtained using reflected ultraviolet sunlight, as this image was, faint markings are visible. These marking change rapidly and reveal high-altitude winds having speeds of the order of 350 km hr^{-1}. (Courtesy of NASA.)

lower layers must be warmer than those above them, to drive the incoming heat from sunlight back towards the top of the atmosphere where it can be returned to space. Because of the great mass of Venus' atmosphere, a sufficient heat flow upward to balance the incoming energy of sunlight is only achieved with a surface temperature of about 730 K.

Heating of the lower atmosphere by incoming sunlight is sufficiently powerful to drive convection from the ground up to an altitude of about 70 km. This convection limits the actual lapse rate (the decrease of temperature with altitude) to about 8 K km^{-1} up to about 50 km. Above this altitude, the temperature declines more slowly with height, becoming roughly constant with altitude above 80 km, where the temperature has dropped to about 200 K. Because there is no ozone layer to strongly absorb ultraviolet sunlight, there is no stratosphere on Venus (i.e. there is no strong preferential heating of an intermediate atmosphere layer leading to the occurrence of a relatively warm high-altitude layer).

In the Venus atmosphere, the temperature is everywhere far too high for the dominant species of CO_2 and N_2 to condense, and there is virtually no free water, so water clouds are not possible. However, the atmosphere contains tiny amounts of sulphur and sulphur dioxide (SO_2). These chemicals have combined with the little available water to form concentrated sulphuric acid (75% H_2SO_4 and 25% H_2O) which condenses into droplets, under the conditions in Venus' atmosphere, at an altitude of about 30 km. These clouds of sulphuric acid extend from 30 km up to about 70 km, and completely cover the planet, reflecting three-quarters of the incident sunlight directly back into space, and preventing any direct view of the surface from space probes above the atmosphere. This very unfamiliar cloud chemistry was actually deduced from terrestrial observations of the infrared spectrum and the polarization of the sunlight reflected from the cloud tops (polarization is the tendency of the reflected light to be brighter at one orientation than at another when viewed through a rotatable polarizing filter such as that used in some sunglasses). Notice again the role of convection in generating clouds.

Because of the great mass of the Venus atmosphere, it takes a very long time (of the order of 10^2 years) for the atmospheric temperature to change substantially by radiation away of heat. This situation is similar to what occurs in the terrestrial oceans, which at great depth do not change temperature by more than a fraction of a degree between winter and summer. Thus, although the time between one noon and the next on Venus (recall that Venus rotates in a *retrograde* direction with a period of 243 days relative to the distant stars) is about 117 Earth days, there is practically no difference in ground temperature between the day and night sides of the planet. Furthermore, the great density of the surface gas makes horizontal heat transport by winds very efficient; horizontal heat flow carried by wind can largely eliminate temperature differences in a time of the order of 10^2 days (10^7 sec). This leads to a temperature difference between the poles and the equator which is never more than about 1 K. Because the planet rotates so slowly that the Coriolis force on a wind (see the preceding section) is unimportant, a direct circulation between pole and equator is possible. It is thought that a simple Hadley cell exists in each hemisphere, with warm air rising slowly near the equator to an altitude of about 60 km and flowing towards both poles, where the gas returns to ground level. The wind speeds of this circulation near the ground are only of the order of 1 m s^{-1} (4 km hr^{-1}) horizontally and 1 cm s^{-1} vertically.

Exercise: The orbital period of Venus is about 225 d, and its rotation period, viewed from a nearby star, is about 243 d in the opposite sense. Make a sketch of the orbital motion of Venus around the Sun, showing the planet's position at four equally spaced times during the Venus year. Put a marker on the planet at one of these positions which is at local noon, and figure out its position relative to the Sun for the other three positions. From this sketch, show that one day on Venus, noon to noon, takes a little more than half of one orbital period.

In contrast, in the thin atmosphere above the cloud tops, large temperature differences occur both between the day and the night side of the planet, and between equator and poles. These temperature differences drive much faster winds – jet streams – at high altitude, with speeds of roughly 100 m s^{-1} (about 350 km hr^{-1}). These winds are directly visible in ultraviolet images of the planet taken from nearby space probes. In these images, the clouds are seen to have large-scale V-shaped markings which travel around the planet in about four days, as seen in Figure 10.6.

10.7 The atmosphere of Mars

The fact that Mars possesses an atmosphere is directly visible from the Earth with the aid of a small telescope. The most prominent feature in visual views of the Red Planet is the presence of a brilliant white polar cap, which is observed to diminish as spring changes to summer, and is gradually replaced by a second polar cap in the opposite hemisphere. Since a polar cap is produced by freezing out of atmospheric gases (water vapour on Earth, which forms polar caps of water ice), the seasonal growth and decay of polar caps is the clearest possible evidence that Mars possesses an atmosphere from which some kind of ice can freeze out. The effects of this atmosphere can also be seen directly in the seasonal changes in colour and contrast of large areas of the surface, and in the virtually complete disappearance of all surface features every few years as a consequence of a planet-wide dust storm. Some effects of the atmosphere are seen in Figure 9.17.

Earth-based spectroscopic observations have provided valuable information about the molecules in the Martian atmosphere (the presence of the principal gas, CO_2, was discovered from Earth). Still more detailed views are possible from passing or orbiting spacecraft and from landers, and much of what we now know about the atmosphere of Mars has been obtained from such missions. Both the USA and the USSR have sent ambitious series of space probes to Mars, and we have already seen many of the results when we studied the surface of the planet in the previous chapter. The study of the Martian atmosphere particularly benefited from the two Viking orbiters and landers in the late 1970's, and from the more recent Pathfinder lander and the Mars Global Surveyor orbital mission. From orbit, these missions provided close-up photographic surveillance of clouds, fog, dust storms and haze on the horizon (look at the planetary limb in Figure 9.15), measurements (using an infrared camera) of surface temperatures over most of the surface for much of a Martian year, and repeated probing of the atmosphere by radio waves as the orbiter passed behind the planet and then emerged on the other side. The two Viking landers and the Pathfinder all measured how the atmospheric temperature and pressure varied with altitude as they descended to the ground, and then carried out repeated observations of the local weather at the landing sites.

The Martian atmosphere revealed by these observations is very different from the atmosphere of the Earth, but perhaps not as strange as that of Venus. Table 10.1 summarizes the main properties. The most fundamental difference between the Martian atmosphere and those of Venus and Earth is that the Martian atmosphere has much less mass, both absolutely and as a fraction of the total planetary mass, than those of the other two terrestrial planets. Mainly as a consequence of this fact, the mean gas pressure at the surface of Mars is only about 0.56 kPa (5.6 mbar), less than 1% of the pressure at the surface of the Earth and less than 10^{-4} of the pressure at the base of the massive Venus atmosphere. The density of the atmospheric gas at ground level is only about 0.017 kg m^{-3}, compared to slightly more than 1 kg m^{-3} at the Earth's surface. As a direct consequence of the very low atmospheric mass, the greenhouse effect on Mars is very weak, and the (globally and annually averaged) surface temperature of about 210 K (−63 C) is only about 4 K higher than would be the case with no atmosphere.

The chemical composition of the Martian atmosphere is found to be very similar to that of Venus, about 95.3% CO_2, 2.7% N_2, and 1.6% Ar. The remainder is made up of small amounts of such substances as CO, O_2, and a very minor amount of H_2O. Like Venus, Mars has much of its CO_2 in the atmosphere rather than buried in carbonate rocks as on Earth, and thus has N_2 as a minor rather than major atmospheric component. The Ar in the atmosphere is overwhelmingly ^{40}Ar, produced by radioactive decay of ^{40}K in the interior of Mars (recall the discussion of radioactive heating in Chapter 6) and released to the surface by volcanic activity, where it becomes an important atmospheric constituent because there is so little of anything else. *Very* small quantities of the non-reactive noble gases neon, argon, krypton, and xenon, a few parts per million or less, are present in the atmosphere.

The atmospheric pressure falls off with altitude essentially as expected, decreasing by half approximately every 8 km. As a result, the surface pressure also varies considerably from place to place as a result of the very large variations in altitude. At the bottom of the huge Hellas basin, the pressure is almost twice as large as its mean value, while at the top of Olympus Mons, the pressure is only a little more than 10% of the average surface value. Even the difference in mean altitude (about 6 km) between the low-lying northern plains and the higher, heavily cratered southern hemisphere leads to an important difference in local surface pressure, which is near 0.75 kPa in the northern plains but roughly 0.4 kPa in the southern highlands.

A surprising discovery by the Viking landers was the fact that the surface pressure varies by about 25% during the Martian year. This is due to condensation of atmospheric CO_2 onto the winter polar cap and the subsequent vaporization as spring arrives; Mars is unique among terrestrial planets in having climatic conditions which cause a substantial amount of the major atmospheric component to freeze at the winter pole. Most of the free surface water on the planet is also trapped in permanent ice caps at both poles, and the atmosphere is extremely dry. Because of the generally low temperatures, and the very cold polar caps, water never makes up more than about 0.1% of the atmosphere of Mars, compared to up to 4% during a tropical monsoon on Earth.

The variations of temperature with height were measured directly by both the Viking landers and by the Pathfinder from above 150 km down to nearly ground level. Figure 10.2 shows a smoothed representation of their measurements, which are probably typical of the situation above the middle latitudes of Mars. Near the ground, the temperature decreases with height as it does in the tropospheres of Venus and Earth, but the rate of decrease does not seem to be fast enough to be imposed by convection as on the other terrestrial planets. Above the equivalent of the Earth's tropopause, at about 40 km, the temperature becomes nearly constant up to a height of around 200 km. There is no stratospheric temperature increase as on Earth; no important absorber of solar radiation is found in this region.

Mars has important similarities with the Earth in the way its surface and atmosphere are heated by the Sun, but it also has substantial differences. Both planets have their axes inclined to the plane of their orbits by about 23°. For this reason both have similar alternation of cold and warm seasons, with winter in one hemisphere coinciding with summer in the other (recall Figure 10.3). This is the reason that one polar cap on Mars grows while the other shrinks, as on Earth. However, the orbit of Earth is almost circular, and the variation in solar heating is only about 3% (the Earth is heated most strongly in January). In contrast, the orbit of Mars is sufficiently eccentric that the input of solar energy is about 40% larger at perihelion (during the summer in the southern hemisphere) than at aphelion. This leads to a considerable difference between the hemispheres: the southern summer is short (because Mars moves faster in its orbit at perihelion than at aphelion) but relatively hot, while the southern winter is long (Mars is moving more slowly) and cold. In the north, the winter is shorter and milder, while the summer is longer but more temperate.

Other important similarities with the Earth are the fact that the planet rotates once every 24.6 hr, close to the Earth's rotation period, and the fact that both planets have atmospheres that are largely transparent to incoming sunlight, so that solar heating occurs largely at ground level, and the atmosphere is heated indirectly, from below, by planetary re-radiation. Thus one might expect to find similar day-night variations on the two planets. However, again major differences intervene to lead to very different results on the two planets. On Earth, the oceans have enormous capacity to store heat, a fact which greatly reduces both the diurnal (day-night) variations and the seasonal variations of temperature on our home planet. The diurnal variations are further diminished by the heat-holding capacity of the atmosphere itself, which limits diurnal variations to 10 or 20 degrees or less in most locations on Earth. In contrast, Mars completely lacks the stabilizing influence of oceans, and the heat capacity of the thin atmosphere is not very significant. We thus expect much larger swings in temperature between day and night.

These expectations were tested by observations from the Viking probes in the 1970's. Both orbiters were equipped with cameras that were sensitive to infrared radiation, which made it possible to determine the temperature at various points on the planetary surface at many times. The landers also carried thermometers, and so could record how the local surface temperature at the landing sites varied with time of day and season. The diurnal variations on Mars are indeed much larger than on Earth; changes of between 50 K and 100 K are normal. The daytime temperature near the equator can rise above the freezing point of water, but at night drops to –70 C.

Similarly, large geographic temperature contrasts are found, especially when one pole is experiencing winter. In the summer hemisphere, daytime temperature does not vary greatly over the hemisphere except directly on the remaining polar cap (they are not too far from the freezing point of water), but in the winter hemisphere, temperatures drop rapidly towards the pole, dipping as low as about 140 K (–133 C!).

More recently, the Mars Global Surveyor has provided very detailed temperature and pressure data from its perch in a nearly pole-to-pole orbit above the planet: it has measured the temperature as a function of pressure up to an altitude of roughly 40 km remotely (by observing the infrared spectrum of atmospheric gases) in a stripe on the day side and an opposite stripe on the night side of Mars once in every two-hour orbit.

Exercise: The Mars Global Surveyor is equipped with instruments which look straight down from orbit onto the surface below. When it first went into orbit around Mars, the satellite observed the local temperature profile almost from pole to pole, but the observations were always taken from above the longitude where the local time (measured by the position of the Sun) was either 2 p. m. or 2 a. m. With a sketch showing the relative positions of the Sun, Mars, and the satellite orbit, explain why vertical (nadir) observations could not be made during these first orbits of regions of the surface at other local times (e. g. over the longitude experiencing 8 a. m.).

Information about the composition and mass of the Martian atmosphere, and the surface heating from the Sun, is enough to allow atmospheric scientists to compute the general overall structure of the Martian atmosphere, and predictions were available even before the first probe went into orbit. It is found that the general circulation in the atmosphere of Mars resembles that of Earth. In the summer hemisphere, where the variation of temperature from equator to pole is not large, it appears that a large Hadley cell develops, which gives rise to steady winds. The rapid rotation of Mars means that the Coriolis force is important, as on Earth, and this leads the winds to flow in a generally east-west direction, as they do on Earth, although these winds have enough north-south motion to transport some heat towards the pole. In the winter hemisphere, the temperature difference between pole and equator is substantially larger, especially during the day, and so the pressure difference is also larger. In this hemisphere the simple Hadley circulation breaks down, and the atmosphere develops large-scale waves which at the surface resemble the high- and low-pressure cyclones that carry heat from the equator to the pole on the winter hemisphere of the Earth, and that are so prominent in photos of the Earth from space.

The winds which are generated by these temperature variations over the planetary surface may exceed 10 m s^{-1} (about 35 km hr^{-1}) near the ground (these winds have been measured by the landers), and are deduced from models to rise to 20 – 100 m s^{-1} (70 – 350 km hr^{-1}; these are real jet streams) high in the troposphere and in the mesosphere.

A very distinctive feature of the atmosphere of Mars is the continual presence of dust in the air. This dust never really settles out; the atmosphere is stirred enough to keep small particles airborne. This dust (due to reddish particles, smaller bits of the red sand on the ground) causes the Martian sky to have a pale pink colour as seen from the surface. When enough dust particles are present, they cause some of the incoming sunlight to heat the atmosphere directly, and thus warm the air.

During some (but not all) northern winters, the winds that develop are not merely enough to add extra dust to the atmosphere, but actually put enough dust into the air to warm the air substantially, which in turn leads to stronger surface winds, which in turn lifts more dust. Sometimes this spiraling cycle of blowing dust and atmospheric warming continues to the point that atmosphere over most of the planet fills with dust up to such a high altitude that even the Tharsis volcanos become invisible. Such events are known as **great dust storms**.

10.8 The origin of the atmospheres of the inner planets

Processes for creating and destroying atmospheres

We now turn from looking at what we know about the present atmospheres of the terrestrial planets to trying to understand more about why they exist at all, and how they may have developed over the 4.5 Gyr age of the solar system.

We start by recalling the general picture of planet formation that was outlined in Chapter 4 and that has come up several times since as we looked at various bodies in the solar system. The observed division of the planets between the rocky terrestrial bodies and the gas giants makes it pretty clear that the planets initially formed in the proto-solar nebula out of the materials that were able to freeze out at various distances from the forming Sun. Close to the sun, where the temperature was relatively high, the solids that formed were mainly rocky and metallic minerals. Farther out, the solids that froze out of the nebula included not only rocky substances but also the principal ices H_2O, CH_4 and NH_3. Nowhere in the nebula was it cold enough for H_2 or He to freeze out.

The planets initially formed by gradual coagulation of these solids into larger and larger bodies, at first simply by collisions, but later with the aid of their mutual gravitational attraction. Eventually a few of the largest bodies swept up most of the rest. In the outer solar system (but not in the region of the terrestrial planets) this initial formation of planetesimals and then planets led to such massive bodies that the new planetary cores were able to sweep up much of the surrounding gaseous material, and thus acquired deep atmospheres of H- and He-rich gas. However, in the inner solar system, the largest bodies were not sufficiently massive to acquire such atmospheres.

This general picture, in which the terrestrial planets formed out of high-temperature condensates such as metallic iron and silicate rocks, suggests strongly that these planets should not have any very significant amount of volatile material. In fact, the observed atmospheres *do* constitute only a very tiny fraction of the planetary mass (see Table 10.1). So now we want to understand how the terrestrial planets came to have any atmospheres at all. What processes contributed small amounts of gas to the forming planets?

We can easily imagine several ways in which the new planets might have acquired some gases.

- As the planets formed, it would not be surprising if they were able to sweep up at least a small amount of the surrounding nebular gases, due to their growing gravitational attraction. Such a sweeping-up process would not be at all selective, but would collect basically all the gaseous material in the nearby nebula, with various chemical elements present in the same proportions as in the nebula. Such an atmosphere would be called a **primary** atmosphere.

- In addition, some of the gas atoms from the nebula would undoubtedly be trapped inside small grains of dust as the refractory materials condensed into solids. This, however, would probably be a selective process, with some atoms or molecules much more likely to be trapped than others due to such effects as easy with which a particular atom could stick to the surface of a dust grain, compatibility of the atom with the crystal structure of the grain, etc.

- The largest bodies formed out of planetesimals eventually became large enough to perturb the motions of many of the smaller bodies into rather eccentric orbits; in fact, this was necessary to allow these new planets to sweep up most of the rest of the available material. Jupiter, because of its huge mass, was particularly effective at doing this, but all the new planets had some effect. This would have led to some mixing of material from the outer solar system into the inner (and *vice versa*), so that planetesimals rich in volatiles (perhaps objects like the carbonaceous chondrites of Chapter 5) would sometimes have been swept up by the future terrestrial planets.

- Another probable source of ices, particularly H_2O ice, would have been collisions with comets coming in from the outer parts of the solar system. Atmospheres produced mainly from gases brought in as part of planetesimals, meteoroids, or comets are called **secondary** atmospheres.

As the terrestrial planets swept up these various volatile-rich small bodies, some of the accreted material would be immediately released into the planetary atmosphere (for example from small comets breaking up in the atmosphere or crashing onto the surface). In other cases, a substantial part of the accreted material would be buried immediately in the crust of the accreting planet, and covered with ejecta. In this case part of the volatile material brought in would gradually be buried deep inside the new planet.

However, this is not the whole story. The new planets would not only accrete volatiles, but at the same time could lose some of this same material back into space. To understand the resulting atmospheres, it is also necessary to look at ways in which volatiles could have been lost, either at the time of formation, or subsequently. Again, several possibilities come to mind.

- Planets near the Sun would have relatively hot surfaces and atmospheres, with temperatures of 200 K or more. In the atmospheres of these bodies, the atoms and molecules move around with typical (thermal) speeds of some hundreds of m s^{-1}. The speeds increase gradually with increasing temperature, and depend quite strongly on the mass of the molecules. For example, at 300 K a single H atom would have a typical speed of about 2.7 km s^{-1}, while for a molecule of CO_2 the speed would be only about 400 m s^{-1}. At any one instant, a tiny fraction of the atoms and molecules would have speeds several times larger than the average; thus an H atom might have a speed of up to 10 or 12 km s^{-1}. This speed is larger than the escape velocity from most of the terrestrial planets. If an H atom finds itself so high in a planetary atmosphere (about 500 km above ground for the Earth) that it would probably not collide with another atom on its way out of the atmosphere, and it happens to have an unusually high speed (directed upwards, of course) it can simply escape from the planet's gravitational attraction altogether. This process is known as **Jeans escape** after its discoverer. Notice that because the *speed* of the would-be escapee decreases strongly as its mass increases, Jeans escape will make loss of normal H atoms easier than loss of D (deuterium, H with both a proton and a neutron in the nucleus) atoms, and thus gradually change the D/H ratio if much H is lost.

- Various chemical reactions that occur high in an atmosphere can give enough energy to the final products that one of the products can escape the planet's gravitational pull. An example is the recombination of an ionized O_2^+ molecule with an electron, $O_2^+ + e^- \rightarrow O + O$. This reaction leads to the breakup of the resulting O_2 molecule, and can leave both the O atoms with enough energy that the one moving upward may escape from the planet. These two mechanisms insure that essentially all the gas atoms can escape, sooner or later, from bodies with relatively weak gravitational attraction such as Mercury or the Moon. These processes collectively are called **non-thermal escape** mechanisms.

- A really large planetesimal impact can literally blow off a significant part of a planet's atmosphere, especially if the planet (like Mars) does not have a very strong gravitational field.

- Finally, just as volatiles can gradually be released from the interior of a planet, they can also be stored there for long periods. As we shall see later, most of the Earth's original CO_2 is currently locked up in carbonate rocks such as limestone.

Clues, and a tentative picture

We can get some very important clues about the origin of the atmospheres of the terrestrial planets by looking closely at the chemical composition of these atmospheres. One of the best clues comes when we look at the relative abundances of atoms of the noble gases Ne (neon), Ar (argon), Kr (krypton), and Xe (xenon). These gases range from being relatively common in the Sun (3390 Ne atoms for every 1000 Si atoms; see Table 2.2) to quite rare (about 0.0042 Xe atom per 1000 Si atoms). They are extremely non-reactive chemically, and remain gaseous to quite low temperatures (e.g. around 120 K for Kr). Thus if they are present in a terrestrial planet that has outgassed its interior in a major way, most of the noble gas atoms will probably be in the planetary atmosphere. Furthermore, these atoms are too heavy to be lost in significant numbers from large planets such as the Earth and Venus.

Now if the atmospheres of the terrestrial planets were primarily composed of gases accreted directly from the solar nebula, we would expect to find about 15 atoms of Ne present for every atom of N. Instead, the Earth's atmosphere contains about 10^5 N atoms for every Ne atom. On Venus we find about 10^4 N atoms per Ne atoms, and about 2×10^4 N atoms per Ne on Mars. We can immediately draw a firm conclusion: the atmospheres of these planets were *not* mainly created by direct, unfiltered accretion of gas from the solar nebula. The terrestrial planets have secondary atmospheres.

This conclusion is confirmed when we look at the relative abundances of the noble gases (excluding isotopes such as ^{40}Ar which are produced by radioactive decay of other species; recall out discussion of heating of asteroids in Chapter 6). The ratios of Ne:Kr:Xe in the Sun are about 812000:33:1. In the Earth's atmosphere the ratios are about 200:11:1, and on Mars about 31:4:1. Venus is similarly enormously depleted in Ne. It appears that unsorted nebular gases cannot make up more than a tiny fraction of the current terrestrial atmospheres.

However, these ratios *are* fairly similar to the ratios of noble gases found in carbonaceous meteorites, where a small number of noble gas atoms were trapped inside the grains of refractory solids as they condensed out of the solar nebula. This trapping process apparently discriminated very strongly against Ne. Thus if volatiles contained in meteorites similar to the carbonaceous chondrites were a major source of the atmospheric gases of the terrestrial planets, this trapping process may have been partly responsible for the very non-solar noble gas ratios.

Another potentially important source of gases is comets. We do not know enough about noble gas ratios in these bodies to obtain any helpful clues there, but one other abundance suggests that these bodies were not the major source of terrestrial atmospheres. That abundance is the ratio of normal hydrogen to deuterium, which has been measured directly in the coma of P/Halley by the Giotto probe, and for other comets spectroscopically from Earth. The result is the D/H ratio is about twice as large in comets as in the Earth's atmosphere. Since the only known processes that would change the terrestrial D/H ratio are ones involving selective loss of lighter H more easily than heavier D, which would *increase* the terrestrial D/H ratio, the fact that the Earth's ratio is smaller than the cometary one probably tells us that comets were not the main source of volatiles for our planet.

Putting the various clues together with our general picture of planet formation, we get the following picture (which still has many incomplete and inconsistent details).

- The atmospheres of the terrestrial planets are definitely composed of heavily pre-selected gases. Unsorted nebular gas makes up at most a tiny fraction of these atmospheres. The terrestrial atmospheres are secondary.

- The atmospheric gases found at present are almost certainly a mixture of volatiles accreted from planetesimals formed in the inner solar system (which probably did not contain a very large volatile fraction), fewer planetesimals from farther out in the solar system (that were probably richer in volatiles), and some comets. The gases incorporated into the interior of the forming planets are probably only incompletely outgassed to the atmosphere. The resulting gas mix was further modified by general and selective loss of some elements, both to space and back into the planetary interior (more on this point later).

- It is plausible to suspect that all the terrestrial planets accreted fairly similar mixes of planetesimals. If this is correct, then they probably all started out with similar fractions of their total mass in H_2O (about 10^{-3} of the total mass of the planet), CO_2 (about 10^{-4} planet mass), N_2 (10^{-5} planet mass), etc. The evidence for this is that we either still find such ratios today, or can identify likely processes that lost or concealed the missing volatiles.

- Mercury is small enough, and has a sufficiently hot surface due to its proximity to the Sun, that it probably was never able to retain a significant atmosphere against Jeans and non-thermal losses.

- It seems probable that the accretion and outgassing of an atmosphere at the same time that the planet is accreting probably greatly influences the fraction of the energy released by infalling planetesimals that is retained by the proto-planet as internal thermal energy. Without any atmosphere, the energy released by accretion heats the layers near the surface, which cool by radiating into space much of the energy released on impact, especially if the impacts are not very frequent. Thus a planet with no atmosphere may still be too cool to allow core separation for a long time after enough infall energy has been released to melt the iron inside, because thermal radiation has been able to rid the planet of most of the heat released. In contrast, after a massive atmosphere (especially containing a lot of water vapour and CO_2) has formed, the atmosphere can act as a powerful blanket (as it does on Venus), strongly inhibiting heat radiation back out into space. In this situation, the ability of the planet to cool by radiating recently released infall energy back into space immediately is greatly inhibited. The result of this situation is probably that a much larger fraction of infall energy release is retained in the interior of the planet, and that the surface soon reaches a high enough temperature (about 1600 K) to melt most minerals, allowing core separation (which itself releases more energy) to begin. Thus the evidence that we have discussed in earlier chapters, indicating that core separation occurred rather early in planetary history, may have a natural explanation due to the formation of a massive atmosphere.

- As the rate of accretion decreased towards the end of the main period of bombardment, the bottom of the blanketing atmosphere would begin to cool and the normal greenhouse effect produced by the sun would begin to assert itself. If the temperature of the gas could descend below the boiling point of water, seas could form as on Earth. If the greenhouse maintained too high a temperature, the water vapour would remain in the air, gradually being destroyed at the top of the atmosphere by breakup due to UV photons followed by Jeans escape of the H, as may have happened on Venus.

A coherent picture of the formation of the atmospheres seems to be emerging. However, there are many details (mostly not discussed here) which do not yet fit nicely into this framework. We are greatly hampered by a shortage of clear clues (after all, the events we are trying to understand took place almost 4.5 Gyr ago; the trail is pretty stale by now), and by our very imperfect understanding of many other events that have happened since the atmospheres formed, which have altered the available clues in ways we have not yet recognized.

10.9 Evolution of the terrestrial atmospheres

Our problem is the following: we suppose that Venus, Earth, and Mars all started out with similar stocks of volatiles (mainly CO_2 and H_2O). However, today they present very different situations. Venus is now practically devoid of water, but its massive CO_2 atmosphere causes a powerful greenhouse effect. The Earth has little trace of its original CO_2 in the atmosphere, but it has an immense stock of (potentially gaseous) H_2O. It has a modest greenhouse effect, raising the temperature from a little below the freezing point of water to a little above. Mars has almost no water in its atmosphere (and generally cannot have liquid water on the surface because its temperature is usually well below freezing), and has far less CO_2 per kg of planetary mass than Venus does.

We could call this the Goldilocks problem: why is Venus too hot, Mars too cold, and the Earth just right?

We will see below that two basic variables appear to control the situation on the terrestrial planets – planetary mass, and distance from the Sun. The fact that

Mars has about 10% of the mass of the Earth and Venus plays a key role in its relative lack of atmosphere. And the small differences in distance from the Sun of the three planets carry them from a region where the equilibrium temperatures are such that water tends to be gaseous (Venus), to where it tends to be liquid (Earth) to where is is usually solid (Mars). These are differences enough to lead similar evolutionary forces to three quite different outcomes.

The Earth

Let us start, as usual, at home. We have a reasonably clear idea of the history of the Earth's climate in the geological record, at least from about 4 Gyr ago. The climate seems to have been generally temperate (or even hot) until about 2.5 Gyr ago, when we find the first clear record of an extended ice age, lasting about 0.5 Gyr. The climate then went back to a warm state until about 0.9 Gyr ago, when another long period of glaciation occurred. Since then we have had alternating periods of warm and of cold. However, there is no indication that the seas have ever frozen completely.

This is actually a rather surprising history. The problem is that our theory of stellar evolution predicts quite unambiguously that the Sun was about 30% fainter than it is now at the time when the solar system first formed, and has only become gradually more luminous in the intervening 4.5 Gyr. If the atmosphere of the Earth had not changed during this time, we would have expected the Earth's seas to be completely frozen until about 2.3 Gyr ago. But some of the oldest known rocks, from 3.8 Gyr ago, are apparently normal sedimentary rocks – that is, they formed in liquid water. So we need to understand how the Earth's atmosphere could have been as warm as now, or even warmer, at a time when the surface was only receiving about 70 or 75% as much heat energy input as now.

Clearly we need to find some way in which the Earth's atmosphere was at least somewhat different in the past than now, and some reason that this change should have acted to stabilize the Earth's climate at close to present conditions.

An obvious possibility is to look for some effect that might have enhanced the current greenhouse effect enough to compensate for the smaller energy input. One way of having a stronger greenhouse would be to have more CO_2 (or some other efficient greenhouse gas) in the atmosphere, to provide better insulation against heat loss by plugging some of the wavelength windows through which the Earth's surface cools by radiating IR energy back into space. (Even the tiny quantities of CO_2 currently present in the atmosphere have an important effect on the efficiency of the Earth's greenhouse; this is why we are concerned that increasing this amount by burning huge amounts of fossil fuel can significantly raise the Earth's surface temperature.) Remarkably, there is a way in which larger amounts of CO_2 could have been present in the past, and even a "feedback" mechanism that would tend to keep the temperature stable over the long run, through what is known as the carbonate-silicate cycle.

To understand how this might work, we need to look at what has happened to Earth's initial endowment of CO_2, which was probably similar to the amount that was deposited on Venus. On Earth, the fate of the CO_2 has been crucially affected by the fact that water on Earth is mostly liquid, in rivers, lakes and oceans. CO_2 in the atmosphere slowly dissolves into the surface waters, up to a saturation point. If nothing else happened, this would not have significantly changed the amount of CO_2 in the atmosphere. However, because the Earth has precipitation and erosion, there is a constant influx of dissolved minerals from weathered rocks into streams, rivers, and eventually the seas. One of the elements that arrives is Ca, from pyroxene ($CaSiO_3$, for example) and feldspar minerals. A series of reactions has the effect of combining some of the Ca atoms with CO_2 to form insoluble $CaCO_3$, which settles to the bottom of the oceans and becomes limestone rock. The reactions below are an example:

$$CaSiO_3 + 2CO_2 + H_2O \rightarrow Ca^{++} + SiO_2 + 2HCO_3^-$$

followed by

$$Ca^{++} + 2HCO_3^- \rightarrow CaCO_3 + CO_2 + H_2O.$$

The HCO_3^- ions are combined with Ca^{++} by marine organisms (mostly a kind of plankton), which use $CaCO_3$ in the construction of their shells. These shells end up in the ooze on the bottom of the sea as these organisms die, and gradually form limestone and other carbonate rocks. (Before the appearance of plankton this function may have been performed by certain types of algae; before the development of living organisms, equivalent reactions probably occurred by purely chemical routes.) The SiO_2 also eventually forms minerals.

An estimate of the amount of CO_2 that is currently stored in limestone and similar rocks, together with the amount that has been subducted into the Earth's mantle, indicates that this reservoir contains a mass of CO_2 similar to the mass currently present in the atmosphere of Venus. Thus our initial idea, that the terrestrial planets started with similar mass fractions of the major volatile elements, seems to be supported. The Earth's initial CO_2 is still here, but only a tiny fraction of it is presently in our atmosphere.

However, CO_2 is not only removed from the atmosphere, but also returned there. Carbonate rocks on the sea floor eventually are subducted into the mantle, where they are intensely heated and compressed as they descend. As a result, the reaction above reverses, giving off CO_2 gas which returns to the atmosphere from volcanos. Thus the present CO_2 abundance in the atmosphere is the result of a balance between reactions which remove CO_2 from the air by depositing it in rock, and reactions which restore CO_2 to the atmosphere.

This balance is actually self-regulating; that is, it has a tendency to keep the atmosphere's surface temperature constant. This occurs because the rate of weathering depends on the surface temperature. As the temperature rises, the amount of evaporation, and hence of precipitation and runoff, increases rapidly. The input of Ca ions to the water system of the world increases, and the rate of extraction of CO_2 also rises. Thus, the rate of loss of CO_2 from the atmosphere increases with temperature. On the other hand, the rate of return of CO_2 to the atmosphere by volcanism does not depend on the surface temperature. If the surface temperature on Earth rises, the rate of extraction of CO_2 increases but the rate of return of CO_2 remains unchanged; the result, predictably, is that the balance shifts in favour of less CO_2 in the atmosphere, which in turn will allow the surface temperature to fall. (Unfortunately, the shift in balance occurs far too slowly to help with our present global warming problem.)

Exercise: Explain why a drop in surface temperature would lead eventually to an increase in CO_2 in the atmosphere, pushing the surface temperature back towards the initial balanced value.

The evidence that the early Earth actually had higher surface temperature that it does at present (no glaciations earlier than 2.5 Gyr ago) is also consistent with this theory. At that time, the continents were almost certainly smaller than they are today (recall the discussion of continent growth in Chapter 8), so the amount of erosion was much smaller, and less Ca was available to immobilize atmospheric CO_2. Hence early in the history of the Earth, the balance between losses and gains of CO_2 to the atmosphere would have been shifted strongly in favour of more atmospheric CO_2 and hence a more effective greenhouse and warmer surface temperature, in spite of the lower solar energy supply.

We now have a reasonable explanation of why the Earth's atmosphere is currently dominated by N_2: the more common volatiles are sequestered elsewhere, water mostly in the oceans and in crustal rocks, and and CO_2 almost entirely in carbonate rocks. N_2 is the next most common volatile among those supplied to the Earth when it formed. But why, unlike any other planet, does the Earth have an atmosphere containing about 20% O_2, a highly reactive substance that ought to be gradually removed from the air by reactions with surface minerals? The answer to this question is connected with the development of life on Earth.

At the time life began on Earth, the atmosphere was probably similar to the present one except for a lack of O_2 and the presence of perhaps 1% H_2. The first micro-organisms probably were constructed from naturally produced organic molecules in the water. They may have derived their energy from reactions between natural organic molecules as well; that is, essentially by something akin to fermentation. They were dependent on the natural supply of such molecules (which were of course in very limited supply). They released as waste products such molecules as CO_2, H_2, NH_3, and CH_4 into the atmosphere. They may have developed as early as 4 Gyr ago.

As the supply of abiotic organic molecules dwindled because of destruction by hungry micro-organisms, new bacterial types arose capable of synthesizing acetate or methane from CO_2 and H_2 in the atmosphere, as present-day methane bacteria do. This greatly increased the range of possible biological activity. This development reduced slightly the H_2 levels in the air, but still left H_2 more abundant than O_2 in the air. Nitrogen fixation may also have developed at this time, perhaps 3.5 Gyr ago.

Half an Gyr later, perhaps, bacterial photosynthesis developed, along the lines of present-day purple and green bacteria. Such photosynthesizing bacteria combined H_2S, H_2, etc., from the environment with C from organic compounds or perhaps from CO_2 in the air. These organisms would have had to deal with the problem of damage by ultraviolet light of $\lambda \sim 2500$ Å, which could pass through the atmosphere because of lack of O_3 to block such rays. This short wave radiation can damage DNA. Some microbes have the ability to repair such damage, a trait perhaps acquired before the development of the ozone layer. Others may have protected themselves under $\sim$ 100 m of water, or by a 100 μm layer of protective purine and pyramidine bases on the outer cell walls, or by hiding under floating layers of organic debris on the water surface, such as algae mats of dead microbes. (Such mats lead to the formation of stromatolites, one of the oldest kind of fossils produced by living creatures.)

Finally, about 2.5 Gyr ago, a microbe developed green-plant photosynthesis, in which organic molecules are synthesized from H_2O and CO_2 using energy from sunlight. Present day blue-green algae operate in this manner and may resemble the first such microbes. Green-plant photosynthesis is chemically more complex than bacterial photosynthesis, and requires numerous enzymes to control reactive intermediate molecules such as HO_2 and H_2O_2.

Green-plant photosynthesis released O_2 into the atmosphere as a waste product, and the development of this type of photosynthesis would have triggered the change of the atmosphere from weakly reducing to strongly oxidizing. Other microbe types would have had to adapt to the newly oxygen-rich conditions, and the ancestors of modern-day anaerobic bacteria, which flourish in muddy lake bottoms, for example, found means of protecting themselves from the toxic O_2.

The oxidizing atmosphere made aerobic respiration possible for organisms, and many, such as nitrifying bacteria, hydrogen bacteria and colourless sulfur bacteria, must have developed quickly. Oxygen greatly reduced the quantity of reduced inorganic compounds in the environment and relegated more primitive microbes to an insignificant role.

The development of an oxygen-rich atmosphere evidently led to the conversion of water-soluble ferrous oxide FeO to the more highly oxidized and insoluble ferric oxide Fe_2O_3. This change caused large amounts of dissolved FeO to precipitate out of the shallow seas as the distinctive **banded iron formations**, thin layers alternately iron-rich and silica-rich that were laid down between 3 and 2 Gyr ago. Such formations are extremely rare in younger rocks.

Oxygen could not become very abundant in the atmosphere until all the ferrous iron in solution and the reduced organic compounds in the environment were oxidized. The first substantial amounts of O_2 appeared in the atmosphere about 2 Gyr ago. This is indicated by the occurrence of **red beds**, which occur when iron is weathered and deposited under oxidizing conditions.

More recently, the rise of oxygen in the atmosphere is hard to document. The new occurrence of metazoa (multicellular creatures, for example jellyfish and annelid worms) about 0.7 Gyr ago required a lower limit on O_2 in the atmosphere of 2% of the present value, while the shell-forming animals that first occur about 580 million years ago required about 20% of the present O_2 level. But there is no obvious reason that O_2 abundance couldn't have risen to substantially higher levels even 2 Gyr ago. The atmosphere has probably been essentially modern for at least one Gyr, and the O_2 it presently contains is quite simply a byproduct of the development of complex living organisms on our planet.

The vanishing atmosphere of Mars

One of the most exciting discoveries made by the wave of space probes sent to the planets in the 1970's was the observation of surface features on Mars that most likely are evidence that at one time liquid water flowed on the Red Planet (Figure 9.16). Since most of the features that suggest running water occur in rather old terrain, it seems that liquid water was somehow possible early in Mars' history. Since the current temperature is almost always too low for water to become liquid, and the amount of warming sunlight available in the distant past would have been even lower than today, it appears that liquid water could only have occurred if there was at one time a much more important greenhouse effect than exists today. The obvious way to achieve this would be with a $10^2 - 10^3$ times higher mass of CO_2 in the atmosphere than is present now.

Could such a (relatively) massive atmosphere have been present at one time? The answer is not really clear. If we assume that Mars originated with a similar mass fraction of CO_2 to those of Earth and Venus, it appears that enough CO_2 could well have been present. Other estimates (relating the amount of CO_2 to the amount of presently observed noble gases, or to inferred initial amount of N_2), while very uncertain, also lead to the same result. (However, it should be pointed out that it is not certain that Mars ever outgassed most of its CO_2 onto the surface; much may remain buried in the mantle. In that case, the theory described below needs important modifications.)

If this much larger amount of CO_2 was once present in the Martian atmosphere, a cycle somewhat like that on Earth probably should have operated. If the surface temperature was high enough to produce liquid water, CO_2 would have dissolved in it, combined with other dissolved minerals, and precipitated as carbonate rock. However, since it appears that Mars never had plate tectonics, the return process would not have involved subduction, but probably would have been due to covering of carbonates with layers of lava from the numerous huge volcanic structures we observe on Mars. Heating and compression would have led to the return of CO_2 to the atmosphere as long as volcanism was active on Mars. A combination of atmospheric CO_2 and H_2O could have provided enough greenhouse action to allow liquid water to exist early in Mars' history.

But Mars is much smaller than the Earth and Venus, and its interior has cooled much more quickly. It appears that Mars has had little or no volcanic activity for more than 1 Gyr. Thus the mechanism to return CO_2 to the atmosphere eventually failed, and only a small fraction of the initial endowment remains above the surface. (The test of this idea is to detect those carbonate rocks on or below the surface of Mars; this is a high priority for current Mars missions.)

It appears that the Mars atmosphere is probably composed of a small fraction of its initial CO_2, a small fraction of its initial N_2 (much may have been lost into space as a result of the planet's relatively weak gravity), and a tiny fraction of the initial water (some would have been lost to space, and the rest is probably present as permafrost in the Martian crust). Mars' present feeble atmosphere is a result of its relatively small total mass.

The atmospheric furnace of Venus

Venus has a total mass very similar to that of Earth, and probably originated with a similar mass of volatiles, particularly H_2O, CO_2, and N_2. Today that original endowment of CO_2 and N_2 is still present in the atmosphere, but the water is almost entirely absent: the atmosphere is extremely dry, and it appears very unlikely that any significant amount of water is found in the hot crustal volcanic rocks. This is almost a mirror image of the situation on Earth, where the CO_2 has been lost from the atmosphere but the H_2O is still very obvious in liquid form. How did a planet so similar to Earth in size, composition, and position in the solar system evolve so differently?

We could start by asking if perhaps Venus actually started with a substantially different composition of its initial volatile content: perhaps it never had much water. This seems unlikely, given that Venus and Earth have very similar total masses of CO_2 and of N_2. In the same way, we can argue that the similar size and position of Venus in the solar system makes it unlikely that water was somehow lost from Venus during accretion, but retained on Earth.

Instead, we find a plausible explanation in the evolution of the atmosphere after it formed. The key difference compared to Earth seems to have been the position of Venus in the solar system, about 30% closer to the Sun than we are, leading to a correspondingly great input of solar energy. During the early stages of accretion and outgassing of volatiles from the planetary interior, a powerful greenhouse would have developed on both planets, combining the blanketing effects of both CO_2 and H_2O. During the main accretion phase, as previously mentioned, this early atmosphere would probably have blanketed both planets strongly enough to allow surface temperatures to rise to 1600 K or higher. However, once the accretion rate dropped off, the temperature at the surface would have declined to a level determined by the input of solar energy and the atmospheric resistance to radiation of surface heat in the infrared.

On Earth, this balance, even with much CO_2 in the atmosphere, led to a surface temperature below the boiling point of water. The water thus stayed in oceans, making possible the removal of CO_2 from the atmosphere by conversion into carbonate rock. Since the rate of removal of CO_2 increases with temperature, the greenhouse effect on Earth was thus self-limiting. On Venus, however, the early surface temperature was higher. It is not clear whether the surface temperature was so high that all the water on the planet ended up as vapour, or whether there were liquid oceans for a while. However, a key feature of a hot, extremely humid atmosphere is a major change in the stratospheric "cold trap" that prevents any significant amount of water from reaching high enough altitudes on Earth to be broken up by UV radiation so that the H can escape into space. In an atmosphere in which water vapour makes up 20% or more of the total gas, this "cold trap" is destroyed. In such a humid atmosphere, water vapour remains an important component of the atmosphere up to very high altitudes, where it can be disrupted, and the H lost by Jeans escape. The higher surface temperature on Venus was enough to tip the atmospheric structure over to this situation, leading to the rather rapid loss of almost all the H_2O from the planet. This in turn would have shut off the possibility of storing CO_2 in the rocks (whatever was already there was soon returned to the atmosphere by the massive volcanic activity of the planet), and the result was the very dry CO_2 and N_2 atmosphere with the powerful greenhouse effect that we find today.

Is there any strong evidence for this theory? One key measurement that strongly supports this idea is the fact that on Venus the deuterium to hydrogen ratio is about 120 times higher than on Earth. Since an atom of D is twice as massive as an atom of normal H, it is lost to space by Jeans escape less efficiently, and this extremely elevated D/H ratio is a probably major symptom of the massive loss of water into space.

Thus it appears that the explanation of the Goldilocks problem is that on Venus the planet was too close to the Sun, and thus too hot, to retain its water, which left a massive CO_2 atmosphere and a powerful greenhouse effect. On Earth, the larger distance from the Sun allowed liquid water to continue to exist, removing almost all the CO_2 and greatly moderating the greenhouse effect, which is however supported at a low level by the return of some CO_2 to the atmosphere by volcanic activity. On Mars, the small size of the planet seems to have shut down volcanism far in the past, and hence stopped the return CO_2 to the atmosphere, leaving most of the volatiles (CO_2 and H_2O) locked in the crust. (Alternatively, limited outgassing and losses into space may have prevented a substantial atmosphere from developing even early in Mars' history, in which case we have to find an alternative explanation for the features that seem to have been made by flowing liquid.)

10.10 Mathematical aspects

The barometric law

The equation that governs the variation of density and pressure with depth in a fluid, if the fluid is at rest in a gravitation field, is the hydrostatic equation, which was derived in Chapter 3. In the simplest case, where density is constant (for example, in a thin layer of water such as an ocean), the hydrostatic equation alone completely describes the situation. This was the case that we considered in Chapters 8 and 9. In more complex situations such as an atmospheric gas, the equation needs to be supplemented with an equation of state for the fluid, and with other equations that regulate the variation of temperature with depth or height, as we saw in Chapter 3 in connection with the solar atmosphere.

The equation of hydrostatic equilibrium is

$$\frac{dp}{dz} = -\rho g, \tag{10.1}$$

where ρ and p are the density and pressure at altitude z, and the acceleration (downward) of gravity is g. Recall that this equation expresses the idea that the *increase* in pressure through a little vertical distance $-dz$ is just enough to support the weight of of that slab per unit area, $\rho g\, dz$. For a fluid of constant density in a uniform gravity field (a terrestrial ocean, for example), Equation (10.1) may be solved immediately because the right-hand side is constant. Then

$$\begin{aligned} p_2 - p_1 &= \int_{p_1}^{p_2} dp = -\rho g \int_{z_1}^{z_2} dz \\ &= -\rho g\,(z_2 - z_1). \end{aligned} \tag{10.2}$$

If the depth from the surface $d = z_2 - z_1$ is used, assuming $p_2 = p_{\mathrm{atm}}$ has the atmospheric value, the equation becomes

$$p(d) = p_{\mathrm{atm}} + \rho g d, \tag{10.3}$$

so pressure increases *linearly* with depth. On Earth, $p_{\mathrm{atm}} = 101$ kPa. Since water has $\rho = 1000$ kg m^{-3}, and $g = 9.8$ m s^{-2}, numerically we find

$$p(d) = 1.0 \times 10^5 + 1.0 \times 10^4 d, \tag{10.4}$$

with p in Pa and d in meters. Thus the pressure due to the weight of water already equals that due to the atmosphere at a depth of about 10 m, and by 1 km the pressure is about 100 atm. (However, even at the bottom of an ocean, at $d \sim 5 \times 10^3$ m, the pressure of about 5×10^7 Pa is still too low to deform rock, and it is only at some depth in the crust that rock is forced to deform.)

An atmospheric gas often obeys a simple equation of state such as the ideal gas law $p = \rho kT/\mu m_{\mathrm{u}}$ (μ is the molecular weight of the gas, 28 for N_2, for example). In this case, the hydrostatic equilibrium equation becomes

$$\frac{dp}{dz} = -\rho g = -\frac{\mu m_{\mathrm{u}} g p}{kT} \equiv -\frac{p}{H} \tag{10.5}$$

If the temperature and gravity are constant throughout the region of interest, Equation (10.5) can easily be solved, since $(\mu m_{\mathrm{u}} g/kT) \equiv 1/H$ is constant:

$$\int_{p_1}^{p_2} \frac{dp}{p} = \ln(p_2/p_1) = -\int_{z_1}^{z_2} \frac{dz}{H} = -\frac{z_2 - z_1}{H}, \tag{10.6}$$

or

$$p_2/p_1 = e^{[-(z_2-z_1)/H]}. \tag{10.7}$$

The quantity H is the distance over which the pressure (or here also the density, since in this situation $\rho_2/\rho_1 = p_2/p_1$) falls by $1/e$. Recall from Chapter 3 that it is called the **scale height** and gives a measure in some sense of the thickness of the atmosphere.

Exercise: Show that the height $h_{1/2}$ used earlier in the chapter is equal to $(\ln 2)H = 0.69H$.

The value of the scale height for Earth's atmosphere is about 8 km for $T = 275$ K, and this is a reasonable measure of the atmosphere's thickness.

Note the physical interpretation of the scale height H that emerges from writing the defining equation as $\mu m_{\mathrm{u}} g H = kT$: the scale height is roughly the height that molecules of molecular mass μm_{u} could rise against the gravitational field by converting the available thermal energy kT into gravitational potential energy $\mu m_{\mathrm{u}} g H$.

If the temperature and/or gravity varies in a known way (for example, the Earth's gravity varies above the surface as $g = GM_{\odot}/r^2$), where r is measured from the centre of the Earth, one can put the appropriate functions into Equation (10.5) and try to solve it.

Exercise: (a) Use the results of this section (and perhaps the discussion of gas pressure in Chapter 2) to estimate the mass of an iron meteorite of $\rho = 7900$ kg m^{-3} for which the mass of a column of Venus atmosphere displaced by the meteorite as it enters the atmosphere is equal to the mass of the meteorite. (Recall that this is a limiting mass below which substantial deceleration by atmospheric friction occurs.) Make the same estimate for Earth and for Mars. (b) Compare the values. Can you explain the difference?

Exercise: Use Newton's second law, $F = d\,(mv)/dt$ to estimate the order of magnitude of the pressure exerted on a house wall, 10 m × 10 m in size, by a terrestrial wind of $v = 50$ km/hr. What is the total force on the wall in familiar units? (Hint: use Newtons's second law by noticing that the wind, on hitting the wall, will lose almost all its forward momentum, and recall that pressure is simply force per unit area.)

Instability and convection

We now look briefly at an important question connected with vertical changes in temperature. Recall from the discussion earlier in the chapter that heat input from the Sun mostly is absorbed by the ground and sea. As the planet re-radiates this energy back into space as IR radiation, some of the radiation is absorbed in the atmosphere, heating it. A basic problem in the theory of planetary atmospheres is to work out what the expected vertical temperature distribution in the atmosphere will be, but this is too complicated a problem for us to attack here. The result of the solution of this problem is that in a reasonably dense atmosphere like that of Earth or Venus, the temperature computed simply from the radiation balance is expected to fall with increasing altitude.

Now one aspect of the vertical temperature structure that we can explore is the question of whether *convection* occurs in a particular altitude region of the atmosphere. Recall the earlier discussion of why a region of the atmosphere develops convection. If a blob of air that rises spontaneously a little way, cooling by adiabatic expansion ("adiabatic" processes are ones in which no exchange of heat with the surroundings occurs), nevertheless finds that after a short upwards excursion it is *warmer* than its surroundings, it will continue to rise. In this case the atmosphere is unstable to convection. Clearly, the criterion that decides whether or not the atmosphere is unstable in this way is whether the vertical rate of change of temperature, dT/dz, in the atmosphere (as set up by radiation balance) is less than (more negative than) the rate of change of temperature with height of a blob rising adiabatically. We can express the condition for occurrence of convection as

$$\left(\frac{dT}{dz}\right)_{\rm rad} < \left(\frac{dT}{dz}\right)_{\rm ad} \qquad (10.8)$$

where the subscript "rad" indicates the temperature gradient computed from radiative equilibrium, and the subscript "ad" indicates the rate of change of T in a blob rising adiabatically, without heat exchange with its surroundings.

Since convection is a very efficient mode of heat transfer, if it occurs in the lower atmosphere, it will carry heat upwards so efficiently that it will prevent the temperature in the atmosphere from declining more rapidly with height than the adiabatic rate. This is observed to be the situation in the tropospheres of Earth and Venus, and is almost certainly also the situation in the atmospheres of the giant planets. It is thus of considerable interest to calculate this minimum temperature gradient, and this is easily within our means.

We will shortly see that we will need an expression for the specific heat of a gas at constant pressure, $c_{\rm p}$. We have already discussed specific heats in Chapter 6 in connection with asteroid heating (see also Table 6.6), but there we looked only at the specific heat (per kg) at constant volume, $c_{\rm v}$. We need first to recall the relationship between these two specific heats.

The first law of thermodynamics states that in a small exchange of heat and work, the change dU in internal energy (we will consider here one kg) is related to the heat input dQ and the work done on the external environment $dW = pdV$ by

$$dU = dQ - dW. \qquad (10.9)$$

If heat goes into our sample with no change of volume, so that $dW = 0$, the heat put in may be expressed as $dQ = c_{\rm v}dT$ (this is basically the definition of $c_{\rm v}$), and since in an ideal gas $U = U(T)$ is a function only of T, we see that $dU = c_{\rm v}dT$. Now consider a small change in our gas *at constant pressure.* In this case,

$$dQ = c_{\rm p}dT = dU + dW = c_{\rm v}dT + pdV, \qquad (10.10)$$

where V is the volume occupied by one kg. Now we may write the ideal gas law, Equation 2.6, as

$$pV = NkT, \qquad (10.11)$$

where V is still the volume of one kg of gas, and N is the number of atoms or molecules in one kg of that gas. Then in a transformation at constant pressure, (10.11) gives

$$pdV = NkdT. \qquad (10.12)$$

Putting this into (10.10) and dividing by dT, we finally obtain

$$c_{\rm p} = c_{\rm v} + Nk. \qquad (10.13)$$

Equation (10.13) allows us to compute the value of $c_{\rm p}$ from $c_{\rm v}$ and a knowledge of the number of atoms (or molecules) per kg.

Exercise: The molecular weight of N_2 is about 28. Show that the number of molecules per kg is about 2.1×10^{25}. The value of $c_{\rm v}$ (Table 6.6) is 742 J K^{-1} kg^{-1}. Calculate $c_{\rm p}$ for N_2.

Now we can go on to the main problem, that of finding the critical vertical temperature gradient that the atmosphere will not drop below. Consider a small vertical displacement of a gas blob in which no heat is exchanged with the surroundings. In this case $dQ = 0$, so the first law tells us that

$$dU + dW = c_{\rm v}dT + pdV = 0. \qquad (10.14)$$

Using (10.11) again, but now *not* assuming that the small change is at constant pressure, we have

$$pdV + Vdp = NkdT. \qquad (10.15)$$

Using this result to eliminate the pdV term in Equation (10.14), and recalling that the volume V per kg is just the inverse of the density (number of kg per unit volume), $V = 1/\rho$, we find

$$Vdp = \frac{dp}{\rho} = (c_v + Nk)dT = c_p dT. \qquad (10.16)$$

Now as the gas blob rises, pressure differences are wiped out so quickly (at the speed of sound) that the blob will remain in pressure equilibrium with its surroundings, and both inside and outside the blob the equation of hydrostatic equilibrium (10.1) will be observed. Using this equation to replace dp by dz in (10.16), we find finally that the vertical temperature gradient which will lead to the onset of convection is given by

$$\left(\frac{dT}{dz}\right)_{\text{ad}} = -\frac{g}{c_p}. \qquad (10.17)$$

Exercise: Calculate the adiabatic temperature gradient at the surface of Venus, assuming an atmosphere of pure CO_2. Confirm that your value agrees approximately with the behaviour shown in Figure 10.2.

10.11 References

S. K. Atreya, J. B. Pollack and M. S. Matthews 1989, *Origin and evolution of planetary and satellite atmospheres* (Tucson, AZ: University of Arizona Press). This 800+ page book contains more than 20 chapters exploring most of the issues suggested by the title. But be warned: most of the chapters were written for professionals in the field.

Bullock, M. A., and Grinspoon, D. H. 1999," Global climate change on Venus", *Sci. Am.*, Mar. 50. The authors argue that the climate of Venus has undergone significant changes during the past several hundred million years, triggered by a major episode of volcanic activity.

Goody, R.M., and Walker, J.C.G. 1972, *Atmospheres* (Englewood Cliffs, N.J.: Prentice-Hall, Inc.). This excellent small book contains a clear description of the physics of planetary atmospheres (mostly that of the Earth, but touching also on Mars and Venus) from basic structure to weather, using only high-school mathematics.

Haberle, R. M. 1986, "The climate of Mars", *Sci. Am.*, May, 54. The theory that the Martian climate evolved from a warmer, wetter past to its current frigid and dry state is discussed.

Hoffman, N. 2001, "White Mars", *Mercury*, Jan. - Feb., 14. Hoffman argues that the surface features on Mars that are usually taken as evidence for liquid water may instead have been produced by pyroclastic flows lubricated by CO_2.

Houghton, J. T. 1986, *The physics of atmospheres* (Cambridge: Cambridge University Press). Houghton's small book is a very clear introduction to the physics of atmospheres, with many useful figures, suitable for physics students from third year on.

Kargel, J. S. and Strom, R. G., "Global climatic change on Mars", *Sci. Am.*, Nov 1996, 80. The atmosphere of Mars has probably changed greatly since the it first formed; this article attempts to reconstruct that history.

Kasting, J. F., Toon, O. B., and Pollack, J. B., "How climate evolved on the terrestrial planets", *Sci. Am.*, Feb. 1988, 90. The enormous differences between the atmospheres of the Earth, Venus, and Mars are described and explained.

J G Luhmann, J B Pollack and L Colin, "The Pioneer mission to Venus", *Sci. Am.*, Apr 1994, 90. Much of what we know about the atmosphere of Venus was learned from the extremely successful NASA Pioneer space probe.

Orgel, L. E. 1994, "The origin of life on the Earth", *Sci. Am.*, Oct., 76. We certainly do not fully understand yet how life originated on Earth. Orgel explains what biologist think may have occurred.

Prinn, R. G. 1985, "The volcanos and clouds of Venus", *Sci. Am.*, Mar., 46. Volcanos on the surface of Venus inject sulphur gases into the atmosphere, substantially modifying the atmospheric chemistry of the planet.

Schubert, G. and Covey, C. 1981, "The atmosphere of Venus", *Sci. Am.*, Jul., 66. The first decade of spacecraft studies of Venus revealed the temperature structure and winds of the planet's atmosphere.

G. Turner, "The development of the atmosphere" in P.H. Greenwood, (ed.), *The Evolving Earth* (Cambridge 1981), p.121. A number of kinds of evidence, both in the present atmosphere and in the geological record, allow one to tentatively reconstruct the history of the Earth's atmosphere.

J.C.G. Walker, 1977, *Evolution of the Atmosphere* (New York, NY: MacMillan Publishing Co.). This book presents a clear discussion of many physical, chemical, and biological aspects of the Earth's present atmosphere, and discusses evidence that allows us to deduce much of its history.

10.12 Review questions

10.1 Approximately how do pressure and density change with altitude in the atmosphere of the Earth? What differences do we find when we look at Venus and Mars, and what physical differences underly these differences?

10.2 What defines the "top" of a planetary atmosphere?

10.3 Physically, why do terrestrial atmospheres decrease in temperature with height above the ground, at least in their lower layers?

10.4 What is the greenhouse effect and how does it operate in a planetary atmosphere?

10.5 What is convection? What makes it occur? How does the presence of convection affect the lower levels of a planetary atmosphere?

10.6 How are gases lost and/or gained by a planetary atmosphere from the top or bottom?

10.7 Why do Mercury and the Earth's Moon have no significant atmospheres?

10.8 How did terrestrial atmospheres originate? What evidence points to this origin rather than some other?

10.9 Were the atmospheres of Venus, the Earth and Mars always enormously dissimilar? Why are they so different today?

10.10 What mechanism tends to maintain a roughly stable temperature on Earth today?

10.11 What drives *horizontal* atmospheric motions?

10.12 Why do clouds form?

10.13 Problems

10.1 (a) Assume that the Earth's atmosphere is pure molecular $^{14}N_2$. Ignoring the variation of temperature T and gravity g with height h above the ground, find the variation with height of $n(h)$, the number of air molecules per m^3. You should use the surface pressure in the Earth's atmosphere, $p(0) = 101$ kPa, to normalize $n(h)$. (b) Now consider the decay of the orbit of a satellite in a low circular Earth orbit. Assuming that energy is lost simply as a result of the satellite accelerating the air molecules with which it collides to its own speed, find an equation which gives an estimate as a function of height of the fractional loss of kinetic energy $\Delta E/E$ *per orbital revolution* due to collision of the satellite with air. (c) For a satellite that has a cross section of 1 m^2 and a mass of 1×10^3 kg, evaluate the altitude at which $\Delta E/E$ reaches 1% per revolution. (Hint: this will require some approximation; you could start by neglecting the difference between the circumference of the orbit and the circumference of the Earth.) Clearly the satellite must be above this altitude to stay in orbit for even a week. How does your altitude compare with the altitude at which space shuttle missions are carried out, about 300 km?

10.2 We can try to estimate the expected daily surface temperature variations in the Earth's atmosphere roughly as follows. Assume for simplicity that a particular place on the Earth's surface receives 12 hours of steady sunshine at an energy input rate of 1.0×10^3 W m^{-2} (somewhat reduced from the usual solar constant to allow for "geometric dilution" of the incoming energy), and that due to a local albedo of $A = 0.40$, a fraction $(1 - A)$ of this energy is absorbed and heats the ground and low atmosphere. The 12 hours of sunlight is followed by 12 hours of darkness. Assume that the energy input is reradiated back into space at a constant rate that just balances the heat input averaged over 24 hours. (a) Calculate the net heating rate (sunlight input minus mean radiative loss) during the daylight hours, and the net cooling rate during nighttime. (b) The mass of atmosphere above the ground is about 1.03 kg cm^{-3} or 1.03×10^4 kg m^{-2}. Find an expression for the total number of molecules (assume that the air is pure N_2) in the volume above one m^2, and evaluate it numerically. (c) Assume that all the gas above a particular square meter is in close thermal contact, so that heat gains or losses result in the same temperature change ΔT at all altitudes. The heat required to increase the temperature of the gas by ΔT is approximately $\Delta E = (7/2)\,k\Delta T$ per molecule. What is the predicted temperature difference between the air at sunrise and at sunset resulting from the 12 hours of net heating? (d) How does the amplitude of the computed temperature change agree with your experience of daily temperature changes? If your experience suggests that the computation does not accurately reflect temperature changes at ground level, what factor(s) might make the estimate differ from your experience?

10.3 Consider the possibility of modeling the structure of the Earth's atmosphere by a gas of pure $^{14}N_2$ at a uniform temperature of $T = 250$ K. (a) Write down the equation of hydrostatic equilibrium that applies, including explicitly the variation of $g_\oplus = GM_\oplus/r^2$ with distance from the centre of the Earth. (b) Integrate the resulting equation to find an expression for the pressure $p(r)$ above the ground, where the pressure is $p(R_\oplus)$; if you do an indefinite integration be sure to evaluate the resulting constant. Check your equation for correct dimensions. (c) Find a simple limiting approximation of the expression you have derived in (b) for heights h above the ground such that $h \ll R_\oplus$, (i.e. take $r = R_\oplus + h$). Confirm that your limiting expression is the same as the usual barometric law for constant temperature. (d) Now calculate the pressure in the solar wind, which is mainly H having a temperature of $T_{\rm w} = 2 \times 10^5$ K and a number density $n = 5 \times 10^6$ m^{-3}. (e) Finally, use your general solution for $p(r)$ from (a) to find the distance r from the centre of the Earth (and the height h) at which your calculated pressure falls to a level about the same as that found in the solar wind. Do you suppose that this level is related to the boundary between the Earth's atmosphere and the solar wind?

10.4 Let's try to model the lower atmosphere of Venus. The atmospheric pressure reaches 1 bar (100 kPa) in the middle of the dense cloud deck, where the temperature is about 350 K. At the surface, the pressure is about 90 bars (9000 kPa). From the surface to the 1 bar level, the temperature $T(h)$ declines at a rate of about $dT/dh = L = -8$ K km^{-1}, close to the "adiabatic lapse rate" of -10 K km^{-1}. (a) Calculate the adiabatic lapse rate using the approximation from Equation (10.17) for pure CO_2, and confirm the value given here. (b) Write down the equation of hydrostatic equilibrium for this case, including explicitly the variation of $T(h)$. (c) Integrate the equation to find the variation of pressure $p(h)$ with height. Evaluate any constants in the resulting equation using the (known) value $p(0)$ and the (as yet unknown) value $T(0)$ at $h = 0$. (d) Now use the known pressure drop from the ground to the middle of the cloud deck, and the known temperature at the 1 bar level, to determine the height h_1 above the surface of the 1 bar level and the temperature $T(0)$ at the surface. (You will have two equations to solve.) Assume that the mean molecular weight is that of a gas of pure CO_2. Compare your values to those shown in Figure 10.2. (e) Compare graphically your calculated variation $p(h)$ with the equivalent expression for an isothermal atmosphere with a temperature which is the mean of the surface value and the value at the 1 bar level.

10.5 The goal of this problem is to get a reasonable model of the variation of pressure with height z in the Earth's (mean) atmosphere. (a) Start by computing the convective lapse rate $(dT/dz)_{\rm ad}$ in the troposphere from Equation (10.17). (b) The lapse rate we compute using (10.17) is actually too steep because this expression neglects the effect of condensation of water as blobs rise. Condensation has the effect of releasing heat energy into the cloud as it rises, making T decrease with height z more slowly than in the "dry" case. We can correct for this by taking the actual lapse rate to be about 2/3 of the value computed in part (a). Make this correction. (c) Now assume that the temperature declines linearly with the corrected lapse rate from part (b) up to 15 km, and is isothermal from there up to 25 km. Find the solution to the hydrostatic equation for $T(z)$ a linear function of z, and use this to compute the variation of $p(z)$ up to 15 km, starting from $T(0) = 290$ K and $p(0) = 1000$ mbar at the ground. (d) From this altitude on up, assume that $T(z)$ is a constant. Starting from the values you found at 15 km, compute $p(z)$ up to 25 km (in the low stratosphere) with the appropriate solution of the hydrostatic equation. Graph the variation of $p(z)$ over the full computed range. Accurate models give about 25 mbar at 25 km altitude. How close are you?

Chapter 11

Giant Planets and their Moons

11.1 Overview

So far we have mainly discussed the terrestrial planets, which resemble more or less closely our own Earth. Because we know quite a lot about the Earth, it has been possible to use it as a prototype in our efforts to understand the other rocky planets of the inner solar system. Now we turn our attention to the giant planets, a group of bodies which are quite different structurally from the Earth, and to their moons, bodies not as unlike the Earth as the giant planets themselves are, but having nevertheless some quite distinctive features not found in the planets and moons of the inner solar system.

The most basic data concerning the four large planets Jupiter, Saturn, Uranus, and Neptune immediately reveals that these are bodies which are quite different from the four terrestrial planets, and justifies grouping them together as the giant planets. (Pluto, the ninth planet, is a body more like the moons of the giants than like any of the other outer planets, and it may be related to the Kuiper belt of comet nuclei. It will be discussed at the end of the chapter.) In contrast to the inner planets, which range in mass from the Earth's mass on down to only about 5.5% of that mass in Mercury, the giant planets are all substantially more massive than the Earth (see Table A.2), ranging from about 15 Earth masses for Uranus and Neptune up to nearly 100 Earth masses for Saturn and over 300 for Jupiter. More than 99.5% of the total planetary mass is found in the four giant planets, more than 70% of it in Jupiter alone. Furthermore, all four giant planets are substantially larger in size than any of the terrestrial planets; the giants range from about 4 Earth radii (Neptune and Uranus) up to more than 11 (Jupiter), while the four terrestrial planets range between about 0.4 and 1.0 Earth radii in size.

Remarkably, in spite of their large sizes, the giant planets are all much less dense than the terrestrial ones. All have densities not very different from that of water (their densities range from 690 to 1640 kg m^{-3}). These densities are several times smaller than those of any of the inner planets (where densities range from 3930 to 5520 kg m^{-3}). It is this fact, taken together with their large sizes, that clearly signals the major difference in chemistry or structure of the giants as compared to the inner planets. Considering that the inner planets are already massive enough that their densities are increased (over the densities they would have if they were, say, only as massive as Ceres, or the Moon) by the effects of gravity in compressing their matter, it is clear that the material making up the giants cannot be the same as that of the terrestrial planets, even approximately, or densities of well over 6000 kg m^{-3} would be found. We shall see later that although all the giant planets have rock (and ice?) cores with masses of the order of 10 – 15 Earth masses, all have massive and deep atmospheres composed mainly of H and He. These atmospheres constitute an important fraction of the total mass of each giant planet, ranging from 10 or 20% of the total for Uranus and Neptune, up to 80% of Saturn and 95% of Jupiter. Such massive atmospheres are completely different from the relatively insignificant atmospheres of the terrestrial planets, which (including all the volatiles, such as water, CO_2, and N_2) constitute no more than 0.01% of total planetary mass.

The four giant planets differ in several other fundamental ways from the terrestrial planets. All but Uranus transport enough internal heat to the surface that they radiate into space roughly twice as much heat as they absorb from incident sunlight. This heat loss from the interior seems to be either radiation of heat released in the interior of the planet from gravitational contraction as it formed, or heat released by gravitational separation of He from H in the planetary interior. This is quite different from the behaviour of the rocky planets, whose internal heat loss is several orders of magnitude smaller than the absorbed and reradiated solar energy, and is due largely to the loss of heat released by radioactive decay of U, Th, and especially ^{40}K. In contrast to the scarcity of moons in the inner solar system, each giant planet has at least one large moon; in fact, each has a system of numerous moons ranging in size from the size of the Earth's Moon on down to a few km in radius. A couple of the moons of Jupiter have densities comparable to that of the Earth's Moon, but most have sufficiently low density that it is clear that they must contain a considerable amount of ice in their bulk composition. All four giants also have ring systems, although only that of Saturn is easily visible from Earth. Thus we are clearly justified in treating both the giant planets and their moons as objects which are really different from the largest bodies in the inner solar system.

We first consider the information available about these remarkable objects from observations, and then look at what is understood about their internal structure, and how they may have formed and developed during the history of the solar system.

Figure 11.1: This image of Jupiter was taken by the Hubble Space Telescope. It clearly shows the complex cloud bands, alternating between light-coloured zones and darker belts. The wave-like and oval shapes in the belts are cloud patterns that reflect complex wind systems in the cloudy atmosphere of the planet. The large oval just below the equator, near the right limb, is the Great Red Spot. The small black dot at the same latitude near the left limb is the shadow of one of the moons of Jupiter.) (Courtesy of NASA.)

11.2 The giant planets

Observational data on the giant planets

What we see when we look at one of the giant planets is very different from the appearance of the terrestrial planets (except for cloud-covered Venus). The visible "surfaces" of the giants are in fact simply the uppermost of several decks of clouds, seen more or less clearly through a light haze high in the atmosphere. In Jupiter and Saturn, the upper cloud layer is composed primarily of ammonia (NH_3) ice crystals. In places it is possible to see down to the next cloud deck of ammonium hydrosulfide (NH_4SH) ices. The atmospheres of Uranus and Neptune are colder than those of Jupiter and Saturn, and so the highest cloud decks, which form the base of the visible atmospheres, are composed of ice crystals of methane (CH_4), and below that, of hydrogen sulfide (H_2S). (Nowhere in the atmospheres of Jupiter and Saturn does the temperature drop to a low enough value for methane to freeze out, hence there is no methane cloud deck on either planet.)

The rather changeable features seen on the "surfaces" of the giant planets are thus mostly due to forms and colorations of the highest cloud layers. Jupiter (see Figure 11.1) displays a disk with alternating white and coloured stripes (called respectively **zones** and **belts**) across its disk parallel to the planet's equator; in fact, these are wide bands of clouds, variously white, tan, light yellow, brown, and even red, that circle the planet at different latitudes. These cloud bands correspond to wind streams, like the jet streams of the Earth's atmosphere, in the planet's upper atmosphere. Near the equator, these winds circle the planet in the direction of its rotation (from west to east) at a speed of about 300 km s^{-1} (relative to the rotation of the planet's deep interior). There are two other regions of high speed winds near $+25°$ and $-25°$ latitude. At other latitudes the winds blow less quickly. These various wind streams seem to be alternately regions of rising and of sinking gases. The cloud tops in the rising gases occur at higher altitude, where the clouds are white ammonia crystals; the sinking gas forms clouds a little lower, where the higher temperature leads to coloured ammonium hydrosulphide ice, thus producing the banded appearance of the planet.

The other prominent feature seen on Jupiter is the **Great Red Spot**, a huge circular storm rather like a terrestrial hurricane. This storm has varied in size (it is presently about twice the size of the Earth) and in the intensity of its red colour through the years, but has been continuously present since it was discovered by the British scientist Robert Hooke (1635 – 1703), a contemporary and competitor of Issac Newton, in the mid-seventeenth century, more than 300 years ago. A number of smaller white circular storms, considerably smaller than the Red Spot, are also present on the planet at any one time, but these are not as long-lived as the Red Spot.

Saturn also presents a banded appearance like that of Jupiter, but much less vivid (Figure 11.2). The cloud colour on the second largest planet is generally yellow, but varies from nearly white to light brown. The pattern of bands is similar to that on Jupiter. There is an equatorial jet stream that flows from west to east around the planet, but the speed of this flow, about 1500 km s^{-1}, is much higher than is found on Jupiter.

Figure 11.2: This image of Saturn, taken by one of the Voyager spacecraft as it approached the giant planet, shows the spectacular ring system as well as faint bands encircling the planet, like the belts and zones of Jupiter. These faint markings reveal the wind systems in the planet's deep atmosphere. (Courtesy of NASA.)

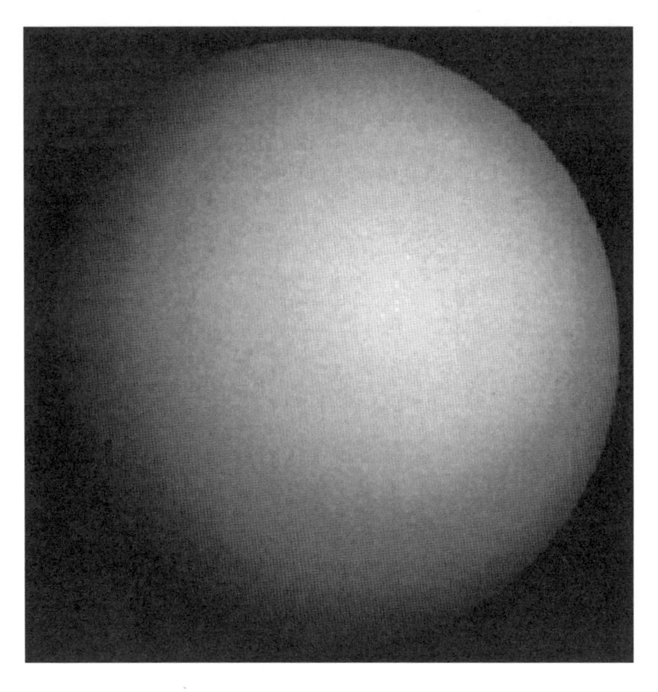

Figure 11.3: The deep atmosphere of Uranus shows no visible features at all except for a slight variation in brightness over the surface. Absorption of red light by methane in the atmosphere gives the planet a deep blue tint. (Courtesy of NASA.)

Small circular storms, like the smaller white ovals on Jupiter, are sometimes seen on Saturn, but they are not nearly as striking as the Great Red Spot, nor as long-lived.

Uranus has a generally blue-green colour. This is caused by methane in the upper atmosphere of the planet: as sunlight flows into the atmosphere where it is reflected back out by haze and the highest cloud layer, the red light is absorbed by the methane, leaving the reflected light rich in blue and green light, and deficient in red. Clouds form only at rather great depths in this cold atmosphere, and are generally obscured by the upper atmosphere haze or smog. Hence almost no cloud features or structure are seen (Figure 11.3. A very striking peculiarity of Uranus compared to all the other planets is that its axis of rotation lies almost in the plane of the ecliptic, so that as the planet circles the Sun, first one hemisphere and then the other passes through a period of complete darkness when the opposite pole is pointing towards the Sun.

Neptune has an even stronger blue colour than Uranus, also due to absorption of red light by methane, but its clouds lie at a somewhat higher altitude and are more easily seen. Like Jupiter, Neptune exhibits giant cyclonic storms. A huge storm, about as large as the Earth, was observed on the planet as the Voyager 2 spacecraft passed through the system. This storm was a darker colour than the planetary disk generally, and is known as the **Great Dark Spot**. White clouds are also seen at a few locations in the atmosphere. Both features are visible in Figure 11.4. The high-altitude winds on Neptune generally circle the planet more slowly than it rotates (that is, they blow from east to west).

As we will discuss later, it is clear that the interiors of Jupiter, Saturn, and Neptune are convecting (this also is assumed to be true of Uranus although we have no strong direct evidence one way or the other). This convection appears to extend up to the visible layers of the atmospheres of the giants. Since convection involves vigorous mixing motions, we could wonder if this means that the atmospheres of the giants have chemical compositions that directly reflect the interior (bulk) compositions of the planets. The answer is: *no*.

The effect that drastically limits the chemical species present in the atmosphere is condensation. In the convecting interior of a giant planet, blobs and streams of gas rise while others descend. In a rising blob of gas, the temperature of the blob will decrease steadily as it rises. This temperature drop is caused by the expansion of the blob, which expends internal energy by pushing its surroundings away. As the temperature decreases in the rising blob, it will reach the temperature at which specific atoms or molecules freeze out, as we have discussed earlier in connection with the cooling solar nebula in which the planets formed. Thus refractory materials such as iron and silicate rock will

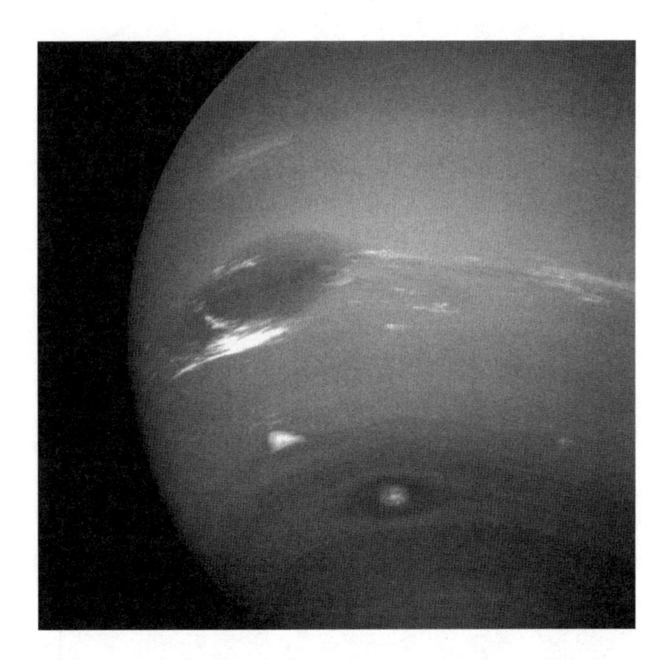

Figure 11.4: This close-up view of the disk of the planet Neptune was obtained by the Voyager 2 spacecraft as it passed Neptune in 1989. Near the middle of the image is a huge cyclonic storm known as the Great Dark Spot. It is roughly a large as Jupiter's Great Red Spot. Below the Great Dark Spot is a smaller storm. Several patches of white cloud are visible. (Courtesy of NASA.)

condense where the temperature is above 2000 K, 1000 km or more below the surface.

The ices will form liquid drops or solid flakes much nearer the surface. In a rising stream of gas in Jupiter's interior, for example, we expect NH_4Cl to condense at about 100 km below the visible surface, water (perhaps mixed with ammonia) will condense at about 50 km below the surface, and NH_4SH at about 20 km down. NH_3 will condense in the visible layers. At the level at which an abundant substance condenses, the droplets or solid particles formed will produce clouds. Within these clouds, the updraft will continue to lift the drops or particles as they grow by further condensation, but when the cloud particles become large enough to not be supported by the rising gases, they will fall back through the cloud layer into the warmer gas below, where they will evaporate again.

We therefore expect that there should be a series of major cloud decks below the visible atmosphere of each of the giant planets. In Jupiter and Saturn, it appears that the highest deck that is really opaque is that of NH_4SH. When we study the chemistry of the atmosphere, we are mainly limited to the layers above this level. Because of condensation of most elements below this cloud deck, the only elements that are expected to have the same relative abundances in the atmosphere as they do deep in the planet are H, C (since the predominant compound of C, CH_4, condenses only at a temperature lower than that reached anywhere in the atmospheres of Jupiter or Saturn), and the noble gases He, Ne, Ar, Kr and Xe (all of which condense only at very low temperatures). Essentially all the other elements, including the abundant and important substances N (in NH_3) and O (in H_2O), will be greatly depleted in the observable layers relative to their contribution to the bulk chemical composition.

We have obtained information about the elements that are present in the atmospheres of the giant planets by a number of different methods. The earliest technique used was to look at the spectrum of reflected sunlight at visible or near infrared wavelengths, and see what additional colours are weakened compared to the directly observed solar spectrum. Such observations may be done from the ground, and reveal the presence of CH_4, some NH_3, and H_2. The possibilities of remote sensing (measurements done without benefit of expensive trips to the outer planets) have been greatly expanded in recent years by the availability of spectrographs on satellites which were used to study reflected ultraviolet sunlight, and the thermal radiation emitted directly by the warm atmospheres of the giants beyond 5 μm in wavelength. Such observations add water, phosphine (PH_3) and several trace hydrocarbons such as C_2H_6 to the observed substances.

The study of the giant planets (and their moons) was completely revolutionized by the data sent back by the two unmanned Voyager spacecraft, and the more recent Galileo probe. Both Voyager spacecraft passed through the Jupiter system in 1979, and visited Saturn in 1980 (Voyager 1) and 1981 (Voyager 2). Voyager 1 passed close to Saturn's largest moon, Titan, and subsequently continued on a trajectory out of the plane of the ecliptic. Voyager 2 continued on in the ecliptic and passed close to Uranus in 1986 and Neptune in 1989. In 1996 the Galileo mission placed a large satellite into orbit around Jupiter, and dropped a probe into the atmosphere of the giant planet. And in 2004 the Cassini space probe is scheduled to go into orbit around Saturn. These missions have made it possible to obtain spectacular close-up views of all the outer planets except Pluto. They have provided us with fascinating images of surfaces and atmospheres as well as with a variety of other measurements such as spectroscopic observations of small surface regions.

The Voyagers and Galileo all carry spectrographs of various kinds that have supplemented in extremely valuable ways the spectra that can be obtained from Earth. But perhaps the most interesting result about chemistry from these missions came from the Galileo project, which included a small probe that actually entered the atmosphere of Jupiter and directly sampled the composition of the gases there, down to layers well below those directly accessible from the outside. The probe was also instrumented to report when it passed though cloud layers. Unfortunately, the probe apparently entered Jupiter in a small region of relatively clear gas (perhaps a column of downflowing gas that had been cleared of most condensible substances), so that the thin cloud layers that it passed through were hardly representative of the rest of the atmosphere.

The results of the observations, both remote and from space probes, are as follows. The main gas present in the atmospheres of all four giant planets is hydrogen, in the form of H_2 molecules, which are detected directly by their absorption lines in the near infrared portion of the spectrum, around 8000 Å. The next most important atomic species in the atmospheres is He, which (because it simply does not form molecules at all) is in atomic form. These two elements account for almost all the atoms in the atmospheres of all the giant planets; all other species (C, N, O, etc) are simply trace elements, present at the level of one or two atoms in a hundred, or less. Cold He cannot be detected in any planetary spectrum, because it has no spectral lines anywhere in the visible or infrared. Its presence and abundance are deduced from the radio occultation experiments carried out by the Voyager and Galileo spacecraft. In these experiments, a pure radio tone (frequency) broadcast by the spacecraft as it passed behind the planet, and again as it emerged on the other limb, was observed from Earth. The refraction (bending) of the radio beam by the planetary atmosphere (which made the spacecraft seem to move at a different speed along its path in space than it was actually moving) was measured. The information about refraction was used to determine the average molecular weight of the atmospheric gas. Since only H and He contribute appreciably to this average molecular weight, the ratio of numbers of He to H atoms may be determined. It is found that for Jupiter, Uranus, and Neptune, He makes up about the same fraction of the total atmospheric gas that it does in the Sun, where there is about one He atom for every ten H atoms (see Table 2.2), so that He makes up about 30% of the total atmospheric mass. However, for Saturn, it appears that He is depleted relative to this value by about a factor of two; only 6% of the gas atoms in the atmosphere are He. The explanation for this interesting fact seems to be the partial separation of H and He in the deep interior of Saturn, as will be discussed in a later section.

The other elements for which abundances might be determined from the spectrum of reflected sunlight are the abundant light elements C, N, and O. (Neon, about as abundant as nitrogen in the sun, has no spectral lines in the visible or infrared spectrum.) The three detectable light elements are almost entirely bound up in the molecules H_2O, CH_4, and NH_3, so one needs to study the spectra of these molecules to derive the abundances of C, N, and O. Determination of the O abundance is quite difficult for all the giant planets because H_2O freezes out as clouds deep in the atmosphere, so that the number of water molecules in the upper atmosphere is greatly depleted. The formation of clouds of ammonia or of ammonium hydrosulphide similarly limits the number of NH_3 molecules in the upper atmosphere, but the abundance of N can be estimated in the atmospheres of Jupiter and Saturn, where it appears to be similar to, or slightly larger than, the abundance found in the Sun. The large abundance of N is confirmed for Jupiter by the Galileo probe, which found that N settled to about three times its solar abundance deep in the atmosphere. The results for Uranus are much less certain, and significant variations in abundance from one latitude to another seem to be found, but it appears that N is somewhat underabundant compared to the Sun. For Neptune, no clear result is available yet.

The best determined of the abundant light elements in all four giant planet atmospheres is C, because methane is sufficiently volatile that it condenses (if at all) only in a high, easily observed region of the atmosphere. C appears to be mildly more abundant in Jupiter and Saturn than in the Sun, by about a factor of three in Jupiter, and six in Saturn. The results for Uranus and Neptune are less consistent, but suggest an overabundance of C, relative to the solar C fraction, of perhaps as much as 20. This may well reflect some mixing up into the atmosphere of the ices that make up a large fraction of the planetary mass of these two bodies.

The heavier noble gases Ar, Kr and Xe appear to be present in Jupiter's atmosphere at about 2 – 3 times their abundances in the sun.

Several characteristics of the giant planets, in addition to those that may be deduced from their atmospheric appearances or spectra, can help us to understand their origins and evolution. One particularly interesting feature is the remarkable difference between the complex moon systems found in the outer solar system, and the comparative rarity of moons around the terrestrial planets. In the inner solar system, only the Earth has a significant (but rather anomalous) moon; Mars has two tiny satellites which probably are left from the period when the planet accreted. The giants, on the other hand, have more than 50 moons among them. These moons form highly ordered systems around Jupiter and Saturn.

Jupiter has four moons comparable in size to the Earth's Moon, which orbit the planet in nearly circular, prograde (i.e. in the direction of the planet's rotation) orbits in the planet's equatorial plane. At least four other small moons also orbit Jupiter in similar orbits. However, the planet also has at least eight moons that orbit it in much larger, inclined and eccentric orbits, some of which are retrograde. These two sets of moons, which we call **regular** and **irregular**, have such different orbital characteristics that it is usually assumed that they must have quite different origins. Saturn also has a large system of regular satellites, at least 18 of them, including one (Titan) which is considerably larger than the Earth's Moon. Saturn has two known irregular moons. Uranus has at least 15 regular moons and two irregular ones, although none are more than about 800 km in radius. Neptune has one large moon (in a retrograde orbit, however!) as well as at least 6 smaller regular moons in small, circular orbits, and one other irregular moon in a very much larger orbit. All four giant planets thus have very similar moon systems, including one or more quite large satellites, a number of moons in regular orbits, and at least one in an irregular orbit. The fact that a large number of moons is found around each of the giant planets strongly suggests that these satellite systems formed as a normal part of the process of planet building, and we shall see that the moon systems contain important clues about giant planet formation.

The giant planets are also all now known to have ring systems. The spectacular rings of Saturn, easily visible in a small telescope (Figure 11.2), have been known since the seventeenth century. They were first seen (quite imperfectly) in 1610 by Galilei, who thought that perhaps Saturn was very non-spherical, or possibly even made up of several bodies close to one another. The nature of the Saturnian disk was first understood in 1659 by the Dutch astronomer Christiaan Huygens. In 1675 the French-Italian astronomer Giovanni Domenico Cassini (1625 – 1712) observed that the ring, which to the casual observer seems to be a continuous, almost solid band (like the brim of a hat, although not attached to the planet), actually has a dark gap about two-thirds of the way out, which divides the ring into a broad inner section and a narrower outer section. This division is clearly visible in Figure 11.2. More recently, other astronomers have observed from Earth that the ring actually shows several dark dividing lanes. Close-up pictures from the two Voyager spacecraft, taken as they passed through the Saturn system in 1980 and 1981, reveal that the rings are actually made up of literally thousands of narrow ringlets, each defining a narrow band around Saturn's equator which is relatively full of the ring material, and separated from neighboring ringlets by equally narrow regions with less material. The distribution of material around each of the ringlets varies in time, often in synchronism with other ringlets, giving rise to patterns like spokes in a wheel.

Rings about the other three giants were only discovered recently. Those of Uranus were observed by chance from Earth in 1977, when astronomers observing the occultation (eclipse) of a distant star by Uranus itself saw the starlight briefly dimmed several times both before and after the planetary occultation, as nine thin rings passed in front of the star. Two more rings were discovered by Voyager 2. Unlike the rings of Saturn, those of Uranus are narrow, dark, and widely separated. One faint, broad, and diffuse ring of dark material was discovered around Jupiter in 1979 by the Voyagers. Earth-based occultation measurements and observations from Voyager 2 show that Neptune has four dark rings, one broad and diffuse like that of Jupiter, and three narrow rings similar to those of Uranus. The rings of Jupiter, Uranus, and Neptune differ from those of Saturn in containing far less material, and in being made of dark material (like rock) rather than bright (like ice).

Composition of the giant planets

We next try to understand the general structure of the giant planets. We shall want especially to determine, as far as we can, what their bulk chemical compositions are, whether they are layered in some way, as the Earth is, and how hot they are inside. The giants are very different in size, in average density, and in general chemical composition from the Earth, and we cannot use the Earth as an approximate starting point as we did for the terrestrial planets. Instead, we must consider a larger range of possibilities.

First we need to see what kinds of material might have gone into the construction of the giant planets. We could imagine trying to somehow determine the chemical makeup element by element, but it is not hard to see that this will give us a problem with so many unknown quantities that we have no hope of finding a unique solution. Instead, we need to pick a small number of plausible chemical substances or mixtures that could reasonably be expected to occur in a giant planet, and see if we can determine the relative amounts of these substances. But how will we do this?

The answer is obtained by looking again at the process of planet formation. Recall from Chapter 4 that we think that the gases in substantial parts of the solar nebula were heated to a temperature well above 1000 K and then cooled, condensing a variety of solid materials in a series of steps as the nebular temperature decreased. As the temperature decreased from 1500 K down to 500 K, the main solids that formed were metallic iron, high-temperature silicate minerals such as Mg_2SiO_4, and sulphur compounds, of which the main one is FeS. As the temperature dropped further through the range of 500 K to 200 K, iron oxidized and was incorporated into silicates, and the minerals took on water and carbon to form rocks such as are found in the carbonaceous chondrites. Below 200 K, water ice began to form, and at still lower temperature, ammonia, methane, nitrogen, and carbon monoxide were able to form minerals in which these substances are embedded in a matrix of water (e.g. the hydrate $NH_3 \cdot H_2O$ and such clathrates as $CH_4 \cdot 6H_2O$, $N_2 \cdot 6H_2O$, and $CO \cdot 6H_2O$. The abundant elements H and He, however, were not condensed at any temperature that the solar nebula could reach.

This condensation sequence suggests a very simple division of chemical elements into three major generic substances that we should be able to treat as the main chemical components in an approximate description of the chemical composition of the giant planets. Let us call "rock" a mix of all the elements that condense above 500 K; this would include approximately solar proportions (see Table 2.2) of Mg, Si, Fe, and perhaps S, and enough O to fully oxidize the Mg and the Si. It is a little uncertain how much O we should include to oxidize iron; we certainly find both oxidized and metallic iron in various settings in the solar system. Because we are interested in the outer solar system, we should probably consider the iron to be oxidized. "Rock" would also include all the minor elements that condense at higher temperature, such as Ca, Al, Na, K, etc, and the O that would oxidize them (but these elements do not contribute much to the bulk of any planet).

A second component would be "ice", a mix of all remaining elements that condense above, say, 50 K, including in particular all the C (probably mainly as CH_4), the N (mainly as NH_3, and all the remaining O (mainly as H_2O). There would also be some N_2, CO, and CO_2, and a little Ne and Ar trapped in the icy matrix. The main feature of "ice" is that it probably contains all the O that did not condense with the "rock", together with solar proportions of C and N, and a tiny fraction of the total H.

The third component, which we call simply "gas", would be the gases that do not condense readily anywhere in the proto-solar system, essentially the He and the roughly 99.5% of the H that did not condense in the "ice" in combination with C, N, and O.

Note that we are using the labels "rock", "ice", and "gas" only to denote particular groups of chemical substances. Do not assume that each substance is in the physical state (solid, liquid, gas) suggested by its name! "Ice", for example, might be present as a solid in the interior of Saturn's moon Rhea, as a liquid under the crust of Jupiter's moon Europa (and in the Earth's oceans), or as a gas in the atmosphere of Jupiter.

Now it seems reasonable first approximation to consider constructing planet models in which we vary the proportions only of rock, ice, and gas. In this way we have only three materials for which we need to adjust the relative abundances, rather than dozens, so the problem of guessing a suitable composition for a planet is much easier. Furthermore, because we know that these three components were naturally produced, and frequently separated from one another, in the early solar nebula, we are using physically reasonable rather than arbitrary materials to build our theoretical planets. In fact, we have already effectively used one of these materials, rock, in our efforts to construct a plausible model of the Earth, and we found that the overall composition of the Earth is not too far from that of the rock that we are considering here. So now we examine more generally what kind of planets we can make from various proportions of these three materials.

Solving the general problem of the structure of a planet made from arbitrary proportions of our three basic materials requires considerable further information, about the behaviour of matter at high pressures. In a planet as massive as Jupiter or Saturn, the great weight of overlying layers will compress the material of the deep interior very strongly, much more than occurs inside the Earth. We need to know about the behaviour of our gas, ice, and rock mixtures at extremely high pressure. Since we will find that the outer planets are quite warm inside, we also need to know about the behaviour of these substances at fairly high temperature.

It is easy to get some idea of what an incredibly high pressure can be reached inside Jupiter. The pressure deep inside the planet must be great enough to support the weight of the material above each square meter. This weight, very roughly, is the product of the average mass of a single cubic meter (the mean density, about 1300 kg m^{-3}), times the height of the column of mass (the radius of the planet, about 70,000,000 m), times the planet's gravity (which at the surface is about 2.5 times greater than that of the Earth, about 25 m s^{-2}). The product of these three numbers is roughly 2×10^{12} Pa, or about 2×10^7 atm, more than 10 million times greater than the typical pressure in Jupiter's (or the Earth's) atmosphere. And as we shall see below, the temperature may be as high as 40,000 K inside Jupiter. So we are going to need information about the behaviour of H (or a mixture of H and He), for example, far outside the range of pressure and temperature covered by Figure 2.6.

We may also estimate the internal temperature inside Jupiter now that we have some idea of the pressure range. At the surface, the atmospheric temperature is measured to be about 170 K. It is found that if heat from the interior is carried outward by radiation or conduction, the excess heat that Jupiter radiates cannot be explained unless the temperature rises very rapidly inward, as both these mechanisms are rather ineffective at carrying heat inside Jupiter. But if the temperature rises rapidly inward, the planetary interior will become unstable to convection, as described in Chapter 10. Convection is a very efficient heat transport mechanism, and is entirely capable of carrying the excess heat out to the surface of the planet. Convection limits the rate at which the temperature can rise inward in the planet; if the temperature rises even a little more rapidly than is needed to keep the convection operating, so much heat is carried out that the temperature quickly adjusts to just the value that will continue the convection. Assuming that the planet is convective inside allows us to estimate that the central temperature of Jupiter will be about 4×10^4 K.

It is actually rather difficult to get the required information about the behaviour of gas, ice, and rock at very large pressures, especially when this is needed for a rather large range of temperature as well. Experiments are possible, for example by enclosing a miniature sample of a substance in between tiny diamond anvils which are then gradually tightened, or even by causing a small projectile to crash into a sample at extremely high speed, and studying the effects of the shock wave that travels through the sample. However, static experiments can only reach pressures of the order of 3×10^9 Pa. Impact experiments can get higher, up to 10^{11} Pa, but even this pressure is substantially less than the expected central pressure of Jupiter. The only possible means of studying the highest pressures at present is theoretically. For simple atoms such as H, this can be done reasonably exactly, but for more complex atoms and molecules such as are found in ice and rock, theoretical results are rather uncertain.

Two specific kinds of information are needed about our substances. First, we need to know about important phase changes that may occur as the pressure or temperature rises; recall the phase diagrams of Chapter 2, which describe water and H_2 (Figures 2.5 and 2.6). Secondly, we need to know how the density of each substance changes with increasing pressure and temperature.

For H, the main phase change of interest to us in connection with giant planet interiors is a transition which occurs at about 10^{11} Pa, where solid or liquid H_2 is so strongly compressed that the atoms find it energetically preferable to dissociate not only from each other (the molecules dissolve), but even to lose touch with their electrons, which join a general swarm of electrons spread out fairly uniformly between the H nuclei. This transition converts molecular H_2 into a structure which resembles a solid or liquid metal. The electrons, no longer attached to individual protons, but free to move throughout the material, conduct electricity and heat very well. We call this state **metallic hydrogen** .

A phase diagram for high-pressure, high-temperature H is shown in Figure 11.5. Compare this figure to Figure 2.6; note that Figure 11.5 has logarithmic (powers of ten) scales for T as well as P, to cover the wide range of values needed, and recall that a pressure of one atm in Fig 2.6 corresponds to $\log P = 5$ on Fig. 11.5. Figure 11.5 contains the boundaries between solid and liquid, and between liquid and gas, that are found in Figure 2.6, but these are now confined to a small corner of the figure. In a phase diagram covering a larger range of P and T, the solid-liquid boundary is seen to occur at constant T only for low pressure; once the pressure has risen above about 10^8 Pa, the boundary moves towards higher T. This reflects the fact that with increasing P, a solid is increasingly difficult to melt; the same effect makes the inner core of the Earth solid even though the cooler outer core is liquid. The boundary between solid molecular and metallic H is the horizontal line above 10^{11} Pa, but for a temperature above about 10^3 K the metallic phase is liquid. Two diagonal dashed lines in the figure near $T \sim 10^4$ K show the boundaries where rising temperature causes molecular H_2 to make the transition to atomic H, and then, at a slightly higher T, the H atoms become ionized.

The pair of dotted lines running diagonally through the figure show the approximate pressure and temperature combinations found inside Jupiter and Saturn, on the assumption that the internal temperature variation is determined by the occurrence of convection. Because of the limiting effect of convection on the rate at which T rises with depth, these lines correspond essentially to the highest T that could occur inside the two giants at each P. As noted above, the excess heat output of the two large giants over the input from the Sun leads us to believe that these "adiabats" actually describe the internal temperature of Jupiter and Saturn rather well. Examining the location of these two lines in the phase diagram, it appears that that the two planets have fluid molecular H_2 throughout their outer regions, but this gives way to liquid metallic H at great depth. These planetary adiabats miss by a wide margin the gas-to-liquid transition made by H_2 at low P and T, and shown in Figure 2.6; this indicates that as one descends into a H-rich atmosphere, there is no distinct

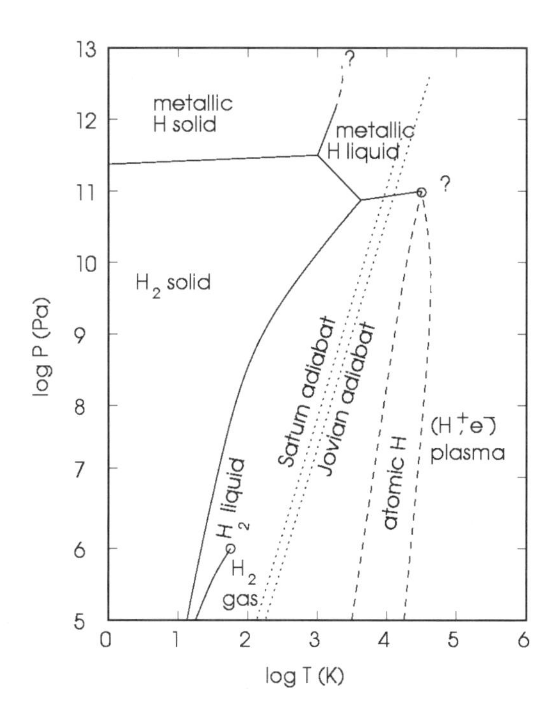

Figure 11.5: Phase diagram of hydrogen, for a much larger range of conditions than are shown in Figure 2.6. The solid and dashed lines show the phase transitions discussed in the text. The dotted lines indicate the range of conditions inside Jupiter and Saturn on the assumption that heat is carried outward by convection. $\log P = 5$ corresponds to 1 atm of pressure. (Adapted from Stevenson 1982, Ann. Rev. Earth Planet Sci., 10, 257.)

boundary where the liquid phase begins. The fluid simply becomes denser and denser as one descends. The atmosphere is "bottomless".

Similar combinations of experiment at (relatively!) low pressure and theory at higher pressure may be used to get some idea of the behaviour of the most water ice and other ices, and of various typical rock minerals. A further complication is that none of the chemical elements is likely to appear alone. H will be mixed with a lot of He (and some Ne, Ar, etc) in the gas component; water ice will be combined with CH_4, NH_3, CO, etc in the ice component, and the rock component will probably contain several minerals including olivine or pyroxene, and metallic Fe. This situation complicates the phase diagrams further.

The other kind of information needed, besides phase diagrams, is the variation of density with pressure for our various components. Such information is obtained from the same kind of combinations of experiment and theory as is used to define the phase diagrams. The way the density varies with increasing pressure for gas, ice and rock is shown in Figure 11.6. The curve for gas shows the variation of density for combinations of pressure and temperature estimated for the interior of Jupiter (see Figure 11.5). The density of the gas increases steadily with increasing pressure, even though at 10^9 Pa the molecules are certainly already in contact (i.e. the gas is really a liquid). At such high pressure, the molecules themselves are seriously deformed by the pressure. The densities of ice and rock are given in this diagram for slightly lower temperature at each pressure than is found in Jupiter; the conditions assumed are similar to those inside Uranus. However, neither the rock nor the ice density is very sensitive to temperature at these pressures, and the relationship shown would not be much different for the conditions inside Jupiter. Like the H-He mix, the ice component increases steadily in density as the applied pressure increases. The more resistant rock only begins to increase significantly in density above 10^{10} Pa.

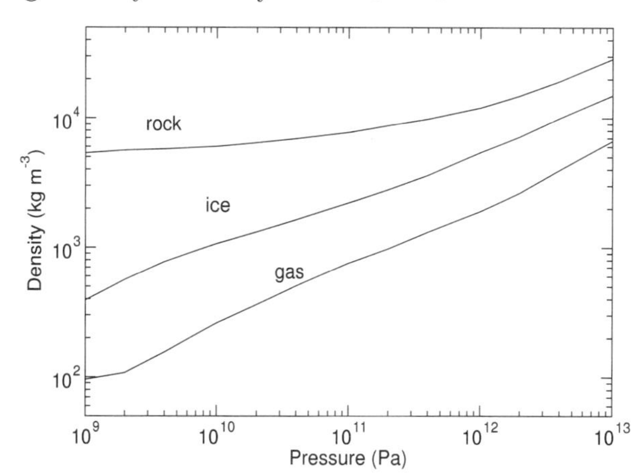

Figure 11.6: The relationship between pressure and density is shown for a solar H-He gas mix, for ice, and for rock. For the gas case, the temperature (not shown) increases with pressure approximately as shown in Figure 11.5 for Jupiter. For the ice and rock mixtures, the assumed T at each P is slightly lower than the curve for Saturn shown in Figure 11.5, and corresponds approximately to conditions inside Uranus. The density values graphed thus include significant effects due to temperature as well as increasing pressure. This is the reason that the density of ice is below 917 kg m^{-3}, its normal terrestrial value, over part of the graph. (Adapted from Stevenson 1982, Ann. Rev. Earth Planet Sci., 10, 257.)

Planetary models

Constructing models of the interiors of giant planets is actually easier than obtaining the information needed about the behaviour of the materials that go into the planets. We must solve a set of equations like those used in getting models of the terrestrial planets. These equations describe how the attraction of gravity at each level varies, depending on the mass inside that level; how the pressure increases, due to the weight of overlying layers; how the temperature varies, due to the effect of convection which carries heat out; and of course, the way in which the density of the assumed material increases with increasing pressure and temperature.

The simplest situation for which to construct models is for material at $T = 0$ K. Figure 11.7 shows how the radius of the resulting models depend on the assumed mass of the planet for planets made of pure gas, pure ice, and pure rock. For a planet made of H or an H-He mixture, the radius of the planet increases rapidly with mass up to about 300 Earth masses, and then stops increasing, as the effect of the large mass acting to compress the gas becomes really important. For larger masses, the size actually starts to decline with increasing mass; this behaviour is characteristic of white dwarf stars, which have the unexpected behaviour that the larger the mass of the star, the smaller it is. Cold planets of ice also increase in size rapidly at first and then more slowly, as increasing mass compresses the material strongly. Rock planets, more resistant to compression, increase steadily in size with increasing mass throughout the mass range shown.

Notice that the low density of H relative to other substances leads to a gas planet being *much larger* at any particular mass than a planet of rock or ice. Each of the four giant planets is plotted at the appropriate point for its mass and size (points noted as J, S, U, and N), and it is clear that if Jupiter and Saturn can be treated approximately as cold planets, they must have compositions dominated by H and He. Even a pure ice planet is far more compressed than either of these planets. On the other hand, Uranus and Neptune could plausibly be modeled as planets made largely of ice (or ice and rock), with only a modest external layer of gas.

Models with more realistic temperatures have also been computed, again for pure gas, ice, and rock. Using the pressure-density relationship of Figure 11.6, one obtains the models shown with dashed lines in Figure 11.7. The size of the rock models is hardly increased at all by the effect of temperature. The ice models are increased in size by a few percent. The gas models, however, are drastically changed, at least for low mass, where the "fluffiness" of H_2 gas makes a warm model much larger than a cold one of the same mass. As the mass of the gas model increases, this effect diminishes as the increasing gravity of the planet compresses the hydrogen. At a mass of 300 Earth masses, appropriate

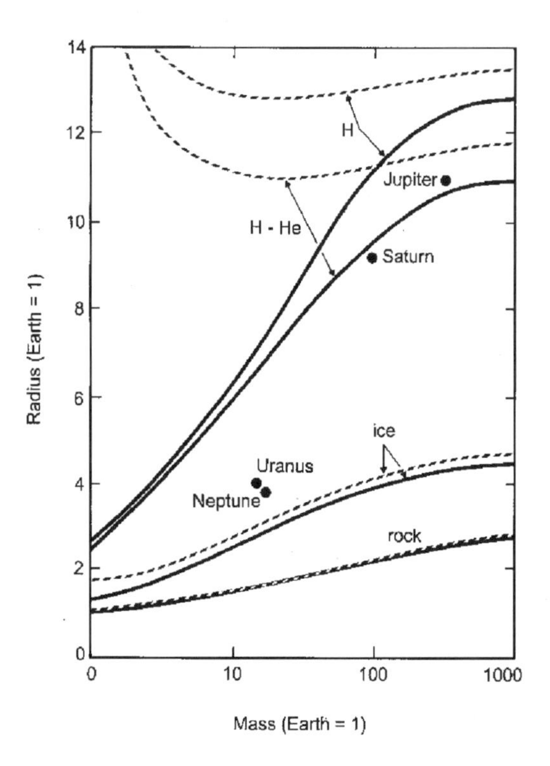

Figure 11.7: The relationship between mass and radius for model planets. The solid lines describe planets at $T = 0$, while the dashed lines correspond to models calculated with the density-pressure relationships of Figure 11.6. The positions of the gas giants in this diagram are indicated by their names. Notice that the mass scale is really logarithmic, while the radius scale is linear. (Adapted from Stevenson 1982, Ann. Rev. Earth Planet Sci., 10, 257.)

to Jupiter, the radius increase caused by finite temperature is only about 10%. It is still clear that among the substances we have chosen to discuss, Jupiter and Saturn must be composed primarily of gas. The fact that both lie a little way below the line for "warm" models of the gas (H-He) mixture means that neither planet can be pure H-He; each must have a modest amount of denser material (some combination of ice and rock) somewhere inside.

Exercise: Why is the difference between "warm" and "cold" models *not* an important distinction for terrestrial planets?

The next step in modeling is to consider layered models, in which for example a shell of gas surrounds a core of rock and ice. In this case the mass of the rock and ice in the core must be determined. One may also choose to vary the ratio of He to H in the gas envelope, to try to determine this quantity directly rather than assuming it. With more free parameters, these models cannot be easily shown in a single graph like Figure 11.7. However, such models begin to approach the level of complexity needed to agree with all the constraints available from observation (mass, radius, the degree of flattening of the planetary shape produced by the rapid planetary rotation, and the external gravity field as measured by space probe fly-bys). All four giant planets have been described by such layered models. Remarkably, all four are found to have dense cores of rock or ice with masses of the order of 10 to 20 Earth masses. They vary in mass and size primarily in the mass and extent of their H-He envelopes, which range from about 20% of the total mass for Uranus and Neptune up to 80% for Saturn and 95% for Jupiter. Both Jupiter and Saturn have molecular H_2 in their outer layers and metallic H inside that, but in Jupiter the metallic H makes up a much larger fraction of the H-rich envelope than in Saturn. In Uranus and Neptune, with less massive gas envelopes and smaller total masses (and therefore internal pressures), H is everywhere molecular H_2.

It is interesting to look at these models more closely. The models for Jupiter all agree on the general structure of the largest planet, although they vary significantly concerning the details. An overview of a typical Jupiter model is shown in Figure 11.8. With it, we may imagine a guided tour of this strange world.... We enter Jupiter from above the atmosphere, through a gas of predominantly H and He in which both density and temperature rise rapidly with depth. Where the pressure is comparable to that at ground level in the Earth's atmosphere, we encounter the first cloud deck, the level at which rising and cooling convection currents reach a low enough temperature for NH_3 to freeze out as ice crystals. Depending on where we enter the atmosphere, the clouds may be yellow, tan, reddish, or white. As we go deeper into the atmosphere, we come to a second cloud deck of ammonium hydrosulphide (NH_4SH) ice, and then a third cloud deck, of water ice. As we continue inwards, the pressure, density, and temperature all rise. By the time we are 700 km below the highest clouds (0.1% of the radius of Jupiter), the temperature has risen to 2000 K. No gas-liquid interface is encountered. However, the H/He-rich atmosphere becomes steadily denser, and at the level where $T \approx 3000$ K and $\rho \approx 100$ kg m^{-1} the fluid in which we are descending resembles a liquid more than a gas. Here the molecules touch one another, and compression of the fluid is much more difficult than it was high in the planet's atmosphere. The fluid is slowly convecting, carrying heat towards the surface.

Slightly below $0.8R_J$, about 140,000 km down from the clouds, we reach a point where $\rho \approx 1000$ kg m^{-1} and $T \approx 10^4$ K. At this level the pressure and temperature are high enough to **dissociate** H_2 molecules into single (atomic) H atoms. This is the first major transition zone; the density rises significantly, though perhaps not abruptly. We continue downward with little change except for steadily rising temperature, pressure, and density, until we reach a depth of about 54,000 km ($0.2R_J$ from the centre) where the surface of the rock core is finally encountered. The temperature here is about 20,000 K. The mass of the rocky core is somewhat uncertain, and it is not know how much ice it includes, but it very likely contains between 10 and 30 $M_\oplus$ (Earth masses). Note that even if we separated all the chemical elements heavier than He out of the H/He envelope (and the presence of CH_4, NH_3, etc in the atmosphere shows that "ices" at least are partly dissolved in the gas envelope), we would be able to make a core of rock and ice of at most about 5 $M_\oplus$. Jupiter clearly has *excess* rock over a purely solar chemical composition. However, only about 5% of the planet resembles a terrestrial planet; the other 95% is in the huge H/He atmosphere.

The structure of Saturn is similar to that of Jupiter, except that observations suggest that the H/He gas mixture has only about one He atom for every 20 H atoms instead of the usual (solar) ratio of about 1 in 10, which is found in Jupiter's atmosphere. We will return to this observation below. As we descend into the atmosphere of Saturn for a tour, we encounter the same series of cloud decks as on Jupiter: a first layer (pale yellow in colour) of ammonia ice crystals, a second of ammonium hydrosulphide ice, and a third of water ice crystals. As we descend into the planet, the density, pressure, and temperature rise steadily. As in the atmosphere of Jupiter, the temperature increase with depth is rapid enough to cause convection, which carries the minor chemical species NH_3, etc to the altitude where the temperature is low enough for the molecules to condense as ice crystals and fall back down. Again as we descend, no abrupt change of phase is encountered; there is no sea below the atmosphere. The atmosphere into which we descend simply becomes more and more dense (and hot). Where the density reaches 50 – 100 kg m^{-3}, the H_2 molecules are in nearly continuous contact with one another, and the fluid makes a seamless transition to a liquid state. At about $0.5R_J$ from the centre, the molecular liquid is transformed by increasing pressure and temperature into an ionic gas, as the molecules of H_2 dissociate into free protons immersed in a swarm of detached electrons. It is thought that in this region He condenses into "raindrops" which fall through the H gas. It is this separation and settling of He which is thought to have gradually depleted the stock of He in the outer envelope of Saturn. At about $0.25R_S$ from the centre, where the temperature is about 14,000 K, we finally reach the predominantly rock core

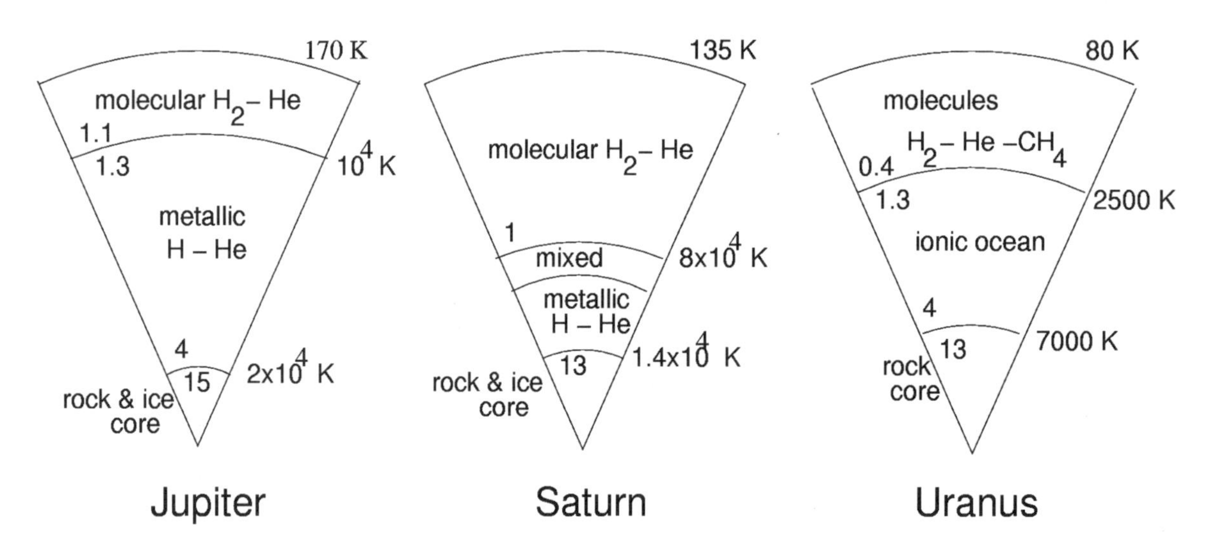

Figure 11.8: Sketches of the interior structure of Jupiter, Saturn, and Uranus. Boundaries between regions are shown at the appropriate fraction of the radius of each planet from the centre; recall that the planets actually have different sizes! Numbers adjacent to boundaries near the left side of each figure are approximate densities, in gm cm^{-3}; those near the right side are approximate temperatures at the boundaries. (Adapted from Stevenson 1982, Ann. Rev. Earth Planet Sci., 10, 257.)

of the planet. As in Jupiter, the total mass of this core is uncertain, but it is believed to be about 20 $M_\oplus$, far more than the 1 – 2 $M_\oplus$ that could be obtained by separating all the heavy elements from a mix of Saturn's mass and solar chemistry.

Uranus and Neptune are similar to one another. They differ from Jupiter and Saturn primarily in having rock cores of much greater relative importance. The rock core of each planet is probably surrounded by an ocean of liquid ice, above which is found the gas atmosphere. The blue colour of these two atmospheres are due to the gaseous methane mixed in with the dominant H and He molecules; this gas strongly absorbs red sunlight, leaving mainly bluish light to be reflected back to the outside observer. As we descend into the atmosphere of one of these planets, (Uranus, say), we first encounter the cloud deck of methane (which cannot freeze out to make clouds anywhere in the atmospheres of Jupiter or Saturn because the temperature is too high at all altitudes). The other cloud decks found in the two largest giant planets occur in the same order below this first cloud layer. Again we descend through an atmosphere which for thousands of kilometers is bottomless, in which temperature and density steadily rise. At about $0.7R_U$ from the centre, where $T \approx 2500$ K, we encounter the surface of an immense ionic ocean of $H_3O^+OH^-$ (ionized water) with dissolved NH_3. The surface of this ocean is marked, not by a gas to liquid transition, but by the abrupt change of chemical composition, and by a change of density from about 400 to 1300 kg m^{-3}. The floor of this ocean, which is some 10,000 km deep, occurs at about $0.3R_U$, where $T \approx 7000$ K. This is the beginning of the rock core of the planet, an object of a few Earth masses. It is possible that the core is differentiated into a silicate mantle and an iron core as in the interior of the Earth.

The solar nebula and the origin of the giants

We now turn to the problem of understanding the formation of the giant planets. It is generally believed that formation of these planets took place during the period when the Sun was forming, out of the material that was orbiting the Sun in the solar nebula. Most of the matter that at one time was in the solar nebula ended up in the Sun, of course. The planets formed from some of the matter that did not, as discussed in Chapter 4.

The material that was to become the Sun and the solar system separated from the parent giant molecular cloud by one or more episodes of gravitational collapse. Some of this collapsing gas, with its embedded dust, fell more or less straight in to the centre of the shrinking cloud fragment, and quickly became part of the forming Sun at the centre. However, most of the gas was rotating too rapidly about the centre of the cloud fragment to fall directly into the centre. Instead, this gas and dust settled into a thick disk-shaped cloud, tens of AU in radius, around the growing central Sun. This disk was the solar nebula.

The disk of gas around the Sun was fairly **turbulent**:

on a large scale, the gas was moving in roughly circular orbit around the Sun, but various individual blobs of gas had somewhat eccentric motions above and below the average plane of the nebula, and in and out. This turbulent, disorderly state meant that individual gas blobs collided with one another frequently. The collisions tended to alter the motion of a gas blob to be more like the motions of other blobs at the same distance from the Sun, and thus these collisions tended to diminish the turbulence by encouraging all the gas to orbit in smooth circular orbits. However, a considerable degree of turbulence was maintained in the disk by blobs and cloud fragments falling into the solar nebula from the parent giant molecular cloud as the Sun developed.

The solar nebula was much warmer than the giant molecular cloud from which the cloud fragments collapsed. This was mainly due to the energy released by fresh gas blobs falling into the nebula, and by the friction of cloud fragments colliding with one another. As the central Sun became more massive and luminous, its radiation also heated the nebula. There is evidence from the meteorites (remember the Ca-Al rich white inclusions in some carbonaceous chondrites?) that some parts of the nebula reached temperatures of 2000 K or so. As the Sun formed, the temperature in the nebula varied from place to place (and also with time, of course), from a maximum of perhaps 2000 K near the Sun, diminishing to perhaps 50 K at the outer edge of the nebula. In the inner parts of the nebula, rock first vaporized and then (as the nebula cooled) condensed as dust grains, while both ice and gas remained gaseous until the process of planet formation was finished. In contrast, in the outer part of the nebula, the generally lower temperature allowed both rock and ice to condense into solid grains.

The turbulence of the nebula insured that tiny grains of condensed solids collided frequently with one another. They must have often stuck together. The size of typical grains grew more or less steadily because of these collisions, gradually producing larger and larger objects. Eventually, we imagine that the solid bodies would have ranged in size from smaller than a grain of salt to larger than an iceberg.

Now we can imagine two rather different ways in which the giant planets could have formed from this rotating, turbulent solar nebula and the many orbiting solid objects it contained. One possibility is that the growth of solid bodies by collisions could have gone on until planetesimals of rock and ice several times more massive than the Earth were formed in the region of 5 to 30 AU from the proto-Sun. Once the largest planetesimals became this large, they would have such powerful gravitational attraction form nearby material that they would begin to accrete *uncondensed* H- and He-rich gas, eventually growing to the mass of the present giant planets. A second possibility is that within the solar nebula, conditions allowed large cloud fragments to collapse directly due to their internal gravitational self-attraction. That is, one might have had within the solar nebula the same kind of gravitational fragmentation and collapse that occurred on a large scale in the giant molecular cloud from which the Sun formed.

The creation of the giant planets by direct gravitational collapse now seems much less likely than the formation first of cores of rock and ice by collisions, followed by sweeping up of gas envelopes from the nebula. The main problems with the direct collapse theory are the following. First, the direct gravitational collapse hypothesis does not offer any obvious reason for the existence of rock (and ice?) cores in the giants; if these planets formed by direct collapse, heavy elements would have tended to remain dissolved in the hot convecting gaseous envelope rather than settling to the centre. Furthermore, the direct collapse theory offers no explanation for the fact that the four giant planets are so different in *total* mass but nevertheless all have similar *core* masses. A related difficulty is that the giants all have excess rock and ice compared to gas, with a *larger* excess of rock in the outer giants. This requires either extraordinary accretion of solids after the collapse phase, or the loss of much of the gas afterwards, with the fractional gain of solids, or the loss of gas, *increasing* towards the outer edge of the solar system. The collapse theory does not provide any explanation for an increasing departure from solar chemistry farther out in the solar system.

Thus, we consider the idea that in the outer solar system, solid planetary cores formed by collisions, and that once they reached some critical size they began to rapidly sweep up the gas and dust around them. This would have increased their gravitational attraction, increasing their sweeping efficiency, until each planet effectively cleared out a large band around its orbit. Computations simulating this process indicate that a core mass of the order of 10 $M_\oplus$, about the size of the cores actually present in the giant planets, would be the mass at which rapid accretion of nebular gases would begin to occur. This process *does* account for the similar core masses in all four giants. Furthermore, since the cores form before gas accretion begins, they are naturally segregated in the planetary centres. However, it is not yet clear what limited the masses to which each giant planet grew. Perhaps accretion of nebular gas came to a halt as the remaining gas was ejected from the solar system by a T Tauri-like stellar wind. Or perhaps the masses of the giants are limited by the total mass of gas in rings swept by each core in the outer solar system at the time when the cores reach a mass large enough to begin "vacuuming up" the nebular gas. In any case, the decrease in density in the nebula with increasing distance for the Sun makes it likely that the core of the inner giants probably accumulated more quickly than those of Uranus and Neptune, and in a denser region of the solar nebula, so that the much larger gas envelope masses of Jupiter and Saturn compared to the two outer giants seems natural. One remaining puzzle, if the outer planets formed from massive "rocky" cores, is why the cores were so much more massive in the outer solar system than in the inner, where the most massive planets only reach 1 $M_{\oplus}$.

Evolution of the giant planets

We have seen that the giant planets probably originated from rocky proto-planetary cores that grew to masses of roughly 10 $M_{\oplus}$ through successive collisions of small solid bodies in the outer solar nebula. Let's look now in more detail at how these cores accreted their massive envelopes, and how the structure of these developing planets changed with time.

Early in the process of planet formation, the solar nebula was swarming with small rocky planetesimals. As these bodies collided with one another and coalesced, the dimensions of the largest objects grew as their number declined. The largest bodies gradually increased in size and mass, first to asteroidal dimensions, then to the sizes of terrestrial planets, and finally, in the outer solar system, to masses of about 10 $M_{\oplus}$. As these largest rocky bodies were growing in the outer solar system, they were also beginning to sweep up and retain gaseous atmospheres from the gas of the solar nebula. Because the rocky cores were moving within the nebula, there was no sharp outer limit to their growing atmospheres. Instead, these atmospheres merged smoothly with the nebula. The outer limit of the atmosphere of one of these large proto-planets simply occurred at a distance from the planet at which the gas ceased to be gravitationally attached to the rocky core, and was instead controlled by the tidal attraction of the growing Sun. In effect, the Sun's gravity forced gas at large distances from the proto-planet to orbit the Sun at a different speed than the proto-planet, rather than remaining close to the planetary core. However, at such large distances from the Sun (between 5 and 50 AU), the size of the region gravitationally controlled by the planetary core was enormous, and so the radius of the thin planetary atmosphere, and the effective size of the growing planet, was hundreds of times larger than the present radius of Jupiter.

As the largest cores grew in mass, the amount of gas that a core could attract and hold also grew steadily. The gas atmosphere grew hotter as it grew in mass, due to the gravitational energy released as material was drawn steadily closer to the growing core. An approximate equilibrium was established, with the gas pressure in the atmosphere at each level (a pressure produced by the compression and heating of the gas) having about the right value to support the weight of overlying gas layers. As more and more gas became attached to the atmosphere inside the growing sphere of influence of the core (which continued to grow in mass by collisions), gravitational compaction of the atmosphere steadily raised its density and temperature so that the pressure balance continued to be maintained.

However, once the internal temperature of the gas atmosphere rose to about 2500 K, at a time when a few Earth masses of gas had been accreted, the H_2 molecules deep in the atmosphere began to *dissociate* into H atoms. This process absorbed a lot of heat, and prevented the temperature of the gas from rising significantly further until the H_2 was mostly dissociated. This in turn upset the pressure balance supporting the huge H/He atmosphere, and this atmosphere quickly shrank to a much more compact state. The shrinkage in turn reduced the pressure holding away the surrounding nebular gas, and much of the nebular gas flowed into the gravitational sphere of influence of the protoplanet. As fresh gas filled the planet's sphere of influence, the total planetary mass increased rapidly, further enhancing the ability of the protoplanet to attract still more nebular gas. The result of this collapse was the rapid accretion of anywhere from about 1 $M_{\oplus}$ (on Uranus and Neptune) to tens or hundreds of Earth masses (Jupiter and Saturn) of atmospheric gas. It is this stage of the accretion process that can be thought of as a kind of "vacuuming up" of the available nebular gas by the rapidly growing planet. At the end of this process, all of the giant planets had reached roughly their present masses.

At this point, the giant planets were in other ways rather different from their present structures. All four giants were considerably hotter inside than they are today, due to the large amount of gravitational energy released by the accretion of the massive gas atmospheres. As a result, they were several times larger in diameter than they are today, and radiated far more infrared energy than now. Jupiter, the most extreme case, probably radiated about ten million times more energy per second than at present; its initial luminosity was about 1% of the Sun's luminosity!

In the 4.5×10^9 years since they were formed, the masses of the giant planets have remained essentially constant. Their structures, rocky cores surrounded by huge gaseous atmospheres, have not changed qualitatively. However, each planet has reached a sufficiently compact state that as heat leaks out from the interior, it is not *not* replenished by further shrinking and release of gravitational energy. Instead, the heat flowing out from the interior and radiating away from the surface simply lowers the internal temperature of the planet. As each giant cools, it does shrink slightly, and as the internal heat energy supply decreases, the intrinsic luminosity (the excess of the planet's luminosity over the input of absorbed solar radiation) slowly decreases also.

When the cooling history of each of the outer planets is calculated, it is found that Jupiter, Uranus, and Neptune all have about the expected radii and luminosities. This fact supplies a powerful confirmation of our ideas about the internal structures of these planets, and our picture of how they have evolved during the 4.5×10^9 age of the solar system.

However, Saturn is about twice as luminous as it is expected to be. It appears that a second important energy source is present inside the planet in addition to the energy available as internal heat released by the formation and subsequent contraction of the planet. This extra energy is probably released by the separation and settling of the He relative to the dominant H of the gas envelope. What we think happens is that as the temperature in the outer layers of metallic H in Saturn drops below about 10^4 K, He becomes partly *immiscible* in (unable to remain dissolved in) the H. Droplets of He form, and since they are denser than the surrounding fluid H, they fall towards the centre of the planet as a kind of exotic hot rain. This separation is thought to release enough energy to account for the part of Saturn's current infrared radiation that is not due simply to solar heating and global cooling of the hot planet. The separation of He from H in the deep interior of the Saturn gradually leads to a general depletion of He throughout the outer envelope, and is probably responsible for the observation (see Sec. 10.2) of a deficiency of He in Saturn's atmosphere compared to the ratio found in the Sun and in the other giant planets.

The interesting fact that Uranus seems not to be radiating any more energy than it absorbs from the Sun each second, while the more distant and quite similar planet Neptune is still losing internal energy, is simply due to the larger input of solar heat into Uranus compared to Neptune. The solar heat input now holds the surface temperature of Uranus approximately constant at the observed 57 K. As the interior continues to cool, the radiating surface can no longer cool at the same pace, and so the efficiency of internal heat transport is greatly reduced, leading to a large decrease in the transport of internal heat to the surface. As a result, internal heat loss now makes up only a small fraction of the total radiation from Uranus.

Exercise: Could a giant planet with a mass of, say, 20 Earth masses have a density as large as that of the Earth? If so, how would such a planet have to differ from the structure of Uranus and Neptune?

11.3 Moons of the giant planets

Observations and exploration

The first moons discovered around a giant planet were the four largest moons of Jupiter, found by Galilei in 1609 with his small telescope (Chapter 1), and easily visible through ordinary binoculars. These "Galilean" moons, named Io, Europa, Ganymede, and Callisto after lovers or companions of Jupiter in classical mythology, are all comparable to the Earth's Moon, with radii ranging from 1560 to 2630 km (similar to the Moon's radius of 1740 km). Saturn has one moon of this size, Titan, found by Christiaan Huygens in 1655. The two largest moons of Uranus, Titania and Oberon, were first seen in 1789 by the planet's discoverer, William Herschel. Neptune also has one large moon, Triton, found by English astronomer William Lassell in 1846, not long after the discovery of the planet itself. These large moons are rather similar in many ways to the terrestrial planets; the largest, Ganymede and Titan, have larger diameters than Mercury, although they are only about half as massive.

During the past two centuries, many somewhat smaller moons having radii of 150 – 750 km were discovered by Earth-based astronomers, and at the start of the 1970's the number of known satellites of the giant planets was over 20 (Table A.3). This number was more than doubled with the discovery between 1979 and 1989 by the Voyager spacecraft of more than two dozen smaller moons, bodies with radii of the order of 50 km or less. It has gradually become clear that each of the giant planets has a *system* of moons, anywhere from eight to 18 or more moons orbiting the main planet. An important and striking feature of these moon systems is that in general the nearer and larger moons travel in nearly circular, concentric orbits around the equator of their planet. The great regularity of the orbits of the moons provides us with an important clue to their origins, as we shall see below.

Although numerous moons were discovered using Earth-based telescopes, little more could be learned about them in this way. The largest moons of Jupiter are not much more than a second of arc across as seen from the Earth, about the same as the typical blurring of images by the Earth's atmosphere. Even using special techniques developed in the past decade to reduce the blurring effect of the atmosphere, or using the

Hubble Space Telescope, one can at best make out the largest features on the nearest large moons. Because detailed images of even the largest and nearest moons of the giants could not be obtained from the ground, even the diameters of these moons were very poorly known before the first space missions to the outer planets. Nothing at all was known about surface features.

The two Voyagers and the Galileo space probe completely changed the situation. These spacecraft carried instruments for several kinds of measurements. Each carried a camera, and we now have an enormous collect of spectacular, detailed images of the surfaces of many of the moons of the giants. Each was also equipped with one or more spectrographs which were used to study both the chemistry of the atmospheres of the planets themselves, and the surfaces of the moons. Several instruments in each probe provide information about the particles and magnetic fields in interplanetary space and in the vicinity of the planets. Finally, the radio signals sent back to Earth by these probes are also studied to provide information about the precise positions and movements of the spacecraft as they pass close to the planets and the largest moons.

Approximate masses of a few of the larger moons had been determined before the era of space exploration by careful study of the apparent motions of various moons about their planets. The orbit of each moon is influenced (perturbed) somewhat by the gravitational pull of the largest nearby moons, and observation of this effect allows one to deduce the masses of the larger moons. More precise masses for a number of the moons were obtained from the Voyagers and Galileo by careful study of the changes in frequency (the Doppler shift) of the radio transmissions from the spacecraft as it passed close to a moon. These frequency changes enabled mission scientists to deduce the acceleration of the spacecraft by the gravitational pull of the moon, from which the moon's mass could be determined. In all, the Voyagers provided new mass measurements for 17 of the moons.

Another extremely important kind of information provided by the Voyagers and Galileo was accurate measurements of the diameters of all but the smallest moons, and determinations of the shapes of some of the smaller irregular objects. (Most of the smallest moons appeared to the Voyagers only as points of light even at closest approach, making accurate size measurements impossible.) The diameters that were determined allowed accurate determinations of the mean densities for about 20 of the larger moons. The mean density, of course, provides us with a very powerful clue to the bulk chemical composition of the object. It is found that the two inner Galilean moons of Jupiter, Io and Europa, both have densities of more than 3000 kg m^{-3}, similar to the density of rock (about 3500 kg m^{-3}). All the other large satellites have densities lying between 2100 and 1000 kg m^{-3}, low enough that these objects cannot be made solely of rock, but must have at least half of their mass made up of ice (density about 920 kg m^{-3}). Most of the large moons apparently are composed of 60 or 70% ice by mass. An important problem, and one which remains unsolved to a considerable extent, is to determine which of these large moons have differentiated into a structure having a rock core and an ice mantle, and which remain more or less uniformly mixed.

Because the moons of the giant planets are solid objects like the terrestrial planets, and generally lack significant atmospheres (although Saturn's largest moon, Titan, has a dense N_2-rich atmosphere, and Neptune's Triton has very tenuous atmosphere), the Voyagers and Galileo have returned a wealth of information about the surfaces of these bodies in the form of thousands of detailed photographs. The large moons were revealed to be an astonishingly diverse group of objects, many of which have histories comparable in complexity to the history of Mercury or the Earth's Moon. Most of the moons have surfaces which are more or less heavily cratered, but two (Io and Europa) are essentially totally free of cratering. Several other moons, in contrast, have a largest crater not a great deal smaller than the moon itself, while still others have few craters with diameters of more than about 50 km. Some moons have huge rift valleys, fractures, scarps, or flows. Two (Io and Triton) have active volcanos. A number of kinds of terrain are unfamiliar and do not yet have generally accepted explanations.

Jupiter's moons

Jupiter has four distinct systems of moons. Close to the planet, between 1.8 and 3.1 Jupiter radii (R_J) and within the faint planetary rings, are four tiny satellites. All travel in direct, nearly circular orbits close to Jupiter's equatorial plane. The innermost two are even within the planet's Roche limit, so they must have some internal strength in order not to be disrupted by tides.

A second system is composed of the four large moons discovered by Galileo Galilei. These also move in nearly (but not exactly) circular orbits within one degree of the planet's equatorial plane, between $5.9R_J$ and $26R_J$ from Jupiter's centre. The orbital periods (recall that the period is the time taken for one revolution around the central planet) of the inner three moons show a remarkable kind of resonance: each time Ganymede makes one complete circuit around Jupiter, Europa makes almost exactly two trips, and Io makes four. The motions are synchronized in such a way that each time Io passes Europa (which happens once for each complete orbit of Europa), Io is at the point in its (slightly elliptical) orbit closest to Jupiter, while Europa is at the point in its orbit farthest from the planet. The moons thus jostle each other in a regular way, which is what maintains the slight eccentricity of the orbits.

The two outer systems of small moons include four at about $160R_J$ in rather eccentric orbits, inclined to Jupiter's equator by nearly 30°, and four in seriously eccentric *retrograde* orbits at around $300R_J$ – these outermost moons orbit the planet in the opposite sense from the inner moons and the planet's own rotation.

Little is known about the physical natures of the small moons. The sizes of the four inner moons are known – all are far from round, with dimensions in the range of about 10 to 120 km – but even this information is quite uncertain for the outer moons. The small moons are all dark and reddish in colour. Distant images from the Galileo orbiter show no surface features on any of the inner moons except for craters.

The four Galilean moons are much more varied and clearly have had complex histories. From the accurate radii derived from probe images, and masses determined from the gravitational deflection of the Voyagers and the Galileo probe by the individual moons, we now have very accurate mean densities for all four moons. Io, with a density of about 3500 kg m^{-3}, must be composed essentially of rocky material, probably similar in composition to the rock component we discussed in connection with the planets themselves; it may have a significant iron core as well. Europa has a density of about 3000 kg m^{-3}, and is thus primarily composed of rock and perhaps some iron, but ice probably makes up roughly 20% of the total mass of the moon. The other two moons have densities a little below 2000 kg m^{-3}, and probably are made up of about 40% rock and 60% ice. The density of the four moons falls systematically with distance from Jupiter.

From careful examination of the gravitational deflections of orbiters during close passes by a moon, it is also possible to get some information about the degree to which matter is concentrated towards the centre of a moon. This information helps to decide whether a moon is differentiated, with a core-mantle structure, or is homogeneous, with its materials uniformly mixed. (Note that some central condensation will occur even in a large homogeneous moon because of compression of matter near the centre by the weight of overlying layers.) Such data definitely indicate that Io, Europa, and Ganymede are differentiated. It is not yet completely clear if Callisto is "somewhat" differentiated or still homogeneous: although the bulk composition of Callisto is similar to that of Ganymede, Callisto clearly does *not* show the same degree of concentration of high-density matter to the centre that the larger moon exhibits.

Models of the three differentiated moons suggest that Io probably has a core of iron and iron sulphide (Fe-FeS) extending from the centre out to somewhere between $0.35R_I$ to $0.60R_I$ (R_I is the radius of Io), surrounded by a mantle of silicate rock extending to the surface. Europa appears to have a crust of water ice between 80 and 200 km thick surrounding a silicate rock mantle. It probably has an Fe-FeS core extending out from the centre to somewhere between $0.30R_E$ and $0.50R_E$. Ganymede, which has a lower mean density than the two inner Galilean moons, probably has a layer of water ice about 800 km thick over a rocky silicate mantle. It seems likely that this mantle overlies an Fe-FeS core having a radius of between $0.15R_G$ and $0.50R_G$. The presence of magnetic fields in Io and Ganymede support the view that these moons have metallic cores.

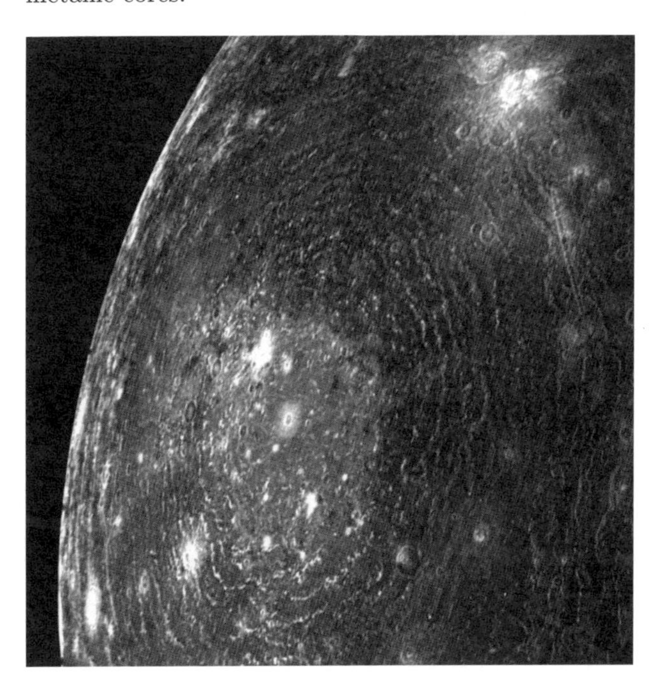

Figure 11.9: This image of Callisto acquired by the Voyager 1 space probe shows the huge impact basin Valhalla. This crater is surrounded by numerous rings that are mainly visible due to colour variations; they have very little vertical relief. This basin resembles the Orientale basin on the Moon, or Caloris on Mercury. The only other visible features are smaller craters. (Courtesy of NASA.)

The surfaces of these four moons are highly distinctive. Callisto, the outermost Galilean moon, and the least differentiated, is a heavily cratered body which shows no clear signs of any past volcanic or tectonic activity. The largest crater on the moon is about 600 km in diameter, about 1/8th of Callisto's diameter, and is surrounded by concentric rings, rather like the Orientale Basin on the Moon (Figure 11.9). Many of Callisto's craters are rather flat, as though the surface is not able to support high relief. This fact suggests that the surface layers may contain large amounts of easily melted water ice, consistent with a bulk composition of more than half water deduced from the mean density, and with spectra of reflected sunlight. Much of the surface is rather dark, so that surface water ice must be mixed to a considerable extent with some other material. The youngest craters are quite light in colour, which suggests that these impacts have excavated relatively clean ice from below the surface. Perhaps a thin surface layer was actually melted early in Callisto's history, allowing rocky material to settle below the surface, and subsequently contaminated with more rocky material by collisions with small asteroids and comets. A puzzling feature of the crater record on Callisto is that there are not as many small craters as one would expect from the number of large craters seen; instead, some smooth, dark material blankets the surface in between craters (Figure 11.10).

Figure 11.11: A full disk image of Ganymede taken by the Galileo orbiter during its first close encounter with the moon in 1996. Notice the division of the surface into two strongly contrasting terrain types, a dark terrain type which on close inspection is found to be heavily cratered, and a light-coloured surface which is observed to be much less heavily cratered but covered with a network of grooves and furrows. (Courtesy of NASA.)

Ganymede is similar in size and overall composition to Callisto, but unlike Callisto, the rocky and metallic materials have settled to the centre beneath the ices, leading to a core-mantle structure. The surface, which in some parts is heavily cratered like that of Callisto, also shows large regions with relatively light cratering that are intensely furrowed or grooved. In spite of similar size and bulk composition, the two moons have clearly had remarkably different histories. The surface of Ganymede, in fact, still presents us with serious difficulties in understanding how the features we see were created. There are two major terrain types present on Ganymede (Figure 11.11). Old regions of the moon, about 40% of the total area, are quite dark in colour, and are heavily cratered. No other significant features are seen in these dark regions except for some vague furrows, probably remains of early giant impacts. The density of craters in these dark regions makes it clear that the crust here is roughly as old as that of Callisto. In contrast, the remainder of the crust is much less heavily cratered, and thus must have been remade long after the early era of bombardment. This younger surface displays terrain covered with a complex network of grooves or furrows (Figure 11.10). A major question has been to guess whether these grooves were produced by cryovolcanism (i.e. lava flows of liquid water rather than liquid silicate rock) or by tectonism (i.e. stretching and distorting of the surface by tidal or other stresses). Since almost no direct evidence of cryovolcanism (volcanic mounts or vents, flow fronts) are found, it seems clear now that most of the features on the grooved terrain were produced by repeated fracturing and stretching of the crust, probably as a result of the effects of large tides at some point in Ganymede's history.

The smallest Galilean moon, Europa, also presents a unique surface. From a distance, the moon's surface is extremely flat (relief of only hundreds of meters) and shows a global system of dark lines rather like a string wound around a ball (Figure 11.12). Only a few craters are visible, and it is clear that the present surface is very much younger than the moon as a whole. The models of interior structure indicate that although the moon contains only a small fraction of ice, that material has floated to the surface and overlies the much larger rocky and metallic interior. This is confirmed by strong evidence for the present of water ice in the spectrum of sunlight reflected from the surface. The surface of Europa thus is covered with a layer of H_2O approximately $1 - 200$ km deep. In recent years it has begun to appear likely that this layer may actually be mostly liquid: Europa may have a global ocean covered with an icy surface only a few km thick, as we will discuss below.

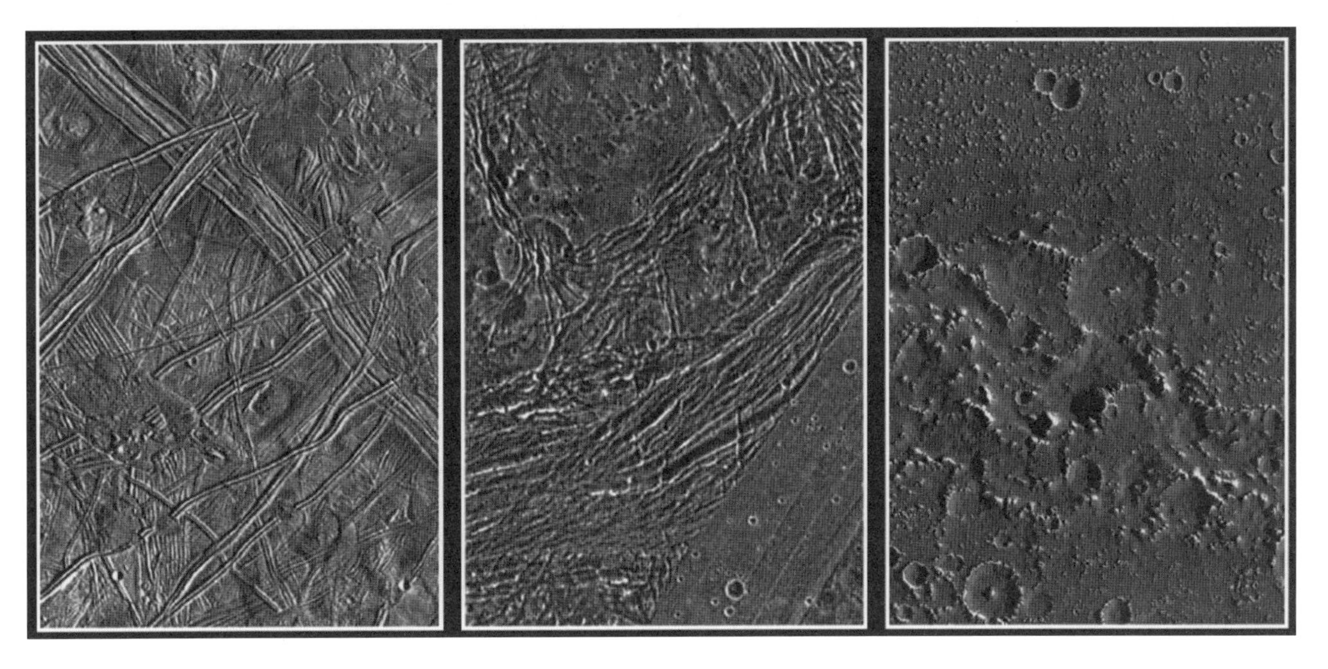

Figure 11.10: This figure shows small regions, about 100 km from top to bottom, on Europa (left), Ganymede (centre), and Callisto. Europa's surface is covered with a network of cracks and fractures, and appears to have been broken and re-cemented many times. No craters are seen. Ganymede shows some crates, but also much evidence of surface deformation and faulting. Callisto's surface shows nothing but craters interspersed with apparently smooth terrain. (Courtesy of NASA.)

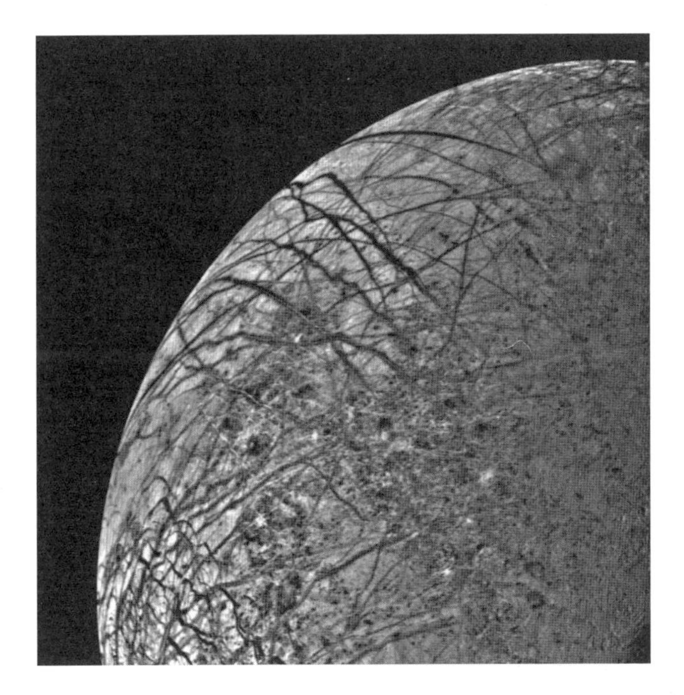

Figure 11.12: This image of about 1/4 of the the visible disk of Europa was obtained by the Voyager 2 probe in 1979. It clearly shows the dark lines criss-crossing the surface of the moon, and the absence of significant craters. (Courtesy of NASA.)

More detailed images from the Galileo orbiter reveal two dominant terrain types. Large regions on the moon are relatively smooth plains, on which the main visible features are long ridges of varying degrees of complexity. These ridges may be as much as a few hundred km long, and vary considerably in complexity. One common type is only about one km wide and about 1 – 200 m high, and is split along its main axis by a steep central valley. Several of these long ridged plains (which are coloured by contaminants that are not yet identified) are visible in the left panel of Figure 11.10. These long ridges appear to have been created by some process of local crustal stretching and cracking.

A second major terrain type is known as "chaos". Such a region is seen to the left of the centre of the expanded view of Europa in Figure 11.13. These seem to be regions of the ridged plains that have been broken into pieces by local heating from below, perhaps set adrift in liquid water, and then re-frozen into a chaotic jumble of fragments.

It is widely suspected that Europa's icy crust may be liquid starting a few km below the solid surface, although this is not yet certain. One kind of evidence supporting this idea is the appearance of the chaos regions, which certainly appear to have existed at some point as icebergs in a liquid sea. Another line of evidence is the shallowness of even the largest craters on the surface. The recent impact crater Pwyll (which is

Figure 11.13: This image shows a small chaos region of Europa, about 35 × 50 km in extent. The surface is illuminated from the right (east). The crust here is clearly made up of fragments of plains terrain which have been broken apart, jumbled, and then re-cemented by introduction of (probably liquid) water in between the fragments. This region looks like what would happen on earth if a region of ice floes or icebergs in the sea froze over completely. (Courtesy of NASA.)

Figure 11.14: This black and white image of Io shows the patchy nature of the surface, but hardly does justice to the profusion of colours seen in the colour images of the moon. The image certainly gives the impression of a body on which lava flows have spread, and many of the dark spots appear to be lava sources. On the right side of this Galileo image, the boundary between light and dark is the terminator, where the solar illumination of the moon ends; near the terminator, several mountains cast sharp shadows. (Courtesy of NASA.)

probably no more than a few million years old) has a diameter of 26 km, but is only about 200 m deep. For comparison, similar sized craters on Ganymede (which also has an icy crust) are more than 2 km deep. One possible explanation for the remarkably shallow form is that the impact on Europa penetrated through a thin crust to liquid water, which then filled in most of the basin. Another possibility is that the surface has slumped and flowed like a terrestrial glacier can – but this would require that the ice temperature be close to the melting point, which would appear to require that the temperature below the crust is quite a lot warmer than the surface, and again strong suggests the possibility of a liquid ocean under the icy crust. NASA is currently considering a mission to the Jupiter system specifically to find out whether Europa does actually have an ice-covered ocean.

The innermost Galilean moon, Io, is a body which is completely unique in the solar system. The first images from the Voyager probes revealed a body resembling a pizza pie in colour, with irregular regions of white, yellow, red, brown and black on a surface pock-marked with spots and blotches. Closer inspection quickly revealed two remarkable facts: first, that the surface has no recognizable impact craters at all, and thus must be very young, and secondly that the moon has a large number of volcanic structures, several of which are actively ejecting lava and/or venting gases into impressive high plumes (Figures 11.14 and 11.15). It quickly became clear that Io is the most volcanically active body in the solar system.

Io has been further investigated using terrestrial telescopes and the Hubble Space Telescope, and also by the Galileo orbiter. These detailed investigations have confirmed the complete absence of detectable craters, a fact which implies that most of the surface of Io is renewed or replaced within about one million years by emplacement of new lavas. The rate at which the surface is covered by fresh lava is estimated to be of the order of 1 m per century on average! The detailed images have also revealed a large variety of volcanic landforms, including active lava lakes, lava flows and huge plumes, volcanic calderas, plateaus and plains. There are also impressive mountains (the highest known rises 16 km above the surrounding plains).

The colours revealed in the Voyager images strongly suggest that the lavas are rich in sulphur (many of the colours mimic those seen in the classic chemistry lab experiment of heating a test-tube containing elemental sulphur). Sulphur compounds are also detected in the spectra of reflected sunlight. These facts led to suggestions that the lava released from Io's interior might be largely sulphur, so that the entire surface

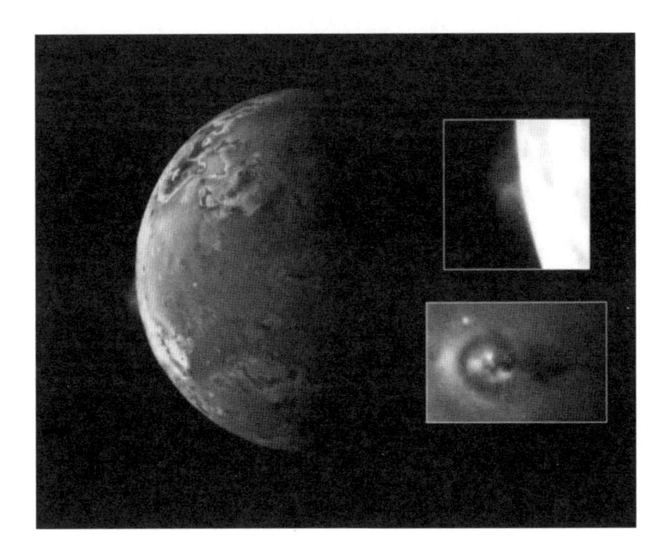

Figure 11.15: This image of Io is similar to the previous one, but reveals in two small close-ups volcano spewing gases to a height of well over 100 km. One volcano is silhouetted on the limb of the moon (left edge of the large image, and upper inset), and the other is seen from above, near the terminator (near the right edge of large image, about halfway down, and lower inset). (Courtesy of NASA.)

could be predominantly composed of sulphur. However, temperature measurements from the Galileo orbiter of the sources of lavas range up to 1700 K, far hotter than temperatures required to melt sulphur-rich lavas, and now it is thought that the lavas may well be magnesium- and iron-rich silicates like those in the Earth's mantle which are simply coloured by the addition of a small fraction of sulphur.

A body which is constantly pouring lava onto its surface can hardly be cool enough inside to have water trapped completely in the interior, so if there is any water in Io, some should be on the surface. The surface appears completely dry, however, and no spectral evidence of water is found. The moon has probably lost into space what little water it originally contained, as well as what it later accreted from impacts of comet nuclei.

Exercise: Why does the Earth's Moon not exhibit as much volcanic activity as Io does?

Origin of the moons of Jupiter

The observed properties of the moons of Jupiter raise a number of very interesting questions about how the system originated and developed. Why are all the inner moons in (almost) circular, coplanar orbits in the planet's equatorial plane? How did the three inner Galilean moons come to have orbital periods in the approximate ratios 1:2:4 – surely they were not formed by chance at just the right relative distances from Jupiter? And finally, why do these four bodies have such very different compositions and surface appearances, ranging from volcanic Io, a completely rocky body, to almost unaltered Callisto, which is about half ice and half rock?

Quite a lot about the moons of Jupiter can be understood by looking at three particular aspects of the moon system: how the moons formed in the first place, how they are heated internally, and how they have interacted through tidal effects with Jupiter and with each other since then.

The facts that the eight known inner moons have nearly circular, coplanar orbits close to the plane of Jupiter's (rotational) equator is strongly reminiscent of the situation of the planets around the sun. Like the moons, the planets orbit in nearly circular, coplanar orbits close to the equatorial plane of the sun. The reason for this regularity, in the case of the planets, is that they initially formed by condensation out of a disk of gas and dust that orbited around the sun as it accreted matter from its primordial cloud. Recall that this disk occurs because much of the material that is falling in towards the proto-sun is also falling *around* it (that is, the material has angular momentum). Infalling gas and dust clouds collide with the disk that is already present and join it. Material close to the sun in the disk is slowed down by friction with slower-moving gas and dust further out, and the inner material spirals gradually in to the central sun. As material condenses out of the disk to form first planetesimals and then planets, these are left orbiting the sun in the plane of the disk, and since the sun acquires most of its material from the disk rather than by "direct hits", the sun's equatorial plane ends up coinciding also with the disk.

The fact that the inner moons all orbit in the planet's equatorial plane strongly suggests that a similar process occurred on a smaller scale as Jupiter accumulated from interplanetary material. In fact, this is exactly what one would expect. In contrast, if the moons were formed separately, somewhere else, and later captured by Jupiter either through drag they encountered from the giant planet's initial, very extended atmosphere, or through interactions or even collisions with bodies already orbiting Jupiter, we would definitely *not* expect to find such a tidy, coplanar moon system.

The densities of the Galilean moons decrease systematically from Io (which has essentially no component of ice matter) to Ganymede and Callisto, both of which are about half ice, half rock and metal. This feature of the moon system is also reminiscent of the solar system as a whole, and confirms our suspicion that these moons formed in a proto-planetary disk. Recall the systematic changes in composition and density in the solar system as a whole, from terrestrial planets, whose composition is dominated by rock and metal, to giants and their moons in which ice is thought to be present in about equal amounts to rock and metals. These variations are explained by the different temperatures that reigned in different parts of the solar nebula, so that ice could condense and form part of the initial planetesimals in the outer solar system but not in the inner. Apparently a similar temperature variation existed in Jupiter's proto-planetary nebula, leading to two inner moons composed mainly of rock and metals, and two outer ones in which ices are an important constituent. Thus, we believe that the overall orderliness of the inner, regular moons, is due to their formation in a proto-planetary disk around the forming planet.

In contrast, the two outer systems of irregular moons are probably the result of capture of one or more stray planetesimals by Jupiter. This would be possible either due to the drag exerted on the initial bodies by an early extended atmosphere, or due to collisions of the initial bodies with other orbiting debris. Quite possibly each of the two presently known irregular groups of moons originated with a single body that has been fragmented and perhaps re-assembled as a result of collisions with other orbiting material, or with comets passing through the Jupiter system.

Thermal evolution of the Galilean moons

Let us now return to the Galilean moons, and try to understand their histories. As these moons formed, each released a rather large amount of gravitational energy – infall motion that was converted to heat as chunks of material fell onto the proto-moons. Enough energy was potentially available from this source to raise the average interior temperatures (from initial values of 100 or 200 K) of Ganymede and Callisto by several hundred K, of Europa by roughly 1500 K, and of Io by nearly 3000 K. Of course, some of this heat was radiated back into space as the moons formed. How large a temperature rise each moon actually achieved depended on how quickly each formed (quick formation would have given little time for heat loss by radiation and so would have led to high internal temperatures), and also on the details of how the material fell onto the moons, neither of which is known.

Since the energy released while the proto-moon is small is also rather small, the heating effect is not significant until the proto-moon has reached a radius of a few hundred km. Beyond that size the heating rapidly becomes more important (unless accretion is very slow, so that most of the heat released can be radiated away as it is released by debris impacts). Thus we expect that the heat deposited in the moon by the accretion process will be distributed quite unevenly. The temperature rise in the outer layers can easily be as large as the estimates given above, but in the deep interior of the forming moon the temperature would have initially been not much higher than the temperature of the nebula in which the moon formed, perhaps in the range of 100 to 200 K.

The heating of the outer layers to a temperature only 200 or 300 K above the nebular temperature would have been sufficient to melt the ice component of the moon outside of a radius of somewhere between 1000 and 2000 km. We would expect this to have occurred in the large icy moons Europa, Ganymede and Callisto, as well as in Saturn's Titan, and possibly in Neptune's moon Triton. In the outer layers of these large moons, then, the rocky component would have settled to the bottom of the melted layer, while water ice and the volatile materials absorbed in it would have risen to form a thick low-density layer which was initially liquid but which would have frozen – at least near the surface – rather quickly. Each of the large moons icy would have found itself with a rather strange density profile: a core of undifferentiated rock and ice with a density of about 2000 kg m^{-3}, then a silicate layer with a density closer to 3000 kg m^{-3}, and finally an ice and water layer of density around 1000 kg m^{-3}. Such a situation is quite unstable, but as long as the moon's core was quite rigid, it would not have changed.

However, the silicates of the core contain naturally radioactive substances just like the materials of the terrestrial planets (though somewhat diluted by the ices). Heat released from this source would have gradually heated the moon's mixed rock and ice core until the core material was soft enough for the denser layer of silicates to sink into the core, and for the water ice in the core to escape into the mantle. This event is known as **core overturn**, and would probably have occurred roughly 1 Gyr after formation of the moon. As a result, the moon would have developed a rocky core, surrounded by a mantle of water and ice, possibly mixed with other volatiles such as ammonia, methane, nitrogen, and carbon monoxide.

How the core of the moon would evolve after this point depends on another unknown of the story – the initial chemical composition of the rocky component of the moon. At one extreme, we might imagine that the rocky material in the moons of the outer planets resembles CI meteorites, with *both* the silicates and the iron highly oxidized and combined chemically in pyroxene and olivine minerals. In this case, the core would continue to heat up, losing heat at the same time by conduction into the surrounding, cold water- and ice-rich mantle. Eventually the core would begin to slowly turn over by solid-state convection like that which occurs in the earth's mantle (see Chapter 8), but this would not greatly alter affairs. The temperature of the core would now probably be somewhat above 1000 K.

At the other extreme, the moon could have formed with a rocky component similar to the composition to the EH (enstatite) meteorites, in which iron is almost entirely in metallic form. (The material that formed the earth may have had roughly this composition.) In this case, the gradual heating of the rocky core would have eventually raised the temperature (1 to 2 Gyr after core overturn) to a high enough value to melt the iron and differentiate the core. In this case the moon would end up with a three-layer structure of a liquid iron inner core, a solid silicate outer core, and and ice and water mantle. Again the core would presently have a temperature above 1000 K, and slow convection would occur in the rocky mantle.(Because the gravity measurements of the Galilean moons by the Galileo probe have not been quite sensitive enough to reveal possible iron cores, we do not yet know whether these moons have iron cores or not.)

In the icy mantle, the situation also depends on the unknown chemical composition. Here, the key unknown is the amount of volatiles other than water the layer contains. This is quite important because substances such as NH_3 can act as powerful anti-freeze agents. The melting temperature of water depends on the pressure, but never drops below about 250 K (−25 C). However, with a few percent of ammonia dissolved in the water, the melting point is depressed to 175 K (about −100 C). This drastically alters the situation in the outer ice-rich layer.

When the moon forms an icy mantle as a result of core overturn, this mantle is initially probably liquid throughout. However, the outer surface of the moon quickly cools to the temperature set by incoming sunlight, around 120 K (−153 C) for the moons of Jupiter. At this temperature the surface freezes solid, and a surface layer of solid ice develops like the ice cover on a lake in winter. What happens next is still uncertain, both because we do not know what substances (besides water) are present in the mantle, and because the behaviour (particularly the conditions for solid-state convection to occur) of ice at low temperature is still not fully understood. But we can roughly bracket the possibilities by looking at extremes.

One possible evolution occurs if the ice mantle contains no important substance that can act as an antifreeze, and if solid-state convection (like that in the Earth's mantle) can occur in the ice where it is not too cold. In this case, the surface temperature of the solid surface ice layer overlying the deep sea is held at the equilibrium temperature set by sunlight, but the bottom layer of the ice layer is at the melting point of water, which is between about 260 and 280 K at various depths. The temperature *difference* across the ice layer is thus held roughly constant at about 150 K, and the inner part of the ice sheet is at a temperature not far below the freezing point. This may make it possible for the lower part of the solid ice lid to convect slowly. This is a very efficient mechanism for carrying heat outwards towards the surface, much more effective than simple conduction of heat through a layer tens of km thick. In this case, the heat transported to the surface per second is easily *larger* than the heat released by radioactivity in the silicate core, so more heat flows out of the mantle from the top than flows in from the bottom. The mantle cools rapidly, and within one or two Gyr the mantle is completely solid ice. From that time to the present, this mantle has been in a state of solid-state convection, simply carrying to the surface the heat released by radioactivity in the core. As the radioactivity level decays, the core and mantle both gradually become cooler.

As the other extreme, we consider the possibility that there is an important antifreeze (such as NH_3) in the material of the mantle. Ammonia is capable of lowering the freezing temperature of the sea by as much as 100 K, to about 170 K. In this case, the top of the surface ice sheet is held at about 120 K, while the bottom is at the melting point of the liquid, only about 50 K warmer. In this case, it seems very likely that convection in the lower part of the surface ice sheet will be prevented by the very low temperature, and with only a small temperature drop across the surface ice sheet, heat conduction out to the surface can easily fall, as the surface ice sheet thickens, to a rate that balances the heat production in the silicate core. In this case, once the surface ice sheet (the lithosphere) becomes thick enough (a few tens of km) for heat loss from the surface to balance production in the core, the low-density mantle almost ceases to cool further. In this situation, a deep liquid sea could still exist today under the solid surface even in a moon such as Callisto that has no significant internal heat source except for radioactive heat release.

If the moon has no important anti-freeze substance in the mantle, but solid-state convection in the ice lid does not occur (there is still dispute on this point), then the lid can still gradually grow to such a thickness that the heat carried out through the ice sheet by conduction falls to a value that balances production in the core. Again, a deep liquid ocean covered by a solid lithosphere of ice would persist up to the present. Thus, it is quite unclear at present whether the large Galilean moons Ganymede and Callisto have liquid seas under their icy surfaces, but it is not unreasonable to speculate that they do.

From this general picture, we would predict that all the Galilean moons, even rocky Io, would have differentiated and developed solid lithospheres billions of years ago. The three ice-rich moons might still have liquid seas deep below the surface, but their surfaces should all be primarily composed of water ice, and heavily cratered.

For Callisto, we indeed find the cratered surface, but recall that the gravity measurements show that this moons is *not* fully differentiated into a silicate core surrounded by an icy mantle, although "some" differentiation seems to have taken place. Furthermore, the surface is not pure ice, but has a lot of dark, probably rocky, material in it. We are thus left with a rather serious puzzle as to how Callisto could have avoided complete differentiation, and how the surface could remain a mixture of ice and rock.

Ganymede has a nearly pure ice surface, and gravity measurements show that it has indeed fully differentiated into a core-mantle structure, as expected. However, recall that the surface shows both regions of heavy cratering, and other that have been heavily modified by tectonic events after the end of the main period of bombardment. Again we have a puzzle.

Gravity measurements of Europa confirm that it is differentiated, and its surface appears to be pure ice. However, it has virtually no craters on the surface, so some effect has reworked the entire surface within the past few millions of years. Io has a surface which does not have a single impact crater, and is covered with volcanic structures and other evidence of tectonic activity. Clearly there is some important part of the story we have so far neglected. This is probably the effect of intermittent heating due to orbital resonances.

Orbital resonances and tidal effects

It appears that both the orbital resonances that are found for the three inner Galilean moons, and the fact that all of their surfaces show evidence of melting long after the formation period, may be due to the effects of tides. Let us recall what kinds of effects might me expected. First, if the moons initially formed with rapid rotation (periods of a few hours, perhaps) around their rotation axes, Jupiter would produce tidal bulges on the near and far sides of each moon. These bulges would be pulled ahead of the Jupiter-moon line by the rapid rotation, and so Jupiter would exert a drag on the rotation of each moon (just as the Moon exerts a drag on the rotation of the Earth). As a result, each of the Galilean satellites would slow down to synchronous rotation within a few million years. In fact, they are all observed to rotate synchronously. While this slowing of the rotation was occurring, each of the moons would be dissipating energy in its interior – there would be strong *tidal heating.* In contrast, the outer small moons are all too far from Jupiter for tides to be effective, and they are not rotating synchronously.

Another tidal effect is that is important is due to the pair of bulges that each moon would raise on Jupiter. Jupiter's rotation about its axis occurs with a shorter period (presently 0.41 d) than the orbital periods of any of the Galilean moons, so the bulges would be carried ahead of the Jupiter-moon line. The extra attraction for the near bulge by the moon causing it would have the effect of slowing (slightly) the rotation of Jupiter, while the bulge itself gives the moon a bit of extra pull, gradually increasing the orbit size (and angular momentum) of the moon. This effect causes the orbits of each of the moons to gradually increase in size, but since the effect falls off rapidly with distance from Jupiter, orbit growth occurs more rapidly for Io than for Europa, and more rapidly for Europa than for Ganymede. This effect has been occuring throughout the history of the Jupiter system, so the moons' orbital sizes are larger than they originally were. Again this is reminiscent of the situation of the Earth and Moon.

The gradual expansion of satellite orbits, with the innermost ones growing most rapidly, has another very interesting effect. As the orbit of Io expanded from it initial rather smaller size, eventually Io came into an orbital resonance with Europa, perhaps a 2:1 resonance like the present one. It appears that the two moons are likely to become trapped in this resonance, so that as Io is pushed farther and farther from Jupiter, it pushes Europa out in front of it, always keeping the 2:1 relationship between the two orbital periods. Eventually, both orbits expand enough that the orbit of Europa reaches a 2:1 resonance with Ganymede. Again trapping occurs. Thus, we do not imagine that the Galilean moons originally formed with orbital period ratios of approximately 4:2:1, but rather evolved into this state. (Eventually all three orbits will expand enough to reach resonance with Callisto too, but this is far in the future.)

As the orbital periods of the two moons approach such a resonance, the regularly occuring pull that each feels from the other causes both orbits to develop a significant eccentricity. That is, the effect of the regularly occurring mutual attraction is to cause each of the moons to vary its distance from Jupiter. Since the amount of tidal stretching of each moon depends on how far it is from Jupiter, the tidal distortion of the shape of each moon varies – it stretches and relaxes, stretches and relaxes – as it goes around in its orbit.

This periodic change in the shape of the moon is a

dissipative process – it deposits energy into the interior of the moon. How much? Roughly the correct amount to explain the heating that must be occurring inside Io to produce the ongoing volcanic activity that we observe. And possibly enough energy is dissipated inside Europa to lead to an ocean below the icy surface. This effect may even have been sufficiently important for Ganymede at the time that it came into resonance with Europa to explain the regions of deformed crust that are not seen on Callisto.

We do not yet have answers for all the interesting questions about the Galilean moons (for example, why are Europa and Ganymede so different in surface appearance?), and some of the ideas discussed above still have important uncertainties. However, it appears that quite a lot of the essential physics of this fascinating moon system is gradually becoming clearer.

The moons of Saturn

In contrast to the moon system of Jupiter with its four large (but very dissimilar) moons accompanied by a dozen or more very small bodies, the moon system of Saturn is dominated by a single large moon, Titan. With a diameter of 5150 km, about 1.5 times larger across than the Earth's Moon, Titan is the second largest moon in the solar system, after Ganymede. Orbiting the ringed planet together with Titan are seven smaller but still significant moons having a variety of sizes: two (Iapetus and Rhea) with diameters near 1500 km, two (Dione and Tethys) with diameters of about 1100 km, two with diameters of around 450 km (Enceladus and Mimas, which are spherical), and one about 300 km (Hyperion, which is potato-shaped). Moons of this intermediate size are not found in the Jupiter system, and it is very interesting to examine them to discover how they differ from moons of the size of the Galilean satellites. An intriguing feature of this group of intermediate-size moons is that the five that orbit inside the orbit of Titan are found in decreasing order of size as one goes inward.

Finally, there are at least ten smaller moons, mostly not not spherical, with characteristic sizes of 250 km or less. The smallest moons known in the Saturn system are only about 20 km across. Unlike the tiny inner moons of Jupiter, which appear to be rocky (as one would expect for bodies formed in the inner part of a warm proto-planetary disk), the smallest moons of Saturn appear to be rich in ices.

The regular structure of the moon system around Saturn strongly suggests that the moons formed in an equatorial disk of material that was accreting onto the main planet, as we have deduced for Jupiter. The fact that all the moons of Saturn have relatively low density, and thus contain a major component of ice, indicates that the accretion disk around Saturn was substantially colder than that of Jupiter, so that more volatile substances could freeze out and be swept up by the forming moons, even close to the planet.

The inner satellites of Saturn, especially from Dione inwards, have been strongly affected by collisions with passing comets. Comets that happen to pass near Saturn are of course strongly attracted by its gravity, and for this reason make a closest approach to the planet that is considerably closer than it would be if Saturn were not attracting them. This effect increases the likelihood of a collision between such comets and the inner moons of Saturn, as well as the typical speed with which the comet impacts the moon. As a result, it is probable that all of the moons from Dione inwards have suffered at least one impact carrying enough kinetic energy to leave a crater with a size comparable to the impacted moon. In many cases these impacts would have been powerful enough to disrupt the satellite, which could later have re-accreted into one or more bodies.

The moons out as far as Hyperion (which is slightly outside the orbit of Titan) appear to have undergone increases in the sizes of their orbits due to tidal effects, just as happened in the Jupiter system. As a result, several orbital resonances have been established. The orbital period of Tethys is twice as long as that of Mimas, as is true of Dione and Enceladus. These 2:1 resonances have been plausibly accounted for as a result of more rapid tidal expansion of the inner orbit than the outer, until the two moons "lock into" a resonant situation. Farther out, Hyperion makes three trips around the planet four every four made by Titan, but the tidal evolution that led to this situation is quite unclear. There are also at least three situations of shared orbits: Janus and Epimetheus, Telesto, Tethys, and Calypso, and Helene with Dione; some of these may be the result of the disruptive collisions mentioned above.

These tidal effects have also strongly affected the rotation of Saturn's moons. All the moons out to Titan are locked by tidal forces into synchronous rotation; each keeps one hemisphere constantly facing Saturn.

Titan (Figure 11.16) is the only moon in the Saturn system which is comparable in size to the Galilean moons, Neptune's Triton, and our own Moon. Because of its size and composition, it is very likely that Titan has undergone an evolution similar to that which has apparently occurred inside Ganymede. Accretion heating probably melted the outer layers of the moon as it formed in the disk of material orbiting the equator of the forming planet, resulting in the formation of a layered moon with an undifferentiated core and a mantle with a dense silicate layer beneath a layer of

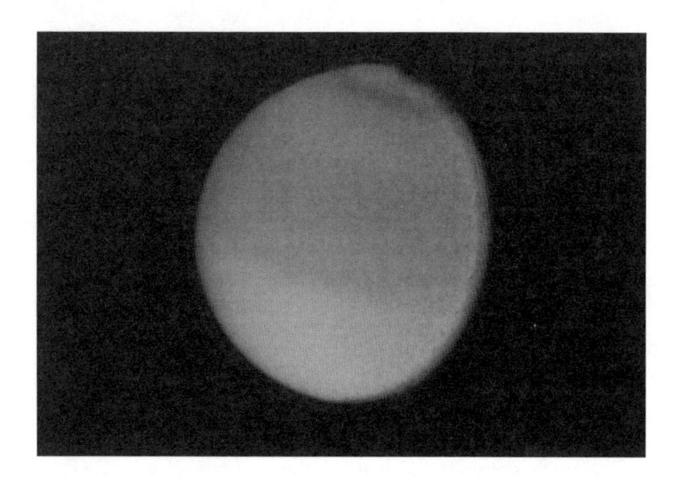

Figure 11.16: Saturn's only really large moon, Titan, is a body composed about half of rock and half of ices. It is probably similar to Jupiter's Ganymede in structure. It has a nitrogen-rich atmosphere; a haze of aerosol particles in the atmosphere makes observation of the surface very difficult. (Courtesy of NASA.)

water and ice. As the core warmed up from radioactive energy release, ice in the core softened, melted, and rose towards the surface, while the dense silicate layer above sank into the core. By about one Gyr after Titan first formed, core overturn was complete. In the mantle, now composed primarily of water and perhaps other volatiles, we again have a competition between the heat that flows into the mantle from the core below, and cooling through the outer icy layers to the frigid surface. As with Ganymede and Callisto, we are not sure how efficient heat loss out through the lithosphere is, so we do not know whether Titan has an ocean deep below its icy surface, or whether the mantle is frozen solid throughout. The Huygens–Cassini space probe mission, which should arrive at Saturn in 2004, will probably help greatly to understand the structure of Titan.

However, Titan is also entirely unique in that it is the only moon in the solar system with a massive atmosphere. Unfortunately, this atmosphere is filled with a haze of small particles (Figure 11.16), and so we cannot see the surface in visible light. Our information on this singular gas envelope comes from observations by both Voyager probes (Voyager 1 was sent quite close to Titan), and from a range of observations from the earth. By observing the way in which the Voyager radio signal changed as the craft passed behind Titan, together with infrared brightness measurements, it was found that the mean molecular weight of the gas making up Titan's atmosphere is close to 28, about the same as that of molecular nitrogen, N_2. The surface pressure is about 150 kPa (1.5 bar), 1.5 times the surface pressure on Earth. Since gravity on Titan is only about 13% of that on Earth, there is about 10 times as much mass of gas over each square m on Titan as on Earth!

The surface temperature is found from infrared observations of brightness to be about 94 K (about −180 C). The temperature declines slowly with height to a low of about 70 K at 30 km. Above this level, the thermosphere begins (Titan has no stratosphere like that of Earth), and the temperature rises to a balmy 170 K (−100 C) at around 200 km above the surface. The atmosphere appears to be convective near the surface.

The chemical composition of the atmosphere is dominated by N_2 (probably about 94% by mass), with a few percent of CH_4 as the principal minor constituent. There are also very small amounts of CO, CO_2, C_2H_6 (ethane), and a number of other compounds of H, C and N. The predominantly nitrogen composition is surprisingly similar to the atmosphere of Earth.

The presence of CH_4 in Titan's atmosphere presents an interesting puzzle. It is found that this gas is rapidly broken up by energetic photons from the Sun into C (which combines with other molecules in the atmosphere to form substances that settle on the surface) and H (which escapes from the moon because of its feeble gravity). All the methane in the present atmosphere would be destroyed in this way in about 30 million yr. This strongly suggests that there is a continuing source that replenishes this molecule as it is destroyed. It is thought that this could be in the form of volcanic activity releasing CH_4 from the interior of the moon – if the interior is hot enough – or in the form of methane lakes on the surface.

How did Titan come to have an atmosphere when none of the Galilean moons acquired one? We can be sure that the moon did not acquire its atmosphere by direct gravitational capture from the proto-planetary nebula in which it formed because in that nebula the abundance of neon was about the same as that of nitrogen, but the current atmosphere of the moon has less than 0.1% of Ne. It also appears that the bulk of the atmosphere was not delivered as a result of cometary impacts, because the ratio of normal hydrogen to deuterium (hydrogen with an extra neutron in the nucleus) is rather different in comets than in Titan's atmosphere. So it appears that the difference between Titan and the Galilean satellites is that Titan acquired a good stock of the gases now found in the atmosphere when it formed, while the Galilean moons did not.

If the gases of the atmosphere were acquired at the time of formation, they were presumably trapped inside ice grains that formed the planetesimals that became Titan, as clathrates. In particular, ammonia (NH_3) is easy to trap in this way, and a significant supply of (more volatile) CH_4 might have been acquired in the same way. It appears that the key difference between the nebulas of Jupiter and of Saturn was probably that temperatures in Saturn's proto-planetary nebula were substantially lower than in Jupiter's, leading to a much greater trapping of volatile molecules in the icy materials that went into forming Titan. The Galilean moons lack atmospheres because the nebula in which they formed was too warm for significant inclusion of suitable volatiles in the ices that formed them.

But was the nitrogen that makes up Titan's atmosphere originally trapped as NH_3, or as N_2? Molecular nitrogen, N_2, was probably the dominant form of N in the *solar* nebula, but could have been converted to NH_3 in the Saturn proto-planetary nebula. If we look at the ratio of current nitrogen in the atmosphere to current argon, which would have been trapped in ices in about the same proportion as N_2, we cannot come to any particular strong conclusion, since the atmosphere of Titan may contain up to about 6% Ar. However, looking at the ratio of ^{15}N to ^{14}N, which is a good indicator of how much N has *escaped* from the atmosphere (remember, the heavier atoms escape less easily than the light ones), we conclude that the early nitrogen atmosphere of Titan was probably about 30 times as massive as the present one! Then the deduced ratio of total nitrogen to observed argon (which is too heavy to escape from the atmosphere) provides a strong argument that the nitrogen was *not* accreted by Titan as N_2. It must have been originally trapped as NH_3, which is quickly converted by solar ultraviolet light to N_2 when it reaches the atmosphere from the interior.

We are still rather unclear about how the CH_4 in the atmosphere was acquired. Planetary scientists eagerly await the arrival of the Huygens–Cassini space probe in early 2004; this probe should help to clear away at least some of the present uncertainties surrounding this particularly moon.

We next turn to the smaller moons. Six of the intermediate moons have known masses (Iapetus, Rhea, Dione, Tethys, Enceladus, and Mimas). All have densities between 1440 and 1160 kg m^{-3}. These bodies are mainly composed of ice, though each must have some rock. No clear pattern of density decreasing with distance, like that observed for the four large moons of Jupiter, is seen here. All six moons show clear evidence, in the way they reflect infrared light between 1 and 2 μm, of water ice on their surfaces, as one might expect from their densities.

All of these moons (except for a part of Enceladus, discussed below) are heavily cratered, a fact evident in the Voyager image of Dione (Figure 11.17). The craters generally have more vertical relief (their walls are high above the central floors) than is found for Ganymede and Callisto. This is probably due to a more rigid crust

Figure 11.17: Saturn's intermediate-sized moon Dione, with a radius of 560 km, is large enough to be quite spherical. The surface is heavily cratered, with more vertical relief than is found on Jupiter's moon Callisto, perhaps because of the colder and more rigid crust of Dione. The strong variations in reflectivity are not yet understood. (Courtesy of NASA.)

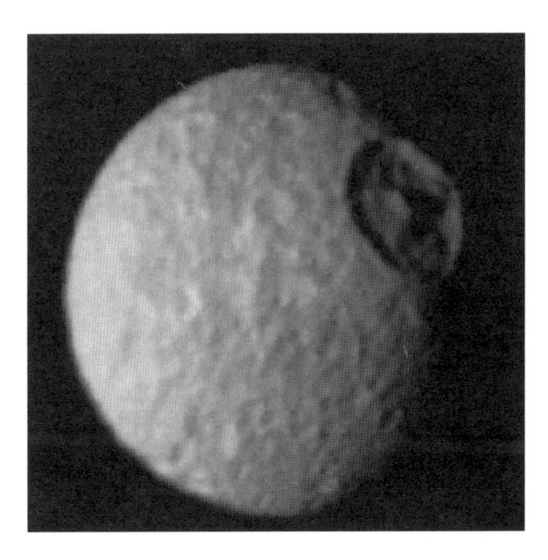

Figure 11.18: Mimas is the inner-most of the intermediate size moons of Saturn, and was not imaged from nearby by either Voyager. However, one huge crater, 130 km in diameter, is easily visible even in this low-resolution image. (Courtesy of NASA.)

on these small and very cold bodies. Impact craters that are so large that it is surprising that the moon survived are found; an impressive example is that of Mimas (Figure 11.18). Several of the intermediate moons show long chasms or cracks that might have been produced as a result of impacts.

Another remarkable feature of the surfaces of several

of the moons is regions of rather low reflectivity. Iapetus is extremely dark (it reflects only 5% of the light striking it) on the hemisphere which faces forward in the moon's orbit around Saturn (the "leading" hemisphere), but is much brighter (an albedo of 50%) on the "trailing" hemisphere. It is thought that Iapetus may have swept up much dark debris broken loose by meteorite impacts from Saturn's very dark outermost moon, Phoebe, which is probably a captured carbonaceous asteroid. In contrast, both the middle moons Rhea and Dione (Figure 11.17) have streaky dark terrain at the centres of their trailing hemispheres, but are elsewhere quite reflective. These dark regions may be the oldest surviving surface on these two bodies; elsewhere the surface has been reworked by the impact of small meteoroids since the moons formed.

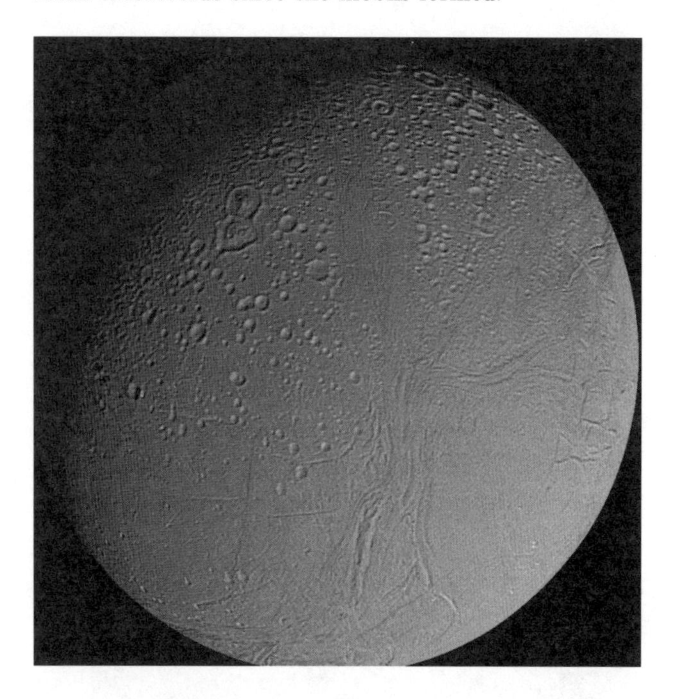

Figure 11.19: The small Saturnian moon Enceladus shows a remarkable variety of surface features, ranging from impact craters to the wide band of grooves that traverse the moon from upper left to lower right. This grooved terrain is reminiscent of that found on Ganymede, and clearly shows that this small moon has undergone important tectonic activity. (Courtesy of NASA.)

Finally, the small, highly reflective moon Enceladus (the second innermost intermediate moon, after Mimas) shows a remarkable variety of terrain, ranging from one hemisphere of heavily cratered terrain to regions which have been resurfaced so recently that they are completely free of craters, but instead are criss-crossed by a network of banded ridges (Figure 11.19). The resurfaced terrain is reminiscent of that on Ganymede. This crater-free hemisphere is almost 100% reflective, like fresh snow or pure, clean ice. The resurfaced hemisphere is estimated, from the absence of large craters, to be less than 1 Gyr old, so this area has apparently been resurfaced in the most recent 20% of Enceladus' history.

Understanding the energy source that provided the heat to melt water and resurface a part of Enceladus has proven to be very difficult. The moon is far too small to have heated significantly during accretion, and its low density shows clearly that it does not have a very large rock component, so that there is certainly not an important radioactive heating source inside (all the major radioactive substances are in the rock component). The only obvious source of heating is tidal friction, the effect that keeps Io's volcanos active. However, the present orbit of Enceladus has rather low eccentricity, and the estimated tidal heat input rate at present is about 300 times too small to provide the energy needed to resurface the moon. Furthermore, the nearby moon Mimas has a *more* eccentric orbit than Enceladus, but it shows few signs of recent surface melting. The energy input that made possible the reworking of Enceladus' surface was probably the result of some tidal resonance with another moon in the past, but the sequence of events that led to the heating is very unclear at present.

The bulls-eye moon system of Uranus

Before the Voyager 2 visit to the Uranus system in 1986, little was known about the moons beyond their orbital properties. Five moons were known, spanning the sizes of the intermediate-size moons of Saturn. All orbit close to the equatorial plane of the planet, in orbits located between about 5 and 23 Uranus radii from the planet's centre. All these orbits are direct, and the rotation of each of the moons is synchronized with the orbital period. These moons get steadily larger as one goes out. First comes tiny Miranda, with a radius of about 240 km, then Ariel and Umbriel, both with radii of about 580 km, and finally Titania and Oberon, with radii of about 770 km. These moons are all well outside the system of dark rings discovered from Earth.

One remarkable feature of the Uranus system is that the equatorial plane of the planet, which is also the orbital plane for the regular moons, is inclined to the ecliptic plane by 97°. Thus the "north" pole of Uranus (if you were above this pole you would see the planet rotating counter-clockwise) is actually slightly below the ecliptic plane. This is different from the other planets, all of which have the north poles of their rotation axes pointing roughly perpendicular to the ecliptic plane on the same side as the north pole of the Sun. Because the rotation axis of Uranus remains fixed in direction as the planet orbits the Sun, a unique seasonal pattern occurs on Uranus, and on its moons. As the system circles the Sun in its 84-year period of revolution, first one of the poles points towards the Sun for some years. The line to the Sun gradually shifts as the planet continues in its orbit, and 21 years later the Sun is over the equator (this will be the situation in 2006). Another 21 years brings the opposite pole to point nearly to the Sun, and so on. This arrangement has the consequence that one hemisphere is constantly illuminated for some years while the other it permanently dark. As the line to the Sun shifts towards the equator, the days begin to alternate like those on other planets, with the rotation period of the planet determining the length of the day for Uranus, and the orbital periods determining the length of days on the moons. As the planet-Sun line shifts towards the opposite pole, the situation reverts to permanent illumination, now of the opposite hemisphere than before.

Exercise: Sketch the Uranus system relative to the ecliptic plane and convince yourself of the correctness of the description above of the seasons. When was the last year in which one of the poles was pointing towards the Sun?

Because of the inclination of the orbit of Uranus to the ecliptic, when Voyager 2 approached the system in 1986 the moon system resembled the bull's eye of a target. The space probe was able to obtain a close-up view of only one of the moons, Miranda, and although the moons all rotated during the time Voyager 2 passed through the Uranus system, only one hemisphere was ever illuminated. At least half of each of the moons has thus still not been photographed.

The Voyager visit made possible the accurate determination of the sizes and masses of all the previously known moons, and led to the discovery of another 10 much smaller moons, all orbiting within the orbit of Miranda in the planet's equatorial plane in nearly circular orbits. These bodies (which are mostly too small to reveal any surface details even to Voyager 2) have radii of between about 10 and 80 km.

Using the newly determined dimensions and masses of the larger moons, their densities are found to range from 1200 to 1710 kg m^{-3}. They are all somewhat denser than moons of similar size in the Saturn system; thus although they are – like the moons of Saturn – composed of a mix of rock and ice, there seems to be somewhat more rock in moons of Uranus than in those of Saturn.

All the moons show some cratering. Two, Umbriel and Oberon (the third and fifth of the intermediate moons, counting outwards) have heavily cratered surfaces, rather like those of Dione or Mimas (see Figure 11.20). The cratering is about as dense as that of the lunar highlands, and probably was produced during the period of intense bombardment that ended about 4 Gyr ago. These moons have apparently been largely inactive since that time.

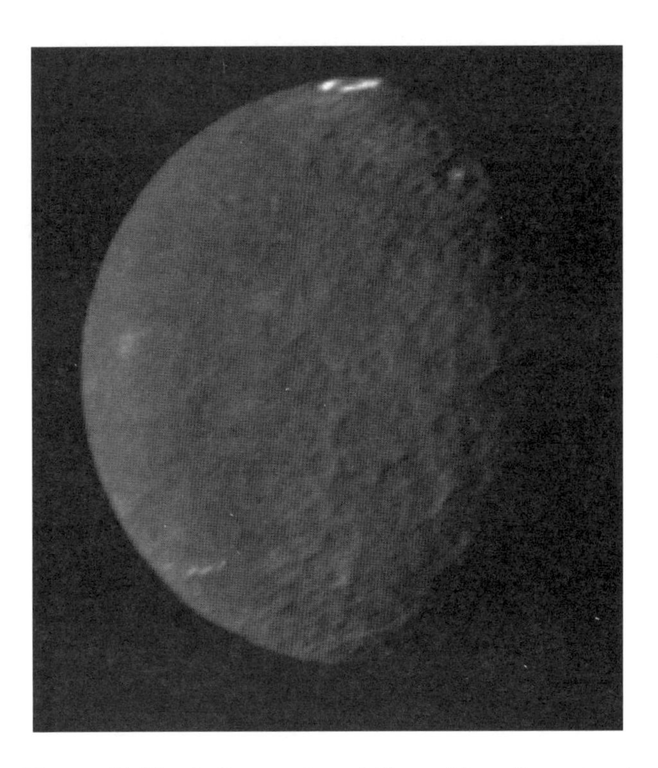

Figure 11.20: A distant view of Uranus' heavily cratered moon Umbriel. Little can be seen on this moon except impact craters; some of the larger ones have central mountain peaks. (Courtesy of NASA.)

Ariel and Titania (the second and fourth intermediate moons from Uranus) also have much cratered terrain, but there are few really large craters like those found on Umbriel and Oberon (see Figures 11.21 and 11.22). Since all four moons must have suffered similar bombardment by large planetesimals during the first half-billion years of their existence, the absence of large craters indicates that the surfaces of these moons must have melted or been covered with "lava" (liquid or slushy water, perhaps mixed with other volatiles such as ammonia) early on. The current crop of craters must date from after this time, and from after the end of the period of heaviest bombardment. In addition to the craters, each moon is deeply scarred by long trenches (grabens) where the crust has cracked open and been partly filled in by liquid or slushy solid from below. The origin of these long cracks is uncertain, but they appear to indicate that the interior of the moon expanded while the lithosphere did not. The result was long fractures in the crust. The most obvious way in

Figure 11.21: This view of Uranus' moon Ariel from Voyager 2 shows clearly that Ariel is cratered but not very heavily, and also that the moon has an extensive system of surface faults that appear to have been produced by expansion of the surface, probably caused by internal heating. (Courtesy of NASA.)

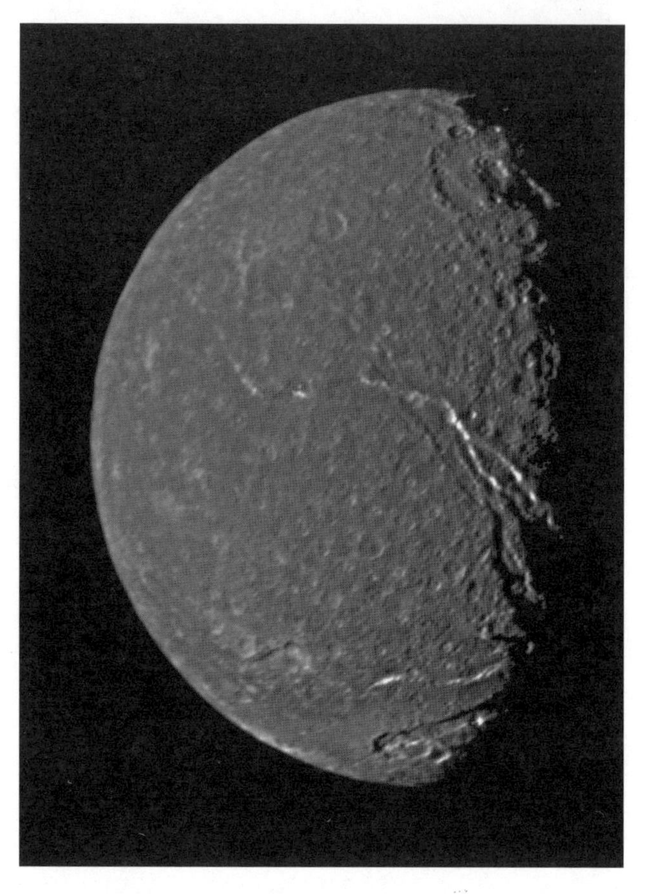

Figure 11.22: A view of Uranus' fourth intermediate moon, Titania. Like Ariel, this moon has moderate cratering (but lacks really large craters such as those seen on Umbriel), and also huge, large-scale faults, perhaps the result of surface expansion. (Courtesy of NASA.)

which this could happen would be if the interior were heated and therefore expanded while the outer layers remained cold.

Finally we come to the smallest and innermost of the major moons, Miranda. It was widely expected that this small body would be heavily cratered but otherwise quite uninteresting. In fact, the images sent back by Voyager 2 revealed what is easily the most puzzling surface of any of the moons of Uranus. Part of Miranda is indeed covered with rolling plains with some cratering, but other parts have largely uncratered oval or trapezoidal regions covered with wide grooves and ridges that seem to follow the outline of the region. A small part of Miranda which shows both kinds of terrain in seen in Figure 11.23. This groove-and-ridge terrain is quite mysterious; one possibility is that this moon has been completely fragmented by impact and then reassembled by gravity, and that the groove-and-ridge terrain is somehow the result of this process. Again we have strong evidence in the relatively young surface, as well as in the strange oval regions, of important resurfacing activity in the moon after the end of the heavy bombardment period.

We have seen in the Jupiter and Saturn systems that accretion and radioactive energy release is important only in relatively large moons such as the Galilean moons and Titan. For moons as small as those of Uranus, the amount of gravitational energy released is not enough to produce a large temperature rise, and radioactive heat produced by the rock component is quickly lost to the surface because of the small size. In the Uranian system the important sources of heating should be destructive impacts and tidal effects.

Consider tidal effects. All the intermediate-size moons of Uranus have orbital periods longer than the rotation period of the planet. The tidal bulges produced on Uranus by each of the moons will be dragged slightly ahead of the planet-moon line by the rotation of the planet. Thus the effects of tides on the moons from Miranda on out will be to increase the sizes of the orbits of the moon. (However, this effect depends on the mass of each moon as well as on it distance, so that the orbit of Ariel is actually increasing faster

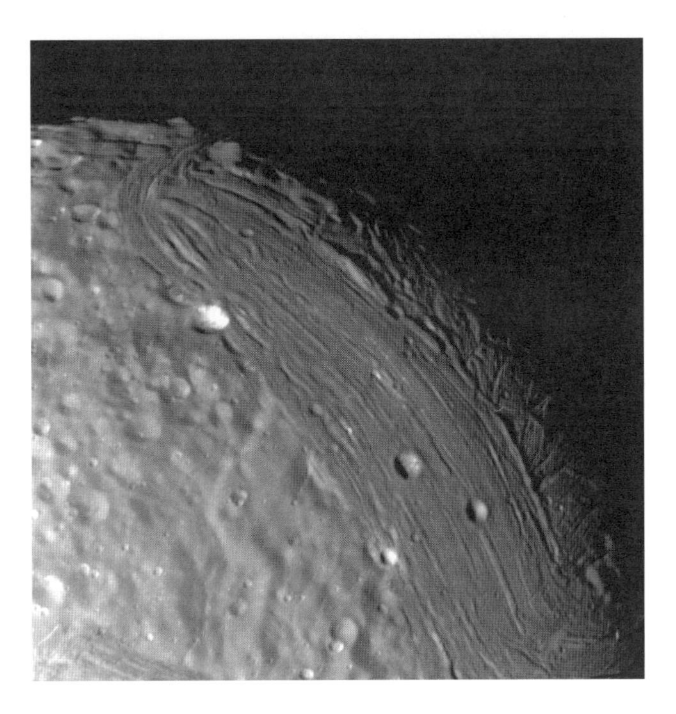

Figure 11.23: The smallest and innermost intermediate moon of Uranus is Miranda. This moon shows a relatively young, lightly cratered surface as well as very strange groove-and-ridge terrain that is not found anywhere else in the solar system. (Courtesy of NASA.)

than that of Miranda even though Miranda is closer to Uranus.) In the past, the moons have certainly had periods during which resonances between orbital periods existed (a past 3:1 resonance between Miranda and Umbriel is responsible for the present 4° inclination of Miranda's orbit to the equatorial plane of Uranus), but the computations of orbital evolution have not yielded any very convincing explanation of the heating of the three moons that have been resurfaced since the end of the period of heavy bombardment. The situation is particularly puzzling for Titania, an evolved moon located in between Umbriel and Oberon, the two moons with the least evolved surfaces. We do not have at present any secure explanation of the heating that led to resurfacing on three of the intermediate-size moons of Uranus.

A final question raised by the Uranus system would be to ask how both the planet and the accretion disk from which its moons system formed came to have such an unusual inclination to the plane of the planetary orbits around the sun. For the planet, this was probably the result of a near-catastrophic off-centre collision between the proto-planet and a second proto-planet of comparable size which drastically altered the direction of spin of the still forming body. However, there is no reason that further material accreting onto the planet would arrive in such a way as to orbit around the planet's highly inclined equator, and thus produce a moon system in this plane. How did the moon system end up forming in the planet's equatorial plane?

The effect that shifted the proto-planetary disk, and the moons that it formed, to the plane of Uranus' equator was again a tidal effect. Rapidly rotating Uranus bulges out at the equator. Because of this, the gravitational pull of the planet not only makes nearby moons and other material orbit around the planet, but any orbit not in the equatorial plane twists steadily around. This motion is rather like that of a spinning top whose axis is not quite vertical, so that the axis of the top moves around in a small cone about the contact point with the floor. This effect, acting on the orbits of moons, guarantees that orbits of different bodies orbiting out of the equatorial plane would sooner or later intersect. The various planetesimals would thus repeatedly collide until the debris settled into the present equatorial plane, where relatively long-lasting moons could finally form by (re-)accretion.

The strange case of Neptune's moons

The Neptune system is relatively poor in moons. It includes a single large moon, Triton, comparable in size to the smaller Galilean moons Io and Europa, as well as at least six small moons (all discovered by Voyager 2) orbiting close to the planet, four of which are even within the planet's Roche limit for ice-rich bodies. A single moon, Nereid, orbits in an extremely eccentric orbit well outside that of Triton.

Unlike the large moons of the other giant planets, the large moon Triton orbits around Neptune in the *opposite* sense to the planet's rotation, in an approximately circular orbit inclined to the plane of the planet's equator by about 23°. The moon's rotation about its own axis, however, is synchronized so as to keep one face always pointing towards Neptune. This extraordinary orbit makes it clear that Triton did not form in an accretion disk around Neptune, but was almost certainly captured more or less intact as it passed close to the planet. This would most likely have been possible as a result of a collision between Triton and a smaller moon already orbiting the planet, which could have slowed Triton down enough to insure that it would lack the energy to escape again from Neptune's gravitational grip.

As Triton gradually settled into a circular orbit from its initially very eccentric orbit (as a result of tidal effects), it would have disrupted any previous moon system, capturing some moons by collisions, and ejecting others from the system or causing them to crash into Neptune. The original satellite system was so greatly

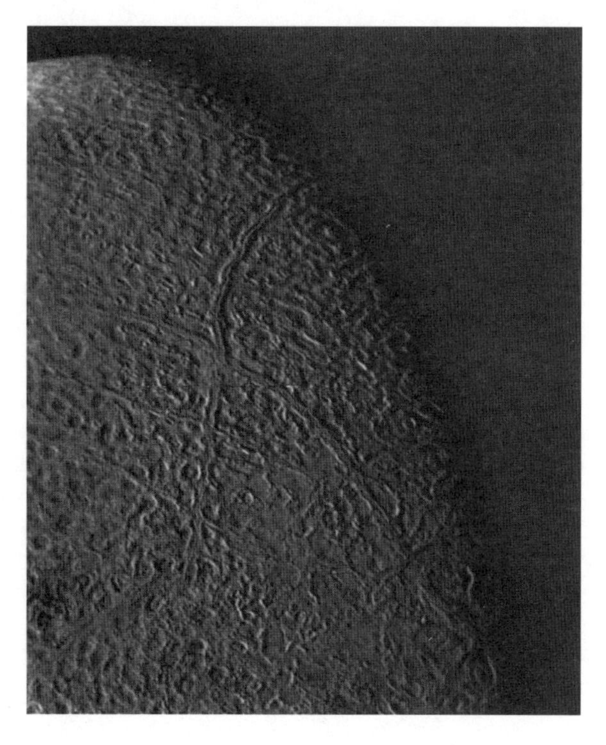

Figure 11.24: The trailing hemisphere of Neptune's single large moon, Triton, shows a vast system of roughly linear ridges that seem to have formed in plains already heavily deformed earlier. These features are probably the result of icy volcanism. Because of its appearance, this part of Triton's surface is known as "cantaloupe terrain". (Courtesy of NASA.)

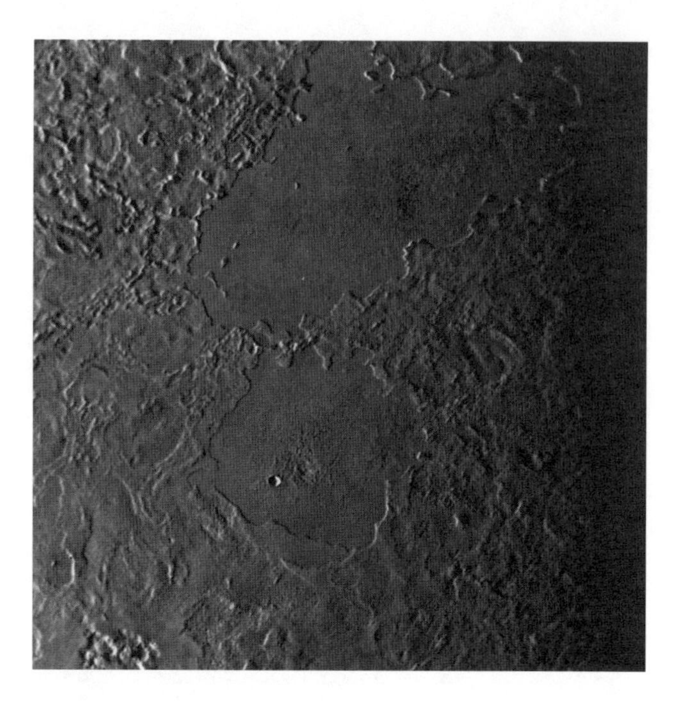

Figure 11.25: Another distinctive surface feature on Triton is several huge calderas or lakes that have been repeatedly filled with liquid water and drained. The lower lake in this image has a single small impact crater; generally, the surface of Triton is sufficiently recent that only a few small craters are found. (Courtesy of NASA.)

disturbed by Triton's arrival on the scene that all the remaining original satellites must have suffered destructive collisions with one another. The current set of small moons close to Neptune probably formed out of the debris of the earlier system, and even these moons have most likely been shattered by comet impacts since they re-formed, only to re-accrete again.

Exercise: Consider Triton shortly after it was captured into a very eccentric retrograde orbit around Neptune. Each time the moon passed close to the planet, it would raise tidal bulges on the near and far sides of the planet. Neptune's rotation would displace these bulges to lag behind the planet-moon line. With a sketch, explain how the near bulge would tend to slow Triton down a little in each close pass by Neptune, and how this would lead to gradual circularization of Triton's orbit.

With a mean density of 2050 kg m^{-3}, rock makes up more than 40% of Triton's mass. The surface of Triton is young, and there is no heavily cratered terrain. This is not surprising; the circularization of Triton's orbit by tidal effects after its capture must have deposited more than enough energy into the satellite to melt and differentiate it completely. The moon now consists of a core of rocky material surrounded by a mantle of ices. As a result of the intense tidal heating, the surface of Triton exhibits a variety of unique tectonic features. The winter polar region is covered with seasonal ice, and the surface there is not clearly visible. On the rest of the moon, the trailing hemisphere (relative to the moon's orbit about Neptune) is covered with terrain that looks like the skin of a cantaloupe: the ground is full of pits and dimples, criss-crossed by long, roughly straight ridges (Figure 11.24). The leading hemisphere is smoother, but has several frozen, terraced lakes, like volcanic calderas (Figure 11.25). In the southern hemisphere two powerful plumes, like geysers, rise to an altitude of about 8 km, where they form dense clouds which are stretched into a long tail by the winds.

Triton has a very thin atmosphere (about 10^{-5} as massive as that of Titan), mainly composed of N_2 together with a small amount of CH_4, but clouds and haze are seen, and this atmosphere is probably responsible for the transport of seasonal ices from one hemisphere to the other.

Little is known about the physical nature of the smaller moons except that they are quite dark in colour and so small that gravity cannot enforce spherical form; all are somewhat irregular in shape.

Exercise: We find planets and moons made primarily of rock, of a mixture of rock and ice, and of rock, ice, and gas. Which other combinations might be able to occur in nature? How might they form?

11.4 Planetary ring systems

Observations of the rings

As we have already seen, all four giant planets are now known to have ring systems. These ring systems exhibit a variety of complex phenomena that were hardly imagined before the 1970's, when the only known planetary rings were those of Saturn, and even for the rings of Saturn little detail can observed from the Earth. Theoretical astronomers have succeeded in explaining some of the observed features of these rings, but other aspects remain mysterious.

Figure 11.26: A view of Jupiter's ring from one of the Voyager probes, seen from behind the planet as the probe was leaving the Jupiter system. The main ring is visible as a distinct arc, while the wider dust halo is visible as a slightly brighter region inside the main arc compared to the dark sky outside. (Courtesy of NASA.)

The four ring systems are amazingly different from one another. Jupiter's single ring (Figure 11.26) is so faint that it can only be seen from behind the planet, and it has been observed only by the Voyagers and Galileo. It is made up of a single distinct main ring of rock and dust about 6000 km wide but only 30 km thick, orbiting Jupiter from about $1.72R_J$ to $1.81R_J$. It is known that the larger particles in the main ring are at least a cm in size, and are quite dark, like rock rather than water ice (note the rather unusual use of the word "particle", which in this setting can mean bodies even many meters in diameter). This ring is embedded in a larger and fainter halo of dust particles that extends inwards towards the planet. Two tiny satellites, Adrastea and Metis, orbit close to the outer edge of the main ring. The ring and these two moons are well within the planet's Roche limit, so each of the moons must be a solid block of rock.

Figure 11.27: This image of Saturn, taken as one of the Voyager spacecraft was leaving the giant planet, is somewhat overexposed for the planetary disk but clearly shows the complex structure of the major rings. In this image the clearly visible rings (starting closest to the planet) are the faint C ring, the bright B ring in which there seem to be many individual strands, the dark Cassini division, the featureless A ring with the faint dark Encke Division near its outer edge, and (as a faint thin line surrounding the A ring but separate from it) the narrow F ring. (Courtesy of NASA.)

Saturn's massive ring system, the only ring system easily seen from Earth, extends from about $0.1R_S$ (6000 km) above the planet's cloud tops out to beyond the Roche limit. The outermost distinct ring is at about $2.32R_S$, but a faint dusty ring extends out to about $8R_S$. The main part of the ring system (the part that can easily be seen from Earth) is about 70 000 km wide. Even from the Earth it can easily be seen that Saturn's ring system is divided by a series of narrow dark rings into separate broad bands (Figure 11.27). These bands are designated by the letters (from the innermost to outermost) D, C, B, A, and F. Only the C, B and A rings are easily visible from the Earth; the D and F rings were discovered by the Voyager probes. Outside these are the very tenuous G ring and the wide, faint dusty E ring. The ring system from C to A is extremely thin compared to its width, only about 50 to 100 m from bottom to top, and when viewed edge-on from

Earth, it vanishes completely.

Although the rings seem fairly complicated when viewed from Earth, the images sent back by the Voyagers revealed a whole new level of complexity. What look like broad, almost featureless rings from Earth turn out to be composed of hundreds of thin, concentric strands. The broad rings also show wave-like distortions, and faint, wedge- or finger-like markings called spokes. The extremely narrow F ring shows kinks, warps, bright knots, and in places seems to be made of two or three thinner rings braided together.

Saturn's rings are quite massive compared to those of the other giant planets; with about 2×10^{19} kg of material in the C, B and A rings, there is nearly as much mass in the rings as in the innermost intermediate moon Mimas. Note that even from space probes we have never actually observed any of the ring particles in any planetary ring; we deduce the range of sizes and other properties of ring particles from the way in which they reflect sunlight, their thermal emission, and how well they reflect radar beams. From such data we deduce that Saturn's bright rings are mostly made of particles between about 1 cm and 5 m across, although there are some tiny dust grains present as well. The ring particles are highly reflective, and the spectrum of reflected light reveals the clear signature of water ice. The Roche limit for water ice lies within the A ring; just outside this are several tiny moons, including two moons whose orbits lie just inside and just outside the F ring.

Exercise: The rings of Saturn can easily be seen from Earth, while the rings of Jupiter and Neptune are not visible from Earth. Can you draw any conclusions from these facts?

The ring system of Uranus (Figure 11.28) is composed of some ten distinct narrow rings that orbit within wider dust bands. The rings are all well within the planetary Roche limit, and are bunched between $1.64R_{\mathrm{U}}$ and $2.00R_{\mathrm{U}}$. All but two of the distinct rings are amazingly narrow, ranging in width from about 1 up to 12 km. Two of the densest rings are wider; the η ring has a width of about 55 km, and the ε ring ranges from 20 to 96 km in width. All the rings seem to be extremely flat, with thicknesses perpendicular to their orbital planes of only a few tens of meters. A final remarkable feature is that most of the distinct rings are clearly slightly non-circular (i. e. they have slight eccentricity).

The outermost and densest ε (epsilon) ring includes particles ranging from dust grains up to boulders at least a meter in diameter, and probably contains most of the mass of the entire ring system. In the other rings the particles present include some dust grains as well as many fragments at least one cm in size. The particles in these rings are as black as soot, and reflect only a few percent of the light striking them. The rings of Uranus have only about 1/4000th of the mass of the rings of Saturn, but they contain considerably more mass than the rings of either Jupiter or Neptune.

Figure 11.28: This view of the ring system of Uranus was obtained by Voyager 2 as it left Uranus behind on its way to Neptune. The part of the ring system imaged includes both the narrow rings that are visible from Earth and the wider dusty bands in which these are embedded. Some of the rings are clearly not symmetric about Uranus. The short oblique streaks are background stars whose apparent place in the sky changed during the time required to obtain this exposure. (Courtesy of NASA.)

The last of the giants to reveal its rings to Earth's inhabitants was Neptune, and again a ring system with many surprising and unique features was found. The rings were first discovered by occultations, and then extensively studied during the Voyager 2 passage through the Neptune system. Five rings are found, two distinct and narrow ones and three that are wider and fainter (Figure 11.29). The most remarkable feature of these rings is the fact that the outermost, narrow ring has several quite distinct bright clumps along part of its circumference, while the inner narrow ring is quite uniform along its length. Three of these clumps are visible in Figure 11.30.

Ring physics

The four giant planet ring systems have turned out to be far more complex and varied than anyone expected from the Earth-based views of Saturn's rings that were available before the start of space probe exploration of the outer solar system. The ring systems have a large

Figure 11.29: Two images of Neptune obtained by Voyager 2 clearly show the two bright,n arrow rings of Neptune. A thinner, more diffuse ring is faintly visible inside the inner sharp ring, and another in between the two distinct rings. (Courtesy of NASA.)

Figure 11.30: This image of Neptune's rings was obtained by Voyager 2 as it left the Neptune system behind (the back-lit disk of the planet is visible at the lower left). Only the two narrow distinct rings are visible. The inner is uniform along its length, but three quite distinct brighter segments are seen along the right side of the outer ring, where presumably some extra mass is concentrated. (Courtesy of NASA.)

range of masses, from the vast system of Saturn to the almost non-existent ring of Jupiter. All of the ring systems are extremely thin (typically tens or hundreds of m) through the ring plane, but individual rings range in radial width from 1 km up to the 70 000 km width of the Saturn's main rings. Most of the rings contain both relatively large particles (up to meters across in the rings of Saturn) and tiny dust grains. Many of the rings have distinct edges, and the wide B ring of Saturn seems to be made up of many thin concentric ringlets. The rings of Uranus are clearly eccentric. One of Neptune's rings has striking clumps, and Saturn's rings show "spokes". Mixed in with the rings are a number of tiny moons only a few km across. These remarkable systems have posed a large number of puzzles to planetary scientists, only some of which have found satisfactory answers up to now.

We can understand some of the phenomena of the ring systems if we recall the basic physical effects governing their orbital motions. The main force directing the motion of the particles that compose the rings is of course the gravity of the central planet, which forces the ring particles to move in essentially circular or elliptical orbits about the planet. A considerably weaker gravitational force is exerted on ring particles by the inner moons orbiting the planet, but as we will see, the weak moon forces can have an important effect on the shapes of rings. The ring particles also exert weak gravitational forces on one another. A third important force comes from the fact that the distinct rings have enough particles in them that collisions between ring particles are frequent, not rare, and this provides a means of changing the structure of a ring that is not available in systems with widely separated bodies, such as the main asteroid belt.

The faint, diffuse rings are mainly composed of dust particles which are subject to the same gravitational forces as the large particles from the central planet, nearby moons, and massive rings. However, in dust rings particle collisions are much rarer, and there are additional important forces such as the pressure of sunlight, effects due to thermal radiation, and even electrical and magnetic forces as these slightly electrically charged particles move through the magnetic field of their planet.

The completely dominant force of gravity from the central planet has the effect that all the ring particles move in orbits around the planet that are quite close to circles or ellipses. However, this fact alone is not enough to explain why rings are confined to a single (nearly equatorial) plane or why the various particle orbits are essentially similar (usually circular) in shape. These features of rings are consequences of the *collisions* between ring particles. As we have already mentioned in connection with the moons of Uranus, the equatorial bulge of the central planet (caused by its rapid rotation about it axis) causes the orbital plane of any ring particle whose orbit is tilted with respect to the equator of the planet to twist around slowly like a tilted spinning top. This effect guarantees that particles in such orbits will collide frequently with other particles in similar orbits. The final result is that the particles settle into orbits very close to the plane of the central planet's equator. Similarly, collisions between various ring particles moving in eccentric orbits will act like a kind of friction, and will cause the various orbits to gradually become circular. Thus, the facts that we find thin rings, very close to the planet's equatorial plane, and that the particles move in nearly circular orbits, are consequences of the occurrence of frequent collisions between ring particles.

Exercise: What disk-like collection of many particles in the solar system has the property that the particles collide only rarely, and are *not* confined to a very thin plane?

However, even when the orbits of ring particles are nearly circular and in the planet's equatorial plane, collisions between particles do not stop (although they become less frequent and less energetic). There are always particles whose orbits are a little different from those of their neighbors, and sooner or later these bodies run into others near them. Thus even when rings have become thin, flat, and circularized, there continues to be a kind of friction acting between particles orbiting the planet at different distances. This friction has the effect of speeding up the slower particles in the outer part of the ring where the orbits are slower, causing these particles to drift outwards into larger orbits. The faster particles in the inner part of a ring are slowed down slightly, causing their orbits to shrink slightly. The overall effect of the friction within a ring is to cause the ring to spread out slowly in width. Similarly, if a ring started out with a sharp inner or outer edge, we would expect this spreading effect to lead fairly rapidly to blurred edges.

Thus, the spreading effect of friction within a ring should lead planetary ring systems to be broad and diffuse. Planetary scientists were puzzled by the existence of gaps in Saturn rings, and even more astonished to find well-defined and extremely narrow rings around the other three planets. Clearly some additional processes must be acting to confine ring particles to distinct rings.

One such process is apparently the gravitational action of moons. Effects are produced by both the large moons outside the Roche limit, and also by smaller moons, usually only a few km across, that orbit close to the rings, often just inside or just outside a narrow ring. An example of such an effect is the outer edge of Saturn's B ring (the inner of the two brightest rings), where the Cassini division begins. Particles at this distance from Saturn have exactly half the orbital period of the innermost intermediate moon Mimas. (We say that these particles are in a 2:1 resonance with Mimas.) Particles orbiting here would encounter Mimas in the same place in their orbits every second revolution, so their orbits would quickly be forced to become quite eccentric, which would lead to collisions with other ring particles. This effect eliminates particles from this orbital radius, and causes the B ring to have a rather sharp edge.

Another kind of effect is "shepherding". Calculations have shown that a pair of tiny moons orbiting just inside, and just outside, a narrow ring are able to confine the particles of the ring, and prevent them from spreading out laterally. The tiny satellites Cordelia and Ophelia are apparently the shepherd moons for the ε ring of Uranus. A number of small moons were observed orbiting within the ring systems by the Voyager spacecraft, and many of the narrow rings may be confined by this mechanism. However, for other narrow rings, no shepherd moons have yet been discovered, perhaps because they were too small or dark to be detected by the Voyager cameras, or perhaps because shepherd moons are not the whole story.

There are at least tentative explanations for some of the other strange phenomena found in rings (eccentricity, clumpiness, waves, braiding, etc) but most of the explanations are rather difficult to understand in a simple way, and so we will not go farther into this problem.

Origin and evolution of ring systems

Perhaps the most interesting question about planetary rings is the question of their origin. Are the rings we see primordial, material that, because of its location inside the Roche limit, was unable to coalesce into moons, and is thus left over from the period when the planet and its large moons formed? A second possibility is that a ring results when a moon drifts inside the Roche limit (perhaps as a result of tidal interaction with the planet) and is torn apart by tidal forces. Similarly, a large comet passing close to the planet might be disrupted by tidal forces, and some of its debris could be captured. Still another possible origin would be that rings are the debris of small moons that are damaged or destroyed by high-speed collisions with passing comets.

Important clues about the origin of rings are found when we try to estimate how long the systems we observe could survive in essentially unchanged form. If we find that the observed ring systems should be able to persist largely unchanged for several Gyr, then a primordial origin is plausible. On the other hand, if the ring systems are expected to change greatly in millions of years or less, then a theory that creates ring systems continually or repeatedly may be more appropriate.

We have a couple of different ways of estimating the ages of the observed rings. For Saturn's bright, icy rings, one finds that over the age of the solar system, each particle should have collided with and accreted roughly its own mass in dark meteoritic dust. However, Saturn's ring particles are only as dark as would be expected after roughly 100 million yr of collisions. We conclude that these particles have *not* been sweeping up meteoritic dust for 4.5 Gyr: they are much younger than the solar system.

A second estimate of the ages of Saturn's rings comes from the tidal interactions between rings and their shepherd moons. The tidal interactions that allow these moons to shape the edges of rings also transfer rotation (angular momentum) between the rings and the moons. For example, the moon Prometheus (located just outside Saturn's A ring) would move the 2500 km that separates it from the A ring in only about 10 million yr. Thus the observed system will change substantially in some millions of years.

Other estimates of ring ages tend to agree that ring systems should change substantially, and perhaps even be completely disrupted or removed, within 10^7 or 10^8 yr. We conclude that the observed rings are probably relatively recent creations, not structures left over from the period of planet formation.

In this case, probably the most common method of making a ring is from the impact of a comet on a small moon. Comets passing close to one of the giant planets will typically be moving very rapidly; a comet passing within $2R_S$ of Saturn will be moving at more than 25 km s^{-1}. If such a comet struck a moon with a diameter of a few tens of km, the impact could completely shatter both the moon and the comet. Calculations based on estimates of how many comets have passed close to each of the giant planets since their formation suggest that any moon close to the Roche limit of Jupiter or Saturn with a radius of less than 1–200 km is likely to have been disrupted at least once by such impacts. Thus the rings of Jupiter, Uranus and Neptune may well have been formed by such impacts.

The case of Saturn is a little more puzzling. Its ring system is so massive that it requires the recent disruption of an intermediate moon; a small one does not supply enough mass. This should have happened only a couple of times since Saturn formed, so the probability of finding the observed ring system at any particular time (e. g. now) is not high. It is of course possible that we have simply been lucky to have such an impressive ring system on hand now. Alternatively, perhaps a really large comet struck a small moon as it passed close to Saturn, disrupting the comet and enabling most of the debris to be captured, but this is also improbable.

The diffuse rings, composed almost entirely of tiny dust particles, are expected to have even shorter lifetimes than the main rings. The dust that makes up these very faint rings is rather easily driven out of the planet system by the steady orbit changes driven by radiation effects, or the particles are slowed by gas drag from the very thin outer atmosphere of the planet and spiral quickly in towards the planet. Thus such rings need almost constant replenishment. However, these rings are often found in orbits near one or another of the small inner moons, and it appears that bombardment of these small moons by fast meteoroids is frequent enough to replenish the dust rings with debris as fast as they are cleared away.

11.5 Pluto and Charon

The outermost planet, Pluto, is a body physically very different from the other planets, although perhaps not so different from some of the moons of the giant planets, or from other bodies in the Kuiper Belt. Furthermore, as the only planet not yet visited by any spacecraft for a close-up look, it remains in many ways uniquely mysterious.

The ninth planet was discovered only in 1930, by Clyde Tombaugh, an astronomer at Percival Lowell's observatory in Arizona. The discovery of the tiny body was the culmination of a long search for fifth massive outer planet, which had been hypothesized to explain what appeared to be irregularities in the orbits of Uranus and Neptune, in the same way that Neptune was discovered through its effects on the orbit of Uranus. (We now know that these orbital irregularities do not exist; no fifth giant planet is expected, or found.) With a position so far from the Sun that it requires 248 years to complete one orbit, it seemed quite appropriate to name the new planet after the Roman god of the underworld, Pluto, especially since the first two letters of the name are also Lowell's initials.

Pluto's orbit is much more eccentric ($e \approx 0.25$) than those of the other planets (except for Mercury), and quite strongly inclined ($i \approx 17°$) to the general orbital plane of the other planets. Because of the large eccentricity of its orbit, Pluto's perihelion ($q \approx 29.7$ AU) brings it closer to the Sun than Neptune for a short part of each revolution, while at its most distant retreat from the centre of the solar system ($Q \approx 49.5$ AU) it is near the outer edge of the Kuiper Belt. One consequence of this large eccentricity is that the solar energy falling on the planet varies by about a factor of three between perihelion and aphelion. The planet passed perihelion on 5 September 1989, and is now moving away from the Sun.

With an orbit that crosses that of Neptune, it would appear that Pluto would be in considerable danger of colliding with the larger planet. However, it is now clear that Pluto is locked in a 3:2 orbital resonance with Neptune (Neptune makes three revolutions about the Sun for two made by Pluto), so that Neptune passes Pluto only when the ninth planet is near the outermost part of its orbit, at a safe distance of about 17 AU from Neptune.

Exercise: Sketch the orbits of Neptune and Pluto and show how the 3:2 ratio of orbital periods leads to Neptune always passing Pluto when the smaller planet is in a particular part of its orbit.

Because Pluto is both small and very distant, for many years after its discovery almost nothing was learned about it except for its orbit. It appeared as an unresolved point of light (less than $1''$ in diameter) in ground-based telescopes, and so its diameter was essentially unknown, except for an upper limit (provided by a stellar occultation that did not occur) of 6500 km. No information at all was available about its mass. One discovery of note was made during this period: in the 1950's it was found that the planet's brightness varies regularly, by about 30%, in a 6.4 day cycle which is clearly the rotation period. This shows immediately that the planet has a surface which is not uniformly reflective.

The situation changed dramatically in 1978 when two astronomers at the U. S. Naval Observatory (only a few km from Lowell's observatory in Arizona) discovered that Pluto has a moon, so close to the planet (less than $1''$ away) that its light blends with that of Pluto except for observations under the best possible conditions. The new moon was quickly named Charon, after the boatman who ferrys the dead to the underworld in Greek mythology. This moon has made possible major advances in our knowledge of the tiny ninth planet.

Careful imaging from Earth, both from the ground and later from the Hubble Space Telescope (see Figure 11.31), showed that Charon moves around Pluto in an orbit with a semi-major axis of about 19,600 km. Furthermore, Charon's orbital period around Pluto is found to be synchronized with the planet's own rotation. The Pluto-Charon system is the only planet-moon pair in the solar system which is fully tidally locked, so that *both* bodies rotate synchronously with their mutual orbit, and each can be seen only from one side of the other. From the orbital period and semi-major axis, the mass of Pluto could be determined for the first time. The tiny planet has a mass of only about 0.0021 of the Earth's mass, less even than the mass of Neptune's moon Triton. (From the relative motions of Pluto and Charon on the sky, which has been successfully observed both from HST and from the ground, Charon's mass is found to be about 12% of that of Pluto.)

Figure 11.31: An image of Pluto and its moon Charon taken with the Hubble Space Telescope when the two bodies were near their maximum apparent separation on the sky. (Courtesy of NASA.)

The plane of Charon's orbit, and of Pluto's equator, is oriented roughly perpendicular to the plane of the solar system, and at present the rotation axes of the two bodies are roughly parallel to the direction of their orbital motion around the Sun. As a result, we had the good luck that only a few years after the discovery of Charon, the Earth moved into Charon's orbital plane, and the planet and moon began to eclipse one another. Timing of these eclipses ("mutual events") made possible, for the first time, accurate measurements of the radii of the two bodies, which were later confirmed by direct imaging by the HST. It is found that the radius of Charon (about 590 km) is about half that of Pluto itself (about 1150 km), making Charon the largest moon, relative to its planet, in the solar system. Combining the planetary radius with the mass, we find that Pluto has a mean density which is about 2050 kg m^{-3}. The planet therefore has a composition, assuming as usual a mix of rock and ice, which is around 60 – 75% rock. This proportion is one of the largest values found among the moons of Saturn, Uranus, and Neptune, which generally have between 50 and 60% rock; only Titan, Oberon, and Triton have similarly large rock fractions. Charon is found to have a similarly large mean density, about 1800 kg m^{-3}, so its proportion of rock is similar to that of Pluto.

One final discovery of note was that of strong evidence in the infra-red spectrum of the presence of CH_4 frost on the planet's surface. Because this ice has an appreciable vapour pressure even at the very low temperature expected on Pluto's surface (roughly 50 K), it was realized that the planet must have a very thin atmosphere. This was confirmed in 1988 when the occultation of a bright star occurred with the kind of gradual dimming expected due to this atmosphere. In contrast, Charon shows no trace of CH_4, but does appear to have water ice at its surface.

Because Pluto has never been visited by a spacecraft, we have no close-up pictures of its surface, and thus no direct evidence as to whether the planet is differentiated or homogeneous. However, there are several reasons to think that Pluto probably is differentiated. Recall that, like the moons of the giants, differentiation occurs if the *ices* are melted, which only requires a temperature rise of about 200 K from the current temperature near 50 K. Some of the arguments pointing towards differentiation are the following. (a) Accretion of the planet could have provided enough energy to melt the ices if most of the gravitational energy released was retained by the planet. (b) With the high rock fraction in the planet, radioactivity would probably have released enough energy by now to cause melting. (c) The observed surface CH_4 frost would not be present if the CH_4 were mixed with other, less volatile ices such as water ice; the surface methane would have evaporated and escaped from the planet, leaving a surface of other, less volatile ices. We deduce that the surface coating of CH_4 may be at least some km thick, which appears to require that differentiation has taken place. (d) Finally (see below), we think that Charon became bound to Pluto after a giant impact somewhat like that now thought to have formed the Earth's Moon; this would also probably have released enough energy to melt the planet.

If we are correct that Pluto has differentiated, a plausible interior model would have a core of rock roughly 900 km in radius, with a layer of mostly water ice above, probably about 250 km thick, that extends to within some km of the surface. Above all is a thin layer, some km thick, of methane ice. The internal temperature could be somewhere in the vicinity of the melting point of water, although the surface is at a chilly 40 to 50 K.

The origin of an apparently unique, tiny planet in the outer solar system has long been a mystery. Pluto's Neptune-crossing orbit led to the proposal that Pluto might once have been a moon of Neptune that suffered a close encounter with Triton, ejecting Pluto from the Neptune system and putting Triton into its present unusual retrograde orbit. This idea now seems very unlikely for several reasons: first, because Pluto is less massive than Triton, Pluto would not be able to reverse Triton's orbit; secondly, because Pluto would leave Neptune in an orbit which would intersect that of Neptune, the two planets would rather quickly collide; and finally, it is not at all obvious how Pluto could get from a Neptune-intersecting orbit into its present strongly Neptune-avoiding 3:2 resonance orbit.

Most scientists now suppose that Pluto formed as an independent body, by accretion of planetesimals, early in the history of the solar system. The recent discovery of hundreds of bodies in the Kuiper Belt, many of which have dimensions approaching those of Charon, certainly makes this origin seem quite plausible. Furthermore, the existence of the many bodies in the Kuiper Belt may offer a reasonable explanation of the origin of the Pluto-Charon system. With probably thousands of bodies in this region, it does not seem too unlikely that Pluto might have suffered a collision with a large one, leading to formation a moon out of the collision debris. Note, however, that because of the small size of the bodies involved, such a collision would have occurred with only about 1/10th the relative velocity that the Earth and its moon had at the time of their collision, so the heating effect – though probably enough to melt Pluto – would have been much less catastrophic. Nevertheless, enough volatiles might have been lost from the Pluto-Charon system to account for its relatively large mean density, and for that of Charon.

Although the solar system's outermost planet is still known quite imperfectly, it is no longer the total mystery it was for the first half century after its discovery. Instead, its particular nature – unique, but clearly related to other objects we have gotten to know – reminds us again of the immense variety and strangeness of the small system of bodies that travel through the Milky Way together with our Sun.

11.6 Mathematical aspects

Gravity, hydrostatic equilibrium, and cooling

Many of the ideas that we have discussed in the Mathematical Aspects sections of earlier chapters are relevant to the giant planets and their moons. For example, we have discussed in Chapters 8 and 9 how the mean density of a planet or moon may be used with reasonable guesses about possible substances making up the body to estimate the relative fractions of these components, and if they are separated, to estimate the size of the core and the mantle.

Exercise: Data about Jupiter's moon Callisto may

be found in Table A.3. Assume that this moon is composed of partly of ice (of density 900 kg m^{-3}) and partly of rock (of density 3500 kg m^{-3}). (a) Show that the general expression relating the mass fractions f_1 and $f_2 = 1 - f_1$ of two composition components of densities ρ_1 and ρ_2 to the observed mean density $\overline{\rho}$ of the moon is simply

$$\overline{\rho} = \frac{1}{f_1/\rho_1 + f_2/\rho_2}. \tag{11.1}$$

(b) Use the measured mean density of Callisto to estimate the fraction of the total mass that is rock, and the fraction that is ice. Do you find that these components each make up roughly half of the moon's mass?

The estimate that you derived earlier (Equation 6.8) for the maximum possible temperature increase that could be produced by the conversion of gravitational accretion energy into internal energy should apply to the accretion of the Galilean moons.

Exercise: Assume that the material from which Europa formed had an initial temperature of 100 K. Could accretion have supplied a large enough temperature increase to melt ice (273 K) and lead to separation of a rocky core from an ice mantle?

We have also seen that internally and in any atmospheres present, the material of these bodies will be approximately in hydrostatic equilibrium, which we examined in Chapters 3 and 8. This fact may be used to estimate conditions both in the deep interior of a planet or moon, and in its atmosphere.

Exercise: Use the reasoning discussed in Chapter 3 to estimate the order of magnitude of the pressure at the centre of Saturn. Does your result agree reasonably with the value you infer from Figure 11.5?

Exercise: At the top of Jupiter's uppermost cloud deck, the pressure is about 6×10^4 Pa. Assuming for simplicity that the gas is all H_2 molecules, estimate the local number density of molecules (number per m^3), and the total mass of gas per m^2 above this level. (You may want to look back at Chapters 3 or 10.)

Another aspect of the giants and their moons that can be studied with physics we have already met is the surface temperatures expected from equilibrium with sunlight. Recall from Equation 7.3 that this depends on the albedos for visible and infrared radiation, as well as the distance of the bodies from the sun.

Exercise: Europa reflects 58% of the visible light falling on it, while Callisto reflects only 13%. Assuming that both moons reflect only about 5% of infrared radiation, determine the average surface temperatures of the two moons. Why is the surface of Europa cooler than that of Callisto? (Hint: don't just directly apply Equation (7.4).)

Growth of a surface ice layer

Yet another problem we can examine is the rate of growth of the ice layer over a sea of water on a moon of one of the giant planets shortly after it first forms. Let's assume that the layer is so thin that the ice layer can be treated as flat, not curved around the moon. We also assume that the only way in which heat is carried out through the icy crust is by thermal conduction; this is the key assumption, because if solid-state convection is able to start in the ice, heat will be transported much more efficiently than by simple conduction. Finally, we assume that the surface layer of the ice is held at a constant temperature T_s by the balance between incoming sunlight and thermal re-radiation [Equation (7.4)], and that the bottom of the ice layer is held at the melting temperature of the water in the sea, T_m (why?).

Now a certain amount of energy will leak out from the sea below to the surface of the ice sheet. We measure this heat leakage by the heat flux q, the energy carried through the ice sheet per m^2 per s. From Equation (6.9), at a time t when the ice sheet has reached a thickness $D(t)$, this heat flux is given by

$$q = k_c \frac{T_m - T_s}{D}. \tag{11.2}$$

This means that in some time dt, the amount of energy lost from one square m of the sea is $q\,dt$. Now let us suppose that the rate of heating of the sea by radioactive energy release in the core is insignificant compared to the rate of heat leakage through the ice layer, which it will be shortly after the liquid water at the surface of the moon starts to freeze. In this case, the heat lost from one m^2 at the top of the sea will have to be provided by freezing a thin layer of ice onto the bottom of the ice sheet; the energy needed will be the latent heat of fusion released by this process. The amount of latent heat released in freezing one m^3 of ice is $L\rho$, where L is the latent heat per kg and ρ is the density of the ice. Thus to provide an amount of energy $q\,dt$ from one m^2 at the top of the sea, a volume $dV = 1 \times dD$ must freeze such that

$$q\,dt = L\rho\,dV = L\rho\,dD \tag{11.3}$$

where dD is the thickness by which the ice layer increases in dt. Then

$$L\rho \frac{dD}{dt} = k_c \frac{T_m - T_s}{D}. \tag{11.4}$$

This equation may be rewritten as

$$D \frac{dD}{dt} = \frac{k_c (T_m - T_s)}{L\rho} \tag{11.5}$$

which is easily integrated (with $D = 0$ at $t = 0$) to yield

$$D(t) = \left(\frac{2k_c(T_m - T_s)}{L\rho}t\right)^{1/2}. \quad (11.6)$$

Thus we see that the thickness of the ice layer grows as the square root of the time elapsed since the start of freezing, rather than linearly with time. (This is the basic reason that most lakes on Earth do not freeze all the way to the bottom during the winter.)

Exercise: Using data from Tables 2.4 and 6.7, estimate the amount of time that would be required for a surface ice layer to reach a thickness of 20 km on Jupiter's moon Ganymede.

Tidal disruption

We next turn to the subject of tidal disruption. Unlike the description of the orbital movement of a small body around a larger one, tidal disruption cannot easily be described exactly. Instead, we look for a way to get an estimate of the size of this effect by suitable approximations.

To treat tidal disruption approximately, recall that the force of gravity exerted by one point mass (or spherical body) of mass M, radius R, and density ρ_M, on another of mass m, radius r, and density ρ_{rmm}, is

$$F = GMm/a^2, \quad (11.7)$$

where G is the gravitational constant and a is the separation of M from m. Now to estimate the tidal effect of M on m, we divide m mentally into two halves, one on the side near M and the other on the side opposite M. Suppose now that the body m is held together by gravity, so that the force holding these two halves together is only gravitational; then the attractive force of gravity F_g of the near half of m on the far half of m is (rather approximately)

$$F_g \approx \frac{G(m/2)(m/2)}{(r)^2} = \frac{Gm^2}{4r^2}. \quad (11.8)$$

Opposing the self-gravity of m is the tidal effect of M. The attraction of M on the near half of m is approximately

$$\begin{aligned} F_n &\approx \frac{GM(m/2)}{(a-r/2)^2} = \frac{GMm}{2a^2(1-r/2a)^2} \\ &\approx \frac{GMm}{2a^2}(1+r/a), \end{aligned} \quad (11.9)$$

where have used a first-order Taylor expansion of the parenthesis in the denominator to get the last approximate equality. Similarly, the gravitational force due to M on the far side of m is approximately

$$F_f \approx \frac{GM(m/2)}{(a+r/2)^2} \approx \frac{GMm}{2a^2}(1-r/a). \quad (11.10)$$

Because of the larger distance of the far half of m from M compared to the separation of the near half of m and M, F_n is somewhat larger than F_f. Thus M will tend to attract the near half of m toward itself more strongly than the far half. This is the origin of the tidal effect. To keep the two halves of m moving together, we need the attractive force F_a of the near half of m on the far half, and the attractive force by the far half of m on the near half to be strong enough that the net force on each half of m equal, so that they follow the same orbits. This requires that $F_f + F_a = F_n - F_a$, or

$$\begin{aligned} F_a &\approx (F_n - F_f)/2 \\ &\approx \frac{GMm}{4a^2}[(1+r/a)-(1-r/a)] \\ &= GMmr/2a^3. \end{aligned} \quad (11.11)$$

Now for the small body to be stable against gravitational disruption, its self-gravity must be large enough to supply the required F_a, so stability occurs for

$$F_g \approx Gm^2/4r^2 \geq F_a \approx GMmr/2a^3, \quad (11.12)$$

or

$$a > r(2M/m)^{1/3} \approx r_{\rm Roche}. \quad (11.13)$$

But now the density of M is just $\rho_M = M/(4\pi R^3/3)$, while $\rho_m = m/(4\pi r^3/3)$, so we may rewrite $r_{\rm Roche}$ as

$$\begin{aligned} r_{\rm Roche} &\approx r(2M/m)^{1/3} \\ &\approx R(2\rho_M/\rho_m)^{1/3} \\ &\approx 1.26R(\rho_M/\rho_m)^{1/3}. \end{aligned} \quad (11.14)$$

From this form it is easy to see that tidal disruption only occurs for separation a not much greater than the radius R of the larger body, and that larger density ρ_m decreases $r_{\rm Roche}$ and promotes stability of m.

Although the derivation above is quite rough, the result shows the correct dependence of $r_{\rm Roche}$ on the two densities, with a coefficient which is of the right order of magnitude. The exact result for two fluid bodies of uniform density is

$$r_{\rm Roche} = 2.45R(\rho_M/\rho_m)^{1/3}. \quad (11.15)$$

This is the value of the Roche limit that should be used for computations.

Note that a single object held together by internal forces that are stronger than gravity (a solid piece of ice, for example) will not be disrupted even if it ventures inside the Roche limit of a larger body.

Exercise: Estimate the Roche limit [using Equation (11.15)], expressed in units of planetary radii, for tidal disruption of (a) the Earth's Moon by Earth and (b) Io by Jupiter. (c) Is the outer edge of Jupiter's ring, at $1.81R_J$, inside or outside the Roche limit for a solid body made of water ice that orbits Jupiter?

11.7 References

Atreya, S. K. et al. 1999, "A comparison of the atmospheres of Jupiter and Saturn: deep atmospheric composition, cloud structure, vertical mixing, and origin", *Plan. Space Sci.*, 47, 1243. Current problems in understanding the atmospheres of Jupiter and Saturn are summarized in detail in this review article.

Binzel, R. 1990, "Pluto", *Sci. Am.*, Jun., 50. Binzel provides a wide-ranging discussion of what was known about Pluto, including first attempts to map its spotted surface, before HST observations began.

Burns, J. A., Hamilton, D. P. and Showalter, M. R. 2002, "Bejeweled Worlds", *Sci. Am.*, Feb., 64. A nicely illustrated view of the rings of the four large outer planets.

Cuzzi, J. N. and Esposito, L. W. 1987, "The rings of Uranus", *Sci. Am.*, Jul., 52. Planetary rings are much more complicated, and probably ephemeral, than we ever imagined. This article discusses some of the puzzles they offer.

Drake, S. and Kowal, C. T. 1980, "Galileo's sighting of Neptune", *Sci. Am.*, Dec., p. 74. Neptune was observed long before it was discovered.

Esposito, L. W. 1993, "Understanding Planetary Rings", *Ann. Rev. Earth Planet. Sci.*, 21, 487. Esposito discusses many of the main problems encountered in understanding planetary rings, and describes some of the answers that have been proposed, in the somewhat technical (but largely non-mathematical) review.

Grasset, O., Sotin, C. and Deschamps, F. 2000, "On the internal structure and dynamics of Titan", *Planet. Space Sci.*, 48, 617. This somewhat technical article describes how the interior of Titan (as well as Ganymede and Callisto) may have evolved since the moon was formed.

Hubbard, W. B. 1984, *Planetary Interiors* (New York: Van Nostrand Reinhold). Chapter 8 of this excellent advanced textbook has a very clear discussion of how we deduce the interior composition and structure of the giant planets and their moons.

Ingersoll, A. P. 1981, "Jupiter and Saturn", *Sci. Am.*, Dec., 90. Ingersoll describes efforts to understand both the interior structure and atmospheres of the two giants in the light of Voyager data.

Ingersoll, A. P. 1987, "Uranus", *Sci. Am.*, Jan., 38. Deductions from the Voyager 2 fly-by of Uranus in 1986 are surveyed.

Johnson, T. V. 1995, "The Galileo mission", *Sci. Am.*, Dec., 44. The most ambitious space probe mission to Jupiter is described, mainly focusing on the technical challenges.

Johnson, T. V. 2000, "The Galileo mission to Jupiter and its moons", *Sci. Am.*, Feb., 40. In spite of major technical problems, the Galileo space probe has made possible a detailed study of Jupiter and its large moons.

Johnson, T. V. et al 1987, "The moons of Uranus", *Sci. Am.*, Apr., 48. Voyager 2 not only discovered 10 new moons of Uranus, but also showed that three of the larger ones have had a geologically active past.

Laeser, R. P. et al 1986, "Engineering Voyager 2's encounter with Uranus", *Sci. Am.*, Nov., 36. A lot of in-flight engineering of Voyager 2 made possible its spectacularly successful fly-by of Uranus.

Malhotra, R. 1999, "Migrating planets", *Sci. Am.*, Sep., 56. Calculations suggest that the orbits of Neptune, Pluto, and some of the bodies of the Kuiper Belt have changed substantially since the solar system formed.

Miner, E. D. 1990, "Voyager 2's encounter with the gas giants", *Phys. Today*, Jul., 40. Miner describes the many technical challenges of the Voyager missions to the outer planets, and summarizes the main scientific results.

Owen, T. C. 2000, "On the origin of Titan's atmosphere", *Planet. Space Sci.*, 48, 747. Owen explains the arguments leading to the present ideas about how Titan's atmosphere originated.

Pappalardo, R. T. et al. 1999, "The hidden ocean of Europa", *Sci. Am.*, Oct., 54. Deep under its icy crust, Europa may have an ocean of liquid water kept warm by tidal heating.

Peale, S. J. 1999, "Origin and evolution of the natural satellites", in *Ann. Rev. Astr. Ap.*, 37, 533. Peale presents a comprehensive (but fairly advanced) discussion of all the satellite systems in the solar system with particular emphasis on how tidal effects have changed both orbits and in some cases internal structure.

Pollack, James B. 1984, "Origin and history of the outer planets: theoretical models and observational constraints", in *Ann. Rev. Astr. Ap.*, 22, 389. This review article discusses theories of the formation of the outer planets and their moons, and how observational data can help to select among competing theories.

Pollack, J. B. and Cuzzi, J. N. 1981, "Rings in the solar system", *Sci. Am.*, Nov., 104. The Voyagers revealed much unexpected complexity in the rings of the outer planets, especially those of Saturn.

Showman, A. P. and Malhotra, R. 1999, "The Galilean satellites", *Science*, 286, 77. This article reviews the many kinds of new information gathered about the four large moons of Jupiter by the Galileo orbiter, and has a lot of useful references to more detailed articles.

Soderblom, L. A. and Johnson, T. V. 1982, "The moons of Saturn", *Sci. Am.*, Jan., 101. The two Voyagers have revealed that most of the moons of Saturn are heavily cratered, and Enceladus shows evidence of complex evolution.

Stern, S. A. 1992, "The Pluto-Charon system", *Ann. Rev. Astron. Astrophys.*, 30, 185. Stern examines the structure and development of both Pluto and its moon in this comprehensive review.

Stevenson, D. J. 1982, "Interiors of the giant planets", in *Ann. Rev. Earth Planet. Sci.*, 10, 257. A clear review describing how we obtain information from a combination of theory and observation about the internal structure of the giant planets.

11.8 Review questions

11.1 How can we determine the mass and radius of a giant planet? Using densities derived from these data, does it appear that all four giant planets have similar chemical composition?

11.2 Why is it useful to simplify the composition of the giants to gas, ice, and rock?

11.3 How is a "model" of a giant planet made? What is the difference between a "cold" model and a "warm" one?

11.4 What are the main ways in which Uranus and Neptune differ from Jupiter and Saturn?

11.5 What processes might have formed the giant planets? What data and arguments allow us to choose one possibility over others?

11.6 How hot are the giants inside? Where does internal heat come from, and how does it reach the surface?

11.7 What can we deduce about the chemical composition of the moons of the giant planets?

11.8 Why does water ice predominate over frozen methane, ammonia, or carbon dioxide in the moons of the giants?

11.9 What heat sources may have powered tectonic activity in the moons of the giant planets?

11.10 How do surface features help us to understand the history of the moons of the giant planets? How can we tell if a moon is differentiated or not?

11.11 How could a moon be captured by a giant planet?

11.12 What processes change planetary rings with time, and cause them to evolve?

11.13 How can shepherd moons exist inside a planetary Roche limit?

11.14 How may rings have formed? Are they probably permanent features of their planets?

11.9 Problems

11.1 Jupiter has about 5×10^{29} molecules of H_2 and 1×10^{29} molecules of He per m^2 above the NH_3 ice cloud tops, where the local temperature is $T_c = 140$ K. (Note: these are *total* numbers of molecules above each square meter, *not* local number densities.) Write down an expression for the pressure p_c at the cloud tops using this information, and evaluate it. (b) Assume that the atmosphere is convective below the NH_3 cloud tops, and that the temperature increases with depth s at the constant adiabatic lapse rate of $dT/ds = 2 \times 10^{-3}$ K m^{-1}. Write down an expression for the temperature $T(s)$ below the cloud tops, and then the equation of hydrostatic equilibrium including explicitly the variation of temperature with depth. (c) Integrate the resulting equation of hydrostatic equilibrium to find the variation of $p(s)$ with depth. Use the known values of pressure and temperature at the NH_3 cloud tops to evaluate any constants. (d) The bottom of the water ice clouds occur at a depth where the temperature is about 280 K.

Evaluate the depth s_w of this level below the level of p_c, and find the pressure $p(s_w)$ there.

11.2 At the top of the NH_3 clouds in Saturn's atmosphere, the temperature is about 110 K and the pressure is about 0.5 bar. Below this level the atmosphere is convecting and the temperature increases with depth s at a constant rate of $dT/ds = 7 \times 10^{-4}$ K m^{-1}. (a) Write down an explicit expression for the value of temperature as a function of depth, $T(s)$, and the expression for the equation of hydrostatic equilibrium including this explicit variation of $T(s)$. (Eliminate density from the equation of hydrostatic equilibrium using the ideal gas law, assuming that Saturn's atmosphere is composed of pure H_2.) (b) Integrate your equation of hydrostatic equilibrium to find an explicit expression for the pressure $p(s)$ as a function of depth below the NH_3 cloud tops. Use the data above to evaluate any constants. (c) Use the ideal gas law and your expressions for $p(s)$ and $T(s)$ to find an expression for the density $\rho(s)$ as a function of depth. (d) The separation of the two nuclei in H_2 is about 7.4×10^{-11} m, so two molecules will essentially touch when their separation is of the order of 10^{-10} m. When the density is high enough for the mean separation between molecules to be of this order, H_2 will surely be essentially liquid rather than gaseous. Imagine for counting purposes that the H_2 molecules in a liquid are arranged in a simple lattice of rows, columns, and layers with all the spacings between adjacent molecules being 1×10^{-10} m. What is the density of H_2 in this state, in kg m^{-3}? (e) Use your results from parts (c) and (d) to estimate the depth below the cloud tops at which Saturn's interior changes from a gas to a molecular liquid.

11.3 Atoms of all atomic numbers have radii comparable to twice the Bohr radius $a_o = 5.29 \times 10^{-11}$ m. In general, one cannot crowd atoms significantly closer together than a mean spacing of $\sim 4a_o$ without providing enough energy to disrupt the electrostatic structure of the atoms (i.e. without providing enough energy to detach at least the valence electrons, thus ionizing the atoms). (a) Calculate the approximate density of liquid hydrogen, of a common rock such as Mg_2SiO_4, and of lead, assuming that in all cases the spacing between atoms is approximately $4a_o$. (Recall that Mg_2SiO_4 has seven atoms, not one.) Compare your estimates to measured values. Considering that this is only an order-of-magnitude estimate, do you think that the assumption of a universal atomic size is roughly correct? (b) Assume that a giant planet of radius R is composed entirely of H, with a (compressed) density of 300 kg m^{-3}. Compute the total number of atoms in the planet, and the gravitational energy released in forming the planet. How large must the radius R be in order for the gravitational energy to be just large enough to provide enough energy to remove the electron from each H atom, assuming that this requires of order $E_{\rm coulomb} \sim e^2/4\pi\varepsilon_o a_o$ Joules per atom? (This is a rough estimate of the minimum mass a planet must have to convert all molecular H into metallic H.) Compare your calculated mass to that of Jupiter.

11.4 (a) Use the measured mean density of Ganymede from Table A.3 to determine the mass fractions of ice (density 900 kg m^{-3}) and rock (density 3200 kg m^{-3}). (b) Assume that Ganymede has separated into a core-mantle structure. Using the mass fractions from (a), determine the radius of the core and the thickness of the mantle. (c) Estimates of the densities of each composition component are always uncertain because of imprecise knowledge of how the moon accreted. Assume that the density of ice is relatively certain, but that the density of the rocky component is uncertain by ± 400 kg m^{-3}. Estimate the corresponding uncertainty in the radius of the core.

11.5 This is problem to examine the break-up of Comet Shoemaker-Levy 9 (SL-9) which struck Jupiter in 1994 (see Figure 7.11). Comet specialists have concluded that SL-9 passed Jupiter in July 1992 at a distance of about 113,000 km from the planet's centre, well within the Roche limit, when the comet broke into a number of fragments. In this problem, we will see that the break-up in 1992 explains very nicely the fact that the pieces arrived at Jupiter in July 1994 over a period of about 1 week, rather than all together. (a) Using the time between the last two approaches to Jupiter and Kepler's third law, determine the semi-major axis of the last orbit of SL-9 around Jupiter. (Be sure to use Jupiter's mass, not that of the Sun!) (b) Now let us assume that the comet was about 5 km across when it broke up, and that it broke up at its closest approach to the planet. Thus the *nearest* pieces of comet to Jupiter were at a distance r_1 about 5 km less than the distance r_2 of the *farthest* pieces. However, at the moment of breakup, all the pieces were travelling at the *same* velocity. Use the *vis viva* equation (Equation 1.14), and the fact that the velocities of all fragments at break-up were the same, to determine the difference between the semi-major axes of the orbits of the "extreme" fragments, 2.5 km closer and farther from Jupiter than the average. (This can be done directly on your pocket calculator if you keep enough decimals, or more elegantly using Taylor expansions.) Then use Kepler's third law again to find the difference in the extreme periods. You should find that the difference in the orbital periods of the fastest and slowest fragments is of the order of some days, neatly explaining the spread in arrival times of the pieces of SL-9.

11.6 One of the major factors in the evolution of the small moons close to Saturn has probably been impacts by comets. In this problem we look at just how destructive a comet impact could be. The problem is to estimate the relative velocity of a plausible comet with a small moon when they collide. (a) Consider a spherical comet composed of water ice and having a radius of 10 km, entering the inner solar system from an aphelion distance of 1×10^4 AU. What is the velocity of this comet as it reaches Saturn's distance from the Sun, 9.54 AU? (b) Now calculate approximately the effect of entering the gravity field of Saturn by using conservation of energy, starting with the velocity calculated in part (a), which we can assume applies at, say, 5×10^6 km from Saturn, to determine the velocity of the comet as it reaches a distance from Saturn of 150,000 km (about the orbital radius of Janus or Epimetheus). (c) Finally, suppose that the comet strikes a small moon at this distance from Saturn. Suppose, to maximize the effect, that the moon is travelling around Saturn in a circular orbit and encounters the comet head–on. What is the approximate relative velocity $v_{\rm rel}$ at the moment of impact? What is the kinetic energy release in the impact, computed as $m_{\rm comet} v_{\rm rel}^2/2$? (d) Consider a moon with a uniform mixture of 0.75 ice and 0.25 rock, of radius $R_{\rm m}$. What is the minimum radius the moon must have for the collision to bring in less energy to the system than the gravitational binding energy of the moon, and thus be unable to completely disrupt the moon?

11.7 As discussed in the text, Titan may have an icy crust with a sea beneath. One way in which this could happen would be if the ices that formed Titan contained a few percent of NH_3, which seems likely. The ammonia would act as an anti-freeze, keeping water liquid down to a temperature of about 170 K. In this case, the cold liquid at the bottom of the icy surface crust would keep the ice so cold that solid state convection would be very inefficient, and most of the heat loss through the crust would be by simple thermal conduction. Assuming that this is the case, we can estimate the thickness of the ice crust on the moon. (a) First, we need an estimate of the heat flowing out of the rocky core of the moon. Assume that the heat loss from the core is approximately equal to the current production by radioactivity. Compute the expected energy output, using data from Chapter 6 (Table 6.5) as necessary. (b) Then assume that this heat production in the moon's core is just in balance with the heat loss through the ice crust, which has its outer boundary at 94 K and its inner boundary at 170 K (the temperature of the ammonia-rich water sea). Find the thickness of ice that is consistent with this balance.

11.8 Let's consider the possible evolution of a disk around a planet, a structure like one of Saturn's rings. We will suppose that the material is in the form of small particles spread uniformly from an inner radius $R_{\rm i}$ to an outer radius $R_{\rm o}$, with a uniform average surface mass density σ (this is the total amount of matter contained in each square m of the ring plane, and is measured in kg m^{-2}). Within this disk the various particles will be orbiting the central planet (of mass $M_{\rm p}$) in nearly circular Keplerian orbits, but we expect that small deviations from circular orbits will produce collisions between ring particles, causing a kind of friction between neighboring orbits, which will have the effect of gradually slowing the innermost particles (and thus decreasing the inner radius of the disk), and of speeding up the outermost particles (increasing the outer radius). Let's suppose that the disk evolves under the influence of this internal friction but without any external torques acting. (a) Write down an expression for the total mass in a narrow ring of radial extent dR. Integrate this expression from $R_{\rm i}$ to $R_{\rm o}$ to find the total mass $M_{\rm d}$ of the disk in terms of $R_{\rm i}$, $R_{\rm o}$ and σ. (b) Write down an expression for the angular momentum dL of the narrow ring of radial extent dR, and integrate this expression to find the total angular momentum L of the disk. (You may compute the velocity $v(R)$ of the ring at R by equating the gravitational acceleration due to the central planet with the acceleration which produces circular motion.) (c) Write down an expression for the total energy $dE_{\rm tot}$, kinetic plus gravitational (which of course is negative) of a small ring of width dR. Use your expression for $v(R)$ to simplify this result. Integrate the result from $R_{\rm i}$ to $R_{\rm o}$ to find the total energy of the disk (this should be negative). (d) Now suppose that the disk spreads out as a result of the friction discussed above to new inner and outer radii $R'_{\rm i}$ and $R'_{\rm o}$, still keeping the same total mass and uniform surface density. This will decrease the surface density to a new value σ'. Find an expression for σ' in terms of σ and the various R's. (e) Because we have assumed no external torques, the expanded disk should have the same value of L as before. Use this requirement to find one relation between the original values of R_i and R_o and the new values. Don't forget that the expanded disk has a different σ than the original one. [Hint: simplify your result using the fact that $a^4 - b^4 = (a^2 - b^2)(a^2 + b^2)$.] (f) Now find an expression for the new total energy E'_{tot} of the expanded disk. Use your result from (c), replacing the σ' by your expression from (d). This will result in an expression in both the old and the new dimensions. (g) Now (finally!) suppose that the original disk extended from $1.5R_p$ to $1.7R_p$, and that the new inner boundary is at $1.3R_p$. Use your result from (e) to find the new outer radius of the disk, and then find the *ratio* of the original total disk energy to the new total energy. The result should be a little larger than 1. Since both energies are negative, this shows that the new disk has *decreased* in total energy; this is where the energy comes from that is dissipated in the disk's internal friction. You have just demonstrated a specific example of a general result, that dissipation resulting in expansion decreases the total energy of a disk, and thus is the way in which the disk will evolve. The disk cannot evolve from a wider to a narrower shape without external energy input.

11.9 Suppose a small spherical icy body is held together mainly by solid body crystal forces rather than gravity, and that it has a tensile strength of 1.5×10^6 N m^{-2} (i.e. it is an iceberg and a force per unit area of 1.5×10^6 N m^{-2} would break it). Could any planet in the solar system disrupt it by tidal forces? Assume a density of 1000 kg m^{-3} and a radius of 1 km for the small body.

Appendix A

Characteristics of planets and moons

Table A.1: Orbits of the planets

Planet or Asteroid	Mean distance a from Sun (AU)	Mean orbital speed v (km s^{-1})	Period of revolution P (yr)	Orbital inclination i (°)	Orbital eccentricity e
Mercury	0.3871	47.9	0.241	7.0	0.206
Venus	0.7233	35.0	0.615	3.4	0.007
Earth	1.0000	29.8	1.000	(0.0)	0.017
Mars	1.523	24.1	1.881	1.9	0.093
Jupiter	5.203	13.1	11.86	1.3	0.048
Saturn	9.585	9.6	29.67	2.5	0.056
Uranus	19.15	6.8	83.8	0.8	0.047
Neptune	29.96	5.4	164.0	1.8	0.009
Pluto	39.3	4.7	246.3	17.2	0.250

Note : Most of these orbital characteristics change slightly with time.
Source: Gupta, R. (ed.) 2002, *Observer's Handbook 2002* (Toronto: Royal Astronomical Society of Canada)

Table A.2: Physical characteristics of the planets.

Planet	Mass (kg)	Mass relative to Earth	Equatorial radius (km)	Equatorial radius relative to Earth	Mean density ρ (kg m^{-3})	Rotation period P_{rot} (day)	Obliquity of rotation axis[a] (°)
Mercury	3.302×10^{23}	0.055	2439	0.383	5440	58.65	0
Venus	4.869×10^{24}	0.815	6051	0.949	5250	243.0	3[b]
Earth	5.974×10^{24}	(1.000)	6378	(1.000)	5515	0.997	23.4
Mars	6.419×10^{23}	0.108	3394	0.532	3933	1.03	25.2
Jupiter	1.899×10^{27}	317.8	71492	11.27	1326	0.410	3.1
Saturn	5.685×10^{26}	95.2	60268	9.46	687	0.444	25.3
Uranus	8.663×10^{25}	14.4	25559	4.01	1318	0.718	82.1[b]
Neptune	1.028×10^{25}	17.2	24764	3.88	1683	0.671	28.3
Pluto	1.315×10^{22}	0.0022	1170	0.181	2000	6.387	57[b]

Notes: [a] Angle between rotation axis and normal to orbital plane
[b] Planet rotates in opposite sense from orbital motion
Source: Gupta, R. (ed.) 2002, *Observer's Handbook 2002* (Toronto: Royal Astronomical Society of Canada); Peale, S. J. 1999, Ann. Rev. Astron. Astrophys., 37, 533.

Table A.3: Orbital and physical properties of the larger moons.

Planet	Moon	Mean distance from planet (10^3 km)	Mean distance from planet (planetary radii)	Sidereal period of orbit (days)	Inclination of orbit to planetary equator (°)	Mass of moon (10^{20} kg)	Radius of moon (km)	Mean density ρ (kg m^{-3})
Earth	Moon	384.40	60.27	27.32	18 – 29	734.9	1 737.5	3 340
Mars	Phobos	9.38	2.76	0.319	1.1	1.08×10^{-4}	11.2[b]	1 900
	Deimos	23.46	6.92	1.262	1.8	1.80×10^{-5}	6.3[b]	1 760
Jupiter	Amalthea	181.3	2.52	0.498	0.4	–	90[b]	–
	Thebe	221.9	3.10	0.675	0.8	–	50[b]	–
	Io	421.6	5.86	1.769	0.0	893.3	1821	3 530
	Europa	670.9	9.33	3.552	0.5	479.7	1 565	2 990
	Ganymede	1 070	14.90	7.155	0.2	1 482	2 634	1 940
	Callisto	1 883	26.20	16.689	0.3	1 076	2403	1 850
	Himalia	11 480	159.52	250.6	28	–	85	–
Saturn	Prometheus	139.35	2.31	0.613	0.0	–	53[b]	–
	Epimetheus	151.42	2.51	0.695	0.3	–	60[b]	–
	Janus	151.47	2.51	0.695	0.1	–	90[b]	–
	Mimas	185.52	3.08	0.942	1.5	0.375	198.8	1 530
	Enceladus	238.02	3.95	1.370	0.0	0.73	249	1 120
	Tethys	294.66	4.88	1.888	1.1	6.22	530	1 000
	Dione	377.40	6.26	2.737	0.0	10.52	560	1 440
	Rhea	527.04	8.74	4.518	0.4	23.1	764	1 240
	Titan	1 221.8	20.25	15.945	0.3	1 345.5	2 575	1 881
	Hyperion	1 481.1	24.55	21.277	0.4	–	146[b]	–
	Iapetus	3 651.3	59.02	79.330	14.7	15.9	718	1 020
	Phoebe	12 952	214.7	550.48	30[a]	–	110	–
Uranus	Portia	66.10	2.59	0.513	0.1	–	55[b]	–
	Puck	86.00	3.37	0.762	0.3	–	77[b]	–
	Miranda	129.8	5.08	1.413	4.2	0.659	236	1 200
	Ariel	191.2	7.47	2.520	0.3	13.53	579	1 670
	Umbriel	266.0	10.41	4.144	0.4	11.72	585	1 490
	Titania	435.8	17.07	8.706	0.1	35.27	789	1 710
	Oberon	582.6	22.82	13.463	0.1	30.14	761	1 630
	Sycorax	122×10^5	477 000	1290	?	–	~ 60	–
Neptune	Despina	52.53	2.12	0.335	0.1	–	74[b]	–
	Galatea	61.95	2.50	0.429	0.1	–	79[b]	–
	Larissa	73.55	2.97	0.555	0.2	–	96[b]	–
	Proteus	117.65	4.75	1.122	0.6	–	209[b]	–
	Triton	354.76	14.33	5.877	23.2[a]	214.7	1 353	2 054
	Nereid	5 513.4	222.7	360.1	27.7	–	170	–
Pluto	Charon	19.41	17.20	6.387	0	19.0	586	2 240

Notes: [a] Motion is retrograde, opposite to sense of planetary rotation
[b] For non-spherical moons the average dimension is given.

Source: Peale, S. J 1999, Ann. Rev. Astron. Astrophys., 37, 533.

Appendix B

Physical and astronomical constants

Table B.1: Physical constants

Gravitational constant	G	=	6.6726×10^{-11} N m^2 kg^{-2}
Speed of light	c	=	2.9979×10^{8} m s^{-1}
Planck's constant	h	=	6.6261×10^{-34} J s
Electron mass	m_e	=	9.1094×10^{-31} kg
Atomic mass unit	m_u	=	1.6605×10^{-27} kg
Mass of H atom	m_H	=	1.6735×10^{-27} kg
Boltzmann's constant	k	=	1.3807×10^{-23} J K^{-1}
Electron charge	e	=	1.6022×10^{-19} C
Gas constant	R_g	=	8.3145 J mole^{-1} K^{-1}
Stefan-Boltzmann constant	σ	=	5.6705×10^{-8} W m^{-2} K^{-4}
Electron volt	1 eV	=	1.6022×10^{-19} J

Table B.2: Astronomical constants

Astronomical unit	1 AU	=	1.4960×10^{11} m
Light-year	1 ly	=	9.4605×10^{15} m
Parsec	1 pc	=	3.0857×10^{16} m
Day	1 d	=	86 400 s
Tropical year	1 yr	=	365.2422 d
Earth mass	$M_\oplus$	=	5.974×10^{24} kg
Earth radius (mean)	$R_\oplus$	=	6371.0 km
Mass of Earth's moon		=	7.349×10^{22} kg
Radius of Earth's moon		=	1 738 km
Solar mass	$M_\odot$	=	1.989×10^{30} kg
Solar radius	$R_\odot$	=	6.96×10^{8} m
Solar luminosity	$L_\odot$	=	3.86×10^{26} W
Solar effective temperature	$T_\odot$	=	5770 K
Solar flux at 1 AU	$f_\odot$	=	1.37×10^{3} W m^{-2}

Index